THE MECCANO SUPER MODELS

Geoff Wright

FRANK HORNBY
1863–1936

New Cavendish Books

LONDON

**First Edition published in Great Britain
by New Cavendish Books—1978.**

Reprinted 1980.

The name *Meccano* has been used by courtesy of *Meccano Limited*.
All archival material by courtesy of M.W. Models, Henley-on-Thames.
Reprinted with the permission of *Meccano Limited*.

The Hornby Companion Series
Edited by Allen Levy.
Design — John B. Cooper
Text production and supervision — Carole Montague

Printed in England by Redwood Burn, Trowbridge.

ISBN 0 904568 07 5

Contents

The author would like to thank:-
Bruce Baxter, Bill Inglis, and the many Meccanoman's Club
members who supplied much of the Leaflet publishing data;
his mother, Bert Halliday, and Tony Knowles for checking
the proofs and making many helpful comments; and Carole
Montague for searching the country and locating Alan Thelwall
who supplied a most elusive Leaflet to complete the Book.

Preface

I will not attempt to conceal my commercial interest in the Meccano hobby. (It would be a forlorn hope to try!) Being a lifelong Meccano enthusiast, I told myself some eight years ago when I opened the Shop, that I must guard against ever becoming a collector of Meccano antiquity myself. That, I was certain, would only lead to bankruptcy!

Then copies of *'Meccano Magazine'* started to pass through my hands, with their fascinating insight into some sixty years of not only Meccano, but general engineering history. It would surely do no harm to keep just a few for reference? Then there were Meccano manuals of instructions, spanning Meccano model building practice of some seventy-five years; the retention of some of these would allow useful comparative study with the Magazines.

Next came some specimens of the famous series of Super Model Leaflets; the setting about collecting the complete series of thirty-seven; the discovery of the various revised versions; and finally the noting of the several different editions of each Leaflet which were apparently printed.... I surrendered — and admitted that I had of course become completely addicted to the collecting instinct. Fortunately ruin appears to have escaped me (so far!).

I hope you will find the study of the dawn of Meccano Super Modelling as fascinating as I have.

Geoff Wright
Henley-on-Thames

MECCANO

A Historical Survey

The purpose of this volume is to bring together, for the first time, all the model leaflets which formed a series of 37 *'Special Instruction Leaflets for Building Meccano Super Models,'* issued by Meccano Limited at intervals during the years 1928 to 1930. In addition, seven leaflets were revised to a greater or lesser extent and reissued in the period 1929 to 1936; these have also been included.

It must be noted, however, that the majority of leaflets were reprinted in the normal way as demand required, and small alterations were often made at the same time. From 1934 onwards, for instance, certain leaflets had criss-cross patterns superimposed on the Flat Plates to coincide with the introduction of the new blue and gold colours, which featured this pattern on many of the blue parts. A full list of all editions known to the author is included on page 331 but the differences between the various printings were insufficient to justify including more than one example of each leaflet in this volume.

In addition to the introduction of the leaflets, Meccano Limited published in 1928 *'The Meccano Book of Engineering'*, a Meccano equivalent to the very popular series, *'Hornby Book of Trains'*. The 'Book of Engineering' was typical of the in-depth information which Frank Hornby provided to stimulate interest in the principles of prototype engineering. The section on cranes in particular is especially interesting, and provided incidentally a great deal of background information on the evolution of what is without doubt the most famous leaflet model of all – No. 4 – 'Giant Block-setting Crane'. In view of this and the insight into the

engineering thought of the time which it provides, this rare publication has been included in its entirety.

Returning to the leaflets themselves, this introduction will cover the history which led up to their publication, and ended with their demise in the mid 1930s. This demise was largely caused by the revolution in Meccano model building techniques brought about by the introduction of Strip and Flexible Plates in 1934. These Plates rendered obsolete the existing 'skeletal' construction, which was employed in the majority of leaflet models.

A later volume will deal with the subsequent development of the Meccano system. Nowadays models have to be of a sophistication far in advance of that of the majority of models featured in these leaflets, if they are to deserve the title, (albeit unofficial) of 'Super Models'.

The very earliest model which should surely deserve the title 'Super Model' was the 'Forth Bridge'. This model is reproduced on page 10 from one of the first manuals published in about 1903 when the sytem, then known as *'Mechanics Made Easy'*, was in its infancy. The model required quantities of parts far in excess of those included in the largest set 'C' of the period. Incredibly enough, however, the set system was subsequently enlarged, until a few years later the largest set did indeed include sufficient parts to build the bridge. Although it measured some 16 feet in length, very little description was required to build it, because of its simple 'repeat' construction. There was also the fact that only seven different types of part were utilised, each of which could readily be identified from the simple diagrams provided.

Model of the Forth Bridge — 'Mechanics Made Easy' period.

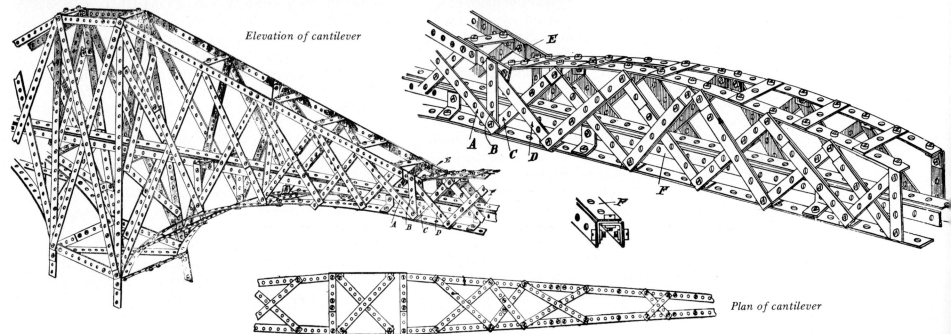

Elevation of cantilever

Plan of cantilever

The need for models to be published as separate model leaflets arose gradually as the models for the larger sets became increasingly complex, employing as they did an ever widening range of different parts in a rapidly developing Meccano system. Thus detailed building instructions began to demand an undue devotion of space in the manuals to do them justice. In contrast, due also to this same factor, some models were included with but minimal illustrations or instructions, which must have posed quite a problem for the would-be constructor of the time. One can only guess at the frustration that must have been caused by the inclusion in the 1916 manual of 'Special Meccano Model No. 318', one of the first published Meccano clocks; the illustration included here constitutes the entire information from which it was supposed to be built.

The 1928-36 leaflets were of course the best known and most comprehensive series to be issued by the Company but it is not so well known that they were preceded by a small series in a double sized vertical format. Although not a leaflet, and therefore rather out of the scope of this volume, there was in addition a comprehensive publication dealing with but one model. This was the *'Meccanograph Manual'*, which conformed to the normal horizontal format of the standard outfit manuals.

The Motor Chassis was destined to have what was perhaps the greatest influence on the evolution of the leaflets. This model first appeared as a prize winner in the famous 1914/1915 competition; the illustrations on pages 12 and 13 are taken from the *'Meccano Prize Models'* published at the time. This chassis was also featured in *'The Light Car'* Magazine for July 7th 1915. Meccano Limited subsequently issued a reprint of the article in a vertical format leaflet, a portion of which is reproduced on page 14. Although not in itself an official leaflet it set the style for the first series of model leaflets which were issued (or reissued) at intervals over the years 1921 to 1927. Four models were included in this series — Grandfather Clock, Loom, Ship Coaler, and a further version of the Motor Chassis. Like the majority of models in both series of leaflets, this Motor Chassis was also

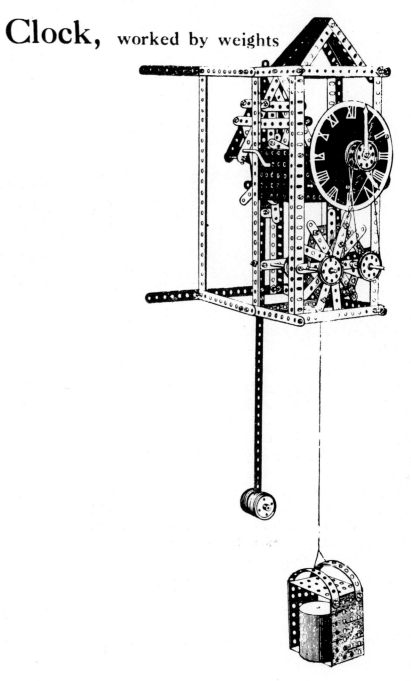

Special Meccano Model No. 318

Clock, worked by weights

*Prize Winning
Model built
by the famous
motoring artist
F. Gordon Crosby*

featured in *'Meccano Magazine'*, in which instructions were also provided for a limousine body designed to be mounted on the chassis, though this required a small alteration to the length of the sideframe members. The complete car is so interesting that illustrations of both body and chassis have been included on pages 15, 16 & 17.

As separate leaflets became available, instructions for the relevant models in the standard outfit manuals of the time were omitted. Instead, a single illustration was provided, and the leaflet (also available separately) was included in the outfit. At the time of the introduction of the main series of leaflets, there arose some discrepancies between these illustrations and the models which were subsequently featured in the leaflets themselves. Some illustrations from the relevant manual pages have been included on page 20, for comparison purposes. It will be seen that the Transporter Bridge was substantially revised and improved when it appeared as leaflet 21, while the 'Tractor' illustrated in the manual bore no resemblance to the vastly more elaborate Traction Engine which appeared as leaflet No. 22. Another anomaly concerned the locomotive in the series. This model as featured originally in *'Meccano Magazine'* was based on an L.M.S. 4-6-2 tank locomotive. When leaflet No. 15 appeared, however, the locomotive represented a Southern Railway 4-6-4 tank. Despite this, an illustration of the L.M.S. locomotive was used for some years to advertise the leaflet. In view of its special interest, two illustrations of this earlier model have been included on page 18. The Aeroscope (page 20) apparently never appeared in leaflet form at all, despite the indication with the illustration from the manual. Although the intention was to issue the model as leaflet No. 20, the model which ultimately appeared in its place was the Electric Mobile Crane.

The importance attached to the Motor Chassis was once more apparent in the choice of a further improved version as the subject for the first leaflet of the 1928-36 series. In

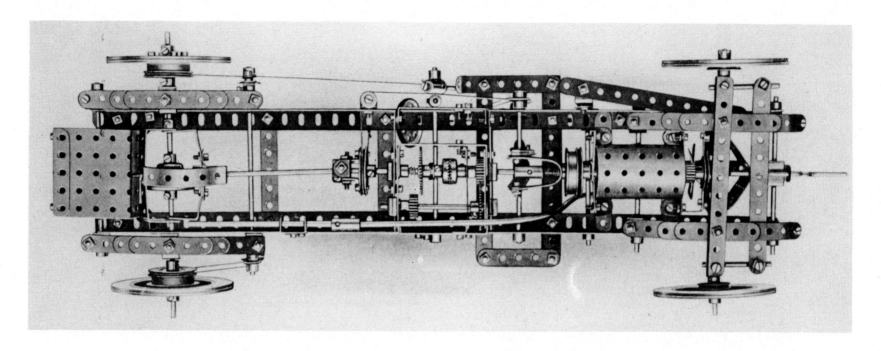

addition, to promote sales of the leaflets, large numbers of these Chassis were built as display models and put on show at large stores throughout the country.

Many of the leaflets have references other than the leaflet number itself; some, but certainly not all, could be built from the contents of a particular outfit of the time. Thus early issues might be allied to either the No. 6 or No. 7 sets of the time; leaflets issued from 1934 onwards might specify 'K' or 'L' set as appropriate. These were the largest sets of their respective periods. In some cases the manual model number was also specified. The majority of the leaflets have a reference in small print, usually at the foot of the front page, which can be used to date the leaflet precisely. For example a reference 328/5 would indicate a leaflet printed in March 1928; the 5 relates to the quantity printed in thousands.

Most, if not all, the 1928-36 leaflets also appeared in a French version. Those about which the author is in doubt are No. 32, Twin Cylinder Steam Engine, and the versions of No. 28, Pontoon Crane, and No. 29, Hammerhead Crane, which were revised to utilise the Geared Roller Bearing.

Leaflet No. 1, Motor Chassis, was also issued in German and Spanish, while No. 14, Grandfather Clock, appeared in German. Whilst on the subject of instructions in other languages, it is relevant here to mention two publications which were prepared in Spain and issued in Spanish in a manual format. These were very advanced models, of an Automatic Mechanical Loom and an Automatic Printing Machine.

At least twelve of the main series of leaflets were also issued in a separate U.S.A. edition.

A complete table of printing references of all editions known to the author of both series of leaflets, including those in different languages, will be found on page 331.

As previously mentioned, the majority of leaflet models were featured also in 'Meccano Magazine', and it was fairly standard practice to include in the same issues substantial

A Chassis built with Meccano

The following consists mainly of extracts which the Editor of "The Light Car" has courteously permitted us to make from an article appearing in the issue of July 7th, 1915

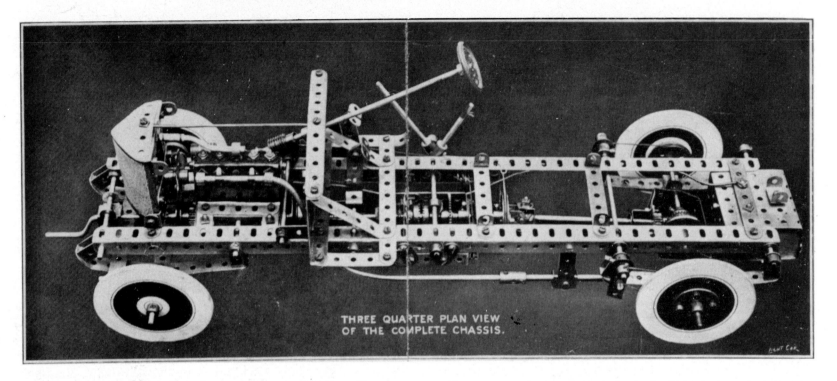

THREE QUARTER PLAN VIEW OF THE COMPLETE CHASSIS.

ABOUT six months ago, the makers of that instructive and interesting mechanical toy. Meccano, promoted a competition and offered £200 worth of prizes for the most ingenious mechanism constructed from Meccano parts. The regulations were that any number of these parts could be used in the construction of the mechanism submitted, but no outside assistance in the way of parts or material was to be employed. The lists closed last March, and the results have just been announced.

This interesting and very ingenious motor-car model, which has been awarded a divided second prize in the recent Meccano Competition, was designed and constructed entirely from Meccano parts by Mr. Gordon Crosby, of Leamington Spa. About 10,000 competitors submitted work from all over the world, and it is interesting to note that one of the prize-winners was M. Léon Bollée, the well-known motor-car manufacturer, of Paris, who sent in a model of a motor-car.

For the benefit of those readers who are not acquainted with Meccano parts, it is advisable to point out that each Meccano outfit comprises a number of flat and angular steel strips perforated with ³⁄₁₆ in. holes at intervals of half an inch, ³⁄₁₆ in. steel rods of varying lengths, small angle brackets, nuts, bolts.

The next item in the transmission is the clutch, which is built up of two disc-wheels — a bush wheel and a flanged-and-grooved wheel — and actuated by a pedal and clutch fork against the pressure of a small coil spring.

The change-speed gear is undoubtedly the most ingenious part of the model. It comprises two speeds of high and low-gear ratios, built into a frame which is bolted to the main frame. The high gear is a direct drive through "dog clutches" arranged by bringing into mesh two small contrate wheels, the teeth of the wheels forming the dogs. The change of speed is actuated by a cross-shaft connected to the change-speed lever, the sliding wheel being operated by a striking-fork cleverly constructed from a flat bracket attached to a collar which can be seen in the centre of the cross-shaft. The bracket is slotted, and the slot is made use of to encircle the gearshaft. When the change-speed lever is pushed over, away from the operator, the two dog clutches are thrown out of mesh, and the movement simultaneously brings the sliding gear wheel into mesh with the low-gear pinion carried on the layshaft. The drive is transmitted to the layshaft by means of a pinion on the main shaft with which a gear-wheel on the layshaft is in constant mesh.

THE CHASSIS FROM THE OFF SIDE NOTE THE VERY COMPLETE STEERING GEAR.

THE COMPLETE CAR BONNET & SEATS.

information on the prototype of the model concerned. Many of the leaflets themselves similarly devoted considerable space to such information; others, however, were 'padded out' with a full-page advertisement on the back for other leaflets in the series.

While many of the models justified the title 'Super Models', this was by no means applicable to all of them; some were, to say the least, rudimentary, and scarcely justified the production of a four page leaflet. The more complex models were provided with eight pages of instructions, and one, Leaflet No. 4, required no less than twelve.

This last was the most famous Meccano model of all time – 'The Block-setting Crane'. Billed as 'The Largest Meccano Model', it was however derived from a somewhat larger previous model. An interesting comparison of the two appears in 'The Meccano Book of Engineering' page 16 & 17, from which it will be seen that the most obvious difference lies in the proportions of the boom. The original version appears very 'front heavy'; the Super Model version, although obviously reconstructed to follow the lines of the prototype shown at the foot of page 17 (Book of Engineering), seems rather over corrected. Careful examination of the original model shows the utilisation of the pre-production version of the Geared Roller Bearing, whose toothed and plain roller races were each fitted with a circle of eight Channel Segments upon which ran pulley wheel rollers. A full description of this early Bearing is given in an article in 'Meccano Engineer' No. 12, June-September 1976. Other differences between the models included the type of Bevel Gears which drove the travelling wheels. At one time the Factory produced yet another version of the Crane for display purposes using the original tower and Bearing, but the later simplified boom. It is interesting to note that the earliest version of the Crane was the one chosen for the front cover of the 1934-1936, and late 1941-1953 manuals. A fundamental technical error was perpetrated in this original model which persisted through others right down Meccano history even to the present day. The error relates to the method of mounting the boom bracing strips on reversed 1½" Angle Girders. Careful

The Meccano Limousine

The Limousine Body

◀ *'The Light Car' reprint issued as separate leaflet*

15

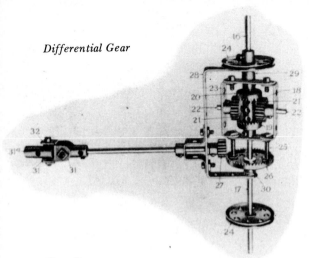

Differential Gear

Gear Box

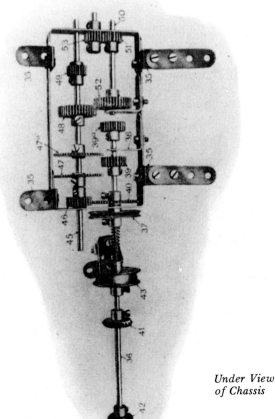

*Under View
of Chassis*

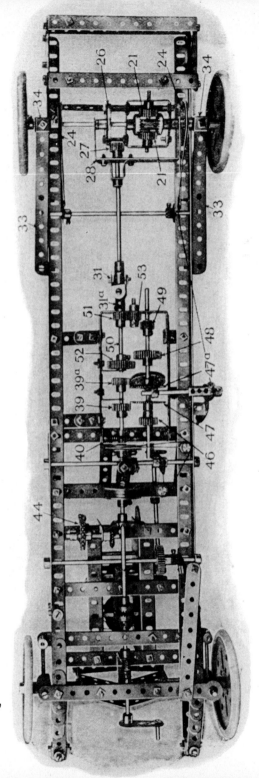

examination of prototype cranes shows that the bracing should instead have been attached to flat gusset plates mounted on the rear of the main channel girder boom members. Controversial discussions have also centred on the proportions of the tower assembly of the Meccano models, the consensus of opinion being that it is too tall. The author believes that it would be nearer the truth to say that the tower was built to a larger scale all round than the boom, and that the boom should be enlarged in all directions to correct the fault. It is surprising that the giant Meccano crane did not apparently appear till 1925, and yet, some twelve years before, the Bing 'Structator' constructional system featured a very large crane on somewhat similar lines and this was the system that Frank Hornby dismissed as 'a showy toy not based on true engineering'! Though the Block-setting Crane leaflet was presumably intended to promote sales of the newly introduced Geared Roller Bearing, its parts list, among other errors, omitted this part altogether; when the model was subsequently featured in *'Meccano Magazine'* in 1929, many corrections were made to the parts list; the corrected version is printed on page 21 for comparison.

Whilst on the subject of the Geared Roller Bearing, another leaflet model to feature this part was No. 8, the Roundabout, but its poor design did not really justify the use of such an elegant part. The model was much too high in proportion to its diameter, and was generally crude. In 1934 leaflets No. 28, Pontoon Crane, and No. 29, Hammerhead Crane, were redesigned to use the Geared Roller Bearing, which helped to clear the way for the withdrawal of the Channel Bearing parts originally used. Though the revised leaflets were labelled as 'L' outfit models, the author can find no evidence that the Bearing was ever included in the outfit.

Another leaflet, No. 32, Twin Cylinder Steam Engine, also featured Channel Segments, which in this instance formed the rims of the flywheels, but here again no evidence has yet come to the author's notice of a revised leaflet being issued when the parts were withdrawn. However, evidence that a reconstructed model was indeed prepared by the Factory does exist, as the illustration from the 1935 edition

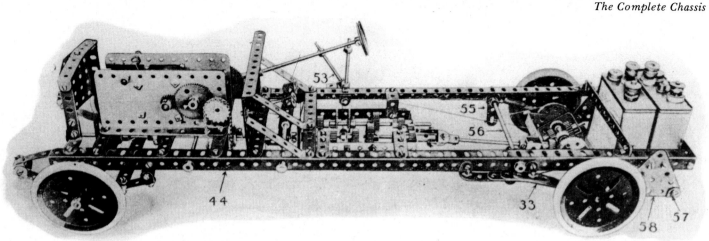

The Complete Chassis

*Brake and
Change Speed
Levers*

Rear Leaf-Spring

*Front of Chassis
showing Steering Gear*

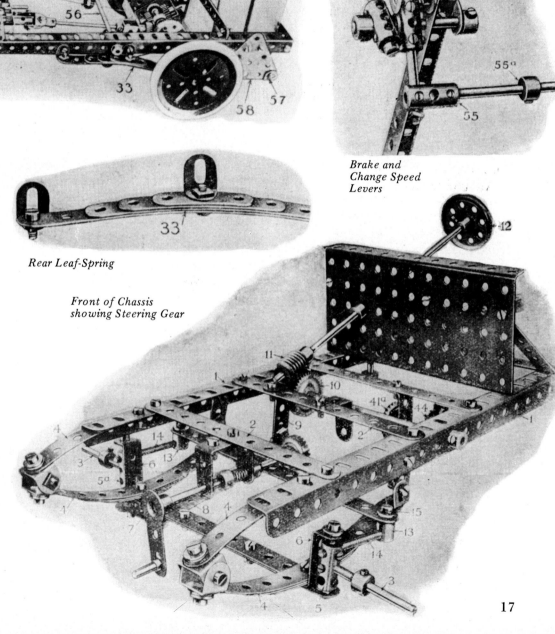

of '*Meccano Parts and How to Use Them*' proves. This shows a portion of the model with Ring Frames (now called Flanged Rings), Part 167b, forming the flywheels instead of Channel Segments, (see page 19).

Similar evidence exists about another Factory reconstructed model; once again it was, as far as the author knows, never published. The model concerned was No. 28, Pontoon Crane, which normally required two Motors to power it, whereas the Set 7 with which it was intended to be built contained but one Motor. As can be seen in this page reprinted from the Set manual, only brief details were given about suitable modifications to permit single Motor operation. The existence of a modified version of the model can be established by examining the three illustrations taken from the 1929 '*Standard Mechanisms*' manual. It will be seen that by this date the early built-up roller race had also been replaced by the new Geared Roller Bearing, (see page 19).

Modifications to leaflets Nos. 28 and 29 have already been mentioned. Other leaflets modified to a certain extent were Nos. 11, 14, & 16, and in these cases the revised leaflets were given an 'a' suffix, becoming Nos. 11a, 14a, & 16a. The advent of the 1929 vertical boilered Steam Engine prompted the reconstruction of model No. 19, Steam Shovel, to employ the engine as motive power, the new leaflet becoming No. 19a. In this case however, the original leaflet

No. 19 was retained, being reprinted in 1934. Brief details of No. 19a were included in the 1929 Steam Engine manual as model S. 31, which reference appears on the leaflet, though according to the manual the leaflet was to be numbered 35. Similar details were included of a steam powered version of Super Model No. 6, as model S. 30; the separate leaflet was to have been No. 6a. However, no evidence has been found of such a leaflet being issued, though in recent years there have been conjectural reconstructions of this model in an attempt to discover how the model would have appeared. One of the best, by Mr. B.N. Love, was fully described in 'Meccano Magazine Quarterly' for October 1973.

Another leaflet to have an 'a' suffix was No. 33a, Double Flyboats; this was not a revised but an alternative model, and was only available bound with leaflet No. 33, Single Flyboats.

The Motor Chassis had the final distinction of being the very last entirely new model to be published in the series of 'Special Instruction Leaflets for Building Meccano Super Models'. This version, introduced in 1934, was based on the contemporary Bentley chassis, and could be built with the contents of the 'L' set of the time.

The model of Quebec Bridge which is depicted on the very attractive coloured cover of this volume is reproduced from the label on the lid of a Meccano set of the early 1930's, and although it was also illustrated in editions of the 'Meccano Book of New Models' of the time, was sadly never issued as a leaflet. However, the 1937-1953 No. 10 outfit manuals included a modified version of the model. Also in these manuals, many of the erstwhile leaflet models were reworked to utilise the new Flexible and Strip Plates. These were the Automatic Ship Coaler, Railway Service Crane, Transporter Bridge, and Giant Block-Setting Crane; the Sports Motor Car could be said to be derived from the earlier leaflets in so far as its chassis was concerned. In late 1954 these manuals were superseded by a series of Number 10 Outfit leaflets. The first two of these featured another version of the Railway Service Crane and a Sports Motor Car, which now featured an integral chassis. Another leaflet, No. 7, was a

The Tank Locomotive – early version as featured in 'Meccano Magazine'.

new Block-Setting Crane. In the author's opinion, these are the sole descendants of the famous series of leaflets which inspired the production of this volume. Other models, though of nominally similar subjects, were entirely new.

As already mentioned, many of the original leaflet models were also featured at about the same time in other Meccano literature, usually *'Meccano Magazine'*. Though the series of 37 basic leaflets had been issued by 1930, further excellent models of equal or greater calibre continued to be featured in the Magazine, but sadly were never issued as leaflets. In view of their importance, and for the sake of completeness, details of those of the early 1930's have been

PONTOON CRANE
The Single Motor version — Manual details and 'Standard Mechanisms' illustrations.

rts required :

of No.			1 of No.		1 of No.		1 of No.	
of No.	2		1 of No.	17				
,, ,,	2A		3 ,, ,,	18A				
,, ,,	3		8 ,, ,,	20				
,, ,,	4		2 ,, ,,	22				
,, ,,	5		7 ,, ,,	22A				
,, ,,	6		1 ,, ,,	23				
,, ,,	6A		5 ,, ,,	24				
,, ,,	7A		4 ,, ,,	26				
,, ,,	8		5 ,, ,,	27A				
,, ,,	8A		4 ,, ,,	30				
,, ,,	8B		3 ,, ,,	31				
,, ,,	9		1 ,, ,,	32	1 of No. 53		1 of No. 97	
,, ,,	9A	135	,, ,,	37	1 ,, ,, 57		2 ,, ,, 99	
,, ,,	9B	58	,, ,,	38	1 ,, ,, 57B		4 ,, ,, 103A	
,, ,,	9D	1	,, ,,	40	62 ,, ,, 59		4 ,, ,, 103B	
,, ,,	12A	1	,, ,,	45	3 ,, ,, 62		1 ,, ,, 103F	
,, ,,	12B	1	,, ,,	48	6 ,, ,, 63		3 ,, ,, 111	
,, ,,	13A	1	,, ,,	48A	4 ,, ,, 70		16 ,, ,, 119	
,, ,,	15	4	,, ,,	48B	3 ,, ,, 76		2 ,, ,, 126	
,, ,,	15A	2	,, ,,	48D	2 ,, ,, 80		2 ,, ,, 126A	
,, ,,	16	2	,, ,,	52	1 ,, ,, 94		5 ,, ,, 133	
,, ,,	16A	2	,, ,,	52A	1 ,, ,, 96			
					2 Electric Motors			

Of the above parts, 5 of No. 7A (18½″ Angle Girders) are required in addition to Outfit 7, but if desired, these parts may be substituted by five 12½″ Angle Girders each bolted ne 9½″ Angle Girder, the two parts being overlapped seven holes.

Also, only one of the Electric Motors is included in the Outfit, but if desired the Motor ked " 1 " in the leaflet may be dispensed with and the luffing and swivelling movements rolled from the other Motor 5, the necessary connection being made by extending the marked 11 in Fig. 4 in the leaflet, and driving it from the Motor 5 through Sprocket n gearing.

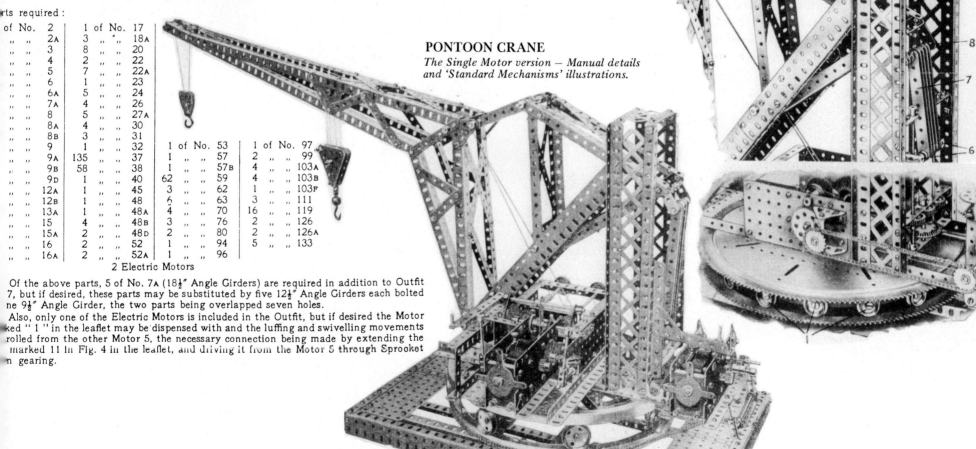

included. They are the Giant Girder Transporting Lorry of 1932, (this model was used to solve route planning problems); the Printing Machine of 1932 (which even incorporated suction feed, using the Meccano Fan for the purpose); the Aerial Ropeway of 1930 (which was practically the only model, incidentally, to employ Channel Segments other than as full circles); the very large scale Outboard Motor of 1934, the Master Clock of 1935, and the LNER No. '10000' High Pressure Locomotive of 1935.

Many of the leaflet models were no doubt inspired by entries to the Meccano model building competitions at various times. In turn the leaflets themselves must have helped to inspire ever greater efforts at 'Super Model' building. It is surely relevant to refer to a few of these models of the period, which must rank as among the finest Meccano

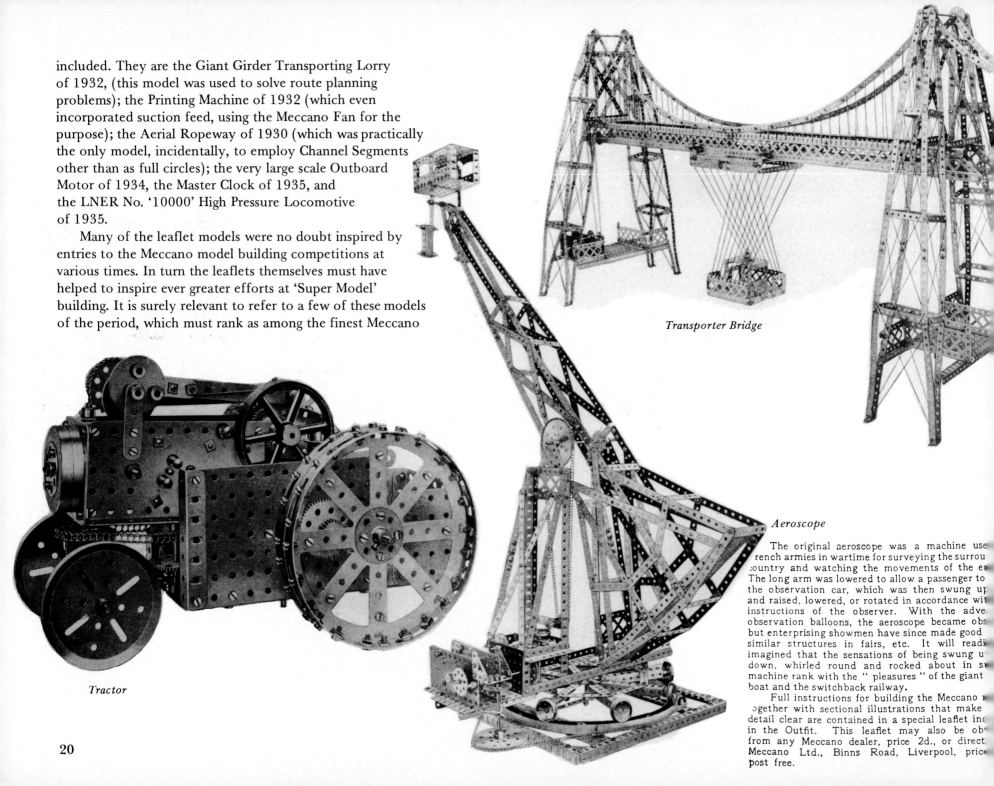

Transporter Bridge

Tractor

Aeroscope

The original aeroscope was a machine use⸍ ⸍rench armies in wartime for surveying the surrou⸍ ⸍ountry and watching the movements of the e⸍ The long arm was lowered to allow a passenger to⸍ the observation car, which was then swung up⸍ and raised, lowered, or rotated in accordance wit⸍ instructions of the observer. With the adve⸍ observation balloons, the aeroscope became obs⸍ but enterprising showmen have since made good⸍ similar structures in fairs, etc. It will readi⸍ imagined that the sensations of being swung u⸍ down. whirled round and rocked about in s⸍ machine rank with the " pleasures " of the giant⸍ boat and the switchback railway.

Full instructions for building the Meccano ▸⸍ ⸍ogether with sectional illustrations that make ⸍ detail clear are contained in a special leaflet inc⸍ in the Outfit. This leaflet may also be ob⸍ from any Meccano dealer, price 2d., or direct⸍ Meccano Ltd., Binns Road, Liverpool, price⸍ post free.

GIANT BLOCK-SETTING CRANE

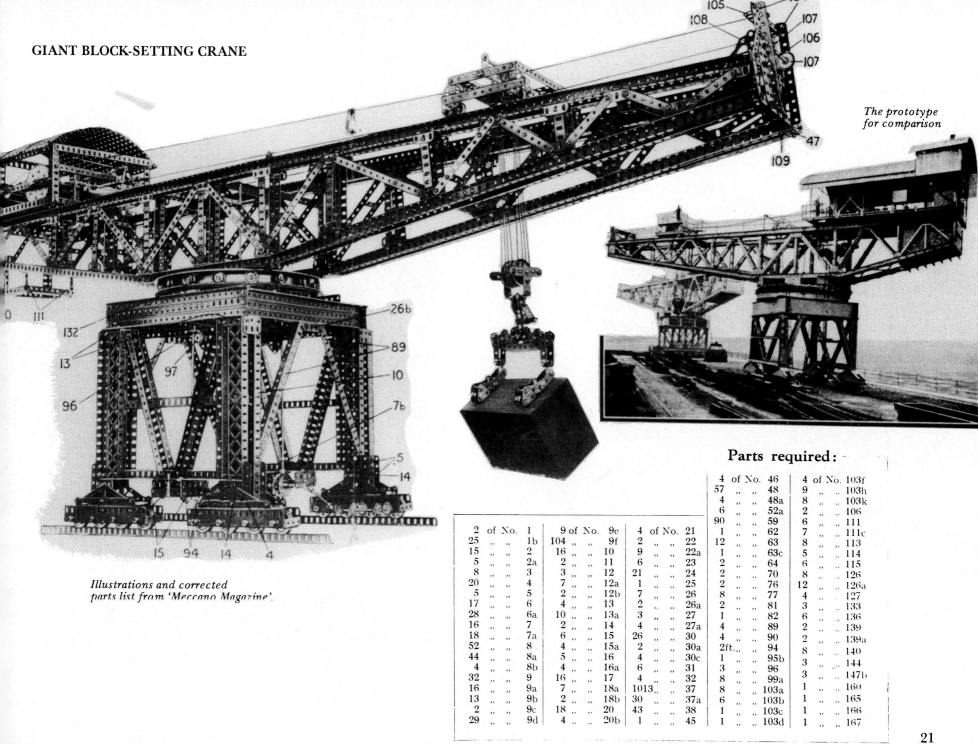

The prototype for comparison

Illustrations and corrected parts list from 'Meccano Magazine'.

Parts required:

2	of No.	1	9	of No.	9e	4	of No.	21	4	of No.	46	4	of No.	103f
25	,, ,,	1b	104	,, ,,	9f	2	,, ,,	22	57	,, ,,	48	9	,, ,,	103h
15	,, ,,	2	16	,, ,,	10	9	,, ,,	22a	4	,, ,,	48a	8	,, ,,	103k
5	,, ,,	2a	2	,, ,,	11	6	,, ,,	23	6	,, ,,	52a	2	,, ,,	106
8	,, ,,	3	3	,, ,,	12	21	,, ,,	24	90	,, ,,	59	6	,, ,,	111
20	,, ,,	4	7	,, ,,	12a	1	,, ,,	25	1	,, ,,	62	7	,, ,,	111c
5	,, ,,	5	2	,, ,,	12b	7	,, ,,	26	12	,, ,,	63	8	,, ,,	113
17	,, ,,	6	4	,, ,,	13	2	,, ,,	26a	1	,, ,,	63c	5	,, ,,	114
28	,, ,,	6a	10	,, ,,	13a	3	,, ,,	27	2	,, ,,	64	6	,, ,,	115
16	,, ,,	7	2	,, ,,	14	4	,, ,,	27a	2	,, ,,	70	8	,, ,,	126
18	,, ,,	7a	6	,, ,,	15	26	,, ,,	30	2	,, ,,	76	12	,, ,,	126a
52	,, ,,	8	4	,, ,,	15a	2	,, ,,	30a	8	,, ,,	77	4	,, ,,	127
44	,, ,,	8a	5	,, ,,	16	4	,, ,,	30c	2	,, ,,	81	3	,, ,,	133
4	,, ,,	8b	4	,, ,,	16a	6	,, ,,	31	1	,, ,,	82	6	,, ,,	136
32	,, ,,	9	16	,, ,,	17	4	,, ,,	32	4	,, ,,	89	2	,, ,,	139
16	,, ,,	9a	7	,, ,,	18a	1013	,, ,,	37	4	,, ,,	90	2	,, ,,	139a
13	,, ,,	9b	2	,, ,,	18b	30	,, ,,	37a	2ft.	,, ,,	94	8	,, ,,	140
2	,, ,,	9c	18	,, ,,	20	43	,, ,,	38	1	,, ,,	95b	3	,, ,,	144
29	,, ,,	9d	4	,, ,,	20b	1	,, ,,	45	3	,, ,,	96	3	,, ,,	147b
									8	,, ,,	99a	1	,, ,,	160
									8	,, ,,	103a	1	,, ,,	165
									6	,, ,,	103b	1	,, ,,	166
									1	,, ,,	103c	1	,, ,,	167
									1	,, ,,	103d			

model building achievements of all time; the Barendrecht Lift Bridge, a very fine example of large scale replica prototype modelling (and this by an enthusiast of but tender years); the Rahm clock, whose creative complexity will long inspire Meccano clock builders; and the Differential Analyser, one of the most outstanding uses of Meccano for research and development work.

Finally, and in complete contrast to all the foregoing, a completely different and novel series of 'Super Models' (not by Meccano Limited) which first appeared in 1926. For a Christmas pantomime, a series of the smaller manual models was built from giant Meccano parts fashioned in wood, (see page 32). The models were of such a size that their 'constructors' could appear to be driving and riding in them in a 'Meccanoland' scene.

THE GIANT GIRDER TRANSPORTING LORRY

Planning the route to be followed through London

The driving mechanism of the lorry seen from below

The Meccano model of the giant girder mounted on the lorry and trailer

THE PRINTING MACHINE

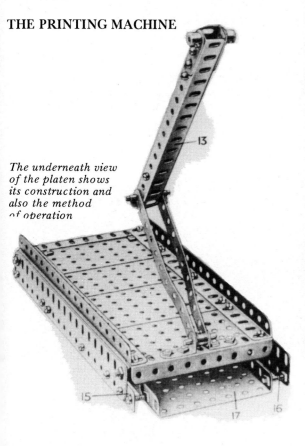

The underneath view of the platen shows its construction and also the method of operation

13

15 2 17 16

This view shows the impression roller with the outer rubber covering removed

20 18 19

55 56 54 50 36 53 15 17 52 47 51 48

49 45 44 11 35 46

This view of the machine shows clearly the inking and delivery rollers. The delivery chains have been omitted in order to show the arrangement more clearly.

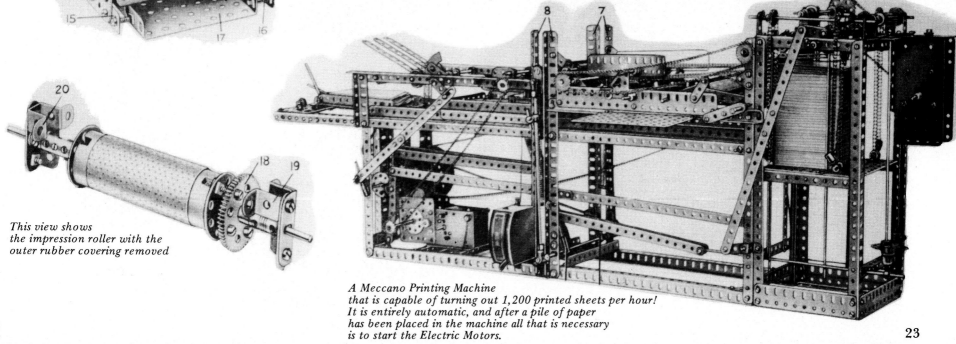

8 7

A Meccano Printing Machine
that is capable of turning out 1,200 printed sheets per hour!
It is entirely automatic, and after a pile of paper
has been placed in the machine all that is necessary
is to start the Electric Motors.

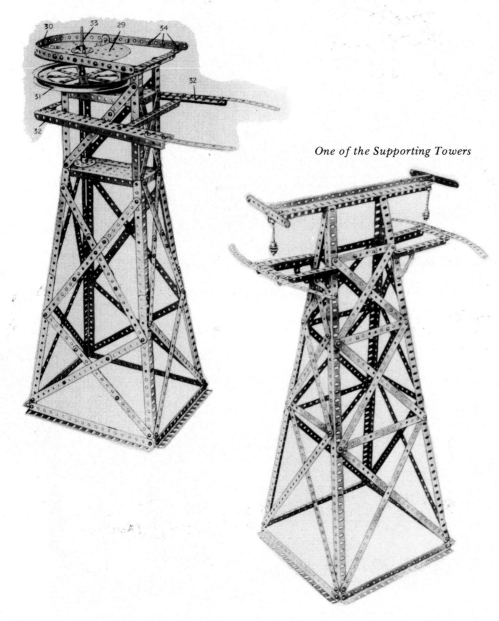

The Return Tower

One of the Supporting Towers

A Meccano A

The Bucket, showing Gripper and Catch

The Trip

erial Ropeway with Automatic Pick-up and Discharging Gear.

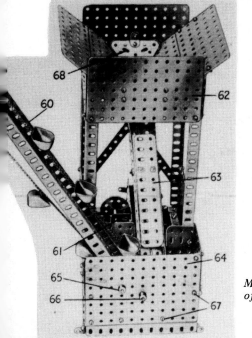

Main Hopper and Driving Gear of Bucket Conveyor

Parts Required to build the Meccano Aerial Ropeway :

43 of No. 1	13 of No. 8	52 of No. 12	1 of No. 19b	1031 of No. 37	28 of No. 59	12 of No. 89	7 of No. 103k	1 of No. 125
22 ,, ,, 1a	32 ,, ,, 8a	10 ,, ,, 12b	3 ,, ,, 19c	6 ,, ,, 37b	14 ,, ,, 62	3 ,, ,, 89a	10 ,, ,, 108	2 ,, ,, 126a
32 ,, ,, 1b	26 ,, ,, 8b	2 ,, ,, 13	2 ,, ,, 20	36 ,, ,, 38	7 ,, ,, 62b	1 ,, ,, 90	3 ,, ,, 111	1 ,, ,, 127
32 ,, ,, 2	17 ,, ,, 9	2 ,, ,, 13a	6 ,, ,, 22	2 ,, ,, 46	9 ,, ,, 63	1 ,, ,, 90a	2 ,, ,, 111a	20 ,, ,, 131
60 ,, ,, 2a	10 ,, ,, 9a	1 ,, ,, 14	2 ,, ,, 22a	2 ,, ,, 48a	1 ,, ,, 63c	6' ,, ,, 94	12 ,, ,, 111c	6 ,, ,, 136
28 ,, ,, 3	2 ,, ,, 9b	1 ,, ,, 15a	7 ,, ,, 23	2 ,, ,, 52	1 ,, ,, 66	4 ,, ,, 96	2 ,, ,, 114	1 ,, ,, 139
5 ,, ,, 4	5 ,, ,, 9c	8 ,, ,, 16	10 ,, ,, 23a	6 ,, ,, 52a	3 ,, ,, 67	2 ,, ,, 102	1 ,, ,, 115	7 ,, ,, 139a
51 ,, ,, 5	8 ,, ,, 9d	7 ,, ,, 16a	5 ,, ,, 24	2 ,, ,, 53	6 ,, ,, 70	1 ,, ,, 103	1 ,, ,, 116	1 ,, ,, 147b
8 ,, ,, 6	3 ,, ,, 9e	2 ,, ,, 16b	1 ,, ,, 26	4 ,, ,, 53a	8 ,, ,, 72	1 ,, ,, 103a	1 ,, ,, 116a	1 ,, ,, 154a
3 ,, ,, 6a	10 ,, ,, 9f	1 ,, ,, 18a	4 ,, ,, 27a	1 ,, ,, 57	5 ,, ,, 76	5 ,, ,, 103c	8 ,, ,, 119	2 ,, ,, 160
12 ,, ,, 7	24 ,, ,, 10	3 ,, ,, 18b	2 ,, ,, 30	12 ,, ,, 58	1 ,, ,, 80a	4 ,, ,, 103d	1 ,, ,, 120	2 ,, ,, 164
22 ,, ,, 7a	1 ,, ,, 11		2 ,, ,, 32		2 ,, ,, 80b	4 ,, ,, 103f		

2 Electric Motors.   30 ft. (approx.) of brass stranded picture wire.   40 ft. (approx.) of fairly thick string.

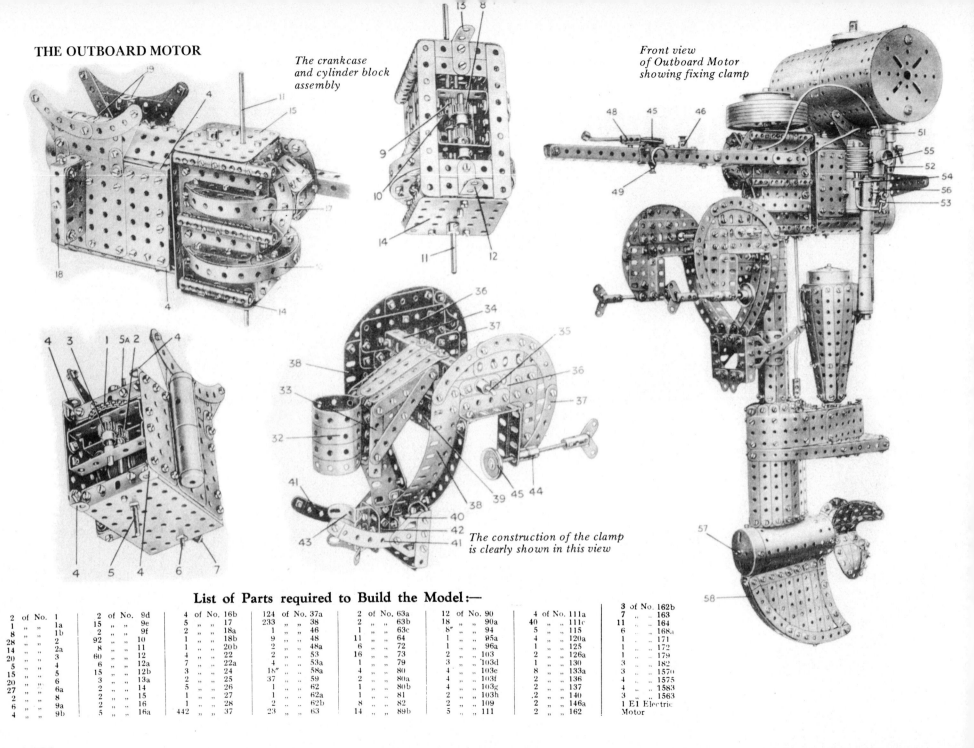

The crankcase and cylinder block assembly

Front view of Outboard Motor showing fixing clamp

The construction of the clamp is clearly shown in this view

List of Parts required to Build the Model:—

Qty	No.	Qty	No.	Qty	No.	Qty	No.	Qty	No.	Qty	No.	Qty	No.	Qty	No.
2 of No.	1	2 of No.	9d	4 of No.	16b	124 of No.	37a	2 of No.	63a	12 of No.	90	4 of No.	111a	3 of No.	162b
1 " "	1a	15 " "	9e	5 " "	17	233 " "	38	2 " "	63b	18 " "	90a	40 " "	111c	7 "	163
8 " "	1b	2 " "	9f	2 " "	18a	1 " "	46	1 " "	63c	8" " "	94	5 " "	115	11 "	164
28 " "	2	92 " "	10	1 " "	18b	9 " "	48	11 " "	64	1 " "	95a	4 " "	120a	6 "	168a
14 " "	2a	8 " "	11	1 " "	20b	2 " "	48a	6 " "	72	1 " "	96a	1 " "	125	1 "	171
20 " "	3	60 " "	12	4 " "	22	2 " "	53	16 " "	73	2 " "	103	2 " "	126a	1 "	172
5 " "	4	6 " "	12a	7 " "	22a	4 " "	53a	2 " "	79	3 " "	103d	1 " "	130	1 "	179
15 " "	5	15 " "	12b	3 " "	24	18" " "	58a	4 " "	80	4 " "	103e	8 " "	133a	3 "	182
20 " "	6	3 " "	13a	2 " "	25	37 " "	59	2 " "	80a	4 " "	103f	2 " "	136	3 "	1570
27 " "	6a	2 " "	14	5 " "	26	1 " "	62	1 " "	80b	4 " "	103g	2 " "	137	4 "	1575
2 " "	8	2 " "	15	1 " "	27	1 " "	62a	1 " "	81	2 " "	103h	.2 " "	140	4 "	1583
6 " "	9a	2 " "	16	1 " "	28	2 " "	62b	8 " "	82	2 " "	109	2 " "	146a	3 "	1563
4 " "	9b	5 " "	16a	442 " "	37	23 " "	63	14 " "	89b	5 " "	111	2 " "	162	1 E1 Electric Motor	

THE MASTER CLOCK

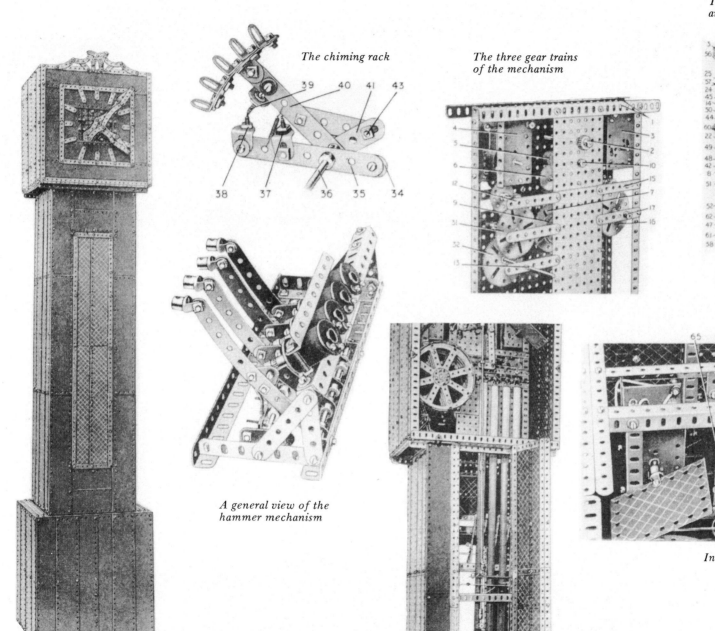

The chiming rack

39 40 41 43

38 37 36 35 34

*The three gear trains
of the mechanism*

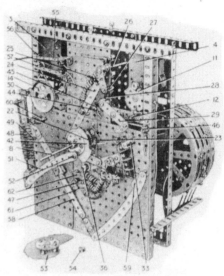

*The complete striking
and chiming mechanism*

*A general view of the
hammer mechanism*

*A rear view of the model
showing the gong tubes*

In this view the govenor fans are shown

27

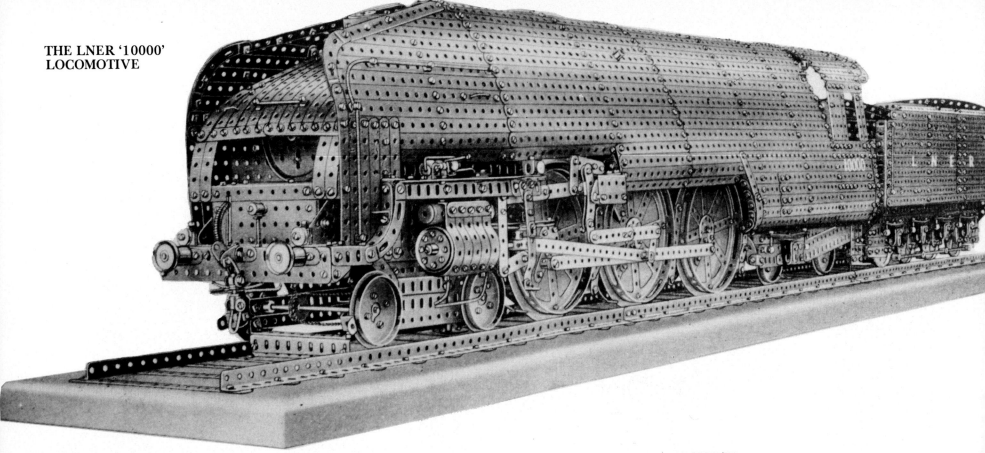

THE LNER '10000' LOCOMOTIVE

A general view of the Meccano Locomotive and tender, showing how well the characteristics of 'No. 10000' have been reproduced

LIST OF PARTS REQUIRED

89 of No. 1	1 of No. 8a	29 of No. 12b	4 of No. 21	4 of No. 48b	11 of No. 64	20 of No. 90	10 of No. 103k	2 of No. 12...
41 „ „ 1a	12 „ „ 8b	8 „ „ 13a	4 „ „ 22	2 „ „ 48c	2 „ „ 67	4 „ „ 90a	8 „ „ 109	12 „ „ 13...
86 „ „ 1b	13 „ „ 9	8 „ „ 14	2 „ „ 22a	4 „ „ 50a	72 „ „ 68	4 „ „ 94	18 „ „ 111	26 „ „ 13...
76 „ „ 2	16 „ „ 9a	8 „ „ 16	4 „ „ 23	10 „ „ 52c	40 „ „ 69	3 „ „ 95	21 „ „ 111a	8 „ „ 13...
98 „ „ 2a	5 „ „ 9b	2 „ „ 16a	8 „ „ 24	9 „ „ 53a	17 „ „ 70	14 „ „ 96	71 „ „ 111c	6 „ „ 14...
47 „ „ 3	4 „ „ 9c	1 „ „ 16b	74 „ „ 25	2 „ „ 58	3 „ „ 72	8 „ „ 103	2 „ „ 114	11 „ „ 14...
47 „ „ 4	6 „ „ 9d	1 „ „ 17	2 „ „ 35	33 „ „ 59	6 „ „ 77	2 „ „ 103a	2 „ „ 116a	2 „ „ 16...
72 „ „ 5	8 „ „ 9e	5 „ „ 18a	1474 „ „ 37	8 „ „ 62	8 „ „ 79	6 „ „ 103b	6 „ „ 118	1 „ „ 16...
16 „ „ 6	11 „ „ 9f	6 „ „ 18b	240 „ „ 37a	1 „ „ 62a	1 „ „ 79a	4 „ „ 103c	2 „ „ 119	4 „ „ 16...
46 „ „ 6a	107 „ „ 10	4 „ „ 19	192 „ „ 38	36 „ „ 62b	1 „ „ 80a	2 „ „ 103d	7 „ „ 120a	11 „ „ 16...
10 „ „ 7	11 „ „ 11	3 „ „ 19s	1 „ „ 43	18 „ „ 63	3 „ „ 81	11 „ „ 103f	3 „ „ 125	1 „ „ 16...
6 „ „ 7a	97 „ „ 12	9 „ „ 19b	10 „ „ 48	2 „ „ 63b	1 „ „ 82	6 „ „ 103g	4 „ „ 126	1 „ „ 16...
7 „ „ 8	6 „ „ 12a	6 „ „ 20b	6 „ „ 48a	8 „ „ 63c	6 „ „ 89a	8 „ „ 103h	6 „ „ 126a	1 „ „ 17...
								1 E.6 Elec... Motor

The main frames as they appear when completed

A FINE LIFT BRIDGE, which is said to be the largest of its kind on the Continent, is now in operation over the Oude—Meuse waterway near Barendrecht in Holland. The present bridge replaces an earlier bridge that consisted of four fixed spans and a swing bridge on the road from Rotterdam to one of the islands of the Dutch province of "Zuid-Holland". Owing to the fact that the old bridge proved a hindrance to the shipping traffic to the town of Dordrecht, it was decided to replace it by a new lift bridge of the balanced counterweight type.

Illustrations of the new bridge appeared in the *"Engineering News"* pages of the *"M.M."* for December, 1934. Each of the side legs of the hoisting towers is a latticed steel structure supported on two masonry piers. Each tower has provision for the winch and counterweight ropes, the supporting pulleys being arranged at the top of the legs a little above the span level. The winch house and control-room is placed on the left-hand side of the bridge in such a position that the operator has a clear view of the roads and the waterway.

On this page we illustrate an enormous Meccano working model of the bridge that has been built recently by a 13½ year old Belgian Meccano enthusiast, Marcel de Wilde of Hoboken.

The model represents the untiring efforts of six months' hard work, and about 8,000 Meccano parts are used in its construction. Although the model has only two fixed spans instead of three as in the original, its total length is slightly over 6½ yards! The height of the vertical towers that accommodate the hoisting machinery for the lift bridge is approximately 6 ft. 6 in., and the length of the lift bridge itself is 4 ft. 9 in. The model is built entirely from Meccano parts and from the illustration on this page it will be appreciated that a tremendous amount of patient work was entailed in carrying out the details of its construction.

The power for raising the bridge is provided by an old type high voltage Electric Motor, the bridge being suspended by means of four sets of two sheave Pulley Blocks at each side. It is interesting to note that over 60 yards of Meccano Cord were required to reeve the blocks and to connect up with the winding gear.

Owing to the great weight of the lift span it was necessary to reduce the load that the Motor had to handle. This was done as in actual engineering practice by the provision of counterbalance weights. These are arranged to move up and down in guides made from Angle Girders and are carefully adjusted so that they just balance the weight of the bridge. With this arrangement very little effort is required to raise the span.

The entire structure is illuminated by means of numerous small electric lamps, and when lit up at night presents a fairy-like spectacle. Some idea of its huge size can be gained from the fact that its builder is able to stand between the main girders of the vertical towers.

There are many praiseworthy features in the model quite apart from the faithfulness with which it reproduces its prototype. For example, the the skilful use of Meccano X Series parts in making the piers and some of the bracing greatly enhances the constructional interest of the model. The Hornby Rails, Points and Rolling Stock with which the roadway of the bridge is equipped play a great part in giving the model a life-like appearance.

The model was constructed from photographs, and as Wilde has never seen the actual bridge, his achievement is all the more remarkable.

This clever young Belgian has been an enthusiastic model-builder since he was five years old, and he built his first really big model when he was only 11. In March 1933 he obtained First Prize in a competition for model cranes, and since that time he has won other prizes.

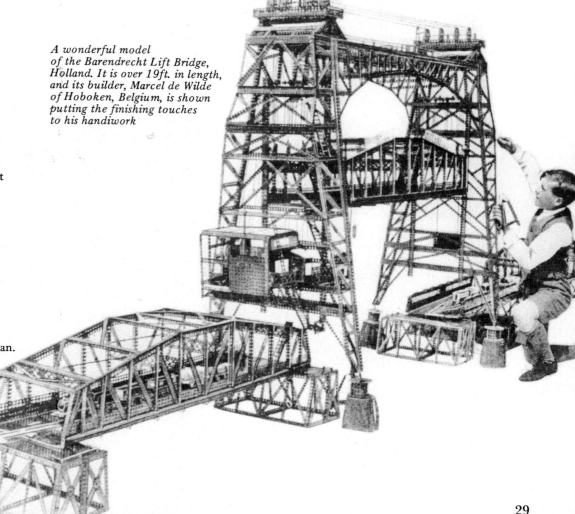

A wonderful model of the Barendrecht Lift Bridge, Holland. It is over 19ft. in length, and its builder, Marcel de Wilde of Hoboken, Belgium, is shown putting the finishing touches to his handiwork

Reprint of article 'The World's Greatest Meccano Model' from *Meccano Magazine*, March 1933.

MECCANO has been employed with outstanding success by scientists, inventors and engineers in the contruction of complicated and delicate apparatus and mechanisms of all kinds; but the greatest triumph of this wonderful constructional toy is to be found in the marvellous astronomical clock constructed by M. Alexandre Rahm, a French Meccano enthusiast. From every point of view this must be regarded as the world's greatest Meccano model.

M. Rahm tells us that the idea of a Meccano astronomical clock came to him as a result of reading two articles that appeared in the French *"M.M."* during 1924, one describing a new Meccano model clock, and the other giving details of that famous mechanical marvel, the clock at Strasbourg Cathedral. From that time onward he devoted all his leisure hours to the study of the problems involved, and the clock that is illustrated and described in this article is the result of years of research and experiment. M. Rahm's first schemes were on a comparatively modest scale, but as his plans proceeded he became more and more ambitious, and the clock in its present form embodies a number of remarkably brilliant solutions of the essential problems of a complete astronomical clock.

THE 'RAHM' CLOCK

This photograph was taken in November 1932 at the premises of Meccano (France) Ltd. Shortly after, the clock was removed to the Magazin du Printemps for exhibition, and in April 1933 was the subject of a lecture at the Sorbonne. The clock still exists today and at the time of writing is in the course of restoration.

The upper portion of the clock giving the following indications:- movements of the planets; standard time; ecclesiastical calculations; time in all parts of the Earth; day of the week; the month; the day of the month; and the day of the year.

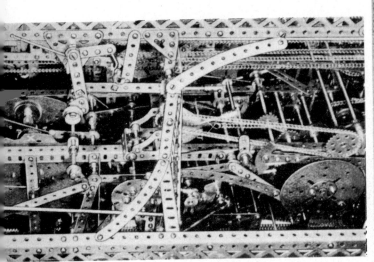

View of a section of the interior of the clock, giving some idea of the extraordinary complexity of the mechanism, and of the manner in which every inch of available space is utilised.
On the left will be noticed a wheel marked with a cross. This wheel makes a complete turn once in 2,500 years!

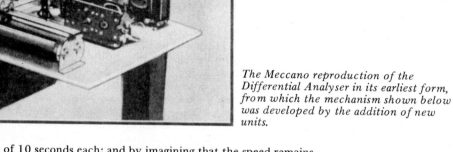

The Meccano reproduction of the Differential Analyser in its earliest form, from which the mechanism shown below was developed by the addition of new units.

Reprint of article 'Machine Solves Mathematical Problems' from *Meccano Magazine,* June 1934.

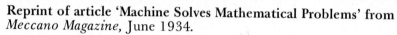

FROM time to time examples have been given in the *"M.M."* of the readiness with which the most complicated mechanisms can be reproduced in Meccano. An excellent instance of this is the wonderful astronomical clock described on page 170 of our issue for March, 1933, which automatically gives a wealth of interesting and useful astronomical information. More recently Meccano has been used in the construction of a remarkable machine that solves in a few minutes complicated equations that otherwise could only be dealt with by laborious calculations occupying many hours. The original of this model is a machine known as the Differential Analyser that was developed by Dr. V. Bush, Vice-President of the Massachusetts Institute of Technology, Cambridge, U.S.A. In constructing this machine, which at present is the only one of its kind in the world, Dr. Bush's purpose was to shorten the labour of making calculations from the complicated equations met with in working out problems in electrical and other branches of engineering, and also in physics and astronomy.

The most important mathematical operation that the machine carries out distinguishes it from other kinds of calculating machine, and makes it unique in the range and complexity of problems to which it can be applied. This operation can best be explained by an example. Suppose that a motor car is starting from rest, and that we have a record of its speed at each moment from the start. This record might be in the form of a graph showing how the speed varied with the time from the start; in handling the problem by the Differential Analyser the information actually would be supplied to it in the form of such a graph. From this information we require to know how far the car goes in, say, two minutes. We can find this approximately by dividing the period of two minutes into smaller intervals, for example into 12

intervals of 10 seconds each; and by imagining that the speed remains constant in each interval, then suddenly changes to another constant value in the next interval, and so on. Thus we can find the distance travelled in each period by multiplying each time interval by the supposed constant speed corresponding to it, and finally add up the distances travelled in successive intervals to find the total distance covered.

Reprint of article 'Meccanoland at Drury Lane' from
Meccano Magazine, December 1929.

MECCANOLAND is a wonderful place! Just when we have finished reading *"Adventures in Meccanoland"* — where Dick dreams of his Meccano models shrinking to miniatures — we learn that there will be giant Meccano models in London this Christmas! Whoever imagined Meccano models 20 ft. in height? Yet huge Meccano cranes and bridges, and Meccano motore cars — big enough to hold real people — will be included in the spectacular Meccanoland scene in "The Sleeping Beauty" at Drury Lane.

In this wonderful Julian Wylie pantomime we shall follow handsome Prince Florizel in his numerous adventures that end happily in the awakening of the Sleeping Beauty. At one stage in the unfolding of this story, the audience will find themselves in Meccanoland, and we can imagine the gasps of astonishment and delight with which Meccano boys (and girls!) will greet this wonderful scene. In it the whole stage at the Theatre Royal will be filled with huge Meccano models, it being Mr. Wylie's idea to show a land where everything is constructed from Meccano. In the background will be a great arch bridge spanning the stage and forming a glittering framework for the whole. Model builders will recognise many old friends, such as the Pit Head Gear, Dutch Windmill, Flip Flap, Hammerhead Crane, etc.

The delights of the scene do not end with the models themselves, for the stage will be occupied by Meccano boys — wearing the regulation jersey — and chorus, the members of which will wear hats crowned by miniature working Meccano models of all kinds. Anxious to help Prince Florizel in his efforts to release the Sleeping Beauty from the Turret Chamber of the Witch's Tower, they show that they possess the practical commonsense of all Meccano boys by relying on their Meccano to get them out of a difficulty. They build a wonderful Aeroplane in which the Prince flies off to the rescue, scatters the demons who obstruct his path, scales the walls of the Tower, and completely defeats the witch! All Meccano boys will rejoice in the part played by their hobby in the downfall of the villain. By no other means could the Prince secure so quickly a machine in which to make the flight to the Tower, and in fact, if it were not for Meccano the release of the "Sleeping Beauty" would be extremely difficult if not altogether impossible!

The models that will be on view in the wonderful Meccanoland scene are built on such a gigantic scale that, at first sight, it seems almost as though the parts come from an Outfit belonging to the children of the Giants that Gulliver encountered in one of his famous voyages! Strips, Girders, Plates, and other Meccano parts are reproduced eight times the size of ordinary parts. From them the models that appear in the scene are constructed in the regulation manner with the aid of giant nuts and bolts. Every model works perfectly and to sit in front of the stage and see these gigantic creations in motion will be an experience long to be remembered. How the workmen who planned and built these models must have enjoyed their task. Making the parts for this wonderful stage scene must have reminded them of the days when they, too, were Meccano boys and built models of the same type!

There is another difference between the "Engineering in Miniature" of Meccano modelbuilding and the make-believe engineering of the Drury Lane pantomime. As everyone knows, Meccano parts are made of stout steel and the box containing each Outfit has a comfortably weighty feel. If steel parts were used in building the gigantic models for Drury Lane's representation of Meccanoland, the huge Angle Girders and Flanged Plates could only be lifted with the aid of a powerful crane! For this reason, wood is used in making the large scale models, but notwithstanding this they have been constructed with as much care as is given to the making of real Meccano parts.

When the Meccanoland scene is "on", the scene will be one of bewildering beauty, enhanced by the art of the theatre electricians working "behind". The immense switchboard at Drury Lane is fitted with every conceivable mechanism to enable any desired effect to be obtained. The lighting can be varied with startling rapidity, and during this scene the men behind the scenes will flood the stage with most wonderful lighting effects. The entire pantomime is planned on a magnificent scale and the gorgeous scene in Meccanoland is one that should not be missed by any Meccano boy who may have the chance of visiting Drury Lane.

THE PANTOMIME 'SUPER MODELS'

Our illustration shows giant Meccano models in the process of construction. We hope every reader who liv in or near London will be abl to see these models in the "Sleeping Beauty" Pantomin at Drury Lane, this Christma: Further details in this article.

The MECCANO
BOOK OF ENGINEERING

PRICE
THREEPENCE

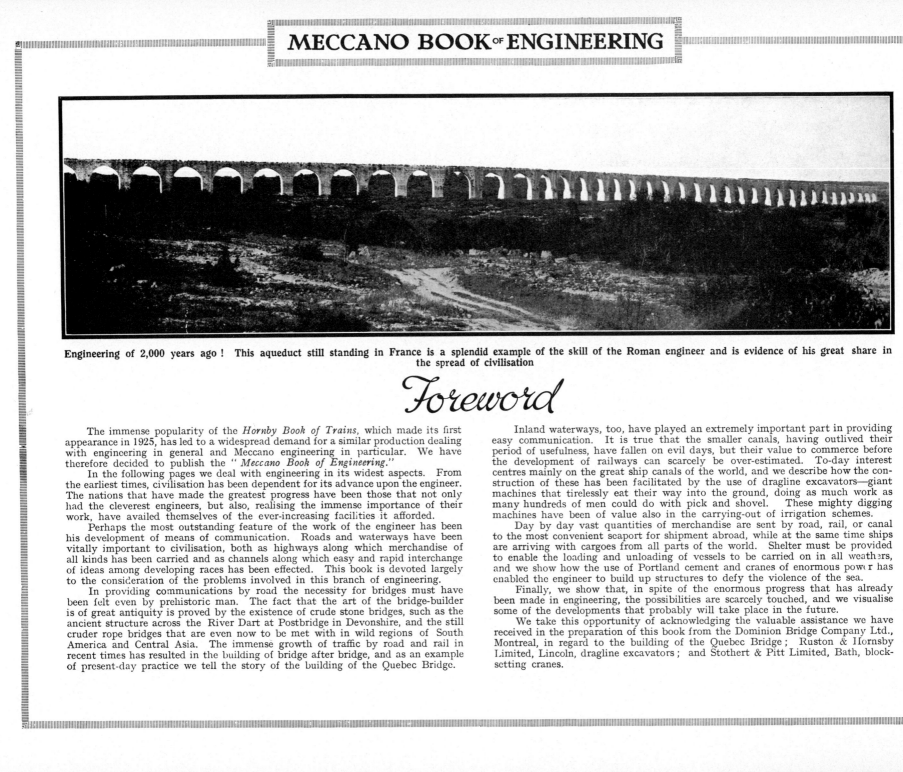

Engineering of 2,000 years ago ! This aqueduct still standing in France is a splendid example of the skill of the Roman engineer and is evidence of his great share in the spread of civilisation

Foreword

The immense popularity of the *Hornby Book of Trains*, which made its first appearance in 1925, has led to a widespread demand for a similar production dealing with engineering in general and Meccano engineering in particular. We have therefore decided to publish the "*Meccano Book of Engineering.*"

In the following pages we deal with engineering in its widest aspects. From the earliest times, civilisation has been dependent for its advance upon the engineer. The nations that have made the greatest progress have been those that not only had the cleverest engineers, but also, realising the immense importance of their work, have availed themselves of the ever-increasing facilities it afforded.

Perhaps the most outstanding feature of the work of the engineer has been his development of means of communication. Roads and waterways have been vitally important to civilisation, both as highways along which merchandise of all kinds has been carried and as channels along which easy and rapid interchange of ideas among developing races has been effected. This book is devoted largely to the consideration of the problems involved in this branch of engineering.

In providing communications by road the necessity for bridges must have been felt even by prehistoric man. The fact that the art of the bridge-builder is of great antiquity is proved by the existence of crude stone bridges, such as the ancient structure across the River Dart at Postbridge in Devonshire, and the still cruder rope bridges that are even now to be met with in wild regions of South America and Central Asia. The immense growth of traffic by road and rail in recent times has resulted in the building of bridge after bridge, and as an example of present-day practice we tell the story of the building of the Quebec Bridge.

Inland waterways, too, have played an extremely important part in providing easy communication. It is true that the smaller canals, having outlived their period of usefulness, have fallen on evil days, but their value to commerce before the development of railways can scarcely be over-estimated. To-day interest centres mainly on the great ship canals of the world, and we describe how the construction of these has been facilitated by the use of dragline excavators—giant machines that tirelessly eat their way into the ground, doing as much work as many hundreds of men could do with pick and shovel. These mighty digging machines have been of value also in the carrying-out of irrigation schemes.

Day by day vast quantities of merchandise are sent by road, rail, or canal to the most convenient seaport for shipment abroad, while at the same time ships are arriving with cargoes from all parts of the world. Shelter must be provided to enable the loading and unloading of vessels to be carried on in all weathers, and we show how the use of Portland cement and cranes of enormous power has enabled the engineer to build up structures to defy the violence of the sea.

Finally, we show that, in spite of the enormous progress that has already been made in engineering, the possibilities are scarcely touched, and we visualise some of the developments that probably will take place in the future.

We take this opportunity of acknowledging the valuable assistance we have received in the preparation of this book from the Dominion Bridge Company Ltd., Montreal, in regard to the building of the Quebec Bridge ; Ruston & Hornsby Limited, Lincoln, dragline excavators ; and Stothert & Pitt Limited, Bath, block-setting cranes.

The Engineer and Civilisation

THE story of civilisation is very largely the story of engineering; in fact it is not too much to say that no nation has ever become civilised without the aid of the engineer. The very earliest beginnings of civilisation appear to have been associated with engineering, for there is good reason to believe that crops of grain for food were raised in prehistoric days on terraces that were cut out on the hillsides near rivers in order that they might easily be supplied with water by means of crude lifting or pumping appliances. The irrigation systems thus set up were the beginnings of the mighty developments that are seen at their best to-day in Egypt and the Sudan, where huge dams have been built to enable the waters of the Nile to be used for renewing the fertility of the soil.

At later periods the nations that rose to greatness were always remarkable for some form of engineering skill. The Egyptians were famous for their Pyramids and their wonderful temples, practically all of which were examples of engineering ability of a very high standard. The largest of the Pyramids, indeed, still possesses the distinction of being the greatest mass of masonry ever erected. Most of the stones of which it is built weigh from 50 to 60 tons, but in spite of their size many were actually raised to a height of 500 ft. above the ground after having been transported from far-distant quarries.

An even more surprising example of the manner in which the Egyptians handled large masses of stone in building is furnished by the stone out of which a statue of King Rameses II was hewn. This was discovered at Thebes, hundreds of miles from the nearest quarry of the red granite of which it is composed. It is 60 ft. in length and its weight has been calculated at not less than 887 tons. The quarrying and transport of such a huge mass would present a formidable problem to the engineer of to-day with all his wonderful machinery and appliances, and it is little short of marvellous that the Egyptians, with their crude mechanisms, should have been able to carry out such a gigantic task. An even more remarkable instance of the engineering capacity of ancient peoples is furnished by the huge block of stone, 69 ft. in length and estimated to weigh 1,500 tons, that has been uncovered at Baalbek, Syria.

The Romans undoubtedly owed a great part of their supremacy to the skilful use they made of engineering principles in the construction of large war machines of the catapult type and in the fortification of their camps. Their engineers were

One of the engineering wonders of a past civilisation. The Great Pyramid of Cheops is the largest mass of masonry in the world. Many of the blocks of stone of which it is built weigh 50 to 60 tons, while the highest stones were raised nearly 500 ft. above ground level.

particularly successful in road making, and the straightness and the wearing qualities of a Roman road are now proverbial. Every country they conquered and occupied was quickly covered by a network of splendid roads, many of which still exist or have become the sites of modern roads. Other signs of Roman occupation are to be seen everywhere in the ruins of the magnificent buildings, bridges and aqueducts that they constructed.

Roads and bridges undoubtedly provided the engineers of early days with their chief opportunities. Both have always been of vital importance in making communication easier and in assisting the development of trade and the opening out of the natural resources of a country. The Romans realised this fully and the road engineer of a province of their vast empire was a very important official.

In Britain roads of a kind had been constructed even before the Romans conquered the island. In Cornwall, for instance, there were tracks made of stone blocks over which most probably tin was carried to the coast where the Phœnician traders awaited it, while similar roads existed in many other parts of the country. The Romans developed and extended the road system extensively, partly to enable their armies to make rapid marches from one fortified camp to another, and partly also to open up the country for trade purposes. Examples of the roads constructed in Britain by the Romans may still be seen, as the efficient drainage provided and the hard nature of the stone used for paving made them extraordinarily durable. No finer roads were built, in fact, until the time of the famous engineer Telford, nearly 2,000 years later.

After the Romans left Britain the wonderful buildings they had erected were treated as quarries, the stone being removed for use in the erection of meaner buildings, and most of the roads fell into disuse and gradually became covered with earth. The partial abandonment of these products of engineering skill was due to the barbarism and lack of understanding of the Anglo-Saxon invaders who soon descended upon the unprotected country, and it was not until these people in their turn began to pay attention to similar necessities that civilisation in Britain moved forward once more.

Progress was very slow until the beginning, about 150 years ago, of the great engineering age. The first important step was taken by Watt, who so much improved the crude steam engines already in use that he is popularly regarded as the

Steam Power changes the World

Railroads make Western Canada

actual inventor. After Watt had made this ample source of power available, amazing strides were made in industry and commerce, most of the credit for which must be attributed to the great engineers.

The most familiar of the uses to which the steam engine was put was in the construction of locomotives. As this development came at a time when a splendid road system had been created by the labours of Telford and his successors, steam locomotives were at first planned to run on the roads. In the meantime, however, railroads had been made in various parts of the country, on which wagons were drawn by horses, and the suitability of these for the new method of haulage soon became evident. Largely through the labours of George Stephenson and his associates in the north of England, and of the pioneers of the Baltimore and Ohio Railway in America, railways as we know them to-day came into existence, and thus the engineer took a great step forward in the work of making communication easy.

Steamships also became of commercial importance. They grew more numerous and progressively larger, until their greater speed and capacity for carrying cargo, together with their comparative independence of weather conditions, enabled them to displace sailing vessels almost completely.

These great engineering developments were productive of results in all parts of the world almost immediately. The steamship brought the old world and the new into closer contact and knitted the various parts of the latter together. Britain especially benefited by the change, as the times required for the journeys to Canada, South Africa, Australia, and New Zealand were greatly shortened. This led to a more rapid development of the resources of these great countries, as the rate of settlement was greatly increased.

Railways also played a great part in the exploitation of the natural wealth of these and other partially developed countries. This was particularly noteworthy in Canada, where far-seeing minds called on the engineer to construct a line to stretch across the prairies to the Pacific

(Above) Crude irrigation in Egypt under the shadow of the Pyramids. The large wooden wheels turned by a camel or bullock raise water in earthenware pots, a method that has been used for thousands of years. (Below) This photograph of the entrance to the Great Pyramid gives a good idea of the size of the building and of the magnitude of the task of its builders. It has been calculated that it contains 2,300,000 blocks of stone.

Coast. A similar scheme had already been carried out further south, and it was thought that the new road would at least make communication between the settlements on the east and west coasts of Canada easy, as the earlier road had already done for those of the United States.

Actually the successful completion of the Canadian Pacific Railway, as the new line was called, did far more. Prior to its construction the easiest route to Winnipeg and the Western Provinces of Canada led through the territory of the United States, while British Columbia was also more closely in contact with the latter country than with the rest of Canada. The railway opened out an easy route north of the Great Lakes and bridged the Rocky Mountains, thus making Canada for the first time a really compact and self-contained territory.

In addition the railroad increased the rate of settlement enormously by providing access to the rich prairie lands and a means whereby the grain that they produced could be exported. The process has since been continuously accelerated by the construction of a second trans-continental railroad and of numerous branch lines. It is no exaggeration to say that Western Canada has been made by engineering, for it could not have become the thriving region that it now is if the railroads had not been constructed.

Examples of the immensely important part played by railways in the development of new countries could be given from almost all quarters of the earth. The first question raised by any country desiring to bring new regions within the sphere of civilisation is invariably that of the construction of a railroad. This holds good in all climates. Kenya in the tropics, and Manchuria in the extreme north of China, are both undergoing development along newly constructed railroads, and into the dense forests of the Congo and of Brazil, the northern prairie lands of Canada, the fertile valleys of China, and the ancient and productive countries in the hinterland of West Africa, railways are being pushed forward as heralds of civilisation.

Waterways that Link the Oceans

The Era of Electricity

The extension of railroads to hitherto inaccessible parts of the earth has not been carried out easily and it has been necessary to learn many new methods of bridging rivers and boring tunnels through mountain ranges. Some of the greatest feats in this direction deserve mention as important agents in the engineer's conquest of the world for civilisation. An outstanding example of a bridge that opened an enormous field for exploitation is that over the Zambesi River near the Victoria Falls. It made possible the extension of the railroad to the valuable gold and copper mines of northern Rhodesia and the borders of the Congo Free State.

Other instances of the influence of the engineer are provided by the Suez and the Panama Canals. Until the former was opened the most convenient route from Britain to India was around the Cape of Good Hope, and Calcutta was reached as easily as Bombay. The shortening of the journey benefited Indian trade and commerce considerably, a fact that was made evident by the phenomenal growth of the port of Bombay. This city displaced Calcutta as the principal port of entry, but nevertheless Calcutta continued to grow and flourish. The Suez Canal in fact made Bombay in exactly the same way as the Canadian Pacific Railway made Western Canada, but in neither case did any other district suffer from the development.

The Panama Canal is proving equally well that the work of the engineer is one of the chief factors in developing and extending civilisation. The mere fact that it is no longer necessary to make the dangerous voyage around Cape Horn is sufficient justification for the existence of the canal, and marks the engineers who constructed it as benefactors to humanity. Beyond this, in the comparatively few years of its existence the canal has already led to a great increase in the importance of the countries on the western slopes of the Andes and of the Rocky Mountains. The

(Above) The Statue of Rameses II found at Thebes. It was carved from a single block of granite transported from Assouan, hundreds of miles away, in spite of its weight of 887 tons. (Below) The largest block of stone ever quarried. Its estimated weight is 1,500 tons, and we can only surmise how it was handled by the ancient inhabitants of Syria, where it was found.

astounding growth of Los Angeles is a striking example. This is due almost entirely to its growing value as a seaport. In the United States it actually ranks second to New York, a position that it owes to its favourable situation as the nearest port in California to the Panama Canal.

Along with the development of the railway and the steamship during last century came the application, on a continually increasing scale, of steam power in industry. Spinning and weaving in all their branches benefited greatly by this, while production in iron and steel-works increased enormously in attempts to cope with the demands occasioned by new applications of machinery. In addition, the coal industry witnessed an almost unprecedented increase in output, as the possession of cheap and abundant fuel became the foundation of national prosperity.

The early attempts to introduce steam-power into industry were received with some hostility, but the greater output made possible by the use of machinery led to increased prosperity in which all classes shared, and the prejudice against machinery has almost completely disappeared.

The civil and mechanical engineers of the last century placed resources hitherto undreamed of at the disposal of mankind, with the result that there has been a great improvement in the general conditions of life in those quarters of the globe where their influence has been exerted. These two were joined later by the electrical engineer. The latter introduced an entirely new power medium that is easily generated from inexhaustible natural sources and may be transmitted to distant points in a very simple manner. The full extent of the usefulness of electricity has yet to be realised. Civil and mechanical engineers, too, have by no means reached their zenith, and it is quite certain that engineering generally will in time play an even more important part in life than it does at the present day.

The Story of the Quebec Bridge

THE Quebec Bridge is one of the three greatest examples of the cantilever type of bridge, the other two being the Forth Bridge in Scotland and the Blackwell's Island Bridge, New York. Of these three, the Quebec Bridge is the largest, and the story of its building is a thrilling one.

The dictionary defines the word " cantilever " as meaning a projecting bracket that supports some other object and a simple cantilever bridge is one in which two shore arms support at their extremities a centre span. These shore arms project outward over the river in the form of huge overhanging brackets, and are known as cantilevers—hence the name given to this type of bridge. The name " cantilever " is derived from the French " cant," meaning angle, and " lever," to raise. The cantilever principle is a very old one, having been used hundreds of years ago in China, Japan and India. These early structures were, of course, very primitive, and the type developed very little until comparatively recent years.

An excellent description of the cantilever principle was given by Sir Benjamin Baker at the Royal Institution in the course of a lecture on the Forth Bridge. On this occasion the lecturer exhibited what he described as a living model of the Forth Bridge, arranged as follows :—

" Two men sitting on chairs extended their arms and supported the same by grasping sticks butting against the chairs. This represented the two double cantilevers. The central beam was represented by a short stick slung from the near hands of the two men, and the anchorages of the cantilevers by ropes extending from the other hands of the men to a couple of piles of bricks. When stresses were brought to bear on this system by a load on the central beam, the men's arms and the anchorage ropes came into tension, and the sticks and chair-legs into compression."

The great advantage of the cantilever system is that it permits the cantilever arms to be built out in pairs on each side of their towers in such a manner as to balance one another during construction, thus rendering external support unnecessary.

In the early cantilever bridges erected in Eastern countries the shore cantilevers consisted of a series of superimposed horizontal wooden beams, each successive beam projecting a little farther over the stream than the one immediately beneath it. When the gap between the two cantilevers had been reduced sufficiently by this means, it was bridged by a central beam, the ends of which rested upon the extremities of the uppermost beams of the cantilevers.

During the past 50 years the cantilever principle has been adopted for bridges constructed of metal and having spans of considerable width. The first true metal cantilever bridge was erected across the Niagara River close to the well-known suspension bridge. This cantilever bridge was opened for traffic in 1883. Two steel piers rising from the stone foundations carried cantilevers having an overall length of 395 ft., and these in turn supported a central or suspension girder 120 ft. in length. The main span, from centre to centre of the piers, was 495 ft.

Some two years later a cantilever metal bridge was constructed across the Fraser River to carry the Canadian Pacific Railway. In this case the clear span measured 315 ft. Subsequently the cantilever principle was adopted for bridges having more than one span, the additional cantilevers being built up on piers having their foundation in the river bed. The most striking example of this type of bridge is the magnificent structure that carries the London and North Eastern Railway across the Firth of Forth. The Forth Bridge has an overall length of 8,296 ft., of which the cantilever portion measures 5,349 ft. and includes three monster double cantilevers and two intervening suspended spans. The total span between the towers of the cantilevers is 1,710 ft. Each cantilever projects 680 ft. and the vertical columns composing their main towers are 361 ft. above high-water level.

Development of Cantilever Type

Fate of First Quebec Bridge

The suspended spans are each 350 ft. in length.

The Blackwell's Island Bridge, New York, is another striking example of the cantilever type. This bridge has a total length of 3,724 ft. and has four cantilevers built up from piers, one on each shore and the other two on the island in the river. The cantilevers are joined together without any intervening suspended spans, and in this respect the bridge differs notably from the Forth Bridge. The five spans of the Blackwell's Island Bridge are all of different lengths, the shortest being 459 ft. and the longest 1,182 ft.

All the foregoing bridges, even that across the Forth are eclipsed by the Quebec Bridge. This bridge was built to enable the provinces eastward of the St. Lawrence River to be linked up with those to the west by means of a great trans-continental railroad. The charter authorising the

Our photograph shows the southern cantilever of the first bridge. The photograph was taken on the 28th August, 1907, immediately before the cantilever collapsed

the clearing of the shores for the erection of the approach structures and the preparations for building the two piers in the river. In 1902 the pier nearest the south shore of the river was completed, and then commenced the great work of building up the south cantilever of the bridge. Month by month the mass of steelwork rose higher and higher, and gradually projected farther out over the river. By the summer of 1907 the south anchor arm and about one third of its cantilever span had been erected, the whole extending over the river for some 200 ft.

So far all had gone well, but one day an alarming incident occurred. It was noticed that the bottom or compression chords of the anchor arm were bending slightly under the tremendous strain imposed upon them. Word was sent hurriedly to the

construction of the bridge was obtained from the Dominion Parliament in 1882. The newly-completed Forth Bridge was regarded as affording positive proof of the superiority of the cantilever bridge, and it was natural, therefore, that the engineers called into consultation proposed that the St. Lawrence should be spanned by a structure of this type. At the place selected for building the bridge the river is nearly 2,000 ft. in width, 200 ft. in depth, and flows between banks 200 ft. in height.

No definite action was taken until 1887, in which year the Quebec Bridge and Railway Company was incorporated. A design for a cantilever bridge was accepted from a New York engineer who had spent some three years over the work. Tenders were invited and ultimately the contract was awarded in 1899 to the Phœnix Bridge Company. According to the contract the bridge was to cost £2,000,000. It was to have a total length of 3,239 ft. including two anchor arms each 500 ft. in length, two cantilever spans of 562 ft. each, and a central suspended span of 675 ft. Constructed to these dimensions the bridge would have had an overall span from centre to centre of the cantilever towers of 1,800 ft., thus exceeding the span of the Forth Bridge by 90 ft. It was to be provided with a single deck 150 ft. in width, and this was to accommodate a road, two pavements and two tramway and two railway tracks.

In due course work was commenced. Among the first tasks carried out were

consulting engineer, no doubt in anticipation that he would order the immediate withdrawal of all workmen from the bridge until it had been minutely examined. For some unexplained reason no command to cease operations came through, however, and work went on as usual.

On 29th August 1907, came swift and terrible disaster. Shortly before work was due to cease for the day, the compression chords of the south anchor arm suddenly crumpled up. The entire cantilever rocked violently, and with a fearful crash collapsed upon its pier, carrying with it the 86 men who had been at work upon the erection at the time. It was obvious that a large number of these men must have perished, but immediate steps were taken to assist the survivors. In spite of all efforts, however, only 11 men were rescued. Of the 17,000 tons of steel contained in the structure, some 8,000 tons had fallen into the deep channel of the river, while the remainder lay astride the pier and along the bank—a gigantic mass of girders and plates 40 ft. in height, twisted and distorted almost beyond belief. Thus in a few minutes was undone the labour of three years.

This terrible catastrophe cast a gloom over the country and created utter consternation among bridge-building engineers. A searching inquiry into the cause of the disaster was instituted at once by the Government, and a Royal Commission was appointed to examine the wreckage. In due course, the Commission

Proposals for New Structures

Salving the Wrecked Bridge

Connecting up web members at the centre of the large post over the main pier

One section of the large link being placed in position at the top of the main pier post

submitted their report, in which they expressed the opinion that the accident had been due to errors in the design and building of the bridge, attributable mainly to lack of practical knowledge of how to plan and prepare for a structure on such a huge scale.

The need for improved means of communication across the St. Lawrence River still remained and was rapidly growing more acute. It was clear that, in spite of the disaster, the bridge must be built, and the Canadian Government took the matter in hand. The shareholders of the Phœnix Bridge Company were compensated for their financial loss, and the Minister of Railways and Canals appointed a Technical Board to design a new cantilever bridge. The plan ultimately put forward by the Board was on a less ambitious scale than that of the Phœnix Bridge Company. It was proposed to build a cantilever bridge 88 ft. in width and having a main central span of 1,758 ft. The reduction of roughly 50 ft. in the length of this span meant that one or both of the existing piers would have to be moved to a new position. The traffic facilities of the bridge also were reduced and consisted only of two railway tracks and two pavements.

Tenders were then invited from prominent engineering firms, and in order that the best possible design of a cantilever bridge might be secured, the Board allowed competing firms the option of tendering either for a bridge as proposed by the Board or for a structure to the firm's own design. This far-sighted policy met with general approval and no less than 35 tenders were submitted. Ultimately the Board selected a tender put forward by the St. Lawrence Bridge Company, an organisation specially formed for the occasion, and combining the interests and resources of the Canadian Bridge Company and the Dominion Bridge Company.

The design submitted by the St. Lawrence Bridge Company contained several features that aroused considerable interest among civil engineers. This was particularly the case in regard to the webs forming the steel bracing of the cantilevers and anchor arms, which were fashioned after the letter "K." Several advantages were claimed for this new system of girder bracing, one being that the various K trusses could be assembled without the necessity of first erecting falsework or temporary supporting members. The new idea was not adopted hastily, and it was not until the Board had considered carefully every orthodox system of girder bracing that they decided that the new method was fully as strong and reliable as any of the others, while it compared very favourably in regard to appearance.

The successful design was for a steel cantilever bridge estimated to cost £1,750,000. It was to have an overall length of 3,239 ft., comprising two approach spans 140 ft. and 269 ft. in length respectively, two anchor arms each 515 ft. in length, two cantilever arms each 580 ft. in length and a central span of 640 ft. The traffic limitations indicated in the Board's own plan were observed in the successful design, in which the side walks were shown as 5 ft. in width and the two railway tracks were placed 32½ ft. apart. One condition of the contract was that £259,000 in cash had to be deposited by the company with the Government as a guarantee of good faith, and this was accordingly done.

The task of salving as much as possible of the pile of tangled steel girders and plates that represented the former partly-built bridge was commenced by a salvage party of 25 men in December 1909. Charges of dynamite were used to break up the heavy masses of distorted steelwork lying astride the stone pier, and oxy-acetylene torches were employed to cut up the material into portable sections. So well did the men work that in nine months they succeeded in removing about 5,000 tons of scrap material, which was sold in Montreal at approximately £2 10s. 0d. per ton. Of the sum thus realised £8,000 was paid to the salvage party. The portion of the wrecked bridge that had sunk into the channel of the river lay too

Re-Building Commenced

The Operation of a Caisson

deep to interfere with navigation and therefore no attempt was made to retrieve it.

A contract in respect to the foundations for and the erection of the piers to support the approach ways and cantilevers was placed with a Canadian firm, M. P. & T. T. Davis. The two piers erected in the river by the Phœnix Bridge Company were in good condition—the south one having suffered little from the collapse upon it of the steelwork—but they were too short and unsuitably placed to be of use for the new bridge and were therefore demolished.

The new pier near the south bank of the river could not be established until the wreckage of the former bridge had been removed, but the contractors soon got to work on the construction of the pier for the north cantilever. On the north shore a large wooden building was erected in which to construct the massive caisson for the north pier. When completed this caisson had an overall length of 180 ft., was 55 ft. in width, 68 ft. in height and weighed roughly 1,600 tons. It was successfully launched and then carefully towed to the pier site, where a cavity to receive it had been excavated in the river bed by dredgers.

The caisson affords a means of sinking foundations in the bed of a river, and in principle it may be regarded as a diving bell of enormous size. It is cylindrical in shape, built either of steel or wood, and in appearance is not unlike a gasometer. The cylinder is closed at the top but open at the bottom and the latter has a sharp cutting edge of steel. When the caisson is sunk, the cutting edge beds itself evenly in the river bottom. The lower part of the caisson is rendered airtight by means of a strong partition fitted across it. The men engaged in the task of excavation work inside the chamber

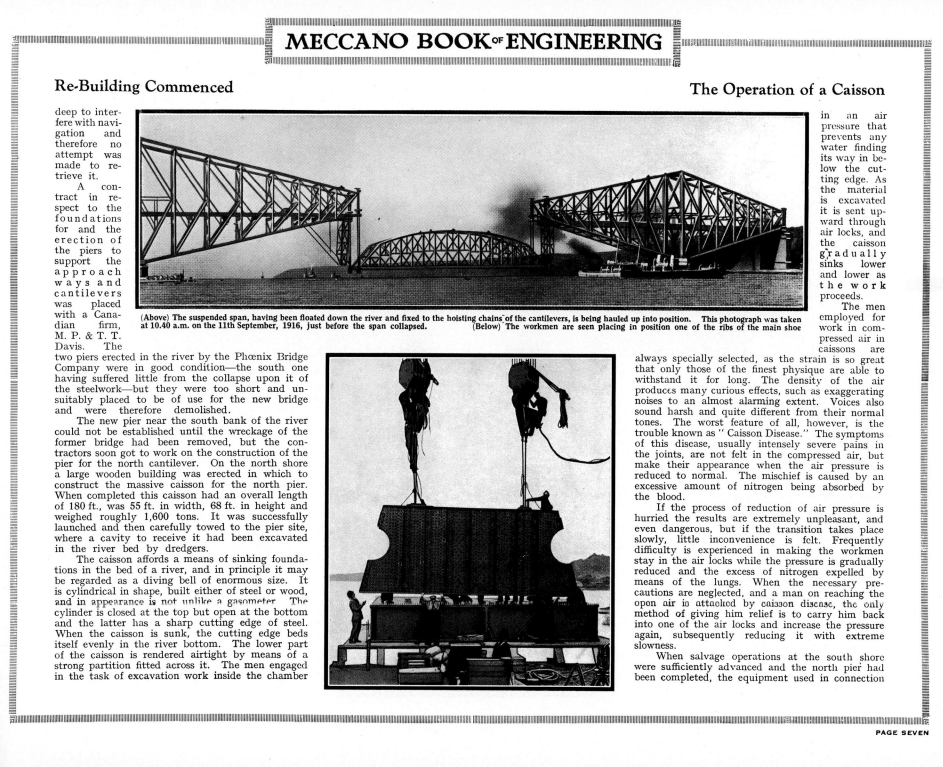

(Above) The suspended span, having been floated down the river and fixed to the hoisting chains of the cantilevers, is being hauled up into position.   This photograph was taken at 10.40 a.m. on the 11th September, 1916, just before the span collapsed.   (Below) The workmen are seen placing in position one of the ribs of the main shoe

in an air pressure that prevents any water finding its way in below the cutting edge. As the material is excavated it is sent upward through air locks, and the caisson gradually sinks lower and lower as the work proceeds.

The men employed for work in compressed air in caissons are always specially selected, as the strain is so great that only those of the finest physique are able to withstand it for long. The density of the air produces many curious effects, such as exaggerating noises to an almost alarming extent. Voices also sound harsh and quite different from their normal tones. The worst feature of all, however, is the trouble known as " Caisson Disease." The symptoms of this disease, usually intensely severe pains in the joints, are not felt in the compressed air, but make their appearance when the air pressure is reduced to normal. The mischief is caused by an excessive amount of nitrogen being absorbed by the blood.

If the process of reduction of air pressure is hurried the results are extremely unpleasant, and even dangerous, but if the transition takes place slowly, little inconvenience is felt. Frequently difficulty is experienced in making the workmen stay in the air locks while the pressure is gradually reduced and the excess of nitrogen expelled by means of the lungs. When the necessary precautions are neglected, and a man on reaching the open air is attacked by caisson disease, the only method of giving him relief is to carry him back into one of the air locks and increase the pressure again, subsequently reducing it with extreme slowness.

When salvage operations at the south shore were sufficiently advanced and the north pier had been completed, the equipment used in connection

Manufacturing the huge Steel Members

Constructing the Cantilever Arms

with the latter was dismantled, shipped across the river to the south side, and there re-erected. The caisson built for the south pier was similar to that constructed for the north pier but was somewhat smaller. Some 3,000,000 ft. of timber and 70 tons of bolts were used in constructing the two caissons.

At that time there were no engineering shops in Canada equipped to manufacture such huge steel members as those required for the bridge. Special workshops built of steel and masonry, and thoroughly equipped for the work, were therefore erected at Montreal at a cost of £260,000. In order

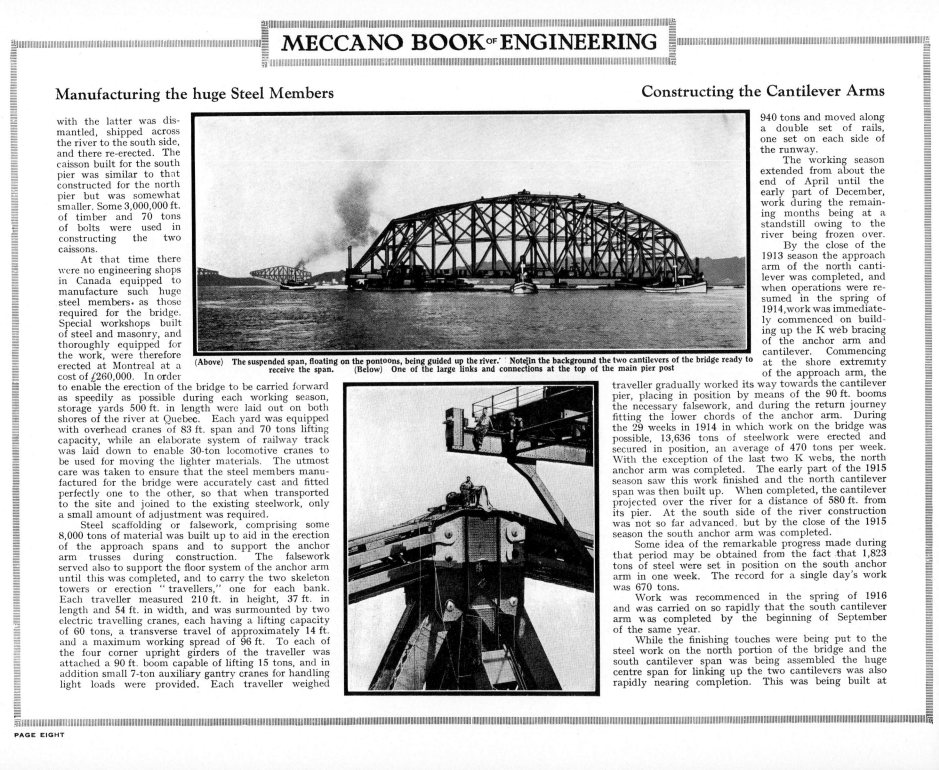

(Above)   The suspended span, floating on the pontoons, being guided up the river. Note in the background the two cantilevers of the bridge ready to receive the span.   (Below)   One of the large links and connections at the top of the main pier post

to enable the erection of the bridge to be carried forward as speedily as possible during each working season, storage yards 500 ft. in length were laid out on both shores of the river at Quebec. Each yard was equipped with overhead cranes of 83 ft. span and 70 tons lifting capacity, while an elaborate system of railway track was laid down to enable 30-ton locomotive cranes to be used for moving the lighter materials. The utmost care was taken to ensure that the steel members manufactured for the bridge were accurately cast and fitted perfectly one to the other, so that when transported to the site and joined to the existing steelwork, only a small amount of adjustment was required.

Steel scaffolding or falsework, comprising some 8,000 tons of material was built up to aid in the erection of the approach spans and to support the anchor arm trusses during construction. The falsework served also to support the floor system of the anchor arm until this was completed, and to carry the two skeleton towers or erection "travellers," one for each bank. Each traveller measured 210 ft. in height, 37 ft. in length and 54 ft. in width, and was surmounted by two electric travelling cranes, each having a lifting capacity of 60 tons, a transverse travel of approximately 14 ft. and a maximum working spread of 96 ft. To each of the four corner upright girders of the traveller was attached a 90 ft. boom capable of lifting 15 tons, and in addition small 7-ton auxiliary gantry cranes for handling light loads were provided. Each traveller weighed

940 tons and moved along a double set of rails, one set on each side of the runway.

The working season extended from about the end of April until the early part of December, work during the remaining months being at a standstill owing to the river being frozen over.

By the close of the 1913 season the approach arm of the north cantilever was completed, and when operations were resumed in the spring of 1914, work was immediately commenced on building up the K web bracing of the anchor arm and cantilever. Commencing at the shore extremity of the approach arm, the traveller gradually worked its way towards the cantilever pier, placing in position by means of the 90 ft. booms the necessary falsework, and during the return journey fitting the lower chords of the anchor arm. During the 29 weeks in 1914 in which work on the bridge was possible, 13,636 tons of steelwork were erected and secured in position, an average of 470 tons per week. With the exception of the last two K webs, the north anchor arm was completed. The early part of the 1915 season saw this work finished and the north cantilever span was then built up. When completed, the cantilever projected over the river for a distance of 580 ft. from its pier. At the south side of the river construction was not so far advanced, but by the close of the 1915 season the south anchor arm was completed.

Some idea of the remarkable progress made during that period may be obtained from the fact that 1,823 tons of steel were set in position on the south anchor arm in one week. The record for a single day's work was 670 tons.

Work was recommenced in the spring of 1916 and was carried on so rapidly that the south cantilever arm was completed by the beginning of September of the same year.

While the finishing touches were being put to the steel work on the north portion of the bridge and the south cantilever span was being assembled the huge centre span for linking up the two cantilevers was also rapidly nearing completion. This was being built at

Launch of the Centre Span

Elaborate Hoisting Arrangements

Sillery Cove, about 3½ miles downstream from the site of the bridge. The Cove proved very favourable for carrying out this work, as it was protected by shallows and yet at high tide admitted sufficient water to float the pontoons upon which the span was eventually to be loaded. The lattice girder sides of the span were arch-shaped and were 110 ft. in height at the centre.

When word was received at Sillery Cove that the bridge cantilevers were ready to receive the central span, preparations were immediately made for transporting this to the bridge site. The span

The collapse of the suspended span at 10.50 a.m. on the 11th September, 1916

had been assembled upon the falsework at a height that allowed the pontoons to be floated beneath it and 2½ hours before high tide on 11th September 1916, this was effected, six pontoons being safely manœuvred into place, three under each end of the span. Each pontoon was constructed of heavy steel framing and steel plate girder bulkheads, and was 165 ft. in length, 32 ft. in width and approximately 11½ ft. in depth.

When the span had been made secure upon the pontoons the whole was floated out into the river and, responding to the tide, moved slowly upstream. Its rate of progress was suitably restrained by five tugs on the downstream side, four of 500 h.p. and one of 1,000 h.p. The 3½-mile voyage to the bridge site was accomplished without mishap and, after much skilful manœuvring, in which two reserve tugs that had accompanied the flotilla lent their aid, the span was brought to a standstill directly beneath the gap between the two cantilevers. The ends of the span were then secured by four 1¼ in. plough steel ropes, controlled by electric hoists on the bridge deck, to cantilever mooring frames, one of which was hinged from the end of each cantilever and hung vertically. Each mooring frame was capable of holding at its lower end a suspended load of 300,000 lb.

Two 30-ton girders, each fitted on the upper side with two shoes, were placed transversely under the ends of the suspension span, each shoe supporting a corner of the span. At the extremity of each cantilever

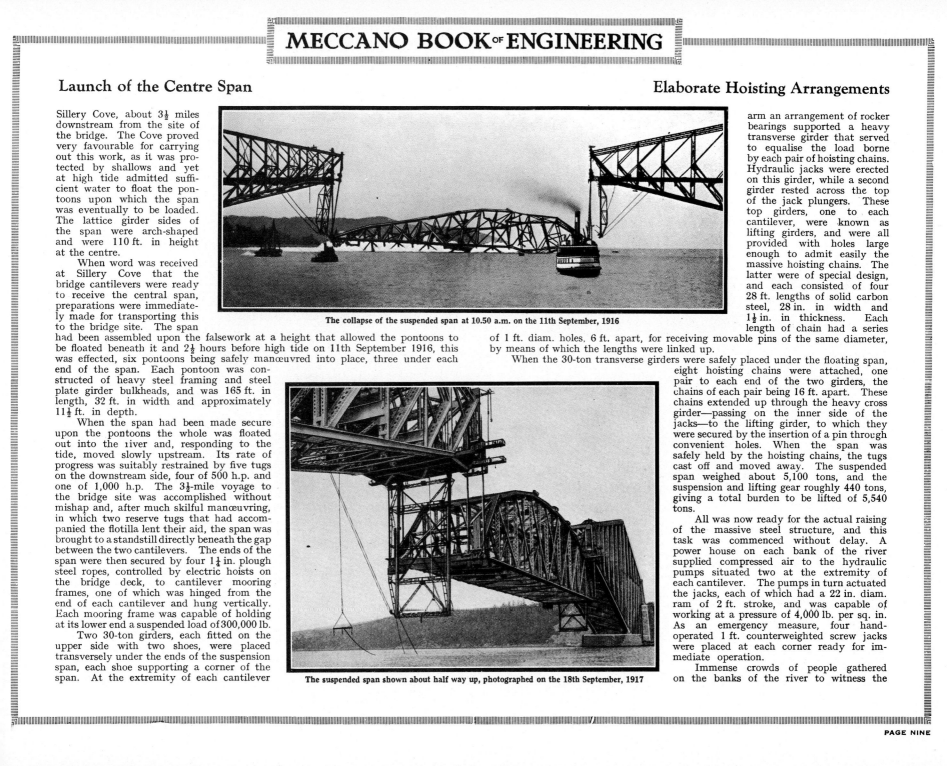

The suspended span shown about half way up, photographed on the 18th September, 1917

arm an arrangement of rocker bearings supported a heavy transverse girder that served to equalise the load borne by each pair of hoisting chains. Hydraulic jacks were erected on this girder, while a second girder rested across the top of the jack plungers. These top girders, one to each cantilever, were known as lifting girders, and were all provided with holes large enough to admit easily the massive hoisting chains. The latter were of special design, and each consisted of four 28 ft. lengths of solid carbon steel, 28 in. in width and 1½ in. in thickness. Each length of chain had a series of 1 ft. diam. holes, 6 ft. apart, for receiving movable pins of the same diameter, by means of which the lengths were linked up.

When the 30-ton transverse girders were safely placed under the floating span, eight hoisting chains were attached, one pair to each end of the two girders, the chains of each pair being 16 ft. apart. These chains extended up through the heavy cross girder—passing on the inner side of the jacks—to the lifting girder, to which they were secured by the insertion of a pin through convenient holes. When the span was safely held by the hoisting chains, the tugs cast off and moved away. The suspended span weighed about 5,100 tons, and the suspension and lifting gear roughly 440 tons, giving a total burden to be lifted of 5,540 tons.

All was now ready for the actual raising of the massive steel structure, and this task was commenced without delay. A power house on each bank of the river supplied compressed air to the hydraulic pumps situated two at the extremity of each cantilever. The pumps in turn actuated the jacks, each of which had a 22 in. diam. ram of 2 ft. stroke, and was capable of working at a pressure of 4,000 lb. per sq. in. As an emergency measure, four hand-operated 1 ft. counterweighted screw jacks were placed at each corner ready for immediate operation.

Immense crowds of people gathered on the banks of the river to witness the

A Second Disaster

Engineers still Undismayed

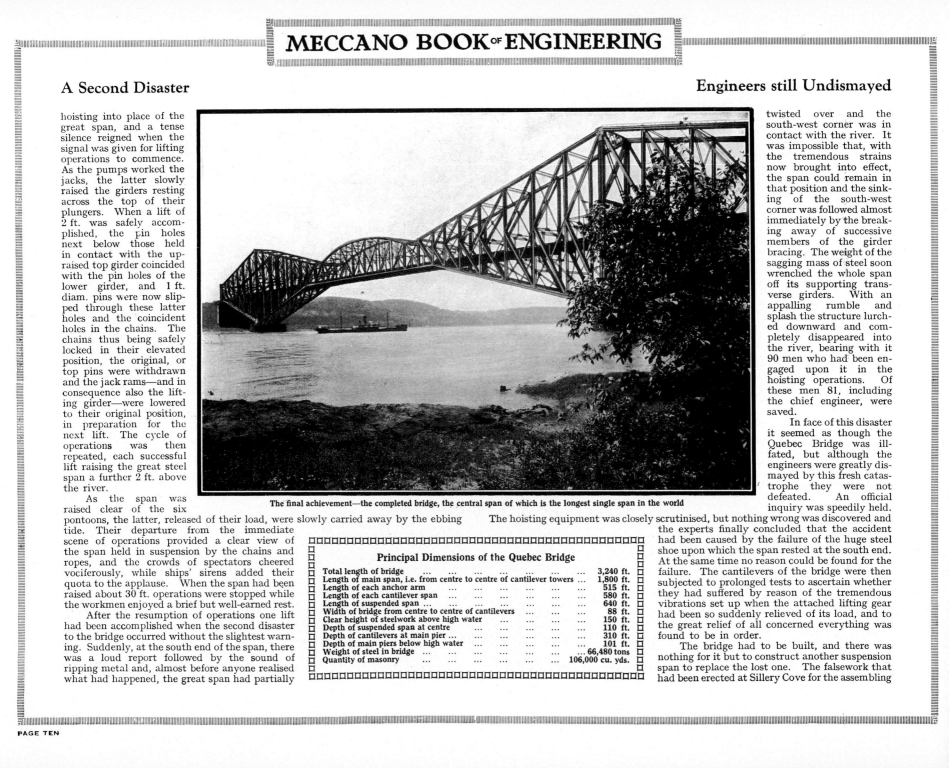

The final achievement—the completed bridge, the central span of which is the longest single span in the world

hoisting into place of the great span, and a tense silence reigned when the signal was given for lifting operations to commence. As the pumps worked the jacks, the latter slowly raised the girders resting across the top of their plungers. When a lift of 2 ft. was safely accomplished, the pin holes next below those held in contact with the upraised top girder coincided with the pin holes of the lower girder, and 1 ft. diam. pins were now slipped through these latter holes and the coincident holes in the chains. The chains thus being safely locked in their elevated position, the original, or top pins were withdrawn and the jack rams—and in consequence also the lifting girder—were lowered to their original position, in preparation for the next lift. The cycle of operations was then repeated, each successful lift raising the great steel span a further 2 ft. above the river.

As the span was raised clear of the six pontoons, the latter, released of their load, were slowly carried away by the ebbing tide. Their departure from the immediate scene of operations provided a clear view of the span held in suspension by the chains and ropes, and the crowds of spectators cheered vociferously, while ships' sirens added their quota to the applause. When the span had been raised about 30 ft. operations were stopped while the workmen enjoyed a brief but well-earned rest.

After the resumption of operations one lift had been accomplished when the second disaster to the bridge occurred without the slightest warning. Suddenly, at the south end of the span, there was a loud report followed by the sound of ripping metal and, almost before anyone realised what had happened, the great span had partially

twisted over and the south-west corner was in contact with the river. It was impossible that, with the tremendous strains now brought into effect, the span could remain in that position and the sinking of the south-west corner was followed almost immediately by the breaking away of successive members of the girder bracing. The weight of the sagging mass of steel soon wrenched the whole span off its supporting transverse girders. With an appalling rumble and splash the structure lurched downward and completely disappeared into the river, bearing with it 90 men who had been engaged upon it in the hoisting operations. Of these men 81, including the chief engineer, were saved.

In face of this disaster it seemed as though the Quebec Bridge was ill-fated, but although the engineers were greatly dismayed by this fresh catastrophe they were not defeated. An official inquiry was speedily held. The hoisting equipment was closely scrutinised, but nothing wrong was discovered and the experts finally concluded that the accident had been caused by the failure of the huge steel shoe upon which the span rested at the south end. At the same time no reason could be found for the failure. The cantilevers of the bridge were then subjected to prolonged tests to ascertain whether they had suffered by reason of the tremendous vibrations set up when the attached lifting gear had been so suddenly relieved of its load, and to the great relief of all concerned everything was found to be in order.

The bridge had to be built, and there was nothing for it but to construct another suspension span to replace the lost one. The falsework that had been erected at Sillery Cove for the assembling

Principal Dimensions of the Quebec Bridge

Total length of bridge	3,240 ft.
Length of main span, i.e. from centre to centre of cantilever towers	1,800 ft.
Length of each anchor arm	515 ft.
Length of each cantilever span	580 ft.
Length of suspended span	640 ft.
Width of bridge from centre to centre of cantilevers	88 ft.
Clear height of steelwork above high water	150 ft.
Depth of suspended span at centre	110 ft.
Depth of cantilevers at main pier	310 ft.
Depth of main piers below high water	101 ft.
Weight of steel in bridge	66,480 tons
Quantity of masonry	106,000 cu. yds.

New Span placed in Position

Completion of the Bridge

of the first span had afterwards been abandoned, and the task of restoring it to fitness prior to building a new span occupied many months. In the meantime the requisite material for the new span was ordered and obtained. The new central span was completed by August of the following year, and early on the morning of 17th September, 1917, pontoons and tugs conveyed it to the bridge site, where in due course it was safely attached to the mooring frames and hoisting gear.

A few minutes after 9 a.m. the signal to commence lifting the span was given, and once more pumps and jacks commenced their responsible task. Mindful of the catastrophe of the previous year, the engineers and workmen exercised the utmost caution, and no attempt was made to work to a speed schedule. Hoisting was carried out in easy stages, each of 15 min. duration. Twelve lifts, each raising the span a further 2 ft., were made on the first day; 22 lifts, equivalent to a rise of 44 ft., were accomplished during the following day, and 26 lifts on the third day, at the close of which the span was suspended within 30 ft. of its final resting place.

At the time that work ceased on the third day there was a rising wind and indications of a storm, and special precautions were taken to make the span secure. During the night the wind attained a force of 35 miles per hour and it was an anxious body of engineers who inspected the span and hoisting gear on the following morning. Everything was found to be in order, and after assuring themselves that the lifting operations could be safely continued, in spite of the high wind still blowing, the engineers gave the signal for hoisting to be resumed. By 3.10 p.m. the hoisting of the span was

(Above) A fine Meccano model of the Quebec Bridge measuring over 15 ft. in length.
(Below) A striking view looking along the above model, showing the double track for Hornby Trains divided by a steel partition.

completed and 50 minutes later the connecting pins had all been driven and the span finally secured in place.

During the following three weeks the floor system of the central span was placed in position by travelling cranes and one of the two railway tracks was laid down and riveted. One month after the suspension span was raised into position the first train passed safely over and on 3rd December, 1917, the structure was completed and opened for regular traffic. The concreting of the side walks for pedestrian traffic and the painting were completed while the bridge was in use.

The building of the Quebec Bridge was a remarkable undertaking in many respects. It is probable that never before has an engineering structure on such a huge scale been carried to completion on the site originally assigned to it after two great disasters, in the first of which the crumpling girders dragged to their death 75 men. These two disasters merely strengthened the determination of the engineers that the bridge should be built and, indeed, scarcely had the account of the second disaster been telegraphed throughout the world before it was followed by an announcement that the bridge would be rebuilt and upon the same plan. As we have seen, this third effort proved entirely successful. The building of the bridge from first to last has enormously increased our knowledge of the problems of compression and tension and of the means for dealing with the effects of distortion in trusses.

To-day the Quebec Bridge carries the trans-continental line of the Canadian National Railways over the St. Lawrence River, reducing the distance between Halifax and Winnipeg by 200 miles, and stands as a monument to the ability, courage and tenacity of its engineers.

Digging by Machinery: The Dragline Excavator

A LARGE proportion of the work of Engineers might be described as consisting of digging holes in the ground. This is the case in such undertakings as cutting canals, boring tunnels, quarrying, excavating reservoirs, and sinking the deep foundations of very large buildings. In ancient times big excavation works involved the employment of vast numbers of men because little or no machinery was available and everything had to be done by manual labour, and this state of affairs continued to a considerable extent up to comparatively recent times. To-day, although large numbers of men have to be employed on any big undertaking, the bulk of the work is carried out entirely by mechanical power. The spade wielded by hand is still necessary, but most of the excavation is done by gigantic shovels operated by steam or electric power, and each capable of doing the work of many hundreds of men.

One of the most familiar of digging machines is the Steam Shovel, often referred to as the Steam Navvy. This consists of a huge shovel mounted on the end of a powerful steel arm or jib and operated by a steam engine accommodated in a cab resembling that of a breakdown crane. Steam shovels are employed in the excavation of railway cuttings, open mines and quarries, and canals and docks. They are capable of accomplishing an enormous amount of work, and they are to be found wherever large scale excavation is in progress. At the same time their scope is limited, for they cannot excavate

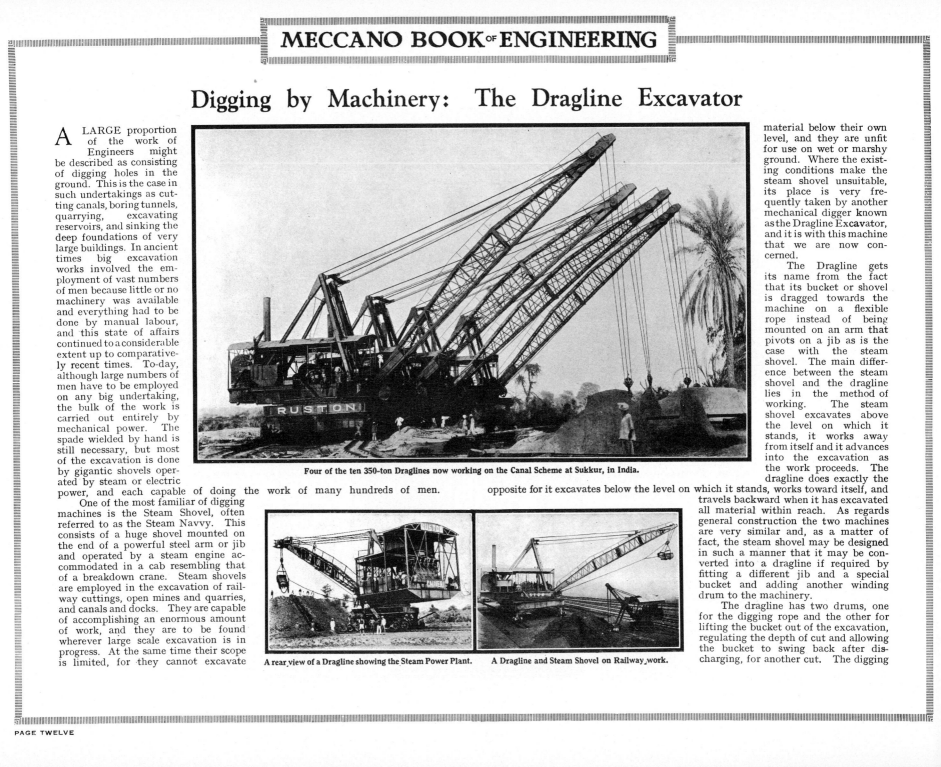

Four of the ten 350-ton Draglines now working on the Canal Scheme at Sukkur, in India.

A rear view of a Dragline showing the Steam Power Plant.

A Dragline and Steam Shovel on Railway work.

material below their own level, and they are unfit for use on wet or marshy ground. Where the existing conditions make the steam shovel unsuitable, its place is very frequently taken by another mechanical digger known as the Dragline Excavator, and it is with this machine that we are now concerned.

The Dragline gets its name from the fact that its bucket or shovel is dragged towards the machine on a flexible rope instead of being mounted on an arm that pivots on a jib as is the case with the steam shovel. The main difference between the steam shovel and the dragline lies in the method of working. The steam shovel excavates above the level on which it stands, it works away from itself and it advances into the excavation as the work proceeds. The dragline does exactly the opposite for it excavates below the level on which it stands, works toward itself, and travels backward when it has excavated all material within reach. As regards general construction the two machines are very similar and, as a matter of fact, the steam shovel may be designed in such a manner that it may be converted into a dragline if required by fitting a different jib and a special bucket and adding another winding drum to the machinery.

The dragline has two drums, one for the digging rope and the other for lifting the bucket out of the excavation, regulating the depth of cut and allowing the bucket to swing back after discharging, for another cut. The digging

How a Dragline Operates

rope passes out of the front of the machine close to the foot of the jib, and is connected to the bucket. The hoisting rope which takes the weight of the bucket and its load runs over the head of the jib and is attached to the bucket.

The jib of a dragline is a lattice-girder and is of lighter design than the jib of the steam shovel. This is made possible by the fact that in a dragline the jib takes only the load due to the lifting rope and this, with the slewing motion, is its only stress. In the steam shovel, however, the jib not only takes the stress from the digging rope, but also bears the whole of the excavating stresses from the bucket arm, with their attendant slewing and digging stresses. In the dragline the stresses at the head of the jib are considerably less than in the case of the steam shovel and so the jib may be made longer. This is an advantage, for it enables the bucket to be thrown out further, and to take a deeper and wider cut.

The bucket of a dragline is of simple construction, and, being open at the front and the top, to a certain extent resembles a coal-scuttle. The digging rope is connected to a cross-bar above the front of the bucket, the hoisting rope being fixed to the body of the bucket farthest away from the machine. The bucket is emptied by hauling upon the hoisting rope, and releasing the digging rope. This allows the bucket to tilt forward, and so discharges the contents from the open mouth.

In the cycle of operations of a dragline the bucket is first lowered, at its extreme radius, to the foot of the excavation. By placing the winding-drum in gear, the digging rope is then wound in, hauling the bucket toward the machine, and dragging it into the material to be excavated.

When the bucket is full, the clutch of the digging drum is thrown out, and the hoisting gear is engaged. The bucket is then

(Above) A 350-ton Dragline arouses the curiosity of the natives.
(Below) A fine Meccano model of a Dragline, in which every movement in the original is accurately reproduced.

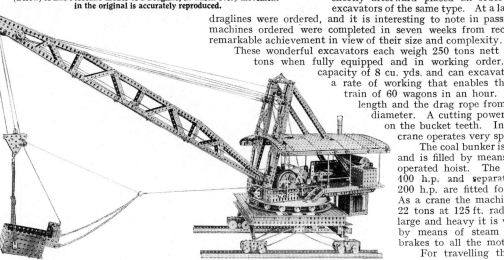

lifted by the hoisting rope, and the digging rope is allowed to run freely, the bucket thus swinging toward the front of the jib. On the machine being slewed over the dumping point, the bucket is discharged in the manner already described.

The largest draglines ever constructed in this country have been built by Ruston & Hornsby Ltd., of Lincoln, for work in connection with the Indian irrigation schemes for the reclamation of millions of acres of barren desert. The work involves the excavation of hundreds of miles of canals and the project as a whole is the largest undertaking of its kind in the world. Some of the channels under construction are over 200 ft. in width and 12 ft. in depth, the excavated material being deposited on the sides to form banks.

In the first place only one dragline was ordered, but this machine gave such satisfaction that the Indian Government shortly afterward placed an order for a further three excavators of the same type. At a later date six additional draglines were ordered, and it is interesting to note in passing that the last two machines ordered were completed in seven weeks from receipt of the order, a remarkable achievement in view of their size and complexity.

These wonderful excavators each weigh 250 tons nett and upwards of 300 tons when fully equipped and in working order. The bucket has a capacity of 8 cu. yds. and can excavate 10 tons at one cut, a rate of working that enables the machine to load a train of 60 wagons in an hour. The jib is 120 ft. in length and the drag rope from the bucket $1\frac{3}{4}$ in. in diameter. A cutting power of 30 tons is exerted on the bucket teeth. In spite of its bulk the crane operates very speedily.

The coal bunker is of four tons capacity and is filled by means of a special steam-operated hoist. The main engines are of 400 h.p. and separate engines of about 200 h.p. are fitted for slewing operations. As a crane the machine will lift a load of 22 tons at 125 ft. radius, and although so large and heavy it is very easily controlled by means of steam clutches and steam brakes to all the motions.

For travelling the machine on rails,

Vast Irrigation Schemes in India

The World's Greatest Barrage

special swivelling bogies are used, all the wheels being driven. In less than one minute the machine digs from seven to eight cubic yards of material and deposits it 200 ft. away from the point where the material was taken out. In other words, the excavator is capable of digging 300 to 400 cu. yds. of material in an hour, and will deposit the material over 120 ft. from the centre of the machine. In order to perform the same amount of work in the same length of time at least 300 men would be required.

In each of these huge draglines there are over 1,000 parts, the heaviest of which weighs over 19 tons. The work of assembling the draglines in India had to be done with inadequate lifting appliances and by native labour under the supervision of the firm's engineers. In these circumstances it is not surprising that considerable difficulties presented themselves. Then there were difficulties of another kind. For instance, one of the engineers in charge dislocated his shoulder, but carried on for a considerable time until help arrived, while another engineer nearly lost his life through being bitten by a snake while oiling the machinery. The engineers had also to contend with stifling desert heat, bad water supply and fever. Notwithstanding all these difficulties, however, four of the excavators were erected in three months, a very creditable performance in the circumstances. Even when the machines were finally erected the difficulties were not over, for the natives had to be educated to drive and operate them. It is interesting to note that the draglines are fitted with searchlights to enable work to proceed at night.

It was on the Sutlej Valley irrigation scheme that the original dragline was first employed in India. The machine began work in April 1924 and on the average excavated 670,000 cu. ft. per day. Some idea of the economy effected in labour may be realised from the fact that this amount of excavation represents the work of 8,000 coolies, who would not only have had to be paid, but fed and housed as well. When completed the Sutlej Valley scheme will irrigate 8,000 square miles, or 5,000,000 acres, of desert. The cost of the work is estimated to be over £7,750,000.

Another scheme at Sarda, in the United Provinces, includes the construction of a great

(Above) How a Dragline digs its way into the Earth.
(Below) A near view of the immense Carriage upon which the Dragline travels.

canal system for irrigation purposes. The work consists of the excavation of 478 miles of canals and branch canals, and no less than 3,370 miles of distributing channels. When complete the scheme will provide for the irrigation of 1,368,000 acres of what is now waste land. It is estimated that the total cost will be over £5,600,000. This scheme affords a good example of work for which the steam shovel would be unsuitable.

Draglines are also being employed in the canals scheme at Sukkur, situated in the province of Sind. In this area the excavators are being used in the construction of 50,000 miles of canals, three of which are to be larger than the Suez Canal. The completed scheme will give control of cultivation of over 7,500,000 acres, of which nearly 6,000,000 acres will be reclaimed sandy desert area, brought into cultivation for the first time. The area made arable will be larger than the whole of the cultivated area of Egypt, and it is estimated that when complete this scheme alone will cause a total annual increase in the wealth of the country by nearly £19,000,000.

Included in the Sukkur scheme is the building of the Lloyd Barrage, a massive masonry dam across the River Indus to control the fluctuations of the river. This will be the greatest work of its kind in the world eclipsing even the wonderful Assouan and Sennar dams in Egypt. It will be nearly a mile in length and over it will be constructed a bridge of 56 spans each 60 ft. in length and each fitted with a massive water-gate 18½ ft. in depth and weighing 50 tons. The top girders of this bridge will be 770 ft. above the foundations.

Work on the Sukkur scheme commenced in October 1923, and although 20,000 men are employed, it is such a huge project that it is not expected that the contract will be completed before the summer of 1930 at the earliest. The total cost will be over £13,000,000, the Lloyd Barrage alone costing £4,500,000 and the canals £9,000,000.

In certain circumstances it is not practicable to utilise steam power. This is the case in connection with excavation work in progress at Metur, presidency of Madras, India. In this district water is scarce and unsuitable for steam boilers and the draglines employed are each driven by their own oil-electric plant.

How the Engineer Holds Back the Sea

(Above) A fine example of a giant Block-setting Crane engaged in building a breakwater in connection with the harbour extension at Madras.
(Below) A photograph of a Gantry Crane lifting a block of concrete from a railway truck preparatory to carrying it down to the harbour.

THE mastery of the Earth that the engineer is acquiring is nowhere shown more emphatically than in the construction of sea-walls and of great harbours in which ships may find shelter from storms and land their cargoes without disturbance. Other engineering achievements such as bridges, tunnels and canals are no doubt impressive, but when the initial difficulties of their construction have been overcome, their maintenance is a comparatively easy matter, whereas sea-walls are subject to continuous hammering from the waves and depend for their continued usefulness on constant observation and repair.

On this account harbour engineering possesses a fascination of its own and the reasons that make sea-walls necessary, and the remarkable methods of under-water construction adopted in building them, are of the greatest interest. The great expansion in shipping, due to the introduction of steam power last century, is mainly responsible for the present-day importance of this branch of engineering, but harbour works became a necessity much earlier in maritime countries such as Great Britain, in spite of the existence of natural harbours. It is on the methods adopted to protect the frail wooden vessels of Tudor times from the fury of the waves that the engineers of to-day have founded their plans.

It is a curious fact that almost every country with a sea coast seems to have at least one natural harbour, and in many cases these are sufficiently large to accommodate large fleets of ships. One of the largest of these natural harbours is the Bay of Rio de Janeiro in South America, which runs in a northerly direction for 15 miles with a width varying from two to seven miles. Surrounded by high mountains, with an entrance less than a mile in width, it is protected on each side by bold headlands.

In Great Britain, Milford Haven in Wales, stretching inland for some 10 miles,

Defects of Natural Harbours

Development of Breakwaters

is unequalled as a sheltered harbour. Other natural harbours are formed by the mouths of rivers. such as the Thames, Mersey, Humber, Forth, and the Seine, but

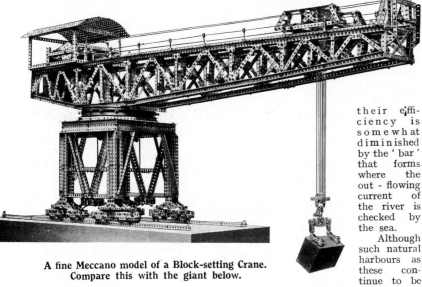

A fine Meccano model of a Block-setting Crane. Compare this with the giant below.

their efficiency is somewhat diminished by the 'bar' that forms where the out-flowing current of the river is checked by the sea. Although such natural harbours as these continue to be useful, they are not all favourably situated. Milford Haven, for instance, is of little importance from a naval point of view, and is too far away from centres of trade and manufacture for use as a commercial harbour. The requirements of modern times have therefore made it necessary to augment the number of harbours, either by improving some natural feature—such as a bay or an inlet—or by constructing more elaborate works and enclosing large areas of the sea by harbour walls or breakwaters.

The branch of engineering under consideration is not concerned with harbour construction only, for sea-walls are very necessary for other purposes, apart altogether from the fact that they often make delightful promenades from which we may enjoy the sea air or cast our fishing lines when on holiday! The constant hammering of the waves soon undermines cliffs, for instance, so that the sea encroaches upon the land and the coast-line becomes completely altered. The construction of protective sea-walls is practically the only method of preventing the evil effects of such encroachment.

Without the aid of mechanical appliances most of the great sea works of the present day would be practically impossible of construction. Foremost among such appliances are cranes of various types and of these the most impressive and at the same time most

interesting are the giant block-setting cranes that handle huge blocks as though they weighed pounds instead of tons.

In order to understand the particular work in which these block-setting cranes are employed, we must look a little further into the methods of harbour construction. In the first place, no two breakwaters or harbours are exactly alike, and almost every harbour requires particular treatment.

In some cases a mound of rubble or stone, deposited in a scattered manner and standing above high-water mark, will serve the purpose, as is the case with the breakwater at Algiers, where a rubble mound is protected by 25-ton blocks heaped on the sea bed. In others currents or storms would soon move such scattered material and break it down. More elaborate methods are then necessary, such as the 'sack-block' system. This employs barges with trap doors. The interior of the barges is lined with sacking and in this concrete is deposited. The sides of the sacking are then brought together and laced over the top, and the barges are towed out to the site of the breakwater. The trap doors are then opened and the concrete drops into the sea, where it is solidified by the action of the water and soon becomes a perfectly hard mass. The sack-block method was used in the construction of the underwater portion of the breakwaters at Newhaven and La Guaira, where layers of blocks weighing 100 tons were successfully laid, each extending across the whole width of the breakwater.

When a natural bay is sufficiently sheltered by a projecting headland, it is only necessary to throw a breakwater across the inlet in order to convert it into a harbour. In such a case the entrance would be between the ends of the breakwater and the headland, if the depth of the water there is suitable. Such harbours as these are found at Plymouth and Cherbourg. Sometimes a single breakwater, thrown from a projecting point of a bay and enclosing a partly sheltered area of water, is sufficient protection, as at Holyhead, Alexandria and Table Bay. Where no headland or sheltered bay exists in a place where a harbour is required, it becomes necessary to form an entirely artificial harbour, which is, of course, a more extensive project.

Lowering a block into position at the end of a breakwater.

Harbour Works at Table Bay

Such harbours as these are found at Kingston, Madras and, nearer home, at Dover.

Although breakwaters thus differ in detail in almost every case, they may be broadly divided into three classes according to the method of construction used. These are (1) the rubble stone or concrete-block mound type, (2) the mound type surmounted by a thick wall, and (3) the vertical wall type, in which a solid wall is carried up direct from the sea bottom.

Mound breakwaters are generally formed by depositing in the sea a mass

Another, and slightly different Meccano model of a Giant Block-setting Crane.

of hard material along the lines previously chosen. Breakwaters of this type are carried a little above high-water level and are placed as squarely as possible to the direction of the heaviest waves, for if placed obliquely the material would soon be scattered. Such breakwaters are generally adopted when an abundant supply of suitable material is close at hand. They are only constructed, however, when the space on the sea-floor that the breakwater will occupy is of no consequence, and where no quay is required to be built.

The mound type of breakwater is well represented by the works at Table Bay and Alexandria. The former breakwater runs in a north-easterly direction from a point to the north of Cape Town, and gives shelter from the north-west where Table Bay opens on to the Atlantic Ocean. It consists of a mound of rubble stone, which the sea has now levelled on the ocean side to a gradient of about 1 in 9 for some distance below low water. The original structure, which was begun in 1860, was 2,400 ft. in length. In 1881 an extension was added, bringing the total length of the breakwater to 3,700 ft. The earlier breakwater was in a depth of 30 ft. but the later works extended it into water 50 ft. in depth.

Although this type of breakwater illustrates the simplest possible construction, it requires a large expenditure of material. At Table Bay this material was at hand in the form of stone excavated from a neighbouring site, so that the consideration of transport of the material did not arise.

In the second type of breakwater a rubble mound—similar in many respects to the mound used in the first type—is surmounted by a massive wall. This type is well represented by the Colombo breakwater. The advantages of the mound

Invention of Portland Cement

and wall type are that it requires less material than the mound type and also that the top of the wall may be used as a quay in fine weather. Sometimes this type of breakwater is modified and additional protection afforded by laying large concrete blocks at random on the seaward side, as is the case with the breakwater at Boulogne Harbour, commenced in 1879.

In the third type of breakwater a massive wall is built of blocks of stone, dove-tailed one into the other in order to present the maximum resistance to the waves. Although this type requires less material than either of the others, it necessitates more careful construction and also involves the employment of divers. It is dependent, too, on the existence of a hard sea-floor at the place where it is to be erected, and the depth of the water must not be too great.

By far the most notable example of this type of breakwater is the Admiralty Harbour at Dover. The construction of the massive breakwaters of that great harbour represents the most modern achievement in this particular branch of engineering. From time to time considerable sums had been spent on improving and extending works erected by such distinguished engineers as Perry, Smeaton, Rennie and Telford, but no satisfactory results were obtained until the invention of Portland cement, which revolutionised this branch of engineering.

Portland cement was invented by Joseph Aspdin, a Leeds bricklayer, and patented in 1824, although the secret is believed to have been known to him as early as 1811. Aspdin found that by mixing limestone with clay he was able to produce a cement that possessed considerable advantages over any other similar material then known. The material derived its name from the fact that when it sets hard it resembles closely the building stone quarried at Portland.

The most valuable use of Portland cement is in the making of concrete, which consists of cement mixed with stone, sand or similar material, so that a solid mass without holes is formed, and it is the use of large blocks of concrete that has made possible the rapid construction of

Two huge cranes at work on a South African Harbour.

The Admiralty Harbour, Dover

Goliath Cranes in Operation

modern harbour works of enormous strength and extent.

The first part of the modern harbour works at Dover was completed in 1871 at a cost of £680,000, and consisted of a breakwater 2,100 ft. in length, extending to a depth of about 48 ft. at low water. For some years this breakwater served the purpose required, but the continued increase in the amount of shipping and the additional requirements for strategical purposes, rendered further work necessary.

Between 1898 and 1909 an additional scheme was carried out and two other breakwaters were built, enclosing a large area of anchorage, now known as the Admiralty Harbour, the construction of which was a great engineering feat. We are better able to gain some idea of the magnitude of the task that confronted the engineers when we learn that the total length of the breakwater is over two miles. The finished harbour is over 610 acres in extent and is sufficiently extensive to shelter a whole fleet. The work included the extension of the former breakwater by 2,000 ft., the reclaiming and excavation of a large portion of the chalk cliffs immediately behind the harbour, the building of a new breakwater at the South end, and a new breakwater, 3,850 ft. in length, at the East end.

The breakwaters are between 50 and 60 ft. in width at their bases, and from 80 to 90 ft. in height. They are constructed of 42-ton concrete blocks, which were formed in special block-making yards erected under the shelter of the cliff. These blocks measure 14 ft. by 7 ft. by 6 ft., and consist of a mixture of gravel, sand and cement. This was poured into wooden moulds in liquid form and, when the mixture had set—for which a week was generally required — the

into the sea floor in groups of six on each side of the line on which the breakwater was to be built. Each group was separated by a distance of 50 ft. and between the two lines of piles was a clear 70 ft. In all, the scheme required half-a-million cubic feet of timber, which was specially selected by an expert sent over to Tasmania for the purpose.

When the massive piles had been satisfactorily driven home into the sea floor by the heavy blows of the powerful pile drivers, cross-girders were placed from one row to the other. It was necessary to give the structure sufficient strength to withstand the violence of the storms to which it would necessarily be exposed before the work was completed, and accordingly these were then braced diagonally by strong ties and laterally by lattice girders. Finally the heavy timber flooring was laid down upon which the two 100 ft. tracks for the Goliath cranes were to be carried. In effect, therefore, two solid piers had been erected with wooden supports and timbered floors, and braced one with another with cross girders. These enabled the gantry cranes to travel out to the end of the piers and to drop concrete blocks at any desired point between the shore and the pier ends. As the blocks were laid the cranes advanced and so laid succeeding tiers, each tier being built up to the level of the finished breakwater before the next was proceeded with.

The blocks were

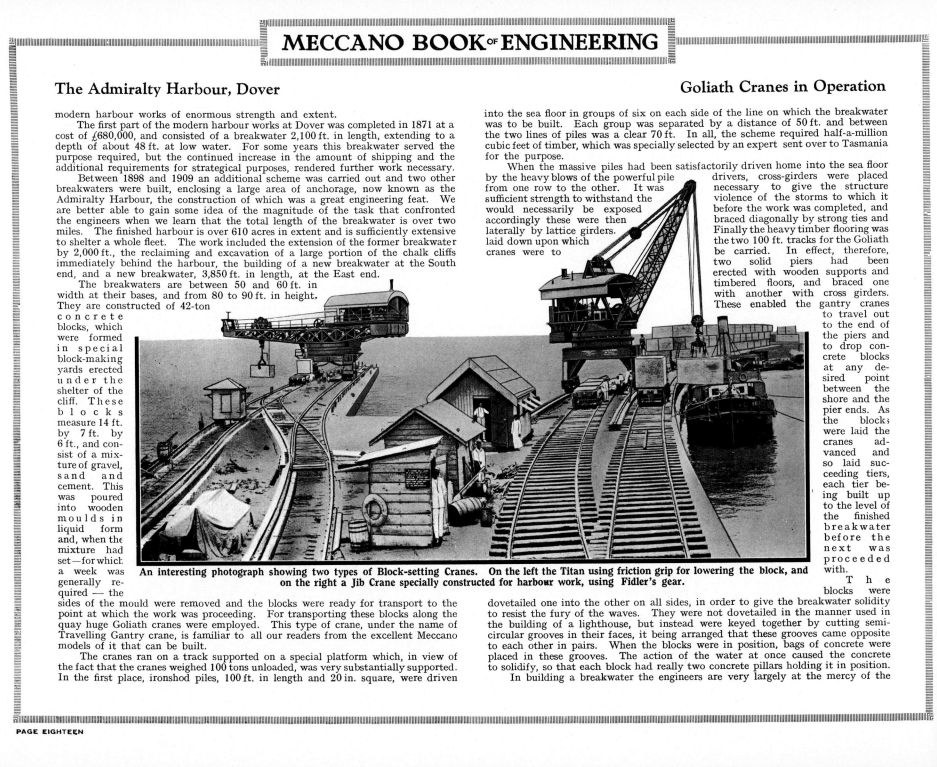

An interesting photograph showing two types of Block-setting Cranes. On the left the Titan using friction grip for lowering the block, and on the right a Jib Crane specially constructed for harbour work, using Fidler's gear.

sides of the mould were removed and the blocks were ready for transport to the point at which the work was proceeding. For transporting these blocks along the quay huge Goliath cranes were employed. This type of crane, under the name of Travelling Gantry crane, is familiar to all our readers from the excellent Meccano models of it that can be built.

The cranes ran on a track supported on a special platform which, in view of the fact that the cranes weighed 100 tons unloaded, was very substantially supported. In the first place, ironshod piles, 100 ft. in length and 20 in. square, were driven

dovetailed one into the other on all sides, in order to give the breakwater solidity to resist the fury of the waves. They were not dovetailed in the manner used in the building of a lighthouse, but instead were keyed together by cutting semi-circular grooves in their faces, it being arranged that these grooves came opposite to each other in pairs. When the blocks were in position, bags of concrete were placed in these grooves. The action of the water at once caused the concrete to solidify, so that each block had really two concrete pillars holding it in position.

In building a breakwater the engineers are very largely at the mercy of the

Three Million Tons of Masonry

Base for the Dover Patrol

weather, for naturally no work can be done when the seas are running high. On the other hand, when the water is calm work continues whenever possible during both night and day. At Dover, even on the best days, it was only possible to work three hours on each tide owing to the strong currents. Notwithstanding this, in one particular month over 600 blocks were laid, showing a progress of over 75 ft. One of the points that had to be carefully watched was the organisation of the block-making yards. In bad weather they had to be kept free from congestion by unused blocks, and in good weather, when the work on the breakwater was being pushed forward with all possible speed, it was necessary to ensure that they were sufficiently well staffed to be able to cope with the increased demands made upon them so as not to delay the work.

In the construction of the first pier at Dover (completed in 1871) only 91 ft. was built during the first 12 months, but in the new Admiralty Harbour 400 ft. of work was constructed in the same period, showing how great was the advance in harbour engineering. In the new harbour over 1,920,000 tons of masonry were used, and as the blocks averaged about 30 tons in weight, the total number required was about 64,000.

The harbour works included the excavation of a portion of the cliff and it became necessary to build a retaining wall to protect the exposed chalk. This necessitated over 1,000,000 tons of blocks and masonry, in addition to that required by the breakwaters themselves.

Besides the East breakwater and the Admiralty Harbour extension, another breakwater had to be constructed to complete the scheme. This is quite separate from the two former, and is known as the Island breakwater. In order to save time the engineers decided to build it at the same time as the other breakwaters.

To this end they set to work to erect a huge steel frame in the sea at the end nearest to the East breakwater, but before the frame was complete a great storm entirely destroyed it. Six months were required to remove the wreckage, so that instead of gaining time, time was actually lost.

After this disaster the steel frame idea was abandoned. In its place the trackway used in the construction of the East breakwater was carried on temporary supports across the south-east entrance to the harbour to the Island breakwater. This enabled Goliaths to bring up the blocks for the Island breakwater from the

block-setting yards, and at the same time allowed the cranes to be withdrawn in bad weather.

In the Dover Harbour we have an excellent example of how, for the time being, man has won a victory over the sea. The great breakwaters have withstood winters of furious storms and the huge waves have not damaged them in any way. The harbour was of incalculable value to the Allies during the War, not only as a port from which troops and munitions might be embarked to France, but also as a base for the Dover Patrol. Here, too, warships, torpedo boats and other craft that were concerned in protecting the cross-Channel traffic from attack by enemy warships, found refuge.

Before leaving the subject of Goliath cranes, which were specially used in the building of Dover Harbour, we must mention that in addition to placing the huge concrete blocks in position these cranes were employed to operate huge clam-shell grabs used for clearing the sea-floor. These grabs were capable of bringing up five tons of material at a time. In many places the ground was too hard for the grabs to get a bite, and then a solid block of iron with three projecting teeth was used. These "breakers," as they are called, were also operated from the Goliath cranes. On being lowered at speed they crashed to the sea-floor, splintering the chalk into large pieces that were gathered by the grab.

The Goliaths were also employed to lower the diving-bells from which the divers set the blocks, telephoning to the crane-man the exact direction so that he could move the crane as required

A striking specimen of a Titan Crane engaged in work on the harbour at Vera Cruz showing the friction grip tackle for placing the block in position

and so set the block in the desired position

Another and larger type of crane used in connection with harbour construction work is that known as the "Titan." This crane has a jib of the cantilever type and the load trolley runs along its upper boom, the whole jib turning on a live ring in a similar manner to that of the large jib cranes. Usually the Titan crane is steam operated, although cranes have been made for use with electric power where current is available.

Titan cranes are frequently constructed of such a size that they weigh 500

Mechanism of a Titan Crane

tons or more and they have been built to operate loads up to 60 tons. This type was evolved when the block system of breakwater construction came into general use. As is the case when Goliath cranes are employed, the concrete blocks are cast in special yards near the scene of operations and are wheeled on special trucks along the pier or gantry to a position near the crane. This picks up the blocks and swings them out into the position in which they are to be fixed in the breakwater. The blocks are then keyed together, as has already been explained, in order that they may present a solid front to the devastating action of the waves.

The Titan crane has the advantage of being mobile, so that it is possible to move it along the pier as the construction of a breakwater proceeds. Even more important is the fact that it is also practicable to withdraw it shorewards for shelter in bad weather.

These cranes are capable of handling concrete blocks over a radius of 100 ft. or more. They do this by means of the long cantilever arm that is mounted on a turntable, which itself rests on a massive under-carriage. The under-carriage is mounted on flanged wheels, running on a special track and driven by means of crown wheels fixed on the inside of the bogie. A bevel gear, which meshes with the crown wheel, transmits motive power from the main engine mounted on the cantilever arm.

The drive is taken to two pairs of wheels, one of which is the foremost pair and the other the rear pair. The drive from the same rod is transmitted to each of the two crown wheels in a very simple manner by means of small bevel wheels. The other pairs of wheels, the innermost on each bogie, are loose wheels and not connected with the driving mechanism in any way. An exactly similar arrangement is carried out on the other side of the track, the front and rear pairs of wheels being driven, and the two inner pairs being loose.

The practice of driving four wheels out of eight on each side of the track is simply one of convenience and depends largely upon the weight of the crane. In the lighter cranes it is not necessary to have four wheels to each bogie.

The cantilever arm and superstructure of all Titan cranes revolves on a ring of live rollers, which in the case of a large crane may have a path of between 30 and 40 ft. in diameter. The bearings are formed by a series of turned steel rollers held in position by a suitable frame and revolving on machined pathways between the upper and lower circular girders. The ends of the rollers can just be seen in the accompanying illustration of a Meccano model of a large block-setting crane immediately below the lower framework of the cantilever arm where it rests upon the massive metal mounting.

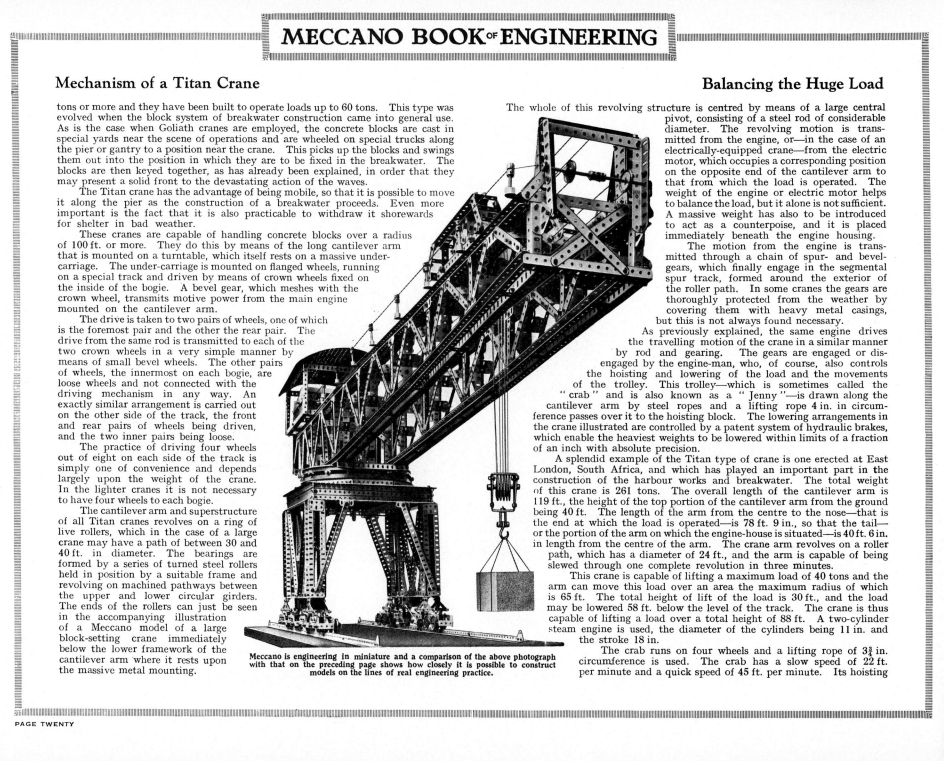

Meccano is engineering in miniature and a comparison of the above photograph with that on the preceding page shows how closely it is possible to construct models on the lines of real engineering practice.

Balancing the Huge Load

The whole of this revolving structure is centred by means of a large central pivot, consisting of a steel rod of considerable diameter. The revolving motion is transmitted from the engine, or—in the case of an electrically-equipped crane—from the electric motor, which occupies a corresponding position on the opposite end of the cantilever arm to that from which the load is operated. The weight of the engine or electric motor helps to balance the load, but it alone is not sufficient. A massive weight has also to be introduced to act as a counterpoise, and it is placed immediately beneath the engine housing.

The motion from the engine is transmitted through a chain of spur- and bevel-gears, which finally engage in the segmental spur track, formed around the exterior of the roller path. In some cranes the gears are thoroughly protected from the weather by covering them with heavy metal casings, but this is not always found necessary.

As previously explained, the same engine drives the travelling motion of the crane in a similar manner by rod and gearing. The gears are engaged or disengaged by the engine-man, who, of course, also controls the hoisting and lowering of the load and the movements of the trolley. This trolley—which is sometimes called the "crab" and is also known as a "Jenny"—is drawn along the cantilever arm by steel ropes and a lifting rope 4 in. in circumference passes over it to the hoisting block. The lowering arrangements in the crane illustrated are controlled by a patent system of hydraulic brakes, which enable the heaviest weights to be lowered within limits of a fraction of an inch with absolute precision.

A splendid example of the Titan type of crane is one erected at East London, South Africa, and which has played an important part in the construction of the harbour works and breakwater. The total weight of this crane is 261 tons. The overall length of the cantilever arm is 119 ft., the height of the top portion of the cantilever arm from the ground being 40 ft. The length of the arm from the centre to the nose—that is the end at which the load is operated—is 78 ft. 9 in., so that the tail—or the portion of the arm on which the engine-house is situated—is 40 ft. 6 in. in length from the centre of the arm. The crane arm revolves on a roller path, which has a diameter of 24 ft., and the arm is capable of being slewed through one complete revolution in three minutes.

This crane is capable of lifting a maximum load of 40 tons and the arm can move this load over an area the maximum radius of which is 65 ft. The total height of lift of the load is 30 ft., and the load may be lowered 58 ft. below the level of the track. The crane is thus capable of lifting a load over a total height of 88 ft. A two-cylinder steam engine is used, the diameter of the cylinders being 11 in. and the stroke 18 in.

The crab runs on four wheels and a lifting rope of 3¾ in. circumference is used. The crab has a slow speed of 22 ft. per minute and a quick speed of 45 ft. per minute. Its hoisting

Block Lifting Devices

Setting on the "Inclined Bond"

speed on slow gear when lifting its maximum load is 8½ ft. per minute, and its speed when racking on low gear with maximum load is 22 ft. per minute. The crane runs on 16 wheels, each of which is borne on springs. The width of the track from centre to centre of the rails is 17 ft.

Apart from the designing, constructing, and the erection on the site of the cranes themselves, there are many other details to which the engineer must give attention. Take, for instance, the question of slinging the huge concrete blocks into position in the breakwater. The least complicated form of hoisting arrangement for slinging concrete blocks is, of course, a simple clip or pair of jaws. There is a large number of designs of these, each being suited for some definite purpose or for some particular conditions of work. Clips of this type depend entirely on friction. In a modified form of the same type of clip—which, however, does not depend upon friction—the lower ends are hook-shaped, the hooks engaging in special recesses moulded in the blocks.

For lifting very large blocks of concrete it is more usual nowadays to use bars passing through vertical holes in which they are retained by various devices. Many of these are self-releasing. These are satisfactory when the

blocks are to be set horizontally in a similar manner to that in which bricks are set in building a wall. In some breakwaters a more complicated setting is required, however, and the blocks are set at an angle or, as it is technically termed, "on the inclined bond." By setting the blocks in this manner, the breakwater is made to present a much more formidable obstacle to the rough seas than would be the case if the blocks were set horizontally.

The problem of slinging the blocks for setting on the inclined bond presents some little difficulty, which has been solved by an ingenious piece of tilting mechanism called "Fidler's Gear." This mechanism consists of a massive beam hanging

from a swivelling joint, the whole suspended by a special four-sheaved pulley. The rotating movement of the beam on the swivel is controlled by a special worm gear, which meshes with a pinion wheel on the vertical swivel bar. A link hangs from the ends of each arm of the beam, which link supports steel cross-heads. From each of these cross-heads there hangs a long Lewis bar with a T end. Two perpendicular holes run completely through the concrete blocks. These holes are of sufficient width across one of their sections to take the T-shaped pieces at the end of the Lewis bars.

What happens in actual operation is this. The concrete block is brought on a special truck from the yard where it was made and laid alongside the Titan crane that is to place it in position on the breakwater. The four-sheaved pulley with Fidler's gear is lowered, and workmen guide the T-shaped Lewis bars through the vertical holes in the concrete block. When these completely penetrate the full depth of the block, the bars are given a quarter turn, which throws the T-shaped end out of register with the hole and thus prevents the rods being withdrawn. Shortly before the Lewis bars reach the bottom of the holes, the rollers on the steel-cross-heads take a bearing on the top of the block and roll across,

altering the relative positions of the points of suspension and the Lewis bars.

The signal is now given to the crane-man to hoist; the engine is started and the block is lifted at the exact angle at which it is to be set in position. The crane hoists the block, swivels round until the block is over its place in the breakwater, and then lowers it as is necessary. When the block rests on the breakwater, workmen turn the T-shaped rods until they are in register with the hole in the block. The crane again hoists and the Lewis bars are easily withdrawn, leaving the block in position set at the correct angle.

Cranes of this type have been employed in the construction of some of the

A striking example of engineering in miniature.
On the left is shown part of a Meccano model of a Giant Blocksetting Crane and on the right is a photograph of the same part in one of the real cranes.
With Meccano it is possible to build models that are actual replicas in miniature of real engineering constructions.

Destructive Power of Storm Waves

best-known harbours of the world, and they have played a very important part in the development of the Empire. Take, for instance, the case of Port Elizabeth, a seaport town some 400 miles east of Capetown. This is the second city in the colony and is situated on Algoa Bay, about seven miles south of the mouth of the Zwartkop River.

The Port owes its prosperity entirely to its harbour and it has become the centre for the trade of a great part of the interior of the country. Previously there were no convenient landing places and so it was impossible for ships to load or unload. Some improvements in this respect were made in 1881 when the old pier 800 ft. in length was constructed. Since that date even more extensive works have been carried out, and the harbour is now one of the finest in South Africa. Port Elizabeth is only one of dozens of similar instances of how giant block-setting cranes help trade.

Looking backward for a moment it is evident that, although progress in engineering has been extremely rapid in all directions in recent times, the development of great sea-works has been one of the most striking features in the history of engineering. As we have already noted, their erection requires great care and thought, as they are subject to continual hammering from the waves throughout the whole term of their existence.

People who only know the sea in its gentler summer moods often find it difficult to realise the destructiveness of the great storm waves. A heavy sea easily moves rocks and boulders weighing many tons. There are many well authenticated instances of this power. For instance, Sir William Matthews, the celebrated engineer, tells us that in 1898 a section of the Peterhead breakwater weighing 3,300 tons was moved bodily by wave action. In 1871 a harbour wall was built at Wick. It was composed of concrete blocks each weighing 100 tons and was capped by two tiers of 80-ton blocks. On top of all was a solid mass of cement weighing 800 tons. The engineers who built this massive structure were thoroughly convinced that it was capable of withstanding all wave action, but to their amazement the sea not only moved the whole mass but actually turned it round and deposited it inside the harbour! As if to show that it could do even more than this, the sea scattered the 80-ton blocks in all directions.

In due course the damage was repaired and the blocks were replaced. This time the engineers, determined to get the upper hand, placed on the top of the concrete blocks a superstructure more than three times as heavy as the original. Once more the sea took a hand in the game and before this 2,600 ton superstructure had been in position two years it was moved and broken in half.

The construction of works to withstand forces that are capable of creating such havoc would almost seem impossible. Nevertheless such works have been erected and their influence on trade and civilisation has been enormous.

Fidler's Gear ready for attaching to a concrete block

(Top) Concrete block held in position by Fidler's Gear. (Bottom) Meccano model of Fidler's Gear, which reproduces all the movements of the original

Development of British Shipping

As a maritime nation Great Britain has always been closely concerned in the engineering problems involved in harbour construction. A few hundred years ago neither the Royal Navy nor the mercantile marine was of sufficient importance to require more harbour accommodation than that provided by the natural inlets and sheltered bays found at such places as Portsmouth, Plymouth, Weymouth, Falmouth and Dartmouth. We find, for instance, that in 1540 there were only four vessels of 120 tons burden registered in the Thames. In Queen Elizabeth's time the shipping of Liverpool amounted to only 223 tons, the largest vessel being of only 40 tons. How different are things to-day, when the shipping of the Thames exceeds 47,000,000 tons and that of the Mersey is nearly 26,000,000 tons!

When we turn to the harbour and dock accommodation provided at our great ports we find a similar change. At the beginning of the 19th century London had not a single dock, whereas to-day there are miles and miles of docks. The docks at Cardiff, Newport, Barrow, Middlesbrough and at many other places did not then exist. Even as late as 1816 Liverpool had only 16 acres of dock area, and Hull and Grimsby were no better than fishing ports, as far as their dock accommodation was concerned.

Taking our survey further afield, we find that the breakwater at Table Bay was not commenced until 1860; that until 1875 Calais Harbour had only 2½ ft. of water on its bar at low water; that Colombo Harbour was not commenced until 1870; that Dover was not selected as a site for a great port until 1845; and that the breakwater at Newhaven was not started until 1878. We might extend the list indefinitely, showing that during the past century work in connection with harbour construction at home and abroad has gone forward by leaps and bounds, and has played a greater part than anything else in the development of civilisation in general and the world's trade in particular.

Even the enormous extensions of recent years have scarcely enabled dock engineering to keep pace with shipping, however. The harbour engineer has encouraged the production of larger vessels by providing better dock accommodation and in turn finds that he is called upon for further efforts. At Liverpool, for instance, the magnificent Gladstone Docks were opened in 1927 and are the largest docks in the world. They cover an area of 58 acres and have an entrance lock 1,070 ft. in length.

Thus the process of expansion continues. Larger docks lead to the production of bigger ships and for the safe handling of these still larger docks are demanded. It is quite clear that harbour-building machinery has not yet reached the limit of its development, and in future we may expect to see even larger cranes in use than the Titans and Goliaths of to-day.

Meccano model of Fidler's Gear for comparison with original on the left of the page

Engineering of the Future

THE progress made in engineering during the past century has been so great that it seems scarcely possible that it can be maintained. Most of us are surrounded by such a mass of engineering achievements of all kinds that we are apt to overlook the fact that in spite of all these developments the engineer has had little opportunity of influencing the world as a whole. In a few countries his work is visible everywhere and his influence has been enormous. But with the exception of the United States these are mainly comparatively small European countries and there are enormous areas of the surface of the earth where one may travel for hundreds of miles without seeing anything but the crudest specimens of man's handiwork. Areas of this kind are to be found in crowded countries such as China as well as in the barren wastes of the Arctic and the Sahara Desert.

There is undoubtedly

In the city of the future, buildings will be larger and higher than they are to-day. This photograph of San Francisco shows the business quarter of that city with the wonderful bay in the distance, and suggests how development will proceed.

the building of bridges, and the boring of tunnels; the arrival of the motor car demands the construction of roads; and with the coming of the aeroplane arises the necessity of providing safe landing grounds.

Although engineers have been busily engaged in the necessary work to meet these demands an observer looking at the Earth from the outside would not be greatly impressed by the results. In a few countries he would see the means of production, machinery, railways and shipping well developed; in other countries he would see the beginning of efforts to supply this demand; but elsewhere he could not fail to be struck by the fact that millions of people are still dependent for their living on the almost unaided efforts of their own hands.

It is the task of the engineer to alter this and there is no doubt that the bulk of his work in the immediate future will

scope for an enormous extension of the activities of the engineer, even in the most unpromising regions. For instance, in many vast stretches of country the inhabitants until recently were dependent for water—the first necessity of life—on an uncertain and fluctuating supply from wells and streams. To-day this is all changed. Huge reservoirs have been constructed and dams erected across the beds of rivers making it possible to maintain an ample supply of water in even the driest seasons. Difficulties due to climate and local conditions have been successfully overcome and the water retained by the gigantic dams has been turned to good use in reclaiming desert areas and in preventing fertile ground from being wasted for lack of water when the rains failed. It is interesting to note that these gigantic schemes have been carried out by British engineers.

Similarly the improvements in the means of transport that have been developed on each side of the north Atlantic Ocean are being extended slowly to other parts of the world. The advent of the steam locomotive in any new country necessitates

be expansion. Railways and roads will spread in all directions in fertile lands to enable the inhabitants to dispose of their produce. Manufactures will follow and the rivers will be harnessed to generate electric power on a vast scale.

As a result of this extension a large demand will certainly arise for materials for the building of bridges, the construction of dams and other works, and eventually this will lead to standardisation of parts and practically to mass production.

Take bridge-building for example. At present the building of great bridges, such as those now being erected to span Sydney Harbour and the Hudson River at New York, is the work of years. When the site and the design of a bridge have been finally settled it is usually necessary to erect special workshops in the neighbourhood and often also to devise new methods and machinery to facilitate the work. Compare this with the task of building a new railway bridge over a narrow country road. Girders and plates of the required size are transported to the spot, and at the appointed hour workmen commence to demolish the old bridge and to

Bridge Building with Standard Parts

place each portion of the new bridge in position. Everything is then made secure and in a few hours trains once more may pass over the bridge which may be said to have sprung into existence ready-made.

Why should not this be done with any bridge irrespective of size ? The chief forms of design are by this time well known and understood, and it is surely not too much to hope that some bridge-building genius will devise systems of construction that will enable any bridge to be built up from easily made standard parts just as models of them may be built up from standard Meccano parts.

The suggestion of the application of mass production methods to bridges as large as, say, the Quebec Bridge over the St. Lawrence River may, at first sight, appear somewhat absurd. It is true that there is no great demand at present for large bridges of this kind, and a commercial traveller carrying samples of them would do well if he made one sale in ten years ! Further, the cost of laying down plant to make the necessary standard parts would be very great. It must be remembered, however, that exactly similar objections were made to Henry Ford's schemes when he entered the motor car industry ; but he persevered because he was convinced that standardisation would mean price reduction and that in consequence a huge market for his cars would be created.

A little thought will show that there is still enormous scope for bridge-building even in Great Britain. A bridge across the Mersey comparable to the Hudson River bridge would be of enormous benefit. Similarly we find South Wales cut off from south-western England, Kent from Essex, and East Yorkshire from Lincolnshire by waterways that easily might be bridged nearer their mouths. Even a bridge across the English Channel is by no means an impossibility.

Another important point is that as a rule bridges are not erected until they are absolutely forced upon us. A world governed by wise engineering principles would foresee the necessity or the advantages to be gained and would proceed to build with the aid of standard parts. It is because the line of the Canadian Pacific Railway was carried across the continent before necessity compelled its completion and in anticipation of succeeding developments that this railway deserves to rank as one of the greatest engineering developments in the world.

Standardisation of parts would be made easier by the introduction of new building materials. At present we are living in the age of iron but in many respects iron is an unsatisfactory metal. It is used on such an enormous scale in industry and in constructive engineering because we do not know a more

The skyscraper cities of the future will not be ugly. Their iron and concrete buildings will be at once graceful and useful, as this photograph of the City Hall of Los Angeles shows.

A Successor to Iron and Steel

suitable metal, but it has the great drawback of being easily corroded and rusted. It has been calculated that the annual loss from rusting and corrosion amounts to no less than £500,000,000, and yet the only practical method that has been available until recently for protecting iron from rusting has been the liberal use of paint. The comparatively recent introduction of rustless steel may possible put an end to this waste and maintain the present position of iron as the world's primary structural metal. Rustless steel is really an alloy containing about 13 per cent. of chromium. It is resistant to most forms of corrosion and is likely to find an increasing number of industrial applications such as in hydraulic pumps, and in dock, bridge and ship construction.

Another important point in connection with the use of iron is that there is a limit to the amount of the metal available. A well-known geologist has stated that if the world's consumption of iron continues to increase at the same rate as before the War, the supply of ore probably will be exhausted within 130 to 150 years. This suggests that the time is approaching when a substitute must be found.

It is difficult to say what new metal or alloy will be developed to take the place of iron and steel. Aluminium or magnesium may come into extensive use in some form or other, as alloys containing them combine lightness with other valuable qualities, and research work may result in the production of alloys having the necessary strength.

As far as reservoir and dam construction and, in a less degree, bridge-building are concerned, the use of reinforced concrete makes standardisation comparatively easy. Ferro-concrete blocks of standard sizes may be made without any difficulty wherever they are required, or alternatively concrete may be poured directly into its final position by making use of standard moulds. This method has been introduced already in America where it is employed in the erection of the huge buildings for which that country is famous. Another interesting and important feature of concrete is that its introduction will help in conserving the supply of iron. A considerably less amount of the metal will be required and in addition it will be protected by the concrete in which it is embedded from the corroding effect of moist air.

The future of engineering must be looked at also from another point of view. The great extensions to which we have referred will not only call for a larger number of trained engineers than are to be found at the present day but will result also in a much more intense study of the science. This study will be carried on by generations that will be more familiar with engineering methods than the present generation,

Future of Transport

Possibilities of Moving Roadways

and we may note in passing that the growing tendency to think in engineering terms is being strongly encouraged by familiarity with the Meccano system of miniature engineering. This study, together with research on the composition and properties of materials of all kinds, will undoubtedly lead to the discovery of new principles and the application of old principles in new forms.

It is impossible to say what new principles will be developed but it is probable that these will be as startling to those who live to see them as the mechanical and electrical methods now in use would be to our ancestors. It must be remembered that the introduction of coaches with glass windows was considered wonderful in the days of Charles II, while at a later period the substitution of stage coaches by railways was regarded as an absolute revolution. The spread of the iron road was thought to be a conquest that involved the complete decay of road travel, but eventually there came another surprise when the motor car made roads more important than they had ever been before.

Surprises of this kind are probably in store for us in the future also. The average prophet visualises the future as bound up with the aeroplane and imagines that the time is coming when passengers and goods will be carried through the air almost to the exclusion of present-day methods. No doubt aeroplanes will be so much improved from the point of view of stability, range and carrying power, that flights round the world will be less exciting than a voyage in a 50,000 ton ocean liner is to-day. But it is far more probable that greater use than ever will be made of improved methods of transport on land and sea. The engineers of civilized races never allow any of their achievements to go to waste. They may allow them to lie neglected for a time, but are always eager to seize any opportunity of improving them. The work of the famous men who built roads in England towards the end of the eighteenth century was not ruined by the coming of the railway, for instance, and it was on the basis of their work that the task of reconstruction and extension was commenced.

What form will transport on Earth take ? It has been suggested that some form of moving way will provide the means of travelling in the future, and that it will be possible to travel from London to Liverpool, for instance, by simply stepping on to a series of platforms moving between the two cities like endless belts. These platforms will move at varying speeds in order that passengers may first

board the slowest and work up to the fastest by stages that do not involve any sudden and uncomfortable increase in speed. Presumably these moving ways would be furnished with adequate waiting-rooms and lounges in order that journeys may be made in comfort at least equal to that of the present-day Pullman coach.

Methods of this kind undoubtedly would prove very valuable especially within the restricted area of a large community or city, but it is doubtful whether they will ever be developed for long-distance communication. They would involve the construction of enormous power plants together with bearings and flexible joints possessing a capacity at present undreamed of for resisting wear and tear. It is true that these requirements may be met as the result of further experiment and research but it seems probable that more economical and equally satisfactory results may be obtained by developments of the moving vehicle and stationary road system at present in use.

The inevitable increase in the speed and volume in vehicular traffic on roadways will bring about a dangerous condition of affairs to cope with which two-way traffic will be abolished in favour of the " one track, one direc-

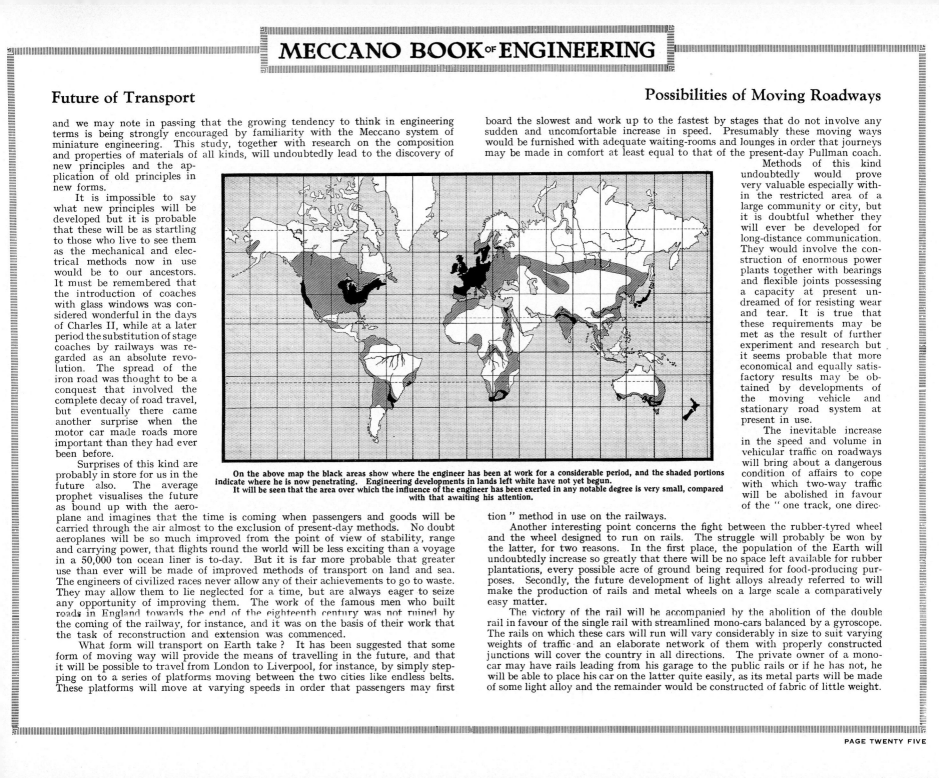

On the above map the black areas show where the engineer has been at work for a considerable period, and the shaded portions indicate where he is now penetrating. Engineering developments in lands left white have not yet begun. It will be seen that the area over which the influence of the engineer has been exerted in any notable degree is very small, compared with that awaiting his attention.

tion " method in use on the railways.

Another interesting point concerns the fight between the rubber-tyred wheel and the wheel designed to run on rails. The struggle will probably be won by the latter, for two reasons. In the first place, the population of the Earth will undoubtedly increase so greatly that there will be no space left available for rubber plantations, every possible acre of ground being required for food-producing purposes. Secondly, the future development of light alloys already referred to will make the production of rails and metal wheels on a large scale a comparatively easy matter.

The victory of the rail will be accompanied by the abolition of the double rail in favour of the single rail with streamlined mono-cars balanced by a gyroscope. The rails on which these cars will run will vary considerably in size to suit varying weights of traffic and an elaborate network of them with properly constructed junctions will cover the country in all directions. The private owner of a mono-car may have rails leading from his garage to the public rails or if he has not, he will be able to place his car on the latter quite easily, as its metal parts will be made of some light alloy and the remainder would be constructed of fabric of little weight.

Coming Era of the Mono-Car

Difficulties of transmission of power over long distances will have been overcome in one way or another by the time that mono-cars have been fully developed, and the single rail may be made to serve as a medium for the supply of electrical power to the gyroscope and to the motor that drives the car. The latter would seem absurdly small to a motorist of the present day, who is accustomed to the heavy masses of metal constituting the petrol engines, gearboxes and back axles of the cars that now rank as the last word in engineering. But the reduction in weight brought about by the use of light alloys and by the absence of dead weight in the shape of gearing, fuel and cooling water will make a very small-powered motor quite sufficient to propel the mono-car of the future at very high speeds.

In addition to the small privately-owned

New Methods of Ocean Transport

is no doubt that some of the steps at present existing between the source of power and the final impelling system will be either abolished or simplified considerably.

It is not altogether impossible that cables will stretch across the ocean, from which ships may pick up current to drive electric motors. Feats that were really more startling than the provision of such wires have often been accomplished by engineers in the past, and the attempt that is to be made to place a string of floating-landing-stages across the Atlantic Ocean like stepping stones may eventually lead to developments of this kind. But if ships continue to run under their own power a form of Diesel engine with electrical transmission seems likely to become prominent and will no doubt hold its own for a considerable period.

The time is approaching

A forecast of a city of the future. Skyscrapers of enormous size will be inter-connected at various levels by roadways and possibly railways, thus relieving the streets below of a great deal of traffic. The building of roadways to connect skyscrapers in this manner has already been seriously suggested in more than one American city. The air passenger of the future will be rushed swiftly upward in an electric elevator to the flat roof of one of these giant buildings, where he will find a completely equipped aerodrome with air liners leaving for, or arriving from, all parts of the world.

cars there will be larger ones available for public use. These will be constructed on somewhat similar lines, but extra provision will be made for the comfort and well-being of the passengers of the future, who, no doubt, will examine the finest of our Pullman coaches reposing in their museums with feelings of surprise that human beings actually travelled in what would seem to them uncomfortable wagons that lurched and staggered at the absurdly low speed of 60 miles per hour!

Turning from land travel to transport by water, it is certain that sea-going vessels will be larger and more commodious. Standardised systems of construction will no doubt be adopted to reduce their cost and the time spent in building them, while their machinery will certainly be much more compact and powerful. The exact form it will take will depend very largely on the future fuel supply, but there

however, when oil as well as coal will fail us. The exhaustion of the supply of these important fuels is not a matter for alarm. Other sources of power will be discovered, or to make a more accurate statement, other methods of using the power derived from the Sun's heat. At present we make use of this immense source of power in a really crude and second-hand fashion. We have begun to make use of such sources of natural power as waterfalls, and probably the time is not far distant when the power of the tides and winds will also be utilised. These indirect methods of using Sun power are not wasteful, but they are somewhat capricious. In time to come more direct methods will be brought into use under the compulsion of necessity, and the total horsepower that will then be available will be immeasurably greater than that with which we struggle on to-day.

Mighty Power Plants in the Tropics

Aeroplanes propelled by Liquid Air

In the days when we rely upon the direct heat radiated by the Sun, plants for power production will be more concentrated. Instead of myriads of little power plants, some obsolete and many inefficient, scattered over the surface of the Earth, there will be several stations distributed around the Earth on or near the equator, where the Sun's radiation is most powerful. The heat concentrated by mirrors or lenses of super-glass will be used to evaporate a liquid in boilers, and the pressure of the resulting vapour will be utilised in giant cylinders.

The liquid used will certainly not be water. At present water is used because it is cheap and plentiful and its boiling point is not inconveniently high. We are so thoroughly accustomed to the use of steam in engines that a suggestion to use any other liquid than water comes with something of a shock. But from an efficiency point of view, better results would be obtained from mercury. This is an expensive liquid with a high boiling point, but it has nevertheless been found possible to use it on a commercial scale for power production, the vapour being condensed after leaving the working cylinders and the heat thus liberated used for steam production. Other liquids may be discovered to have thermal properties equal to those of mercury, and with greater experience in building boilers and cylinders to withstand higher temperatures, there seems little doubt that one of these will come into use instead of water.

The power produced by the great plants to be erected in the tropics must then be transmitted to other regions of the Earth. The forms in which the transmission will be made will depend very largely upon the purpose for which power is required. Electricity will certainly play a very important part, and already it is comparatively easy to transmit high-voltage current to enormous distances by cables. Attempts have been made to do this without wires, but so far there seem to be serious difficulties in the way of wireless power transmission, the amount of power received at any one place being a very small fraction of that radiated. Some development of the beam system may solve such difficulties, or an entirely new method may be introduced ; but in any case great modifications will be necessary in wireless apparatus if a really satisfactory proportion of the power developed

Perhaps Piccadilly will look like this in the year 2000, with lines of fast suburban electric trains taking the place of the motor traffic of the present day.

at the generating station is to reach a distant point in this manner.

Wherever transmission of electricity by wire or any other means is possible, this method of power distribution will no doubt be adopted. But for aeroplane propulsion, and for ships, either surface or submarine, liquid air may prove to be valuable. It may be produced in compressors at the great power plants near the equator and stored under pressure in cylinders that are easily transportable.

This power medium may be used in two forms. In one it will be allowed to expand in some kind of turbine, where, because of its enormous pressure, it will be far more effective than steam is at the present day. For an aeroplane, in which additional weight makes additional power necessary, machinery and propellers will be omitted altogether, the liquid air being allowed to expand through nozzles directed to the rear of the planes, to propel it forward like a rocket. This is by no means a visionary scheme and suggestions for using liquid air in this manner have already been made. Its use is not, of course, feasible at the present day on account of its high cost.

The fantastic stories that we often read of the enormous power that will be obtained in future from the disintegration of atoms may be disregarded. It is quite true that the temperature of a chunk of radium is higher than that of its surroundings, and that this remarkable source of heat continues to operate for incredibly long periods. A few tons of radium would thus be very valuable—but so far the total amount that has been extracted is only one pound, and there is no indication that any such quantity as a ton exists in the Earth within easy reach.

It may be noted that we do actually make use of the energy of disintegrating atoms, as this source of energy seems to play a great part in maintaining the temperature of the Sun. To make use of it directly is another matter altogether. Very few elements radiate energy of this kind spontaneously, and while there is no doubt whatever that enormous stores of energy lie within all atoms and would be available for use in some form if liberated by their break-up, it would require more energy or power to decompose them than would be set free. On the average the cost is at present something like 100,000 times the gain !

Development of Skyscraper Cities

Meccano Boys—Engineers of the Future

The break-up of atoms of aluminium may be taken as an illustration of this. This metal would yield the inflammable gas hydrogen on bombardment with the rays from radium. But if the rays from the entire stock of radium in the world were projected into a sheet of aluminium for the next seven years, only one cubic millimetre of hydrogen would be produced. We can find better uses for radium than this.

Summing up, it may be said that the two things that the engineer calls for in all circumstances are ample supplies of improved materials and power. We have seen how these wants will probably be supplied, the former by standardisation and research on non-rusting metallic alloys, and the latter by making more direct use of the Sun's heat. With his resources thus increased, the engineer will continue to play an increasingly important part in life.

In future we shall live in cities that will be planned and erected by engineers, who have already invaded the building world in America. The great heights to which the steel and concrete erections of American cities have been taken is a measure of what will be done throughout the world as the population increases. The difficulty of supplying clean fresh air to those who live and work on the lower floors of the great buildings will be solved by the use of carefully planned ducts through which filtered air will be supplied, while lamps that radiate a scientific blend of infra-red and ultra-violet rays in addition to the usual light rays will be more beneficial to them than sunlight itself.

The continued increase in the number of people per square yard in crowded business and residential areas will also make the provision of overhead means of transport necessary, as may be realised from the fact that if the Woolworth Building and other skyscrapers on Manhattan Island in New York discharged all their occupants at once there would not be standing room for them in the streets in the immediate vicinity. The buildings of the cities of the future will therefore be connected by bridges at various heights for foot and vehicular traffic so that it will not be necessary for all their occupants to follow the same route in entering or leaving.

High-speed escalators will be provided, in addition to express lifts, and if the occupant of an office on the fiftieth floor of a building near the Bank of England in London gets tired of travelling to his home north of Hampstead on the mono-rail cars that run through the city at different levels, he may proceed by a series of escalators that take him north while bringing him nearer the ground.

A suggestion of this kind has already been made quite seriously in Chicago, a go-ahead American city that promises to produce many splendid ideas in the future. It has been proposed to erect a line of skyscrapers along the Lake Michigan frontage of that city, with the tallest buildings in the middle of the line, the heights decreasing towards the ends. The tops of these buildings will be bridged by a roadway, along which those who work in the buildings will pass on arrival or departure, while they will leave their cars during the day in the garages arranged on the uppermost floors. A scheme of this kind will relieve congestion of traffic in the streets and thus prevent waste of valuable time.

The engineer will also rule in factories and in agriculture. In the former he will find new methods of carrying out the fundamental processes, and he will be greatly assisted in this work by the results of a more scientific study of lubrication as well as by the new alloys that the metallurgists will produce. Agricultural machinery is in special need of improvement, but at present the lack of power prevents developments. Both steam-engines and petrol motors are being used more frequently, but the complete mechanization of this industry will not become possible until cheap electrical power is widely distributed.

The last place in which power on any comprehensive scale will be introduced is the home, but in the days to come power will be so cheap in comparison with human labour that the latter will be displaced almost universally. There is, in fact, no sphere where the efforts of the engineer will not be productive, for in addition to his utilitarian work he will join forces with others to give practical expression to many ideas and discoveries that will add greatly to the enjoyment of life and increase the general standard of comfort.

This brief summary of the engineering of the future is necessarily incomplete. In 1828 George Stephenson was in a position to visualise the great changes in transport methods that the introduction of the steam engine would bring about, but he would have been quite unable to foretell the introduction of the petrol engine, and of electric lighting and power. Similarly, principles that to us would be new and startling will almost certainly be commonplace features to the engineers of the future, who are the Meccano boys of to-day.

An impression of the great land liners of the future, careering along special elevated roadways, the triumph of the engineer.

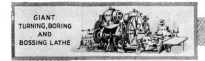
GIANT TURNING, BORING AND BOSSING LATHE

ELECTRIC TRAIN

SUBMARINE

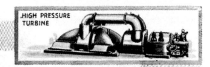
HIGH PRESSURE TURBINE

THE FIRST PASSENGER LOCOMOTIVE

THE FLYING SCOTSMAN.

CUGNOT'S ROAD VEHICLE

MODERN RACING CAR

WRIGHT'S GLIDER

"SUPERMARINE NAPIER" SEAPLANE

AN EARLY "AEROSTAT"

DIRIGIBLE AIRSHIP

The Boyhood of Famous Inventors

Most of the world's famous inventors and engineers showed their love of mechanical subjects in their young days. How they would have welcomed Meccano then! The schoolboy, James Watt, amazed his friends by building a small electric shocking-machine, therein displaying that love of "making things work" that afterwards led him to fame and fortune as the inventor of the first practical steam engine. Samuel Smiles, in his biography of John Smeaton, the famous lighthouse builder, tells us that "the only playthings in which he seemed to take any real pleasure were models of things that would work." Young James Nasmyth, the future inventor of the steam hammer, spent hours in laboriously turning wooden spinning tops and making small brass cannon. George Stephenson, during most of the little spare time he had when a boy, constructed models of pumping and winding engines out of clay. Edison, as a boy, experimented with a telegraphic instrument in which the wires were wrapped in old rags and glass bottles served as insulators. How much easier would the tasks of these famous men have been had they had Meccano to assist them with their experiments!

The Joy of Inventing

Inventing new models and movements in Meccano is the greatest fun in the world, and there is little doubt that the inventors and engineers who will make their mark in the future are at the present moment building Meccano models.

The Meccano system is peculiarly adapted to experimenting and inventing, not only because of the interchangeability and scope of the parts but also because of their exceptional precision. All the strips, girders and brackets have equidistant holes, half-an-inch apart and spaced to the 1/1000 part of an inch, enabling perfect connections to be made. The gears and pinions are machine-cut from the finest brass. They mesh correctly, with the correct amount of play, and they operate in exactly the same manner as the gears and pinions used for big machines. It is interesting to note that many large engineering firms always keep a stock of Meccano on hand with which to carry out experiments and to test new ideas.

As soon as he has built all the models shown in the Manuals, every Meccano boy should set about improving them or building others according to his own ideas. New and valuable parts are constantly being added to the Meccano system and each enables boys to build a whole series of new and better models.

Every Meccano boy should try his hand at inventing, for there is nothing in the world comparable with the joy and satisfaction of creating something new. When he succeeds in producing a new model he should enter it in one of the Meccano Model-building Competitions, announced every month in the "*Meccano Magazine*." Splendid prizes are waiting to be won by inventive boys!

ENGINE OF EARLY STEAMBOAT

GIANT MARINE ENGINE

EARLY TRIP HAMMER

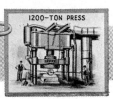
1200-TON PRESS

HAND LOOM OF 1825 — MODERN LOOM — H.M.S. NELSON.

EARLY STEAMBOAT

MECCANO
A SELECTION OF SUPER MODELS

Motorcycle and Sidecar

This is an excellent example of Meccano miniature engineering. The Sidecar is of streamline design and is mounted on springs. The Motorcycle is complete with lamps, horn, exhaust pipes, spring-mounted saddle, etc.

Motor Chassis

Replicas of this model are used by motor car manufacturers and agents to demonstrate to car buyers all the movements of a first class automobile. The model runs perfectly under its own power.

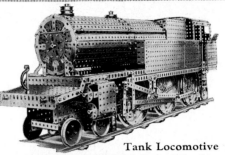

Tank Locomotive

Here is a model that will delight the railway expert. A very interesting feature is the accurate reproduction of Walschaerts' valve gear, every detail of which has its counterpart in the Meccano model.

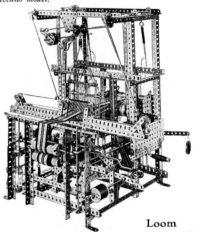

Loom

This is perhaps the crowning achievement in the long list of Meccano successes. The material produced by the Meccano Loom is marvellously woven and could be used for neck-ties, hat-bands, etc.

Travelling Gantry Crane

This is a realistic and powerful model. It demonstrates a number of interesting movements, all of which may be actuated separately or simultaneously by means of the 4-volt Electric Motor embodied in the structure.

The models illustrated on this page show the wonderful possibilities of Meccano. They comprise a selection from a range of super models that have been specially produced by our expert designers. Each one in the series is a masterpiece and there is not a boy in the country who will not be eager to build them all.

These models are so important that we have engaged expert engineers to describe them, and a special leaflet with beautiful half-tone illustrations and detailed instructions has been written for each of them.

A descriptive leaflet, giving full particulars of all the models in the series and the prices of the special Instruction Leaflets that are published in connection with them, may be obtained free of charge from your dealer, or direct from Meccano Limited, Binns Road, Liverpool.

Steam Shovel

A splendid model of a giant excavator of the type used in making canals or railway cuttings. The travelling and rotating movements and luffing motion of the jib are operated by an Electric Motor.

Log Saw

This is a model of a machine used in saw mills for the preliminary cutting and shaping of the tree trunks as they arrive from the logging camps. The saw is driven rapidly to and fro whilst the work table travels slowly beneath it.

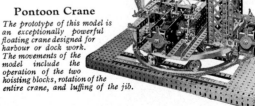

Pontoon Crane

The prototype of this model is an exceptionally powerful floating crane designed for harbour or dock work. The movements of the model include the operation of the two hoisting blocks, rotation of the entire crane, and luffing of the jib.

MECCANO

The Toy that made Engineering famous

Engineering for Boys

The Meccano system is composed of over two hundred different parts, mostly made of steel or brass, each one of which has a specified mechanical purpose. These parts combine to form a complete miniature engineering system with which practically any mechanical movement may be reproduced in model form. More can be accomplished with Meccano than with any other constructional toy, for no other system has such possibilities. The genius is in the parts and the youngest boy can commence to build models as soon as he gets his Outfit home.

Hundreds of Models

There is no limit to the number of models you can build with Meccano—Cranes, Clocks, Motor Cars, Ship-Coalers, Machine Tools, Locomotives—in fact everything that interests boys. The most wonderful thing about Meccano is that it is *real engineering;* it is fascinating and delightful and yet so simple that even an inexperienced boy may join in the fun of building models without having to study or learn anything. A beautifully illustrated Book of Instructions showing how to make hundreds of models is included with every Outfit and a screw-driver is the only tool required.

Meccano Boys Build and Invent

The training of the eye, brain and hand in erecting Meccano is considerable, but there is also developed a faculty of immense value to every boy. No boy is content to build the models exactly as he finds them; it is always possible to improve, and he sets to work to do this almost at once. It is a boy's nature to venture into unknown fields, and the Meccano hobby opens up a new and wide world for him to explore. He very soon proceeds to invent, and new models and designs, the creation of his own brain, make their appearance.

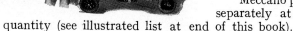

How to Begin

Meccano is sold in nine different Outfits, numbered 00 to 7. All Meccano parts are of the same high quality and finish, but the larger Outfits contain a greater quantity and variety of parts, making possible the construction of more elaborate models. Each Outfit may be converted into the one next higher by the purchase of an Accessory Outfit (see page 41). Thus, if a No. 2 is the first Outfit bought, it may be converted into a No. 3 by adding to it a No. 2A. A No. 3A will then convert it into a No. 4 and so on up to No. 7. In this way, no matter with what Outfit you commence, you may build it up by degrees until you possess a No. 7.

Meccano parts may be bought separately at any time in any quantity (see illustrated list at end of this book).

The Meccano Service

The Meccano boy of to-day will be the famous engineer of to-morrow. When you want to know something more about engineering than is now shown in our books, or when you strike a rough problem of any kind, write to us. We receive over 200 letters from boys every day all the year round. Some write to us because they are in difficulty, others because they want advice on their work or pleasures, or about their choice of a career. Others, again, write to us just because they like to do so—and we are glad to know that they regard us as their friends. We publish a special Magazine for them (see page IV of cover).

Although all kinds of queries are addressed to us on all manner of subjects, the main interest is, of course, Engineering. No one has such a wonderful knowledge of engineering matters as that possessed by our staff of experts, and this vast store of knowledge, gained only by many years of hard-earned experience, is at your service.

THE FINEST HOBBY IN THE WORLD

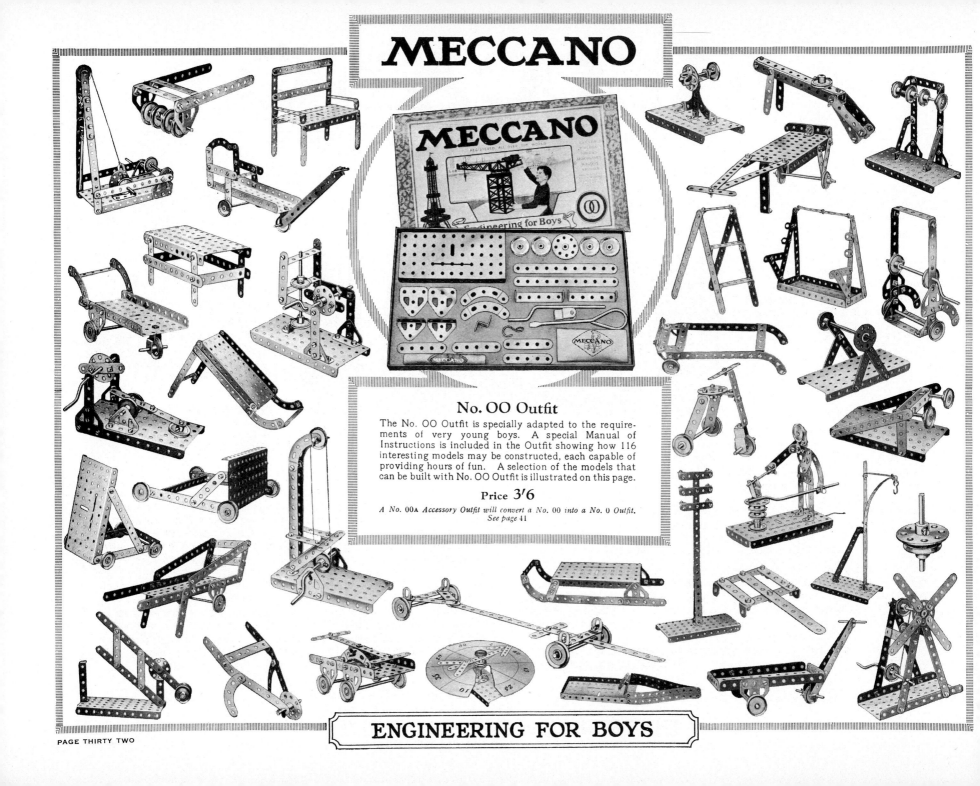

MECCANO

No. OO Outfit

The No. OO Outfit is specially adapted to the requirements of very young boys. A special Manual of Instructions is included in the Outfit showing how 116 interesting models may be constructed, each capable of providing hours of fun. A selection of the models that can be built with No. OO Outfit is illustrated on this page.

Price 3/6

A No. 00A Accessory Outfit will convert a No. 00 into a No. 0 Outfit.
See page 41

ENGINEERING FOR BOYS

MECCANO

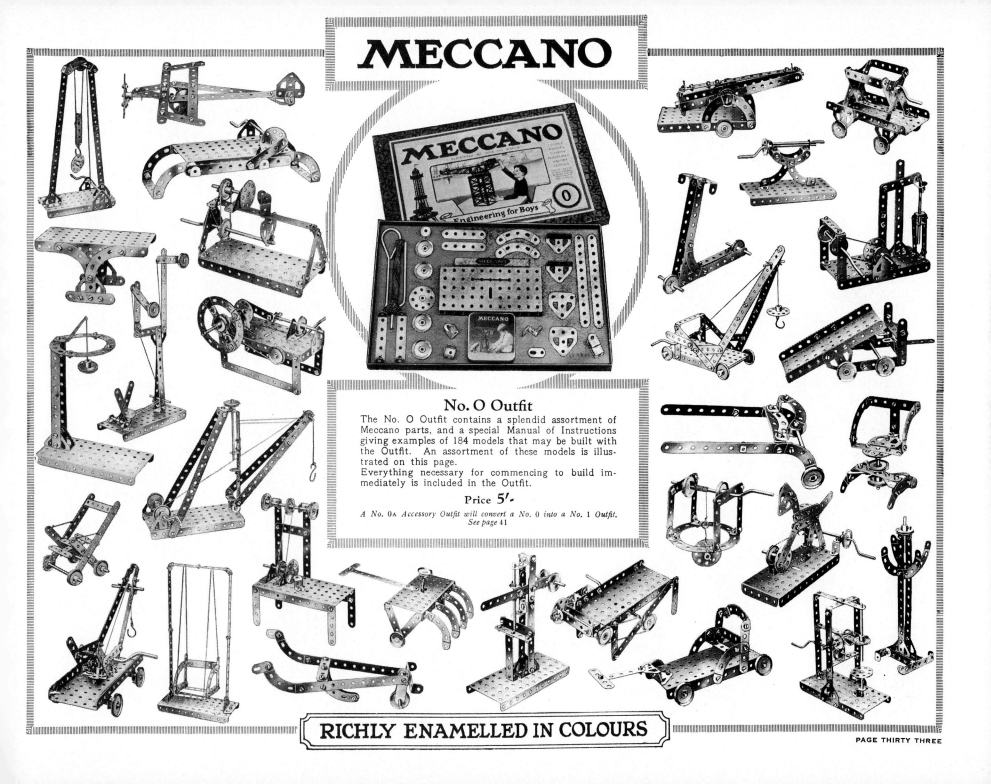

No. O Outfit

The No. O Outfit contains a splendid assortment of Meccano parts, and a special Manual of Instructions giving examples of 184 models that may be built with the Outfit. An assortment of these models is illustrated on this page.

Everything necessary for commencing to build immediately is included in the Outfit.

Price 5'-

A No. 0A Accessory Outfit will convert a No. 0 into a No. 1 Outfit.
See page 41

RICHLY ENAMELLED IN COLOURS

MECCANO

HAND LOOM

DROP STAMP

MECCANOGRAPH

LETTER BALANCE

TELPHER SPAN

LAWN MOWER

TOWER WAGON

WINDMILL PUMP

BICYCLE

MECHANICAL STAMP

ROTATING CRANE

GIANT FOUNDRY LADLE

No. 1 Outfit

This Outfit contains a large number of Meccano parts with which a splendid range of models may be built. The possibilities of the No. 1 Outfit may be judged from the fine selection of models illustrated on this page. A big Manual of Instructions is included, giving examples of 348 models that may be built with the Outfit.

Price 10'-

A No. 1A Accessory Outfit will convert a No. 1 into a No. 2 Outfit. See page 41

MECHANICAL SHOVEL

POTTERS WHEEL

RACING MOTOR-CAR

LORRY CRANE

ELEVATED JIB CRANE

BAND SAW

DRILL

ELECTRIC ELEVATOR

AEROPLANE

MOTOR VAN

ANTI-AIRCRAFT GUN

TRAVELLING CRANE

HELVE HAMMER

NEW PARTS, BETTER MODELS, MORE FUN

MECCANO

CARRIER TRICYCLE

TRAVELLING JIB CRANE

AEROPLANE

COASTER

EMBOSSING MACHINE

RAILWAY BRIDGE WITH SIGNALS

HIGH-LEVEL BRIDGE

PIT-HEAD GEAR

ELECTRIC TRUCK

CANDY PULLER

No. 2 Outfit

The fortunate possessor of a No. 2 Outfit is able to build up models of a more complicated and interesting type. A selection of these fine models is illustrated on this page.

All the models are designed on correct engineering principles, and full instructions for building 396 are included in the Outfit.

Price 16/-

A No. 2A Accessory Outfit will convert a No. 2 into a No. 3 Outfit.
See page 41

SIFTER

STEAM LORRY

FIRE ESCAPE

MAT FRAME

TURNTABLE

HAY TEDDER

ROUNDABOUT

WINDMILL

ANTI-AIRCRAFT GUN

STAMPING MILL

TRY-YOUR-STRENGTH MACHINE

MECCANO BOYS BUILD AND INVENT

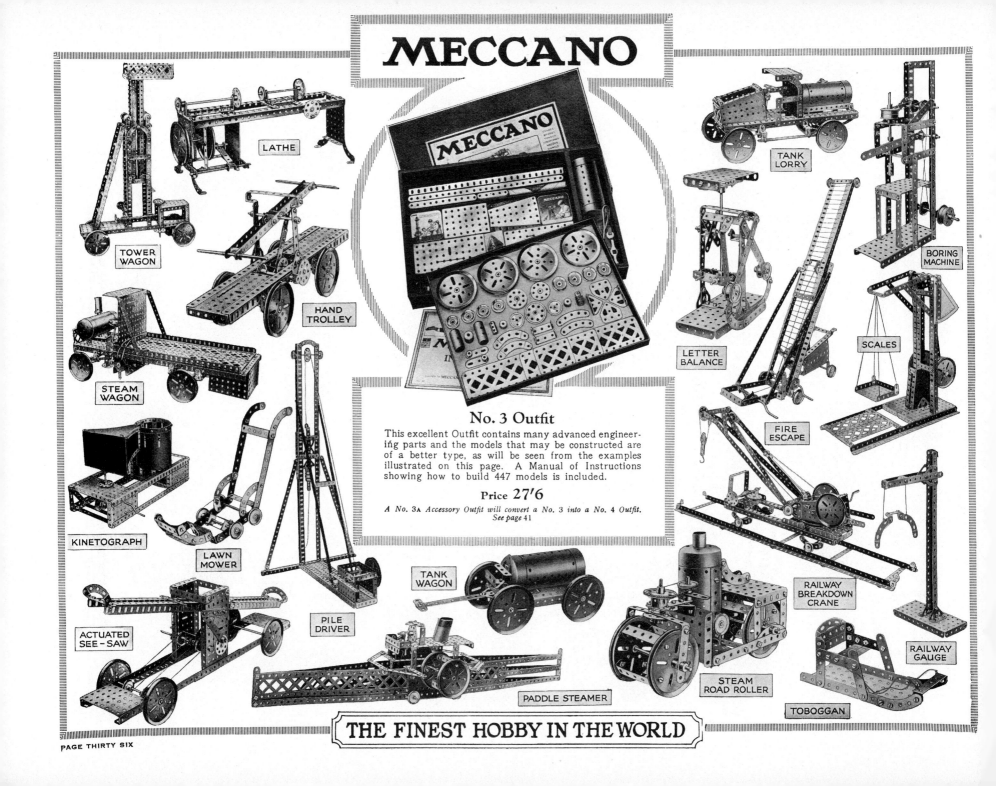

MECCANO

LATHE

TOWER WAGON

HAND TROLLEY

STEAM WAGON

KINETOGRAPH

LAWN MOWER

ACTUATED SEE-SAW

PILE DRIVER

TANK WAGON

PADDLE STEAMER

TANK LORRY

BORING MACHINE

LETTER BALANCE

SCALES

FIRE ESCAPE

RAILWAY BREAKDOWN CRANE

STEAM ROAD ROLLER

RAILWAY GAUGE

TOBOGGAN

No. 3 Outfit

This excellent Outfit contains many advanced engineering parts and the models that may be constructed are of a better type, as will be seen from the examples illustrated on this page. A Manual of Instructions showing how to build 447 models is included.

Price 27'6

A No. 3A Accessory Outfit will convert a No. 3 into a No. 4 Outfit.
See page 41

THE FINEST HOBBY IN THE WORLD

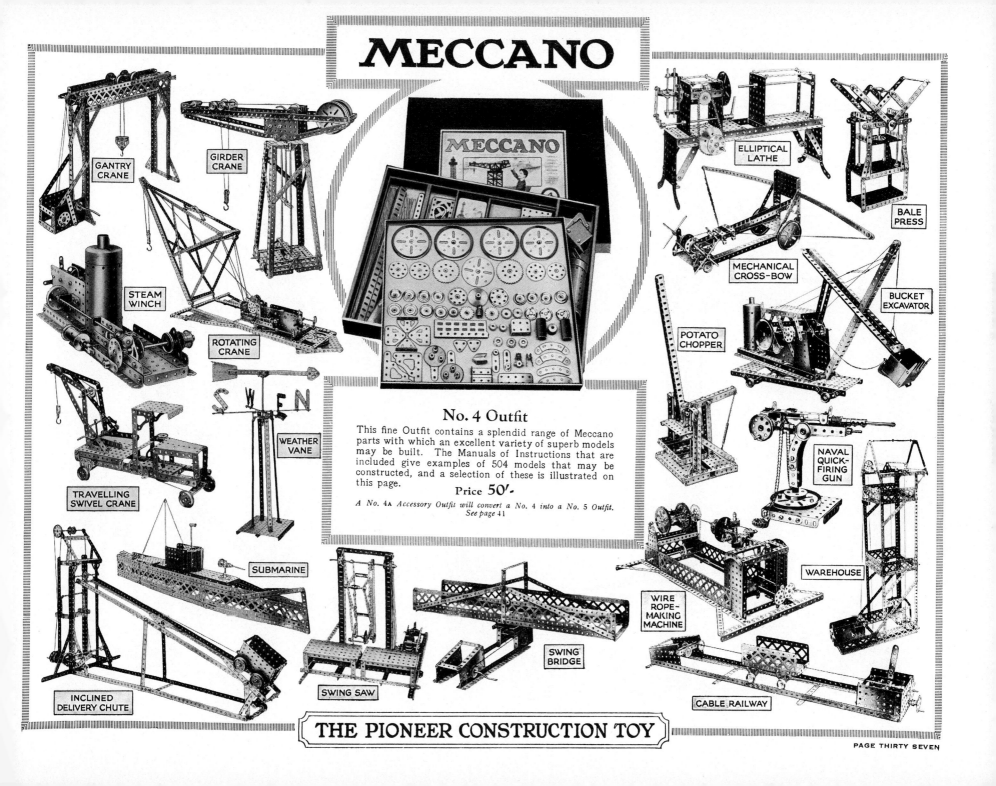

MECCANO

GANTRY CRANE

GIRDER CRANE

STEAM WINCH

ROTATING CRANE

TRAVELLING SWIVEL CRANE

WEATHER VANE

ELLIPTICAL LATHE

BALE PRESS

MECHANICAL CROSS-BOW

BUCKET EXCAVATOR

POTATO CHOPPER

NAVAL QUICK-FIRING GUN

WIRE ROPE-MAKING MACHINE

WAREHOUSE

No. 4 Outfit

This fine Outfit contains a splendid range of Meccano parts with which an excellent variety of superb models may be built. The Manuals of Instructions that are included give examples of 504 models that may be constructed, and a selection of these is illustrated on this page.

Price 50'-

A No. 4A Accessory Outfit will convert a No. 4 into a No. 5 Outfit.
See page 41

SUBMARINE

INCLINED DELIVERY CHUTE

SWING SAW

SWING BRIDGE

CABLE RAILWAY

THE PIONEER CONSTRUCTION TOY

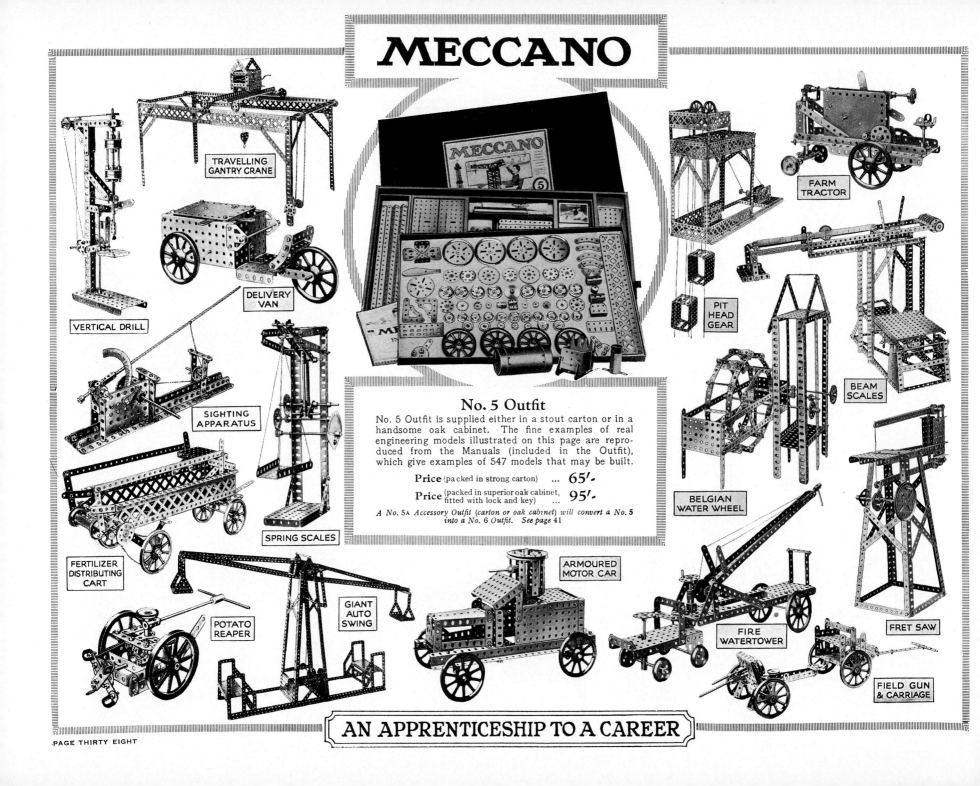

MECCANO

TRAVELLING GANTRY CRANE

VERTICAL DRILL

DELIVERY VAN

SIGHTING APPARATUS

SPRING SCALES

FERTILIZER DISTRIBUTING CART

POTATO REAPER

GIANT AUTO SWING

ARMOURED MOTOR CAR

FARM TRACTOR

PIT HEAD GEAR

BEAM SCALES

BELGIAN WATER WHEEL

FIRE WATERTOWER

FRET SAW

FIELD GUN & CARRIAGE

No. 5 Outfit

No. 5 Outfit is supplied either in a stout carton or in a handsome oak cabinet. The fine examples of real engineering models illustrated on this page are reproduced from the Manuals (included in the Outfit), which give examples of 547 models that may be built.

Price (packed in strong carton) ... **65/-**

Price (packed in superior oak cabinet, fitted with lock and key) ... **95/-**

A No. 5A Accessory Outfit (carton or oak cabinet) will convert a No. 5 into a No. 6 Outfit. See page 41

AN APPRENTICESHIP TO A CAREER

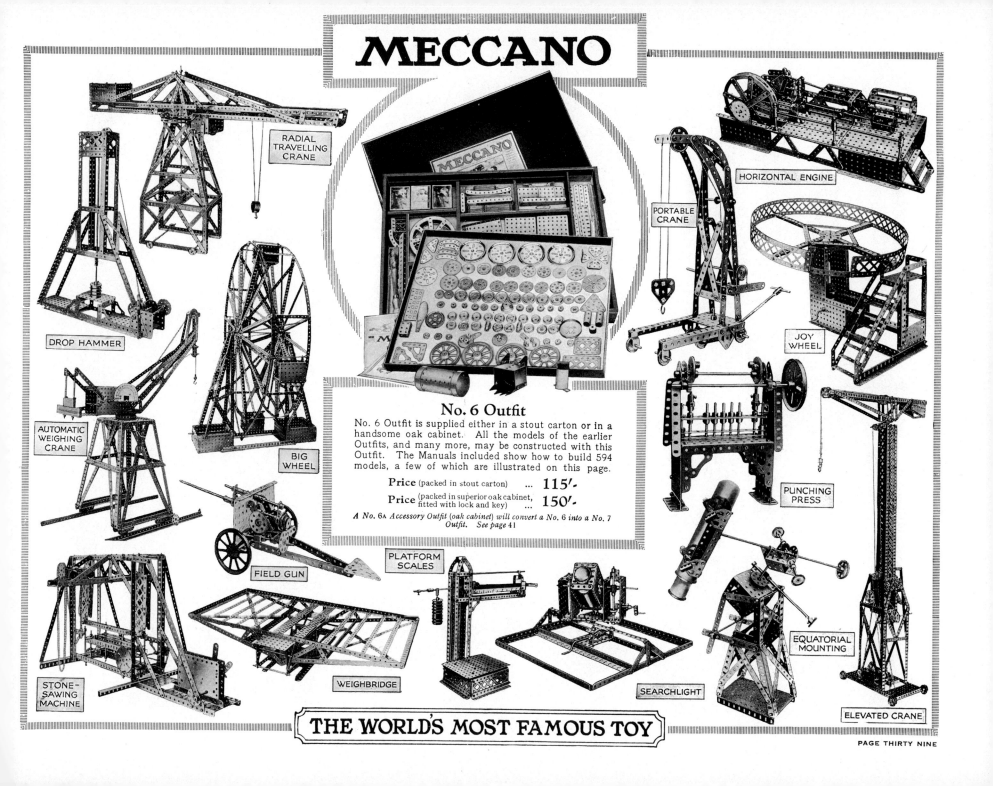

MECCANO

RADIAL TRAVELLING CRANE

HORIZONTAL ENGINE

DROP HAMMER

PORTABLE CRANE

JOY WHEEL

AUTOMATIC WEIGHING CRANE

BIG WHEEL

No. 6 Outfit

No. 6 Outfit is supplied either in a stout carton or in a handsome oak cabinet. All the models of the earlier Outfits, and many more, may be constructed with this Outfit. The Manuals included show how to build 594 models, a few of which are illustrated on this page.

Price (packed in stout carton) ... **115/-**

Price (packed in superior oak cabinet, fitted with lock and key) ... **150/-**

A No. 6A Accessory Outfit (oak cabinet) will convert a No. 6 into a No. 7 Outfit. See page 41

PUNCHING PRESS

PLATFORM SCALES

FIELD GUN

STONE-SAWING MACHINE

WEIGHBRIDGE

SEARCHLIGHT

EQUATORIAL MOUNTING

ELEVATED CRANE

THE WORLD'S MOST FAMOUS TOY

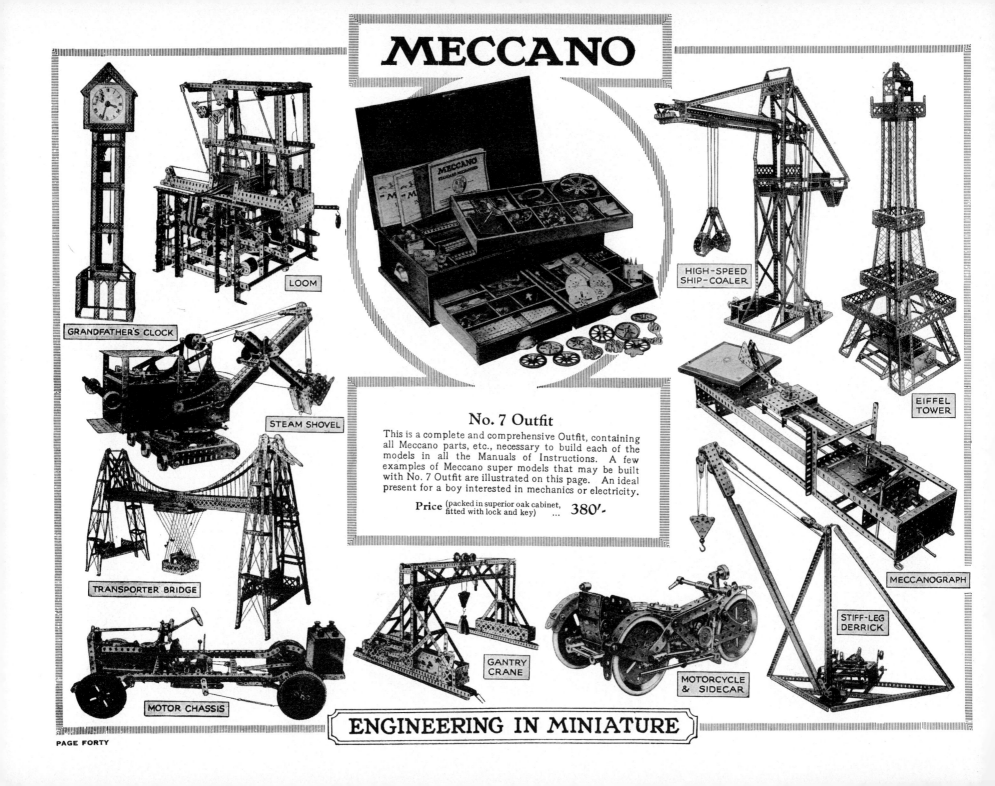

MECCANO

GRANDFATHER'S CLOCK

LOOM

STEAM SHOVEL

TRANSPORTER BRIDGE

MOTOR CHASSIS

HIGH-SPEED SHIP-COALER

EIFFEL TOWER

MECCANOGRAPH

STIFF-LEG DERRICK

GANTRY CRANE

MOTORCYCLE & SIDECAR

No. 7 Outfit

This is a complete and comprehensive Outfit, containing all Meccano parts, etc., necessary to build each of the models in all the Manuals of Instructions. A few examples of Meccano super models that may be built with No. 7 Outfit are illustrated on this page. An ideal present for a boy interested in mechanics or electricity.

Price (packed in superior oak cabinet, fitted with lock and key) ... **380'-**

ENGINEERING IN MINIATURE

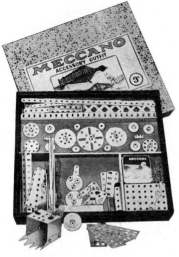

No. 3a Accessory Outfit

The Purpose of Meccano Accessory Outfits

Meccano Accessory Outfits connect the main Outfits from No. 00 to No. 7. They may be aptly described as the stepping stones to bigger and better models. A No. 2 Outfit may be converted into a No. 3 by adding to it a No. 2a Accessory Outfit, and a No. 3a would then convert it into a No. 4. In this way, no matter with which Outfit a boy commences, he may build it up by degrees until he possesses all the parts contained in the largest Outfit.

The Meccano No. 3a Accessory Outfit is shown in the accompanying illustration.

Price List of Meccano Accessory Outfits

No. 00a	(converts a No. 00 Outfit into a No. 0)	...	...	...	Price	1/6
„ 0a	(„ „ 0 „ „ „ 1)	...	...	...	„	5/6
„ 1a	(„ „ 1 „ „ „ 2)	...	...	...	„	7/-
„ 2a	(„ „ 2 „ „ „ 3)	...	...	...	„	12/6
„ 3a	(„ „ 3 „ „ „ 4)	...	...	...	„	23/6
„ 4a	(„ „ 4 „ „ „ 5)	...	...	...	„	15/-
„ 5a*	(„ „ 5* „ „ „ 6*)	...	...	...	„	50/-
„ 5a†	(„ „ 5† „ „ „ 6†)	...	...	...	„	80/-
„ 6a†	(„ „ 6† „ „ „ 7)	...	...	...	„	215/-

Carton.   †*Wood.*

Special Inventor's Outfit

This Outfit makes a valuable addition to any keen model-builder's equipment. It is intended specially for boys who already have Meccano and who wish to satisfy their inventive inclinations by building models from their own designs. The parts contained include four large Pulley Wheels with Dunlop Tyres, Ball Race, Ship's Funnel, Pulley Blocks, Channel Bearing, Crane Grab, and many others.

Price 17/6

Storage Boxes for Meccano Parts

Almost every Meccano boy purchases additional Meccano parts from time to time, but he sometimes has difficulty in finding suitable accommodation for them. We are now pleased to announce that we can supply strongly-made boxes that have been specially designed for the purpose, enabling such extra parts to be stored neatly and methodically so that they are always easily accessible. There are three different sizes, each of which is illustrated and described below.

No. 1 Storage Box

Stained and varnished rich oak effect, and fitted with partitions as shown in the illustration. The lid is hinged and is secured by means of lock and key.   Price 10/6

Dimensions :

Length   15½ ins.
Width   8¾ ins.
Depth   2¾ ins.

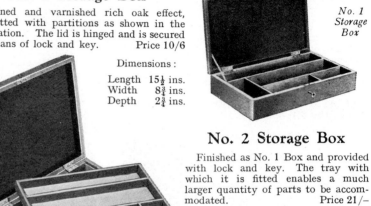

No. 1 Storage Box

No. 2 Storage Box

No. 2 Storage Box

Finished as No. 1 Box and provided with lock and key. The tray with which it is fitted enables a much larger quantity of parts to be accommodated.   Price 21/-

Dimensions : Length 14½ ins. Width 11 ins. Depth 3¾ ins.

The full range of Meccano Accessory Parts is illustrated and listed at the end of this book.

No. 3 Storage Box

This box is a perfect receptacle for Meccano parts. It is finished similarly to the Nos. 1 and 2 Boxes and provided with lock and key. The two partitioned trays with which it is fitted enable a very large number of Meccano parts to be stored.   Price 30/-

Dimensions : Length 20 ins. Width 14 ins. Depth 5½ ins.

No. 3 Storage Box

MECCANO BOYS BUILD AND INVENT

Meccano Electric Motor No. 1

(4 volt)

The 4-volt Motor is specially designed to build into Meccano models. It may be run by a 4-volt accumulator or, by employing the Transformer described below, from the main. It is fitted with reversing motion, provided with stopping and starting controls, and the gearing is interchangeable. 15/6

Important.—The 4-volt Motor will not run satisfactorily from dry cells.

Transformer

By means of this transformer the Meccano Electric Motor No. 1 (4 volt) may be driven from the house supply (alternating current only). It is available for all standard supply voltages, from 100 to 250 inclusive, at all standard frequencies. The supply voltage and frequency must be specified when ordering. Complete with length of flex and adapter for connection to an ordinary lamp socket. Price 30/-

Meccano Accumulators

These excellent accumulators have been specially adapted to drive the Meccano Electric Motor No. 1. 4 volt 8 amps. Price 17/6   4 volt 20 amps. Price 25/-

Meccano Resistance Controller

By employing this variable resistance the speed of the Meccano Electric Motor No. 1 (4 volt) may be regulated as desired. The controller is connected  in series with the motor and accumulator, or with the motor and transformer if a transformer is used as the source of power. It will not regulate the speed of a high-voltage motor connected to the main. Price 3/6

Run your Meccano Models with a Meccano Motor

If you wish to obtain the fullest possible enjoyment from the Meccano hobby you must operate your models with a Meccano motor. Just imagine the thrill of setting in motion your Crane, Ship-coaler, Motor Car, Windmill or any other model you build. You push over the control lever of the motor and immediately the model commences to work in exactly the same manner as its "big brother" in real life.

Meccano motors are strongly made and the utmost care is taken in their manufacture to ensure that they will give satisfaction to their owners. The side plates and bases are pierced with the standard Meccano equidistant holes, which enable the motors to be built into any Meccano model in the exact position required.

Various combinations of gears may be mounted on the motors for the purpose of reducing the speed of the driving spindles, and thereby increasing the lifting power. An instance of what is possible in this connection is shown by the illustration below.

All the motors have forward and reverse movements, a feature that greatly enhances the fun of running the models.

This illustration shows how easy it is to mount gearing on a Meccano Electric Motor. In this example the final shaft of the gear train rotates once in every 171 revolutions of the armature, thus providing a slow, powerful drive.

Meccano Electric Motor No. 2

(100-250 volt A.C. or D.C.)

This Electric Motor is specially adapted for driving Meccano models, into which it may be built. It is designed for connection with the electric light main—100-120 volts or 200-250 volts, alternating or direct. A 6 ft. length of flex, fitted with a plug for connection with the motor terminals and an adapter for connection with an ordinary lamp socket, is included. A suitable resistance is required when the motor is run with a 200-250-volt current, and this is supplied by connecting a 60-watt lamp in series with the motor. A board, on which are mounted a suitable lamp holder (lamp not included) and a switch, is provided separately. Price 32/6
Lamp board (with lamp holder and switch) ,, 4/6

Meccano Rheostat

(For high voltage Motors)

This Rheostat is for controlling the speed of the Electric Motor No. 2 or the Hornby Metropolitan Train H.V. It may be connected to the house lighting system by means of an adapter and may be used with either alternating or direct currents ranging from 100 to 250 volts. A 60-watt lamp (not supplied) is required for use with the Rheostat. Price 18/6

Meccano Clockwork Motor

This is a splendid motor for driving Meccano models. It is fitted with starting, stopping and reversing levers, and all its movements are fully explained in the instructions that accompany it. Price 7/6

RUN YOUR MODELS WITH A MOTOR

Meccano No. 4-7 Manual

Meccano Bound Manual

Meccano Standard Mechanisms Manual

The Meccano Manuals of Instructions

The Meccano Manuals are all beautifully printed and the illustrations are in half-tone throughout. Every Meccano boy should possess a copy of each of the 00-3 and 4-7 Manuals in which a total number of 626 models is illustrated, and also a copy of the Standard Mechanisms Manual in which a fine selection of real engineering movements that may be built with Meccano are reproduced. These Manuals may be purchased as separate units, or attractively bound in full cloth cover, lettered in gold.

The prices of the full range of Meccano Manuals are as follows :—

No. 0 Manual of Instructions	...	...	...	...	...	...	Price	4d.
No. 00-3 „	„	...	...	...	...	...	„	1/6
No. 4-7 „	„	...	...	...	...	...	„	1/6

Standard Mechanisms Manual	...	...	...	...	...	Price	1/-
Bound Manual of Instructions (comprising a 00-3 Manual, a 4-7 Manual and a Standard Mechanisms Manual)	...	...	...	...	„	7/6
Meccano Book of New Models	...	...	...	...	...	„	6d.

Meccano Lubricating Oil

Before commencing to operate a Meccano model, all gears and bearings should be oiled thoroughly with Meccano Lubricating Oil. This oil is specially prepared and is of the right consistency for the purpose.

Price, per bottle, 6d.

Oil Can No. 1

This is a miniature Oil Can that will give every satisfaction. It is strongly made and it functions perfectly. Price 6d.

Oil Can No. 2 ("K" Type)

This miniature Oil Can operates perfectly. The oil is ejected drop by drop by depressing the valve.

Price 3/6

Meccano Enamel

The Meccano enamel has been introduced to enable model-builders to convert nickel parts to colour or to touch up coloured parts should such treatment become necessary through mishandling. It is available in red and green, each colour being identical in shade with the enamels used in the Meccano Factory for spraying Meccano parts.

Price, per tin, 8d.

Meccano Saw Bench

This model Saw Bench is suitable for use with an Electric or Clockwork Motor. By means of the equidistant holes in the base it may be built into a Meccano Model Workshop. Beautifully finished in black enamel and nickel. Price 4/-

Meccano Shafting Standards

These Shafting Standards are designed on the Meccano system, with equidistant holes. Our illustration shows how strong and serviceable shafting may be constructed from Meccano parts with the aid of the Large Standard.

Standard only, Large	...	Price	1/-
„ „ Small	...	„	8d.

ENGINEERING FOR BOYS

MECCANO ACCESSORY PARTS

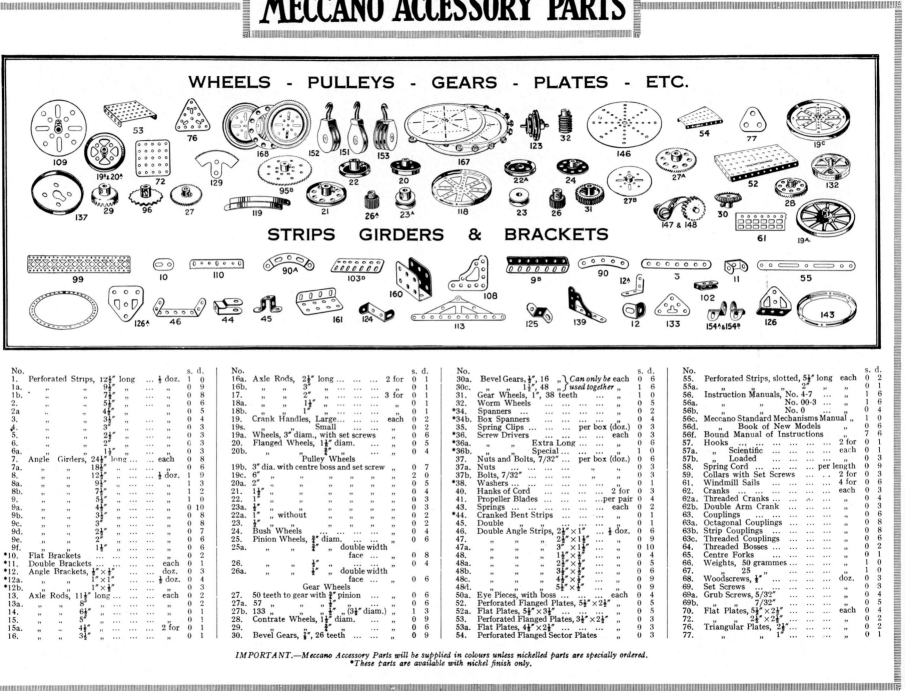

WHEELS - PULLEYS - GEARS - PLATES - ETC.

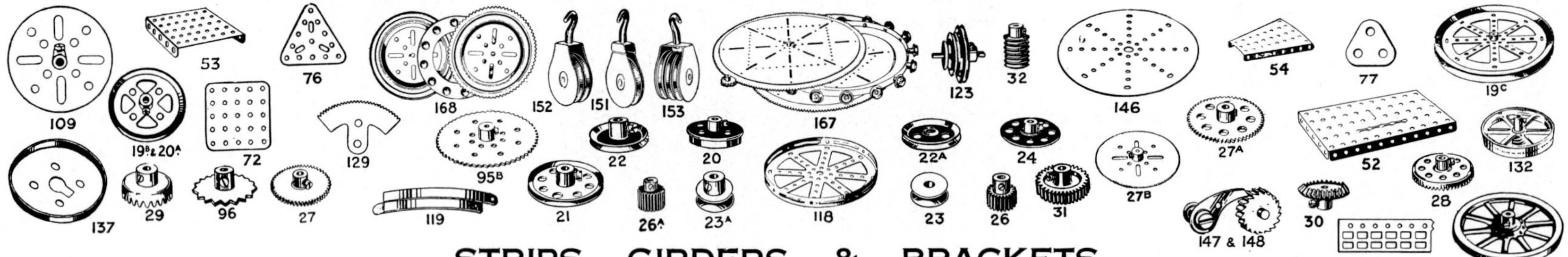

STRIPS GIRDERS & BRACKETS

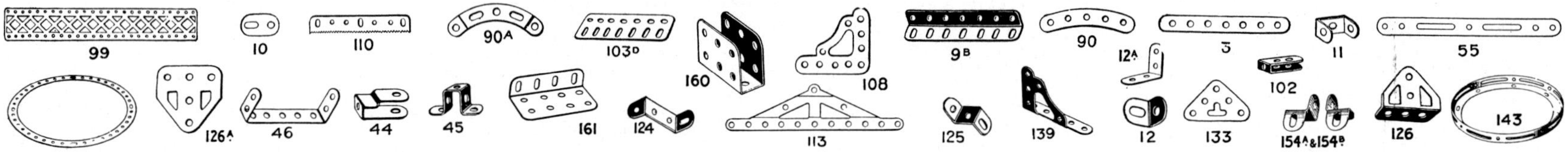

No.			s.	d.
1.	Perforated Strips, 12½″ long ...	½ doz.	1	0
1a.	„ „ 9½″ „ ...	„	0	9
1b.	„ „ 7½″ „ ...	„	0	8
2.	„ „ 5½″ „ ...	„	0	6
2a	„ „ 4½″ „	„	0	5
3.	„ „ 3½″ „ ...	„	0	4
4.	„ „ 3″ „ ...	„	0	3
5.	„ „ 2½″ „ ...	„	0	3
6.	„ „ 2″ „ ...	„	0	3
6a.	„ „ 1½″ „ ...	„	0	3
7.	Angle Girders, 24½″ long	each	0	8
7a.	„ „ 18½″	„	0	6
8.	„ „ 12½″	½ doz.	1	9
8a.	„ „ 9½″ „	„	1	3
8b.	„ „ 7½″ „	„	1	2
9.	„ „ 5½″ „	„	1	0
9a.	„ „ 4½″ „	„	0	10
9b.	„ „ 3½″ „	„	0	8
9c.	„ „ 3″ „	„	0	8
9d.	„ „ 2½″ „	„	0	7
9e.	„ „ 2″ „	„	0	6
9f.	„ „ 1½″ „	„	0	6
*10.	Flat Brackets	„	0	2
*11.	Double Brackets	each	0	1
*12.	Angle Brackets, ½″×½″	doz.	0	3
*12a.	„ „ 1″×1″	½ doz.	0	4
*12b.	„ „ 1″×½″	„	0	3
13.	Axle Rods, 11½″ long	each	0	2
13a.	„ „ 8″ „	„	0	2
14.	„ „ 6½″ „	„	0	1
15.	„ „ 5″ „	„	0	1
15a.	„ „ 4½″ „	2 for	0	1
16.	„ „ 3½″ „	„	0	1

No.			s.	d.
16a.	Axle Rods, 2½″ long	2 for	0	1
16b.	„ „ 3″ „	„	0	1
17.	„ „ 2″ „	3 for	0	1
18a.	„ „ 1½″ „	„	0	1
18b.	„ „ 1″ „	„	0	1
19.	Crank Handles, Large...	each	0	2
19s.	„ „ Small	„	0	2
19a.	Wheels, 3″ diam., with set screws	„	0	6
20.	Flanged Wheels, 1⅛″ diam. ...	„	0	5
20b.	„ „ ¾″ „ ...	„	0	4
	Pulley Wheels			
19b.	3″ dia. with centre boss and set screw	„	0	7
19c.	6″ „ „ „ „ „	„	2	0
20a.	2″ „ „ „ „ „	„	0	5
21.	1½″ „ „ „ „ „	„	0	4
22.	1″ „ „ „ „ „	„	0	3
23a.	½″ „ „ „ „ „	„	0	3
22a.	1″ „ without „ „ „	„	0	2
23.	½″ „ „ „ „ „	„	0	2
24.	Bush Wheels	„	0	4
25.	Pinion Wheels, ¾″ diam.	„	0	6
25a.	„ „ ¾″ „ double width face ...	„	0	8
26.	„ „ ½″ „	„	0	4
26a.	„ „ ½″ „ double width face ...	„	0	6
	Gear Wheels			
27.	50 teeth to gear with ¾″ pinion ...	„	0	6
27a.	57 „ „ „ ½″ „ ...	„	0	6
27b.	133 „ „ „ ½″ „ (3½″ diam.)	„	1	3
28.	Contrate Wheels, 1½″ diam. ...	„	0	9
29.	„ „ ¾″ „ ...	„	0	6
30.	Bevel Gears, ⅞″, 26 teeth	„	0	9

No.			s.	d.
30a.	Bevel Gears, ½″, 16 „ } *Can only be*	each	0	6
30c.	„ „ 1½″, 48 „ } *used together*	„	1	6
31.	Gear Wheels, 1″, 38 teeth ...	„	1	0
32.	Worm Wheels	„	0	5
*34.	Spanners	„	0	2
*34b.	Box Spanners	„	0	4
35.	Spring Clips	per box (doz.)	0	3
*36.	Screw Drivers	each	0	3
*36a.	„ „ Extra Long	„	0	6
*36b.	„ „ Special	„	1	0
37.	Nuts and Bolts, 7/32″ ...	per box (doz.)	0	6
37a.	Nuts ... ... „	„	0	3
37b.	Bolts, 7/32″ ... ... „	„	0	3
*38.	Washers	„	0	1
40.	Hanks of Cord	2 for	0	3
41.	Propeller Blades	per pair	0	4
43.	Springs	each	0	2
*44.	Cranked Bent Strips	„	0	1
45.	Double „ „	„	0	1
46.	Double Angle Strips, 2½″×1″ ...	½ doz.	0	6
47.	„ „ „ 2½″×1½″ ...	„	0	9
47a.	„ „ „ 3″ ×1½″ ...	„	0	10
48.	„ „ „ 1½″×½″ ...	„	0	4
48a.	„ „ „ 2½″×½″ ...	„	0	5
48b.	„ „ „ 3½″×½″ ...	„	0	6
48c.	„ „ „ 4½″×½″ ...	„	0	9
48d.	„ „ „ 5½″×½″ ...	„	0	9
50a.	Eye Pieces, with boss	each	0	4
52.	Perforated Flanged Plates, 5½″×2½″	„	0	5
52a.	Flat Plates, 5½″×3½″	„	0	5
53.	Perforated Flanged Plates, 3½″×2½″	„	0	3
53a.	Flat Plates, 4½″×2½″	„	0	3
54.	Perforated Flanged Sector Plates	„	0	3

No.			s.	d.
55.	Perforated Strips, slotted, 5½″ long	each	0	2
55a.	„ „ „ 2″ „	„	0	1
56.	Instruction Manuals, No. 4-7 ...	„	1	6
56a.	„ „ No. 00-3 ...	„	1	6
56b.	„ „ No. 0 ...	„	0	4
56c.	Meccano Standard Mechanisms Manual	„	1	0
56d.	„ Book of New Models	„	0	6
56f.	Bound Manual of Instructions	„	7	6
57.	Hooks	2 for	0	1
57a.	„ Scientific	each	0	1
57b.	„ Loaded	„	0	3
58.	Spring Cord	per length	0	9
59.	Collars with Set Screws	2 for	0	3
61.	Windmill Sails	4 for	0	6
62.	Cranks	each	0	3
62a.	Threaded Cranks	„	0	4
62b.	Double Arm Crank	„	0	3
63.	Couplings	„	0	6
63a.	Octagonal Couplings	„	0	8
63b.	Strip Couplings	„	0	8
63c.	Threaded Couplings	„	0	6
64.	Threaded Bosses	„	0	2
65.	Centre Forks	„	0	1
66.	Weights, 50 grammes	„	1	0
67.	„ 25 „	„	1	0
68.	Woodscrews, ½″	doz.	0	3
69.	Set Screws	„	0	3
69a.	Grub Screws, 5/32″	„	0	4
69b.	„ „ 7/32″	„	0	5
70.	Flat Plates, 5½″×2½″	each	0	4
72.	„ „ 2½″×2½″	„	0	2
76.	Triangular Plates, 2½″...	„	0	2
77.	„ „ 1″	„	0	1

IMPORTANT.—Meccano Accessory Parts will be supplied in colours unless nickelled parts are specially ordered.
**These parts are available with nickel finish only.*

MECCANO ACCESSORY PARTS

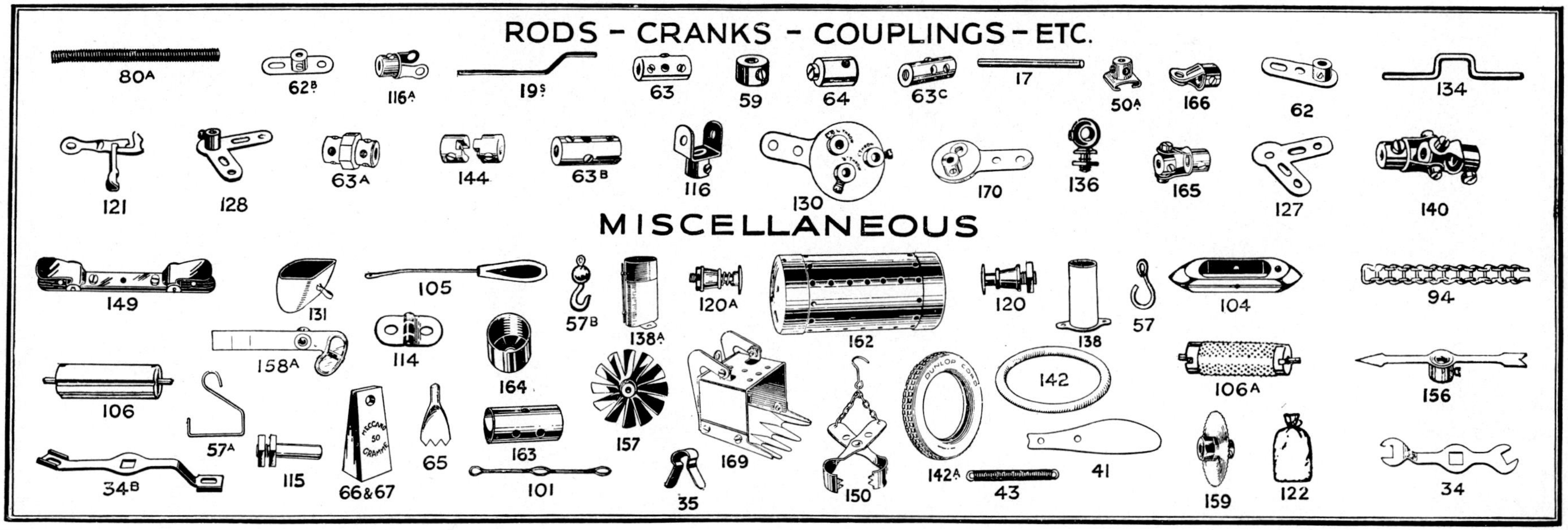

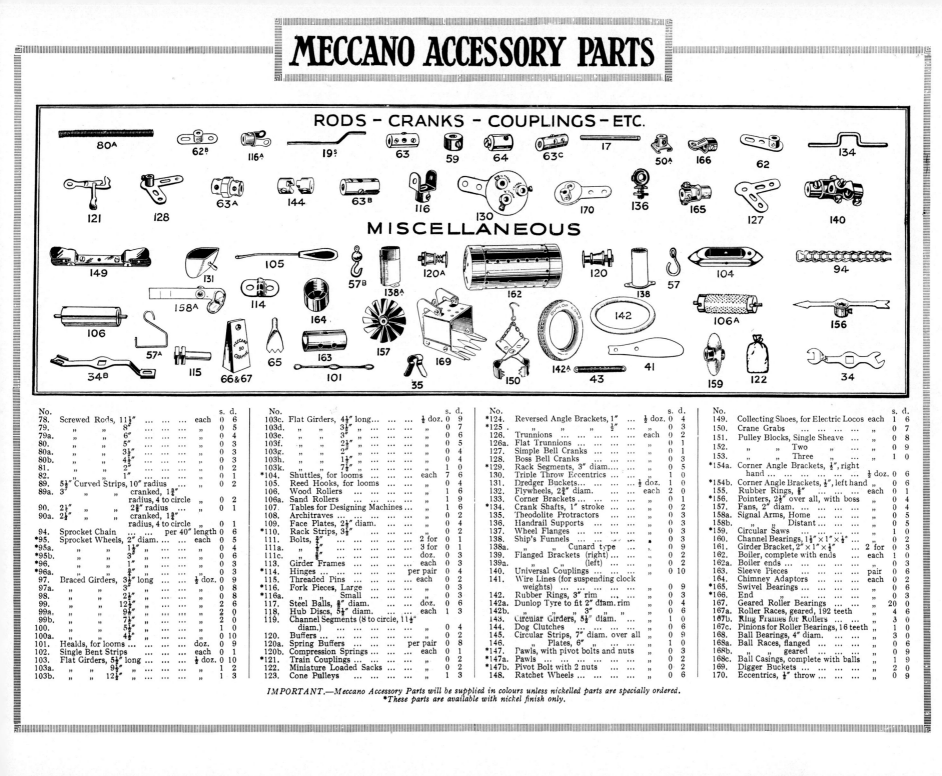

No.			s.	d.
78.	Screwed Rods, 11½″ … … …	each	0	6
79.	" " 8″ … … …	"	0	5
79a.	" " 6″ … … …	"	0	4
80.	" " 5″ … … …	"	0	3
80a.	" " 3½″ … … …	"	0	3
80b.	" " 4½″ … … …	"	0	3
81.	" " 2″ … … …	"	0	2
82.	" " 1″ … … …	"	0	1
89.	5½″ Curved Strips, 10″ radius …	"	0	2
89a.	3″ " " cranked, 1¾″ radius, 4 to circle	"	0	2
90.	2½″ " " 2⅜″ radius …	"	0	1
90a.	2½″ " " cranked, 1¾″ radius, 4 to circle	"	0	1
94.	Sprocket Chain … …	per 40″ length	0	6
*95.	Sprocket Wheels, 2″ diam. … …	each	0	5
*95a.	" " 1½″ " … …	"	0	4
*95b.	" " 3″ " … …	"	0	6
*96.	" " 1″ " … …	"	0	3
*96a.	" " ¾″ " … …	"	0	3
97.	Braced Girders, 3½″ long … …	½ doz.	0	9
97a.	" " 3″ " … …	"	0	8
98.	" " 2½″ " … …	"	0	8
99.	" " 12½″ " … …	"	2	6
99a.	" " 9½″ " … …	"	2	0
99b.	" " 7½″ " … …	"	2	0
100.	" " 5½″ " … …	"	1	0
100a.	" " 4½″ " … …	"	0	10
101.	Healds, for looms … … … …	doz.	0	9
102.	Single Bent Strips … … …	each	0	1
103.	Flat Girders, 5½″ long … … …	½ doz.	0	10
103a.	" " 9½″ " … … …	"	1	2
103b.	" " 12½″ " … … …	"	1	3

No.			s.	d.
103c.	Flat Girders, 4½″ long… … …	½ doz.	0	9
103d.	" " 3½″ " … … …	"	0	7
103e.	" " 3″ " … … …	"	0	6
103f.	" " 2½″ " … … …	"	0	5
103g.	" " 2″ " … … …	"	0	4
103h.	" " 1½″ " … … …	"	0	4
103k.	" " 7½″ " … … …	"	1	0
*104.	Shuttles, for looms … … …	each	7	6
105.	Reed Hooks, for looms … …	"	0	4
106.	Wood Rollers … … … …	"	1	6
106a.	Sand Rollers … … … …	"	1	9
107.	Tables for Designing Machines …	"	1	6
108.	Architraves … … … … …	"	0	2
109.	Face Plates, 2½″ diam. … …	"	0	4
*110.	Rack Strips, 3½″ … … …	"	0	2
111.	Bolts, ¾″ … … … … …	2 for	0	1
111a.	" ½″ … … … … …	3 for	0	1
111c.	" ⅜″ … … … … …	doz.	0	3
113.	Girder Frames … … … …	each	0	3
*114.	Hinges … … … … …	per pair	0	4
115.	Threaded Pins … … … …	each	0	2
*116.	Fork Pieces, Large … … …	"	0	3
*116a.	" " Small … … …	"	0	3
117.	Steel Balls, ⅜″ diam. … …	doz.	0	6
118.	Hub Discs, 5½″ diam. … …	each	1	3
119.	Channel Segments (8 to circle, 11½″ diam.) … … … …	"	0	4
120.	Buffers … … … … …	"	0	2
120a.	Spring Buffers … … …	per pair	0	8
120b.	Compression Springs … … …	each	0	1
*121.	Train Couplings … … … …	"	0	2
122.	Miniature Loaded Sacks … …	"	0	2
123.	Cone Pulleys … … … …	"	1	3

No.			s.	d.
*124.	Reversed Angle Brackets, 1″ …	½ doz.	0	4
*125.	" " " ½″ …	"	0	3
126.	Trunnions … … … … …	each	0	2
126a.	Flat Trunnions … … … …	"	0	1
127.	Simple Bell Cranks … … …	"	0	1
128.	Boss Bell Cranks … … …	"	0	3
*129.	Rack Segments, 3″ diam.… …	"	0	5
130.	Triple Throw Eccentrics … …	"	1	0
131.	Dredger Buckets… … … …	½ doz.	1	0
132.	Flywheels, 2¾″ diam. … …	each	2	0
133.	Corner Brackets … … … …	"	0	1
*134.	Crank Shafts, 1″ stroke … …	"	0	2
135.	Theodolite Protractors … …	"	0	3
136.	Handrail Supports … … …	"	0	3
137.	Wheel Flanges … … … …	"	0	3
138.	Ship's Funnels … … … …	"	0	3
138a.	" " Cunard type …	"	0	9
139.	Flanged Brackets (right) … …	"	0	2
139a.	" " (left) … …	"	0	2
140.	Universal Couplings … … …	"	0	10
141.	Wire Lines (for suspending clock weights) … … … … …	"	0	9
142.	Rubber Rings, 3″ rim … …	"	0	3
142a.	Dunlop Tyre to fit 2″ diam. rim	"	0	4
142b.	" " " 3″ " "	"	0	6
143.	Circular Girders, 5½″ diam. …	"	1	0
144.	Dog Clutches … … … …	"	0	6
145.	Circular Strips, 7″ diam. over all	"	0	9
146.	" Plates, 6″ " … …	"	1	0
*147.	Pawls, with pivot bolts and nuts	"	0	3
*147a.	Pawls … … … … … …	"	0	2
*147b.	Pivot Bolt with 2 nuts … …	"	0	2
148.	Ratchet Wheels … … … …	"	0	6

No.			s.	d.
149.	Collecting Shoes, for Electric Locos	each	1	6
150.	Crane Grabs … … … …	"	0	7
151.	Pulley Blocks, Single Sheave …	"	0	8
152.	" " Two " …	"	0	9
153.	" " Three " …	"	1	0
*154a.	Corner Angle Brackets, ½″, right hand … … … … … …	½ doz.	0	6
*154b.	Corner Angle Brackets, ½″, left hand	"	0	6
155.	Rubber Rings, ⅝″ … … …	each	0	1
*156.	Pointers, 2½″ over all, with boss	"	0	4
157.	Fans, 2″ diam. … … … …	"	0	4
158a.	Signal Arms, Home … … …	"	0	5
158b.	" " Distant … … …	"	0	5
*159.	Circular Saws … … … …	"	1	0
160.	Channel Bearings, 1½″ × 1″ × ½″ …	"	0	2
161.	Girder Bracket, 2″ × 1″ × ½″ …	2 for	0	3
162.	Boiler, complete with ends …	each	1	0
162a.	Boiler ends … … … … …	"	0	3
163.	Sleeve Pieces … … … …	pair	0	6
164.	Chimney Adaptors … … …	each	0	2
*165.	Swivel Bearings … … … …	"	0	6
*166.	End " … … … …	"	0	3
167.	Geared Roller Bearings … …	"	20	0
167a.	Roller Races, geared, 192 teeth	"	4	6
167b.	Ring Frames for Rollers … …	"	3	0
167c.	Pinions for Roller Bearings, 16 teeth	"	1	0
168.	Ball Bearings, 4″ diam. … …	"	3	0
168a.	Ball Races, flanged … … …	"	0	6
168b.	" " geared … … …	"	0	9
168c.	Ball Casings, complete with balls	"	1	9
169.	Digger Buckets … … … …	"	2	0
170.	Eccentrics, ½″ throw … … …	"	0	9

IMPORTANT.—Meccano Accessory Parts will be supplied in colours unless nickelled parts are specially ordered.
**These parts are available with nickel finish only.*

THE
"MECCANO MAGAZINE"

A fine Engineering Monthly for Boys

The *Meccano Magazine*, published in the interests of boys, contains splendid articles on such subjects as Famous Engineers and Inventors, Electricity, Bridges, Cranes, Railways, Wonderful Machinery, Aeroplanes, Latest Patents, Nature Study, Stamps, Photography and Books—in fact it deals with those subjects in which all healthy boys are interested. New Meccano models and new parts are announced from time to time; interesting competitions are arranged for Meccano boys, and there are special articles for owners of Hornby Trains.

The *Meccano Magazine* has a larger circulation than any similar boys' magazine, and is read in every civilised country in the world. It is published on the 1st of each month, and has a circulation of over 60,000 copies each month. It may be ordered from your Meccano dealer or newsagent, price 6d. If desired, it will be mailed direct by Meccano Ltd., Binns Road, Liverpool (post free) for six months 4/-, or twelve months 8/-. Send 6d. for a specimen copy, post free.

MECCANO LIMITED   Binns Road   LIVERPOOL

Published by
Meccano Limited
Liverpool

1028/60

Summary

Special Instruction Leaflets

New Meccano Motor Chassis

Special Features:—

Three-speed forward and Reverse Gear Box, Differential Gear, Ackermann Steering,
Friction Clutch, Torque Rods, Internal-expanding Brakes, Foot Brake on Cardan Shaft,
Radiator Fan, Semi-elliptic Laminated Springs, Disc Wheels, Dunlop Tyres, etc.

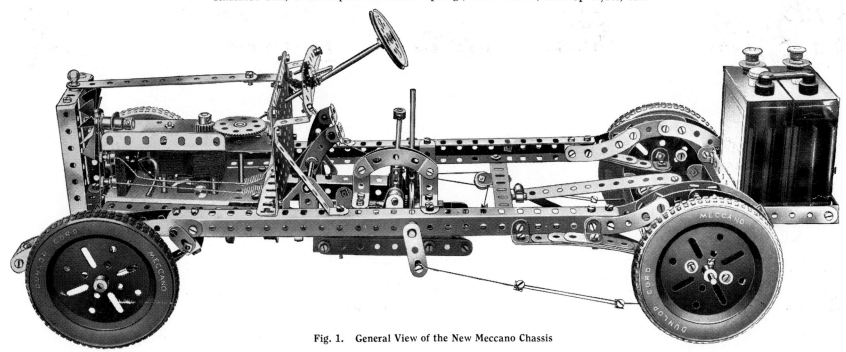

Fig. 1.　General View of the New Meccano Chassis

THE Meccano Motor Chassis forms not only an excellent example of the adaptability of the Meccano parts but also a striking illustration of the educational value of the Meccano system. It shows how, with the aid of a number of ordinary Meccano parts, any intelligent boy may build a complete working model that demonstrates the principles of modern motor engineering so well that replicas of it have been used to instruct pupils in numerous technical schools.

The motor chassis about to be described embodies numerous improvements upon models of a similar type that have been published previously, and it may be regarded as representing the latest Meccano practice. Amongst the improvements may be mentioned the unit principle of construction that has been adopted. The motor, clutch and gearbox are all mounted on a rigid frame, which may be detached from the chassis merely by loosening two or three screws. The differential and rear axle casing, with torque rods, etc., also form a complete unit, the removal of which is the work of a few seconds only.

Published by MECCANO LIMITED, BINNS ROAD, LIVERPOOL　　　　　Printed in England. 528/5

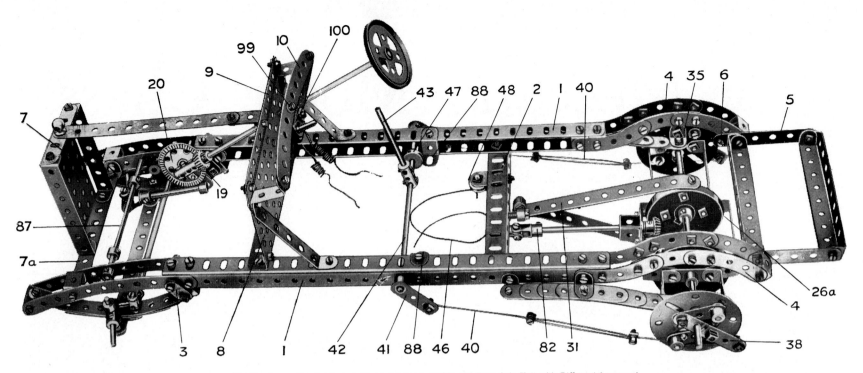

Fig. 2. Frame, showing Springs, Steering Column, Brakes, and Rear Axle Unit with Differential removed

The gearbox provides three speeds forward and reverse gear, and is controlled by a central gear-change lever sliding in a quadrant that retains it in position after each change is effected. The clutch is controlled by a foot pedal and is fitted with a small Meccano Rubber Ring, the resilient nature of which enables the drive from the motor to be taken up very smoothly and gradually and transmitted to the road wheels. The differential gear has been improved and made more compact. The back axle unit is mounted on cantilever springs and any twisting tendency set up by the thrust of the propeller shaft is counteracted by torque rods attached to the main frame by a spring connection.

The steering gear is designed according to the Ackermann principle, which provides for a different angle of turning movement in each front road wheel. Internal expanding brakes are attached to the rear wheels and a pedal-operated brake is fitted to the cardan shaft immediately in front of the universal joint. Other refinements of the model include a radiator cooling fan and a motor starting switch mounted on the dashboard.

The chassis will carry easily the weight of the Meccano 8 ampere-hour Accumulator, even on top gear. The Accumulator should be placed on the luggage carrier at the rear of the model, thus converting the chassis into a self-contained power unit.

The construction of the model should be commenced by building the main frame, which is shown more clearly in Fig. 2. Each side consists of two $12\frac{1}{2}''$ Angle Girders 1 bolted together in the form of a channel section

to give maximum rigidity. The side girders are held together by a cross member 2 composed of a $5\frac{1}{2}''$ Angle Girder and their front ends are extended by $5\frac{1}{2}''$ Curved Strips to carry the ends of the front semi-elliptic springs. Each inner $5\frac{1}{2}''$ Curved Strip is secured to the upper Girder of its respective side member by means of two Angle Brackets. Two of the bolts that serve to secure the Curved Strips also serve as pivots for the shackles (Flat Brackets 3) supporting the rear ends of the front springs (see also Figs. 4 and 6). The bolts should be secured to the side members by two locked nuts (see Meccano Standard Mechanism No. 262) so that the Flat Brackets are quite free to turn on their shanks.

The Frame and Springs

The main frame is extended and carried over the back axle by means of a series of $2\frac{1}{2}''$ large radius Curved Strips 4 bolted together in the manner shown. The luggage carrier 5 is composed of two $3''$ Strips connected by four $4\frac{1}{2}'' \times \frac{1}{2}''$ Double Angle Strips. The carrier is bolted to the end holes in the main frame, and nuts on bolts 6 inserted in the end holes of the $3''$ Strips strike against the Curved Strips 4 and thereby maintain the carrier in a horizontal position. The carrier is designed to hold the Meccano 8 amp. Accumulator, and when not in use it may be folded back.

The radiator is represented by a $3\frac{1}{2}'' \times 2\frac{1}{2}''$ Flanged Plate 7 with two $3\frac{1}{2}'' \times \frac{1}{2}''$ Double Angle Strips bolted at the sides. It is secured to a $4\frac{1}{2}''$ Strip 7a mounted between the front $5\frac{1}{2}''$ Curved Strips of the frame. The

$5\frac{1}{2}'' \times 2\frac{1}{2}''$ Flat Plate 8 is secured to a $5\frac{1}{2}''$ Angle Girder bolted to the main side Girders 1 and is extended at the top by a $5\frac{1}{2}''$ Strip 9 secured at each end by Flat Brackets. The dashboard 10 consists of a $5\frac{1}{2}''$ Strip and a $5\frac{1}{2}''$ Curved Strip attached to the Plate 8 by means of two 1'' Reversed Angle Brackets. The outer ends of these Brackets should be bent slightly to obtain the correct angle for the dashboard.

The springing is a very important consideration in the construction of any motor vehicle. The springs must be so designed that they will stand up to the strains imposed by heavy loads or violent shocks, and yet be so sensitive that they will absorb lesser vibrations. Those included in the Meccano Chassis are a faithful reproduction of the type used in the majority of motor cars.

It will be seen from Fig. 6 that the front springs are of the semi-elliptic type, and that each consists of one $5\frac{1}{2}''$, one $4\frac{1}{2}''$, one $3\frac{1}{2}''$, one $2\frac{1}{2}''$, and one $1\frac{1}{2}''$ Strip placed one upon the other and slightly bent. Each end of the $5\frac{1}{2}''$ Strip is secured to a Double Bracket. The rear Double Bracket is bolted pivotally (S.M. 262) to the pair of Flat Brackets 3, which form the shackles by means of which the rear ends of the springs are attached pivotally to the frame. The front Double Bracket is mounted on a $\frac{3}{4}''$ Bolt passing through the side frame members (Fig. 4).

The rear springs are of the cantilever type, and one of them is shown in detail in Fig. 9. Each spring is built up from the same components as the front springs and is attached rigidly to the frame by two Angle Brackets (see Fig. 2).

Principles of Ackermann Steering

It has already been mentioned that the steering gear is based on the Ackermann principle but the importance of the different angularities of the front wheels may be a point that has escaped the notice of many Meccano boys. Perhaps it will not be out of place, therefore, to insert here a brief summary of the principle of the gear.

When a car turns a corner the near side road wheels describe a sharper curve than the outer wheels. This will be clear on reference to Fig. 3. The drawing is intended to represent a car turning a corner, and in doing so it will be apparent that the wheels must describe an arc or portion of a circle whose centre is shown at A. Now although both front wheels must turn about this centre they are situated at varying distances from it. This means to say that the right-hand front road wheel must follow an arc having a radius equal to AB, and the left-hand wheel must follow an arc struck from a larger radius AC. For the wheels to describe an arc of a circle with the least possible friction on the road surface, each must be situated at a tangent to its respective circle. But it is obvious that both wheels cannot lie at their respective tangents and at the same time remain parallel to each other.

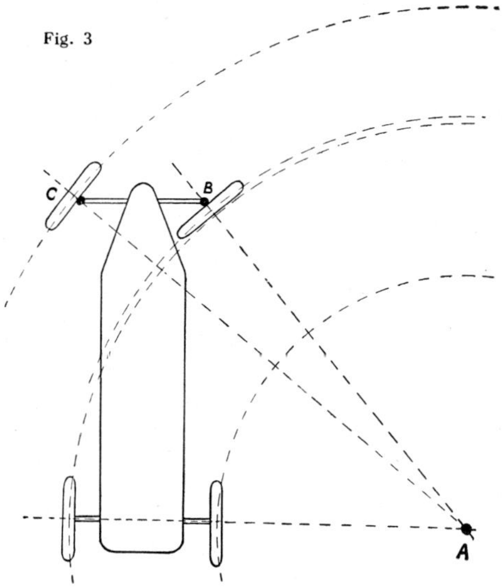

Hence it becomes necessary to incorporate in the steering gear

Fig. 3

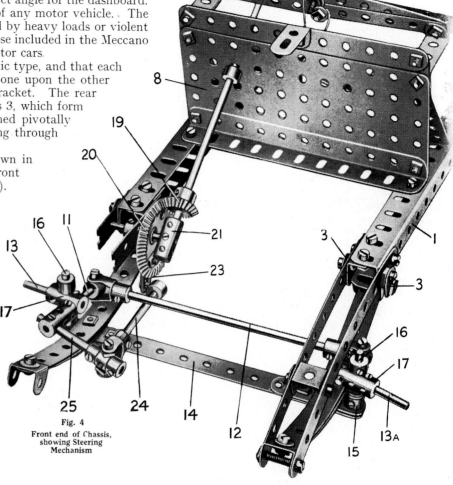

Fig. 4
Front end of Chassis,
showing Steering
Mechanism

some method by means of which a greater angle can be given to the wheel that is nearest to the centre of the circle, no matter whether the car be turning to right or left. The arrangement by which this object is achieved constitutes what is known as Ackermann steering gear. In actual practice, the gear consists essentially of two short levers rigidly connected to the stub axles and projecting either forward or backward. These levers lie at a slightly obtuse angle to the stub axles. The correct angle is arrived at by fixing the levers so that their centre lines, if produced, would meet on the centre line of the car. The exact meeting place varies according to the size of the car and length of the levers, but as a rule it is found to be just in front of the back axle. The levers are connected one to the other by a tie rod.

The Chassis Steering Gear

In Meccano practice it has been found a little difficult to secure the necessary angles in the levers and at the same time maintain a perfectly rigid construction, and therefore, a slightly different method has been adopted. This comprises short Rods 11 and 11a (Figs. 4 and 5) secured just behind the stub axles and protruding backward.

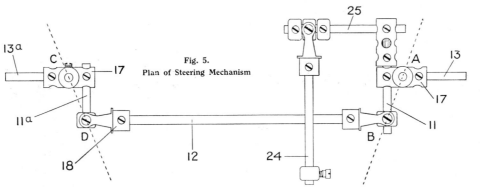

Fig. 5.
Plan of Steering Mechanism

They are connected together by a 5″ Rod 12. A plan view of this linkage is shown in Fig. 5, and it will be seen from the drawing that imaginary lines AB, CD drawn through the pivotal mountings of the stub axles and through the points where the tie rod 12 is attached to the rods 11 and 11a correspond roughly to the angles at which the levers would be placed in actual practice.

Now if the car is to be turned to the right when looking at the gearing as in Fig. 5, the road wheel on the stub axle 13 must be deflected in that direction and the imaginary lever AB will be moved through a certain number of degrees to the left. In doing so it pushes the lever corresponding to CD in our sketch in the same direction, but owing to the difference in angularity between the two levers, lever CD and therefore the road wheel attached to its stub axle 13a, moves through a lesser number of degrees. If the car moves to the left exactly the opposite occurs, the lever CD moving through a greater number of degrees than the lever AB.

Therefore this arrangement of the linkage fulfils the essential requirements of the Ackermann steering gear, that is, it imparts a greater angular movement to the inner road wheel when the car turns a corner.

The mounting of the stub axle 13a is shown in detail in Fig. 6. The fixed front axle 14 consists of two 5½″ Strips overlapped two holes and supporting at each end a Crank 15. A 1½″ Axle Rod 16 secured in each Crank 15 serves as a vertical swivel pin upon which a Coupling 17 carrying the stub axle (a 1″ Axle Rod) is free to turn. The Coupling 17 in Fig. 6 carries the 1″ Rod 11a, to which is secured a Swivel Bearing 18 (Part No. 165). The fork of the latter is fixed to the tie rod 12, the other end of which is connected to the other stub axle by another Swivel Bearing secured to the 1½″ Rod 11 (Figs. 4 and 5).

The connections between the steering wheel and the road wheels form another important point that must be considered in connection with the

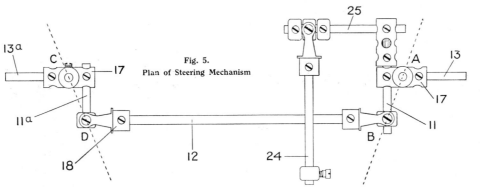

Fig. 6. Detail of Left-hand Stub Axle

steering gear. The gear ratio, or extent of movement of the road wheels to a given movement of the steering wheel, must not be too high, otherwise a slight twist of the wheel would result in a considerable deflection of the car, which would be dangerous and might easily cause accidents. On the other hand, if the ratio is too low the car would be slow to respond to the wheel and therefore difficult to manage in dense traffic. In actual practice the gear reduction is effected in various ways, principally by worm and nut mechanism, but in the Meccano model the most convenient method was found by gearing a ½″ Bevel 19 with a 1½″ Bevel Wheel 20, Fig. 4. The latter is free to turn on a 1½″ Rod journalled in the side frame member and secured in the centre of a Coupling 21. One end of this Coupling forms a journal bearing for the end of the steering column 22, which consists of an 8″ Rod carrying a 2″ Pulley Wheel to represent the steering wheel.

A Flat Bracket 23 bolted to the 1½″ Bevel Wheel 20 forms the steering lever, and a set-screw passed through its elongated hole is used to secure a Collar to the 2½″ Rod 24. The other end of this Rod 24 carries a Swivel Bearing, the collar of which is free to turn between two Collars and set-screws on the 2″ Rod 25. Nuts should be placed on the bolts against the collar of the Swivel Bearing, to hold the bolts rigid without gripping the Rod 25. The latter rod is fixed in a Coupling secured to the 1½″ Rod 11. It will now be seen that the movement of the steering wheel is transmitted to the right-hand road wheel via the Bevel Wheel 20 and linkage 24 and 25, and the left-hand wheel is caused to move simultaneously but at a different angle, as has been explained already, by means of the Rods 11 and 11a and tie rod 12.

The fixed front axle 14 is secured to the front chassis springs by means of ⅜″ Bolts. The Cranks 15 should be bent so that the fixed swivel pins 16 are slightly out of the vertical, with their upper ends pointing outward. This brings the points of contact between the front wheels and the ground as nearly as possible beneath the centres of the swivel pins. In actual practice the object of canting the swivel pins in this way is to save the driver from fatigue and road shock, for if the centre line of each road wheel was parallel with the centre line of the swivel pin, all shock or vibrations in the road wheel would act on the steering wheel with a leverage equal to the distance that separates them. It is specially important in cars fitted with four-wheel brakes, for the application of such brakes on a car where

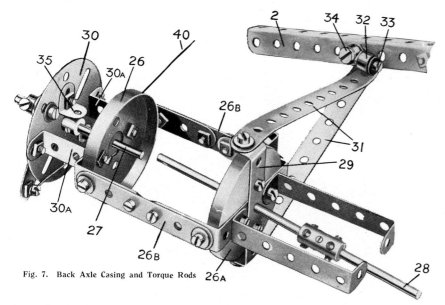

Fig. 7. Back Axle Casing and Torque Rods

Besides carrying the weight of the vehicle, it must absorb the torque or twisting reaction set up by the propeller shaft, and also transmit the thrust of the road wheels to the chassis. The torque set up in the back axle will be understood more clearly by studying the action of the drive transmission between the propeller shaft and the road wheels. Suppose that this is effected by a bevel pinion on the propeller shaft driving a larger bevel gear secured to an unbroken axle carrying the two road wheels : when the engine rotates, the small bevel pinion on the propeller shaft will endeavour to rotate the bevel wheel on the back axle but since this naturally is somewhat difficult to move, the pinion will tend to *travel round the bevel wheel* while the latter remains stationary. This state of affairs possibly might result in a snapped propeller shaft and even broken springs, owing to the twisting movement imparted to the axle casing.

It is to counteract these stresses and strains that motor vehicles are fitted with what are known as torque rods. Many car manufacturers obtain the required results by enclosing the propeller shaft in a torque tube, which not only forms a torque reaction resistance, but also receives the forward thrust of the back axle. In the Meccano model the torque rods are shown quite separately from the propeller shaft, so that their functions may be understood more readily.

The torque rods consist of two $5\frac{1}{2}''$ Strips 31 secured to the ends of the $2\frac{1}{2}'' \times \frac{1}{2}''$ Double Angle Strip 29. These $5\frac{1}{2}''$ Strips taper together at their other ends, where they are secured to a Collar 32 by means of an ordinary bolt inserted in place of the grub screw. Two Washers should be placed beneath the head of this bolt to prevent its shank from binding on the $\frac{1}{2}''$ Bolt 33, about which the Collar is free to pivot. The latter bolt, in turn, is inserted in another Collar 34 that is capable of turning about a Pivot Bolt secured to the $5\frac{1}{2}''$ Girder 2, which forms the main cross member of the frame (see Fig. 2). A Compression Spring (part No. 120b) is placed between the Collar and the Girder to act as a shock absorber when the back axle is forced up and down by irregularities in the road surface.

It will now be seen that the torque rods 31 effectively counteract any twisting tendency in the back axle without interfering with the free vertical movement of the latter as a whole or the independent movement of one or other of the rear wheels.

pin and wheel are parallel would tend to " toe out " the wheels.

Back Axle and Torque Rods

The back axle, which really consists of a fixed hollow casing, is represented in the model by a framework of Strips, etc., that provides suitable bearings for the two axle shafts and also forms a rigid connection between the fixed portions of the rear wheel brakes (see Fig. 7).

The differential is housed in the back axle between two Wheel Flanges 26 and 26a, each of which is bolted against the inner side of a $2\frac{1}{2}'' \times 1\frac{1}{2}''$ Double Angle Strip. These Angle Strips are secured rigidly together by means of 3″ Strips 26b, and their centre holes form the inner bearings for the axle shafts 27 and 28. In addition, shaft 28 passes through the centre hole of a $2\frac{1}{2}'' \times \frac{1}{2}''$ Double Angle Strip 29 bolted to the Wheel Flange 26a. One Washer should be placed between the Wheel Flange and the Angle Strip 29 on each of the bolts that hold the latter in position. The rear wheel brake mountings consist of two Face Plates 30 bolted rigidly to the back axle casing, one being secured to the ends of two 1″ Reversed Angle Brackets and the other to the ends of two $2\frac{1}{2}'' \times \frac{1}{2}''$ Double Angle Strips.

The rear axle casing (Fig. 7) performs several important functions in addition to that of providing rigid bearings for the shafts secured to the road wheels.

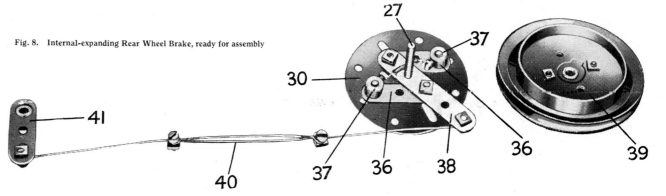

Fig. 8. Internal-expanding Rear Wheel Brake, ready for assembly

The back axle casing is secured to the rear cantilever springs by an Angle Bracket 35 secured to each Face Plate 30. These Angle Brackets are bolted to the end holes of the springs. as will be seen in Fig. 2.

Brake Mechanism

One of the rear wheel brakes is shown in detail in Fig. 8, and it will be seen that it is of the internal expanding type. Two ½″ Bolts are passed through opposite slots in the Face Plate 30 and their ends, after passing through 1½″ Strips 36, are secured in Collars 37, which form the brake shoes. Each ½″ Bolt carries a Washer under its head and two on its shank between the Face Plate and the 1½″ Strips, 36. The latter Strips are pivoted by means of bolts and lock nuts to a 2½″ Strip 38 that is free to turn about the axle shaft 27. When the 2½″ Strip is moved, the Collars are thrust outward along the slots by means of the links 36 and pressed against the inside periphery of a Wheel Flange 39 bolted to the inside of the road wheel. Three Washers should be placed on the axle 27 between the Strip 38 and the Face Plate. Care should be taken to see that the ½″ Bolts are able to move quite freely to and fro in the slots of the Face Plate.

The grub screws in the Collars 37 have been replaced by 7/32″ Meccano Bolts, and these are used to secure a short length of Spring Cord. The latter serves to withdraw the brake shoes 37 and return the brake to the "off" position when the Strip 38 is released. The road wheel should be placed on the axle 27 with the Wheel Flange 39 towards the Collars 37, care being taken to see that the latter have plenty of room to move before the road wheel is secured rigidly to the axle.

Each brake rod 40 (see Figs. 2 and 8) consists of two Meccano loom Heads bolted together (a length of cord will serve almost as well in their place if preferred). The Heads are connected pivotally at one end to the Strip 38 by means of a bolt and two nuts (see S.M. 262) and at the other end by a similar method to a Crank 41 secured to a 6½″ Rod 42 (Fig. 2). This Rod 42 carries a hand lever 43 (a 2½″ Rod) by means of which the brakes are operated.

A second brake is fitted to the chassis and is operated by the foot pedal 44, the mounting of which is clearly shown in the general view of the power unit (Fig. 10). It will be seen that the lever consists of a 2½″ large radius Curved Strip pivoted by its centre hole to a 3½″ Rod 45 journalled in two Trunnions. A length of cord 46 (Figs. 2 and 10) is tied to the second hole of the lever and is led under the ½″ loose Pulley 47 (Fig. 2), round a second ½″ Pulley 48 (mounted on a Pivot Bolt secured in the end of a Single Bent Strip bolted to the cross member 2) and thence round the groove of a 1″ Pulley 49 (Fig. 10) secured to the cardan shaft. The cord is finally brought back and tied under the head of the Pivot Bolt carrying the Pulley 48. A slight pressure on the pedal 44 tightens the cord round the Pulley 49 and thereby retards the motion of the cardan shaft. When the brake is off the lower portion of the pedal rests against a ¾″ Bolt 50 secured in one of the Trunnions, and the pedal is held thereby in a convenient upright position.

The Power Unit

The 4-volt Electric Motor representing the engine, and the gearbox, clutch, etc., are all rigidly connected together, so that they form a complete unit that may be removed from the chassis simply and

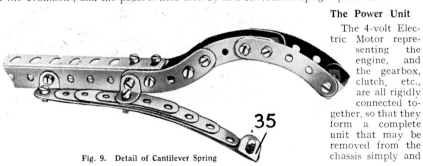

Fig. 9. Detail of Cantilever Spring

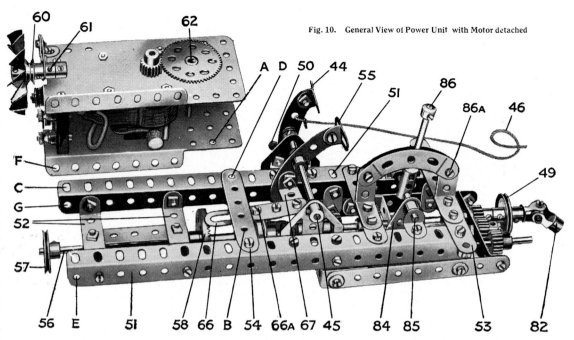

Fig. 10. General View of Power Unit with Motor detached

quickly. This method of construction ensures that the gear wheels and other working parts will always be in proper alignment with each other, and that their functions will not be affected in any way by stresses and strains set up in the chassis frame.

The main frame of the unit consists of two 9½″ Angle Girders 51 connected together by two 2½″ × ½″ Double Angle Strips 52 and a 4½″ Strip 53. The Motor is secured to the frame by a bolt passing through hole A in its side and hole B in the 3½″ Strip 54, and by two other bolts engaging the holes C and D of one of the 9½″ Girders. A Washer is placed on each of these bolts between the Motor and the frame. It will be observed that the Motor rests on the far side 9½″ Angle Girder (Fig. 10) only, and is bolted thereto. The near 9½″ Angle Girder is not attached to the Motor except by the 3″ Strip 54.

A 2½″ × ½″ Double Angle Strip bolted across the two Double Angle Strips 52 forms a bearing for the 5″ Rod 56, which corresponds to the crankshaft of an actual car. This Rod 56 carries a 1″ fast Pulley 57, a 1½″ Contrate Wheel 58, and a 1″ fast Pulley 59 (Fig. 11). A length of cord connects the Pulley 57 with the ½″ fast Pulley 60 (Fig. 10) secured to the shaft of the radiator cooling fan, which is free to rotate in the boss of a Crank 61. The latter is bolted by its end hole to an Angle Bracket secured to the top of the Motor. When the engine is in motion the fan rotates at a considerable speed immediately behind the radiator.

Transmission—The Clutch

The drive from the Motor armature is first led to a secondary shaft 62, on the lower end of which is secured a ½″ Pinion, boss downward, engaging with the 1½″ Contrate Wheel 58. The 1″ Pulley 59 on the 5″ Rod 56 forms the male portion of the clutch (Fig. 11) and is fitted with a Meccano Rubber Ring (Part No. 155), which provides the resilient surface required in a frictional contact clutch of this type. The female clutch member consists of a Flanged Wheel 63, with set-screw removed, placed on the end of a 3½″ Rod 64.

The Flanged Wheel must slide on the Rod 64 and yet be mounted in such a way that when it is engaged by the clutch member 59 it transmits power to the Rod 64. This is accomplished in the following manner : two Angle Brackets bolted to the Flanged Wheel by ⅜″ Bolts and spaced therefrom by Collars engage by their slotted holes with the shanks of two set screws inserted in the "spider" or central collar 65 of a Universal

Coupling. This " spider " is secured to the Rod 64 and a portion of a Compression Spring 65a (part No. 120b) is inserted between it and the boss of the Flanged Wheel. For this purpose it will be necessary to cut the spring approximately in half. The Spring 65a normally holds the Flanged Wheel in engagement with the Rubber Ring on the Pulley 59, but the Flanged Wheel can be forced back on the Rod 64 to an extent just sufficient to throw it out of gear with the clutch member 59.

The clutch withdrawal mechanism consists of a 2″ Slotted Strip 66 (Fig. 10) bolted to a 1½″ Strip, the latter in turn being bolted to a 1″ × ½″ Angle Bracket 67 that is connected by a bolt and lock-nuts to the second hole of the pedal 55. The slot of the Strip 66 engages the Rod 62 immediately behind the Pinion driving the Contrate Wheel 58. The Rod 62 thus forms a guide for the Strip 66, which moves in a direction parallel to the Rod 56. It will be found that when the pedal 55 is depressed the shank of the bolt 66a engages with the rim of the Flanged Wheel 63, and the latter is thereby withdrawn from contact with the clutch member 59.

Gear Box

The gear box provides three speeds forward, neutral, and reverse gears. It is built up from two 4½″ Strips connected together at the front end by a 2½″ × 1″ Double Angle Strip and at the other end by a 2½″ × ½″ Double Angle Strip (Fig. 11). It is bolted to the Angle Girders 51 in the position shown in Fig. 10 by means of four Flat Brackets.

The 3½″ Rod 64 carrying the clutch member represents the primary driving shaft. It is provided with a ¾″ Pinion 68 and a 1″ Gear Wheel 69, and its inner end is journalled in the 1″ × 1″ Angle Bracket 70. The countershaft consists of a 6½″ Rod 71 that is slidable in the end Double Angle Strips of the gear box. This Rod carries the following parts, reading from left to right in Fig. 11 ; two Collars (acting as stops to limit its sliding movement), a 50-teeth Gear Wheel 72, 1″ Gear Wheel 73, two more Collars, one of which (74) is free on the Rod, ¾″ Pinion 75, 1″ Gear Wheel 76, and ½″ Pinion 77. These parts should be secured carefully in the positions indicated in Fig. 11.

The driven 3″ Rod 78 is journalled in the end Double Angle Strip of the gear box and in a second 1″ × 1″ Angle Bracket 70a. It carries a 50-teeth Gear Wheel 79, 1″ Gear Wheel 80, ½″ Pinion 81, the brake pulley 49, and the Universal Coupling 82. A Washer should be placed between the ½″ Pinion 81 and the Double Angle Strip. This Pinion is in constant engagement with another ½″ Pinion 83, which is free to turn upon a ¾″ Bolt secured to the end Double Angle Strip by two nuts.

An ordinary 7/32″ Bolt passes through the elongated hole of the Crank 84 and enters the threaded bore of the Collar 74. A nut placed upon it is secured tightly against the Collar in order to prevent its shank touching the rod 71 and also to ensure that the Crank is quite free to pivot about the bolt. The Crank is secured to a 2″ Axle Rod 85 (Fig. 10) journalled in Angle Brackets bolted to the Angle Girders 51 of the power unit, and a Coupling secured to this Rod carries the gear change lever 86.

It will be seen that the lever moves in a quadrant constructed from two 2½″ small radius Curved Strips bolted one on each side of 1″ × 1″ Angle Brackets secured to the top of the power unit. The Curved Strips are spaced away from each other by the thickness of the supporting Angle Bracket and one Washer placed on each connecting bolt. In this way the Curved Strips are caused to apply a certain pressure to the lever 86, which pressure is sufficient to hold the lever firmly in position after each change of gear is effected.

The different speeds are obtained as follows. Assume that the sliding rod 71 is at the furthest limit of its travel to the left in Fig. 11. Then the drive from the engine is led through the following gears : 68, 72, 77, 83, and 81. The power is transmitted to the road wheels from the Rod 78 by means of the Universal Coupling 82 and the propeller shaft. When the mechanism is so placed the chassis runs backward, and the speed ratio between the propeller shaft and the driving rod 64 is 1 in 2.

A slight movement of the gear change lever disengages the Pinion 77 from Pinion 83, and " neutral " gear results, the secondary shaft revolving idly without engaging any of the wheels 79, 80 or 83. Further movement of the lever slides the Rod 71 further to the right and causes the following gears to be engaged : 68, 72, 75, and 79. This gives first speed forward, the ratio between shafts 78 and 64 being 1 in 4. Continuing the movement of the lever, the second forward speed is obtained, the drive now being directed as follows : 69, 73, 75, and 79. Ratio : 1 in 2.

When the lever is hard over and the rod 71 at the limit of its travel to the right, the gears in engagement are 69, 73, 76, and 80. This represents top forward speed, with a ratio of 1 in 1. Owing to the high speed of the Electric Motor, the total ratio of speed reduction between the motor armature and the back road wheels is fairly considerable. In reverse gear the total gear reduction is approximately 1 in 48. In first forward gear it is about 1 in 96, in second forward gear it is roughly 1 in 48, and in " top " gear the road wheels rotate approximately once in every 24 revolutions of the Motor.

The power unit is mounted in the chassis as follows. First remove the radiator by unscrewing the Strip 7a (Fig. 2) on which it is mounted ; remove the bolt 86a (Fig. 10) from the change gear lever quadrant, and draw out the 5″ Rod 87 (Fig. 2). Now place the power unit in position and bolt the end holes of the 4½″ Strip 53 to the ½″ Reversed Angle Brackets 88 (Fig. 2), and replace the 5″ Rod 87, passing it through the holes E, F, G, of the Motor and power unit frame (Fig. 10). Collars on the Rod 87 are next screwed tight against the power unit, and the bolt 86a replaced in the gear lever quadrant. (This bolt was taken out merely to obviate the necessity of removing the Rod 42, Fig. 2, which passes through the centre of the quadrant). Replace the radiator and secure the cord 46 of the foot brake in the position previously described.

Having secured the power unit in position, attention may be given to the final stage in the transmission, i.e., the propeller shaft and differential.

Differential Gear

In explaining the design of the steering gear it was pointed out that when a car travels in a curved or circular path the two front road wheels must each describe an arc struck from the centre of the circle or portion of a circle in which the car moves, and the outer wheel must naturally follow an arc of greater radius than the wheel that is nearer the centre (see Fig. 3).

The difference in speed thus set up between the two wheels is not important in the case of the front wheels, for they are both free to turn on their individual axles ; but it is obvious that since the rear or driving wheels are similarly placed in regard to the central point A, Fig. 3, the same rule must apply to them. To state this more plainly, the rear wheels must rotate at different speeds when the car moves in a curve, otherwise slip must take place between the tyres and the road surface, which would result, at least in the heavier types of car, in damage to the tyres and in more or less severe inconvenience to the steering. But both these wheels must be driven constantly from the engine and each must receive an

Fig. 11. Gear Box and Clutch

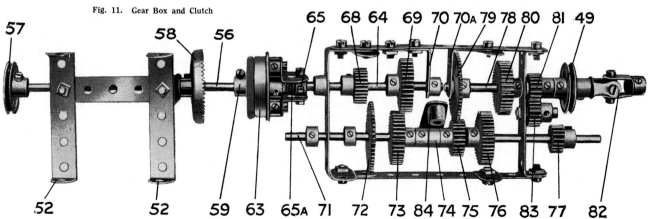

57 58 56 65 68 64 69 70 70A 79 78 80 81 49

52 52 59 63 65A 71 72 73 84 74 75 76 83 77 82

equal amount of driving power; therefore it is necessary to incorporate in the back axle some device that will transmit the power evenly to the wheels and at the same time allow for the difference in speed that arises immediately the car deviates to any extent from the straight.

The mechanism that fulfils these functions is known as a "differential" or "balance" gear. In some cars, especially in heavy commercial vehicles, the differential is incorporated in a secondary shaft that is journalled in the main frame and connected at each end to one of the road wheels by means of chain or belt drive. The object of this is to reduce to a minimum the weight of the back axle, which is subjected to a continuous series of road shocks when in motion. In the Meccano model, the differential forms part of the back axle unit, and the principles of the mechanism should be clear from the following description.

The back axle shaft is in two sections, 27 and 28 (see Fig. 7). The former consists of a 3″ Rod and the latter of a 4½″ Rod and a 2″ Rod connected end to end by a Coupling as shown. The inner ends of the shafts 27 and 28 are journalled in opposite ends of a Coupling 89 (Fig. 12), in the centre transverse hole of which is secured a 2″ Rod 93 that serves to carry the two ⅞″ Bevel Gears 90. The set-screws of these Bevels should be removed so that they are free to turn about the 2″ Rod. They engage with two similar Bevels 91 and 92 secured to the shafts 27 and 28 respectively.

The outer ends of the 2″ Rod carrying the Bevels 90 are passed through the elongated holes of 1″ × ½″ Angle Brackets. The latter are secured rigidly by means of ½″ Bolts to opposite holes in the 1½″ Bevel Gear 94, and are spaced therefrom by means of Collars placed upon the bolts between the Brackets and the Bevel Gear. This Bevel Gear is free to revolve independently about the axle shaft 28, its set-screw having been removed.

The propeller shaft consists of a 3½″ Rod 95, one end of which is secured in the Universal Joint 82 (Fig. 11) and the other end, after passing through a Double Bent Strip and the side of the differential frame, is secured in the ½″ Bevel Gear 96, which engages with the 1½″ Bevel Gear 94. Two Collars 98 should be secured to the shaft 28 in the position shown to maintain the various gears in correct alignment and to prevent the gears 94 and 96 from slipping or binding against each other. A Washer should be placed between the outer Collar 98 and the Double Angle Strip forming the end of the differential frame, and two Washers should be placed against the boss of the ⅞″ Bevel Gear 91.

Care should be taken to see that the various parts of the differential gear work quite freely and that the several Bevel Gears are all placed in the correct positions in relation to each other. Everything should operate smoothly and easily when the shafts 27 and 28 are twisted between thumb and finger, whether simultaneously and in the same direction, or separately and in opposite directions.

If one of the road wheels revolves at a greater speed than the other the Bevel Gears 90 begin to rotate and thereby adjust the difference in speed between the Bevel Gears 91 and 92. If the vehicle is running in a perfectly straight course the axles 27 and 28 and Bevel Gears 90, 91 and 92 must all rotate as one unit, since the road wheels are travelling at the same speed.

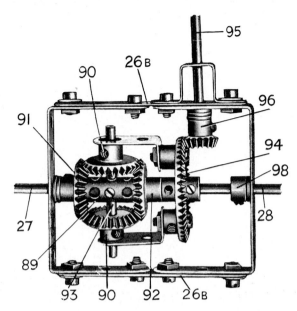

Fig. 12. The New Differential Gear

The construction of the differential frame will be obvious from Fig. 12. The two 2½″ × 1½″ Double Angle Strips shown in this illustration may also be seen in Fig. 7, but in the latter case they are shown bolted to Wheel Flanges 26 and 26a and incorporated in the back axle casing. When the gear is ready to assemble, the differential frame (formed by the 2½″ × 1½″ Double Angle Strips and 3″ Strips 26b) should first be incorporated in the fixed back axle (Fig. 7). The gearing should then be placed in the frame and the shafts 27 and 28 inserted in their respective positions. It will be noticed that a Washer is placed beneath the head of the bolts at each corner of the differential frame (Fig. 12); this is to prevent the shanks of the bolts fouling the sides of the Wheel Flanges 26 and 26a (Fig. 7).

Electrical Connections

All that now remains to complete the model is the wiring between the Motor, dashboard switch, and the Accumulator. Either the Meccano 8 amp. or 20 amp. Accumulator may be used, but the former is of a more convenient size. As previously pointed out, it may be mounted on the luggage carrier at the rear of the model.

One wire should be led direct from the Motor terminal to one terminal of the Accumulator, and another wire should be led from the second Motor terminal to a 6BA bolt 99 secured to the dashboard (see Figs. 2 and 4). This bolt is insulated from the 5½″ Curved Strip of the dashboard by means of a Meccano Insulating Bush and Washer. The switch handle consists of a Threaded Pin secured to a Flat Bracket 100, which is attached to the dashboard by another 6BA Bolt. An ordinary metal Washer should be placed on each side of the Flat Bracket, but the bolt is insulated from the dashboard by means of an Insulating Bush and Washer. A wire secured to its shank is led to the second terminal of the Accumulator. The Motor is started by sliding the Flat Bracket 100 over the head of the bolt 99, thus completing the electric circuit.

In connecting up the wiring care should be taken to see that the insulation is not damaged in any way, otherwise short circuits may be caused by the current leaking to the metal frame of the chassis.

It is scarcely necessary to add that all the working parts of the Chassis, with the single exception of the actual frictional surfaces of the clutch, should be lubricated at frequent intervals. Great care should be taken to prevent any oil coming in contact with the Rubber Ring on the clutch member 59 (Fig. 11), for the oil would cause the clutch to slip, of course, without transmitting the drive to the road wheels.

If the Meccano Chassis is to be used for demonstrating the actual working of a motor car, it will obviously be inconvenient to allow the model to run about on its wheels. A good plan, therefore, is to jack up the model on suitable supports. A stand for this purpose can easily be devised by any boy from ordinary Meccano parts.

When the Chassis is raised in this way, with the wheels free to revolve, the various features of the mechanism may be studied while actually in motion and the different movements, such as starting and stopping the Motor, clutching and declutching, gear-changing, reversing, and steering, etc., may be easily demonstrated.

List of Parts Required to Build the complete Motor Chassis

11 of No. 2	8 of No. 11	2 of No. 16A	2 of No. 23	2 of No. 30c	2 of No. 48B	5 of No. 89	1 of No. 115	2 of No. 147B
9 ,, ,, 2A	24 ,, ,, 12	1 ,, ,, 16B	1 ,, ,, 23A	4 ,, ,, 31	4 ,, ,, 48C	14 ,, ,, 90	2 ,, ,, 120B	1 ,, ,, 155
4 ,, ,, 3	4 ,, ,, 12A	5 ,, ,, 17	2 ,, ,, 25	178 ,, ,, 37	1 ,, ,, 53	2 ,, ,, 90A	4 ,, ,, 124	1 ,, ,, 157
6 ,, ,, 4	4 ,, ,, 12B	5 ,, ,, 18A	4 ,, ,, 26	38 ,, ,, 37A	1 ,, ,, 55A	4 ,, ,, 101	2 ,, ,, 125	2 6BA Screws
6 ,, ,, 5	1 ,, ,, 13A	3 ,, ,, 18B	2 ,, ,, 27	40 ,, ,, 38	3″ ,, ,, 58	1 ,, ,, 102	2 ,, ,, 126	2 6BA Nuts
9 ,, ,, 6A	2 ,, ,, 14	4 ,, ,, 19B	1 ,, ,, 27A	1 ,, ,, 45	42 ,, ,, 59	2 ,, ,, 109	1 ,, ,, 136	2 Insulating
4 ,, ,, 8	2 ,, ,, 15	1 ,, ,, 20	1 ,, ,, 28	2 ,, ,, 46	5 ,, ,, 62	5 ,, ,, 111	4 ,, ,, 137	Bushes
2 ,, ,, 9	1 ,, ,, 15A	1 ,, ,, 20A	4 ,, ,, 30	2 ,, ,, 47A	9 ,, ,, 63	8 ,, ,, 111A	5 ,, ,, 140	2 Insulating
12 ,, ,, 10	5 ,, ,, 16	3 ,, ,, 22	2 ,, ,, 30A	9 ,, ,, 48A	1 ,, ,, 70	9 ,, ,, 111C	4 ,, ,, 142B	Washers

Meccano Motor Chassis

Built with Meccano Outfit L

Special Features :—

Four-speed forward and reverse gear-box ; differential gear ; single plate clutch ; four-wheel internal expanding brakes with hand and foot control ; underslung axles ; Ackermann steering, etc.

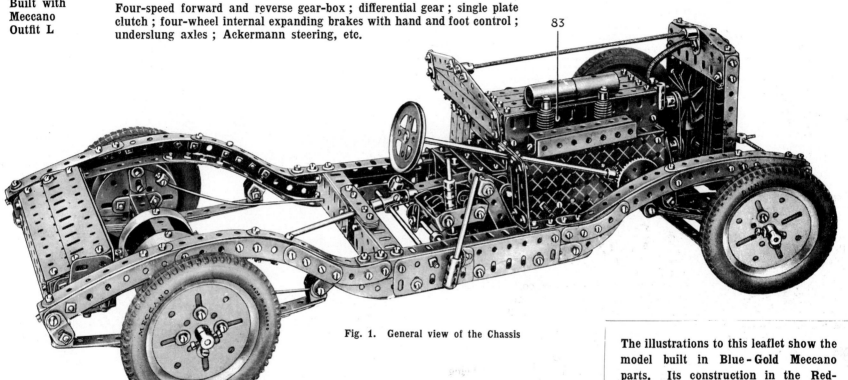

Fig. 1.   General view of the Chassis

The illustrations to this leaflet show the model built in Blue - Gold Meccano parts.   Its construction in the Red-Green Meccano parts is exactly the same.

The Meccano Motor Chassis described and illustrated in this leaflet is an entirely new model, embodying all the main features of an actual up-to-date chassis, and also many of the smaller refinements. It represents a great advance on the chassis described in the No. 1 Leaflet, and it is even more suitable for demonstrating the principles of motorcar construction and operation.

The motor unit, an El Electric Motor, is placed, together with the clutch and gear-box, in the position occupied by the engine in the actual car.   In this manner the appearance of the model is kept as close to that of the original as possible.   The brakes, which in actual practice are controlled by rods, are controlled in the model by bowden cables, as this form of construction makes the model simpler to build.

21/1134/5   *Published by* MECCANO LIMITED, BINNS ROAD, LIVERPOOL 13   Printed in England

The Prototype

THE Meccano model is, as far as possible, a replica of the new Bentley chassis that is now being manufactured by the makers of the Rolls-Royce cars. This car is fitted with a 3½-litre six-cylinder engine, having a nominal cylinder capacity of 3,669 c.c. The complete power unit is flexibly mounted in the chassis at the rear on two rubber pads, and at the front on a flexible beam fitted with a shock absorber.

The gear-box is of the four-speed forward and reverse type, the drive being taken from this through a substantial open propeller shaft. It is interesting to note that neither torque rods nor torque tube are fitted, the entire driving strain being taken up by the rear springs. Each of the four wheels is fitted with a large diameter internal expanding brake, operated through a disc clutch-type mechanical servo motor mounted on the gear-box. All brakes are compensated relative to each other, a hand adjustment being provided for the front pedal brake.

The performance of this car is remarkably high although this can be really appreciated only when driving on roads where some of the 120 b.h.p. may be unleashed in safety. On the revolution counter, which is scaled up to 5,000 r.p.m., a red mark has been introduced at 4,500 r.p.m., this being considered the desirable limit speed of the engine. This engine speed gives a road speed of 94 m.p.h., when travelling in top, and when in third gear the speed is about 75 m.p.h. Similarly, second gear gives a little over 54 m.p.h., and first a little over 34 m.p.h.

The chassis is of deep section in the centre, tapering considerably to each upswept end. The springs are all of the half elliptic type, and hydraulic shock absorbers are fitted to each, but on account of their small size these have been omitted in the model.

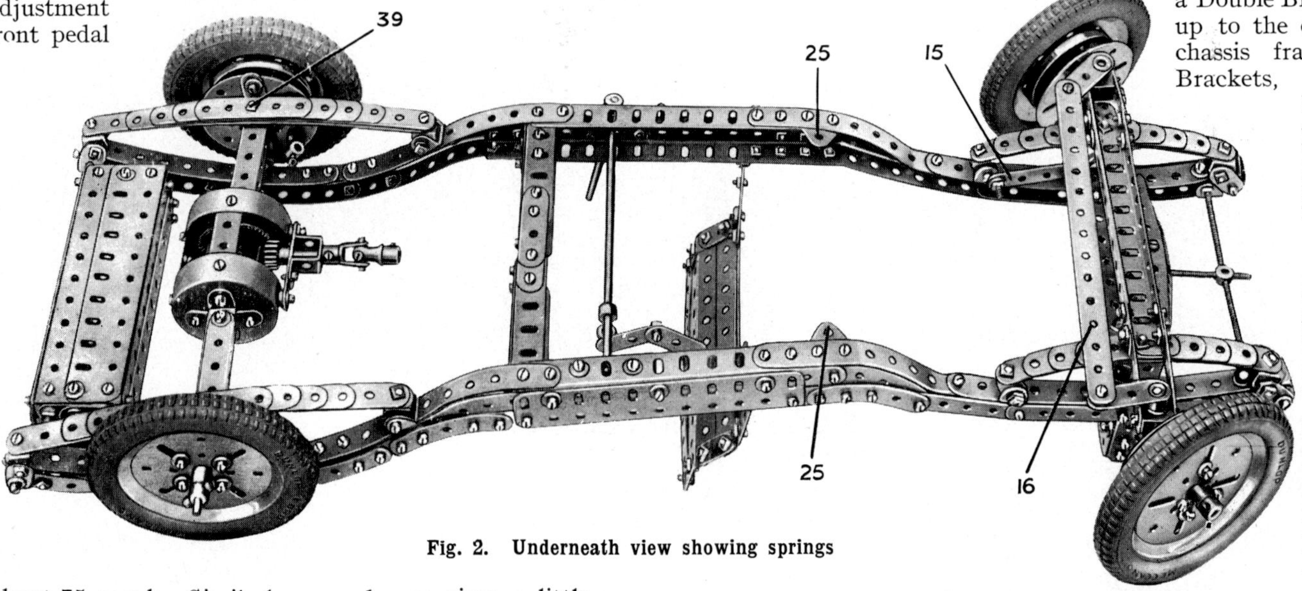

The Main Frames

One side of the chassis frames is shown in Fig. 3, the forward end being at the right-hand side of the illustration. A 7½″ Angle Girder 1 is attached to a 5½″ Angle Girder by means of a 5½″ Flat Girder as shown. The rear end of this complete member carries at its broad side two 2½″ large radius Curved Strips, and these are connected together by a bolt at the point 2. This bolt carries also a Flat Bracket that will later form part of the spring suspension

Fig. 2.   Underneath view showing springs

link. A 2″ Strip is now fitted and this carries at its outer end a 4″ Curved Strip prolonged by means of a 5½″ Curved Strip, the Curved Strips overlapping each other four holes. The 4″ Curved Strips are not contained in the Outfit, and if desired each one may be replaced by two 2½″ large radius Curved Strips. The Strips 3 and 4 are now fitted, these being built up from Strips of varying lengths as illustrated.

The fore end is constructed in a similar manner to the end already described, except that two 5½″ Curved Strips are used in place of one 4″ and one 5½″ Curved Strip.

The rear spring shackles are built up in the following manner. Two Flat Brackets, one of which has already been mentioned, and the other of which is bolted to a ½″ × ½″ Angle Bracket, are fitted with a pivotally attached Double Bracket that carries one end of the rear spring. The other end of the spring also is fitted with a Double Bracket that is linked up to the extreme end of the chassis frame by two Flat Brackets, lock-nutted bolts being used for this purpose. The inside Flat Bracket of the last-mentioned pair is attached to a ½″ × ½″ Angle Bracket. The spring shackle at the other extremity of the frame is a copy of that described already. The inner front shackle, however, consists of two Double Brackets held together by lock-nutted bolts. The rear spring is built up from two 7½″ Strips, together with one 5½″, one 3½″, and one 2½″ Strip. These are all secured together at a common centre by means of a ½″ Bolt. The construction of the front spring is similar to that of the rear, but it is represented by two 5½″ Strips together with one 3½″ and one 2½″ Strip.

When both side girders have been built they must be connected together as shown in Fig. 2. The main connection consists of a substantial girder built up from two 2½″ and two 3″ Angle Girders, together with two 3″ Flat Girders. These parts are bolted together to form two short deep section girders, and when complete are connected together by a series of 2½″ and 1½″ Strips as shown in Figs. 1 and 2. In addition to this, the side girders are further interconnected by the front axle. This part is composed of two 5½″ Angle Girders and four 2½″ large radius Curved Strips. The arrangement is illustrated in Fig. 4.

The petrol tank also adds to the structural strength of the model, although this arrangement of course is not in accordance with actual practice. The tank top is represented by two 5½″ Flat Girders, and this is secured to the front face of the tank by means of ½″ × ½″ Angle Brackets, the front face being constructed similarly. The tank bottom consists of four 4½″ Flat Girders. Two 3½″ Angle Girders, overlapping three holes, form the connection between the tank bottom and front side. The rear face of this part of the model consists of a 5½″ Flat Girder held in place at its upper edges by two ½″ × ½″ Angle Brackets.

Each end of the tank consists of two 1½″ Flat Girders that are held in place by means of two 6½″ Rods and one 8″ Rod. These Rods pass through ½″ × ½″ Angle Brackets, Collars being used to hold the Flat Girders in place. The outer extremities of the 8″ Rods are locked on the inside of the main chassis members by Collars.

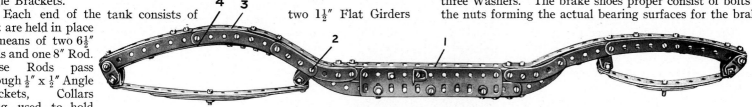

Fig. 3. One of the main frames removed from the chassis

The Front Wheels and Steering Mechanism

In Figs. 2, 4, and 6 the front portion of the chassis is shown, Fig. 4 giving a striking impression of the low raking lines of the model. Each side of the front axle is fitted with a pair of 2½″ large radius Curved Strips as already described, and these carry a pair of Double Brackets 5. These two parts form bearings for a short Rod, the lower end of which is fitted with a Crank 6, which is spaced away from the bearing by two Washers. The upper end of the Rod carries a Coupling 7, four Washers being used at this point for spacing purposes. The outer end of the longitudinal bore of this Coupling is fitted with the stub axle, a 1½″ Rod, which supports a Face Plate 8.

Six Washers are now placed on the stub axle, and these hold the road wheel in its correct position. The wheel is prevented from falling off the axle by means of a Collar. A Wheel Flange is attached to the 3″ Pulley forming the centre of the road wheel, the boss of this latter part being fitted with two bolts and nuts forming a knock-off nut. These knock-off nuts are a conspicuous feature of nearly all modern sports cars.

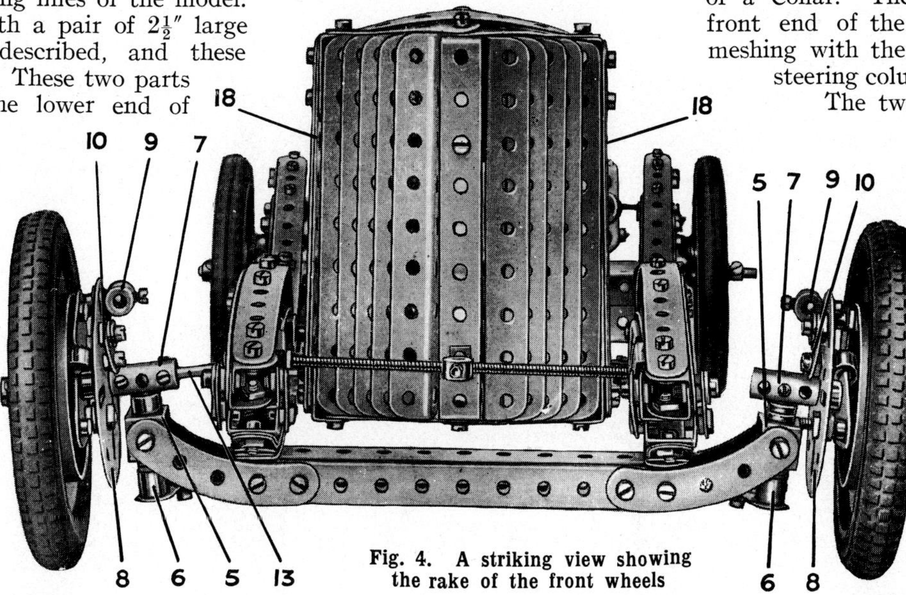

One of the front brakes is shown in detail in Fig. 10. A Collar 9 is first

Fig. 4. A striking view showing the rake of the front wheels

secured to the Face Plate, the unoccupied tapped hole of which carries a bolt that forms the locking bolt for the end of the bowden cable. A Flat Bracket 10 is now pivotally attached to the Face Plate by means of a ⅜″ Bolt, the end of which forms the support for a Collar 11, this being locked in place by means of its Grub Screw.

The brake shoes are now fitted. Each of these consists of a 1″ Triangular Plate held in place by a ½″ Bolt, and spaced away from the Face Plate by three Washers. The brake shoes proper consist of bolts fitted with two nuts, the nuts forming the actual bearing surfaces for the brake. The Spring Cord 12 holds the brake in the off position.

The Coupling 7, shown on the left-hand side of Fig. 4, carries a 1½″ Rod 13, the end of which is connected by means of two Collars 14, Fig. 6, to one end of a 3½″ Strip 15. This Strip is slightly bent as shown, and is fitted at its free end with a Flat Bracket by means of which it is secured to a 1½″ Bevel Gear. This Gear is fixed on a short Rod that is fitted with a Coupling and is mounted at its inner end in a Double Bracket. It is prevented from moving laterally by means of a Collar. The bore of the Coupling supports the front end of the steering column that carries a ½″ Bevel meshing with the 1½″ Bevel. The method of mounting the steering column is shown in Fig. 1.

The two Cranks 6 are now connected together by a 7½″ Strip 16. This Strip forms the track rod and is bent at each end slightly in order to allow for the rake of the front wheels.

The front support for the engine is now fitted. This consists of two 4½″ Strips 17 attached at each end by a ½″ Reversed Angle Bracket. The method of securing the engine to this will be described later.

The Radiator

This section of the model next occupies our attention. The frame consists of two pairs of 4½″ Strips 18 fitted at each end with a 1″ × ½″ Angle Bracket. At the lower end these Brackets are connected together by means of two 2″ Strips, Fig. 5, and at the point where they are joined a 4½″ × ½″ Double Angle Strip is fitted. The 1″ × ½″ Angle Brackets at their upper ends are secured together by two

2″ Strips and a 3½″ Strip. These Strips are bent slightly in order to arrive at the correct shape in the completed radiator. Two ½″ × ½″ Angle Brackets are now fitted, and these carry the 3½″ Flat Girder 19. The centre of this Girder is fitted with a Flat Bracket 20 that carries in its upper hole the Threaded Boss 21.

It should be noted here that the Double Angle Strip already mentioned is secured at its upper end to the centre connecting bolt of the two upper 2″ Strips.

The imitation radiator shutters are composed of a series of 4½″ Angle Girders. They are connected together by means of two 4½″ Threaded Rods and are spaced apart by Washers, four Washers being placed between each two. The 4½″ × ½″ Double Angle Strip is fitted with two Double Brackets 22 and 23, the first being secured in place by a nut and bolt. The Bracket 23, however, is secured to the Double Angle Strip by a 2″ Threaded Rod shown in Fig. 4. Full use must be taken of the slots in the Angle Girders in order to arrive at the necessary curve characteristic of the Bentley radiator.

The radiator, when complete, is secured to the chassis by means of four ½″ × ½″ Angle Brackets 24. These are arranged in pairs, each pair being bolted together to form a corner angle bracket. The 4½″ Strips 17 form the point at which the radiator is attached to the chassis. It is further secured by a 2″ Threaded Rod, holding the Double Bracket 23 in position. A " spider " taken from a Swivel Bearing is passed on to the Threaded Rod and it supports in its transverse tapped holes the ends of two 3½″ Threaded Rods. These are attached at their opposite ends to ½″ × ½″ Angle Brackets and also to the chassis frames, nuts being used to lock them in position. Care must be taken to see that these last-mentioned Threaded Rods hold the " spider " exactly central, as shown in Fig. 4.

The 1″ Triangular Plates 25 are now fitted as shown in Fig. 6. These will be used later for carrying the two rear engine supports.

The Rear Axle

Probably one of the greatest difficulties experienced in the building of a Meccano Chassis is that of constructing a compact and efficient differential and back axle casing. In Figs. 7 and 8 one solution to the problem is illustrated, and it is very doubtful whether a smaller complete back axle casing is possible with the use of Meccano parts only. The

Fig. 5. Rear view of radiator

differential is shown detached from the casing in Fig. 8. A Coupling 26 is fitted in its centre plain hole with a 1½″ Rod carrying at each end a Collar. These Collars are held in place by the 1″ Threaded Rods 27 by means of which the Coupling is secured to a 1½″ Contrate Wheel 28, representing the crown wheel.

Between the Coupling and Contrate 28 a ¾″ Contrate 29 is fitted, three Washers being used for spacing purposes. The 4½″ Rod 29A, on which this last-mentioned Contrate is carried, forms one side of the back axle, the opposite side of which consists of a similar Rod 30 carrying the Contrate 31. The planetary pinions are now fitted. Each of these consists of a ¾″ Pinion secured, boss outward, to the Coupling 26 by means of a Pivot Bolt. These Pinions mesh with the ¾″ Contrates already described.

The Rod 29A is now fitted with a Boiler End 32, spaced away from the Contrate 28 by means of six Washers. In a similar manner a second Boiler End 33 is fitted, two Washers being used to space this from the differential. Three 2″ Strips, one of which is shown at 34, are now fitted on the inside of the Boiler Ends. A fourth 2″ Strip 35 is also fitted but this is attached to the outside edges of the Boiler Ends. ⅜″ Bolts are used for securing this Strip in position, and two Washers are placed between the Strip and the Boiler Ends on each Bolt ; one Washer is also placed under the head of each Bolt. A Double Bent Strip is now bolted to the 2″ Strip in the manner shown in Fig. 7, and this, together with one of the holes in the Strip 35, forms a bearing for the Rod 36. The inner end of this Rod is fitted with a ½″ Pinion that meshes with the crown wheel 28. The Rod at its outer end is fitted with a Universal Coupling.

The construction of the rear axle casing can be followed fairly easily from Fig. 7. Three 2½″ × ½″ Double Angle Strips are first secured to the Boiler End 33, being arranged to form a channel section girder. The outer turned-up ends of these are bolted to a Face Plate, and care must be taken to see that the centre hole of the Boiler End is in accurate alignment with the hole in the boss of the Face Plate.

The 2½″ Strip 37 must now be fitted. This part is secured to the ½″ × ½″ Angle Bracket 38, which in turn is bolted to the Boiler End 33. The opposite end of the Strip is fitted with a ½″ Bolt 39 by means

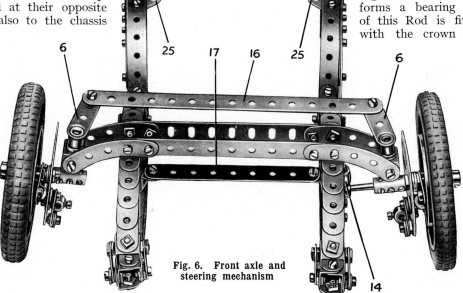

Fig. 6. Front axle and steering mechanism

of which a $1'' \times \frac{1}{2}''$ Angle Bracket is held in place. The elongated hole of this Bracket is bolted to one of the outer holes of the Face Plate, this form of construction being necessary in order to allow the leaf spring to be accommodated on the inner face of the Bracket. It should be noted here that the long bolt shown holding the rear spring together in Fig. 3 is only included during the early stage in the building of the model, and may be withdrawn immediately the complete rear axle is ready to be fitted.

The opposite side of the rear axle casing is now built, its construction being carried out in an exactly similar manner to that already described.

Brakes are next dealt with, and no difficulty should be experienced with these if the instructions given for building the front wheel brakes are carefully followed. In the illustration showing the complete back axle, the bolt heads are shown used as the brake surfaces in place of nuts shown in Fig. 10. This arrangement was adopted in order to allow narrow rubber tubing to be placed over the bolt heads, thereby increasing the efficiency of the brakes. If desired, however, the front wheel arrangement may be used in place of this.

The back axle is now ready for fitting into the chassis, and this is accomplished in the following manner. The temporary bolts used for holding the leaves of the rear springs together are first removed, after which the shanks of the bolts 39 are passed into the vacant holes. By careful manœuvring, this will be accomplished without difficulty. When the bolts are finally in place the securing nuts are fitted as shown in Fig. 2. The rear wheels are now fitted, these being similar to those used at the front. They are locked on the axle, however, and knock-off nuts are represented by Collars fitted with two bolts.

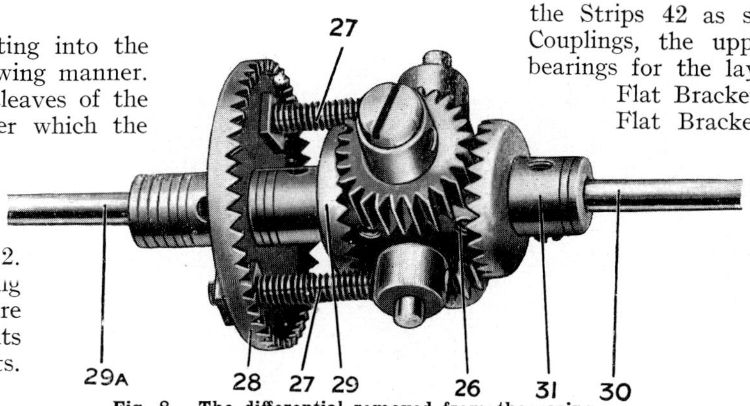

Gear-Box

This is probably the most difficult section of the model to construct, and strict attention should therefore be given to the following description. Care must be taken also in lining up the various shafts and bearings, as upon

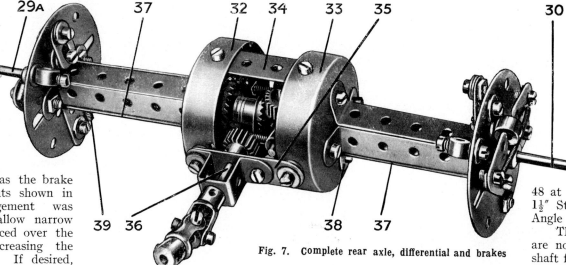

Fig. 7. Complete rear axle, differential and brakes

Fig. 8. The differential removed from the casing

this depends the successful working of the model. It is of the four forward speed and single reverse type, and although its various gears are not in constant mesh, as with most modern gear-boxes, it gives an excellent insight into the operation of an actual gear-box.

The frame consists essentially of two $3\frac{1}{2}''$ Angle Girders 40 and 41, connected together by four $2\frac{1}{2}''$ Strips and four Angle Brackets 42. These four cross members form a rectangle $3\frac{1}{2}''$ long and $2\frac{1}{2}''$ wide. A $2\frac{1}{2}''$ Angle Girder 43 is also fitted, the purpose of which will be described later. A $3\frac{1}{2}''$ Strip 44 is bolted to the inner flanges of the Strips 42. This Strip 44 forms the support for two $1\frac{1}{2}'' \times \frac{1}{2}''$ Double Angle Strips 45 and 46 that form the bearings for the driving and driven shafts respectively.

Each built-up girder 42 carries at each end a $1\frac{1}{2}''$ Strip, and these support a $2\frac{1}{2}''$ Strip 47 at one end of the gear-box and a similar Strip 48 at the other end. In addition, the $1\frac{1}{2}''$ Strips form supports for two $2\frac{1}{2}''$ Angle Girders 49 and 50.

The layshaft guides and supports are now fitted. In Fig. 11 the layshaft for third and top gears is shown. A $4\frac{1}{2}''$ Rod 51 slides in holes of the Strips 42 as shown. It carries a Collar 52 and also two Couplings, the upper holes of these latter parts forming the bearings for the lay-shaft 53. The Collar 52 is fitted with a Flat Bracket, part of which is shown at 54, Fig. 12. The Flat Bracket is held in place by a $\frac{3}{8}''$ Bolt, under the head of which is placed two Washers. Two Washers are also placed for spacing purposes between the Flat Bracket and Collar 52, the Bolt passing through the slotted hole of the Bracket at its inner end. The Flat Bracket will now be found to bridge the gap between the Girder 41 and the Strip 44, and its ends must be bent inward slightly until they press lightly against these two parts. By this means the Rod 51 is prevented from turning. It is able to slide horizontally, however, and its movement in this direction is limited by the bolt head 55 on one side and the securing bolt of the Double Angle Strip 45 on the other.

The slide on the other side of the gear-box must be fitted before proceeding further with the construction. This is built up and fitted in an exactly similar manner to that already described, with the exception that the two Couplings carrying the lay-shaft are arranged differently. Their positions are indicated at 56 and 57 in Fig. 11.

The driving shaft 58 is a $2\frac{1}{2}''$ Rod and carries a Collar and $\frac{3}{4}''$ Pinion 59 between the Strip 48 and Double Angle Strip 46. On the opposite side of the Double Angle Strip is fitted a $\frac{1}{2}''$ Pinion 60. It should be noted that this Pinion is only occupied for half its length by the Rod 58, the remaining portion of the hole forming a support for the inner end of the Rod 61. This Rod is $3\frac{1}{2}''$ in length, and is fitted with the $\frac{1}{2}''$ Pinion 62 and $\frac{3}{4}''$ Pinion 63, which are secured on the Rod between the Double Angle Strip 45 and Pinion 60. Between the Double Angle Strip and $2\frac{1}{2}''$ Strip 47 a $1''$ Gear 64 is locked in place on the Rod, being secured as near to the $2\frac{1}{2}''$ Strip as possible without actually touching. The boss of this Gear must fall inward in order to give the Pinion 65 sufficient clearance. A Collar is now secured outside the gear-box on the Rod 61 in order to prevent that Rod from moving laterally.

The lay-shaft 53 is next fitted. This is journalled in the upper plain holes of the two Couplings secured to the Rod 51. It consists of a $2\frac{1}{2}''$ Rod and it is fitted with a $\frac{1}{2}''$ Pinion 66 and $\frac{3}{4}''$ Pinion 67. The boss of the Pinion 66 and the Collar 68 prevent the Rod from moving laterally, independently of the Rod 51. As already mentioned, this lay-shaft operates the third and top gears, which are arranged as follows. When the Rod 51 is moved to its extreme rear position, Pinions 59, 66, 67 and 62 are in engagement, and this results in top gear. Neutral is obtained by moving the lay-shaft partly to the front. When the Rod is into the forward position the two

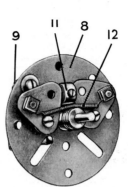

Fig. 10. One of the front brakes with its road wheel

Pinions 60 and 62 are locked together by the Pinion 67, thus resulting in a straight-through drive that is used for third gear.

The gear-box is now ready for receiving the second lay-shaft. The disposition of each of the Couplings supporting this has already been described, and the $2\frac{1}{2}''$ Rod forming the lay-shaft may be fitted. Between the two Couplings are fitted a $\frac{3}{4}''$ Pinion 69 and Collar 70. To the left of the Coupling 57 a $\frac{1}{2}''$ Pinion indicated at 71 is secured, and this forms one of the second gear and reverse gear Pinions. The bottom gear pinion 65 consists of the pinion taken from an E1 Electric Motor. This will be found to mesh accurately with the $1''$ Gear 64 when the lay-shaft is adjusted properly. First and second gears are obtained in the following manner. When the Rod 61 is in its mid position, the Pinions 60 and 69 are in mesh together with the pinion 65 and $1''$ Gear 64. Slight movement forward results in the pinion 65 and Gear 64 being thrown out of mesh, and gives neutral gear. Further forward movement brings the Pinions 63 and 71 into mesh, while Pinions 60 and 69 still remain in mesh.

Two corner angle brackets formed from $\frac{1}{2}'' \times \frac{1}{2}''$ Angle Brackets are now fitted, the positions of which are shown in Fig. 11. The inner flanges of these two parts form bearings for a $3''$ Rod carrying a $\frac{1}{2}''$ Pinion 72 and Collar 73. The two parts are spaced slightly apart in order to accommodate the end of a Pawl 74 that is secured on a Rod 75 journalled in the holes of the two ends of the gear-box as shown. A Collar limits the backward movement of the Rod 75. The Pinion 72 is normally held by the gate in the position shown, as will be described later, and is only thrown into gear when the first and second gear lay-shaft is in neutral. It is then moved to the rear and engages with Pinions 63 and 71. Thus the drive-

Fig. 9. The engine unit with one side removed to show the internal construction

for reverse gear is taken through Pinions 60, 69, 71, 72 and 63, and the resulting gear ratio is midway between second and third gears of the forward speeds. Figs. 9 and 12 should be constantly referred to, as they will make the construction of the gear-box considerably simpler. A 3½″ Strip 76 is next fitted as shown in Fig. 9, forming a bracing member for the Double Angle Strips 45 and 46.

The Engine Casing

A 5½″×3½″ Flat Plate 77, Fig. 12, is fitted at the front end with a 3½″ Angle Girder. This is connected to a 2½″ Girder by four 2½″ Strips and one 2″ Strip, a space being left above the second 2½″ Strip from the bottom in order to accommodate the Rod carrying the fan pulley 78. A Flat Bracket is bolted to each 3½″ Angle Girder in order to partially close the gap, and also to form supporting points for the shanks of two ½″ Bolts. The Bolts secure the Wheel Flange and Bush Wheel 79 in place. The bottom hole of the Bush Wheel carries a Threaded Pin by means of which the front engine mounting, an End Bearing, is held in place. The top hole of the 3½″ Girder is fitted with a 2″ Girder, and this is held in place by means of a vertical 1½″ Strip.

The rear of the 5½″×3½″ Flat Plate 77 is fitted with a 1½″ Angle Girder attached to a similar Girder 80 by means of two 2½″ Angle Girders. The space enclosed by these four short Girders is filled in with two 1½″ Strips. The horizontal flange of the lower 2½″ Angle Girder is fitted at one side with a 3″ Angle Girder 81 and at the other with a 1½″ Angle Girder 82. It should be noted that many of the 1½″ Strips used in the construction of this part of the model are only used for " filling in " purposes and may be dispensed with if necessary.

The gear-box is now fitted, by adding the nut and bolt 83, Fig. 9. The nut and bolt 83A is that which supports one of the built-up corner angle brackets mentioned earlier. The bottom Girders of the gear-box are now connected by two 1½″ Strips and one 2″ Strip to the Girders 81 and 82 respectively, and the bottom holes of the 2″ Strips support a 2½″×½″ Double Angle Strip 84. The same bolts that secure this last-mentioned part also hold in place the two 1½″ Strips 85, Figs. 12 and 13. Washers are placed for spacing purposes between the ends of the Double Angle Strip 84 and the 2″ Strips. The 2½″ Strip 86 is now fitted in the position indicated in Fig. 9.

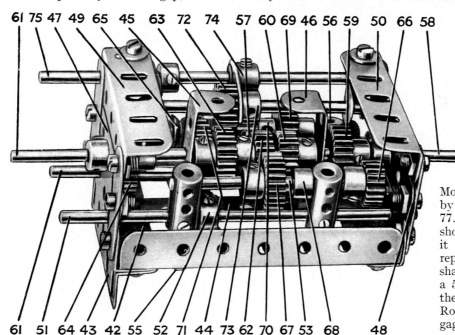

61 75 47 49 65 45 63 72 74 57 60 69 46 56 59 50 66 58

61 51 64 43 42 55 52 71 44 73 62 70 67 53 68 48

Fig. 11. The complete four-speed forward and reverse gear-box

Reference to Fig. 1 shows the form that the right-hand side of the engine takes. This consists of a 5½″×2½″ Flat Plate secured at the front end to the 2½″ Angle Girder already mentioned, and at the rear to the Strip and Girders forming the side of the gear-box.

A 5½″ Flat Girder 83 is fitted at its lower edge with an Angle Girder of similar length. This Angle Girder supports the bottom ends of two 2″ Threaded Rods each of which carries a Worm and the shank of a Spring Buffer held in place by a Nut. Collars are used in order to raise the Worms slightly. These two fittings represent the S.U. Carburetter fitted to the original machine. They are both connected together by a balancing pipe represented by three 3½″×½″ Double Angle Strips.

This section of the engine carrying the carburetters is held in position by a bolt that enters the transverse tapped hole of a Threaded Boss secured on the inside of the top of the engine. This arrangement enables the 5½″ Flat Girder to be fitted when the remainder of the engine has been built. The bolt by means of which the Threaded Boss is attached to the top of the engine also secures in place a Sleeve Piece, and this, together with a second similar part, represents the air-intake.

Fitting the Power Unit

When the construction has reached this stage the Electric Motor can be incorporated, which is done by temporarily removing the Flat Plate 77. The method of carrying the Motor is shown in Fig. 9, and it should be noted that it cannot be secured until Plate 77 is replaced. The front end of the armature shaft carries a 1″ Gear that meshes with a 50-teeth Gear locked on the Rod carrying the Pulley 78, as shown in Fig 12. This Rod is also fitted with a ½″ Pinion that engages with a 57-teeth Gear 89. The 5″ Rod carrying this Gear also carries a ½″ Pinion 90 meshing with a second 57-teeth Gear 91 that is free to rotate on the Rod 58 of the gear-box. Between this Gear and the end of the gear-box a collar and portion of a Compression Strip is fitted as shown in Fig. 12. A ½″ loose Pulley fitted with a ⅝″ Rubber Ring is now passed on to the Rod and is held firmly against the face of the Gear 91 by a ⅞″ Bevel 92. This Bevel is locked on the Rod and forms the fixed member of the clutch.

The clutch withdrawal mechanism is shown in Fig. 9. It is operated by a Crank 93 fitted with a 1½″ Strip 94, and this is connected by a Double Bracket and Strip, as shown in Fig. 12, to the clutch pedal 95. The Plate 77 is now replaced and the dynamo 97 and exhaust system fitted. When these

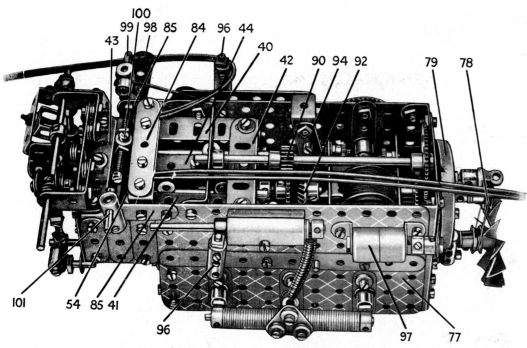

Fig. 12. Underneath view of complete engine unit

are in place the rear engine supports 96 are fixed in position, the threaded shanks of the Threaded Pins being used to secure the engine to the 1″ Triangular Plates 25 mentioned earlier. The method of fitting the front engine support has already been described. To complete the transmission the cardan shaft and Universal Couplings are fitted, as shown in Fig. 1.

The construction and operation of the " gate " and gear selectors are shown in Figs. 9, 12 and 13, and therefore need no further description.

The Brake Mechanism

The foot brake pedal 98, when depressed, presses against a 1″ Rod 99, and this action operates a Collar carrying the $\frac{1}{2}$″ Bolt 100. This Bolt holds a second Collar firmly in position, and carries in its two opposite tapped holes two $\frac{3}{4}$″ Bolts round which pass the wires, which are connected at their opposite ends to the Flat Brackets of the brakes. These wires form the inner cores of bowden cables, the outer sheathing of which is represented by Spring Cord. The sheathing is secured in place at the brake drum ends in the Collars 9 as already described. The other ends of the lengths of Spring Cord are clamped between the $2\frac{1}{2}$″ Strip 84 and a $2\frac{1}{2}$″ × $\frac{1}{2}$″ Double Angle Strip as shown in Fig. 12.

The hand brake lever, which is secured to a transverse Rod journalled at its free end in a $1\frac{1}{2}$″ Angle Girder, is limited in its movement by a $\frac{1}{2}$″ × $\frac{1}{2}$″ Angle Bracket and $\frac{3}{8}$″ Bolt as shown in Fig. 1. The link mechanism, by means of which it is connected to the 1″ Rod 101, Fig. 12, is shown in Fig. 2.

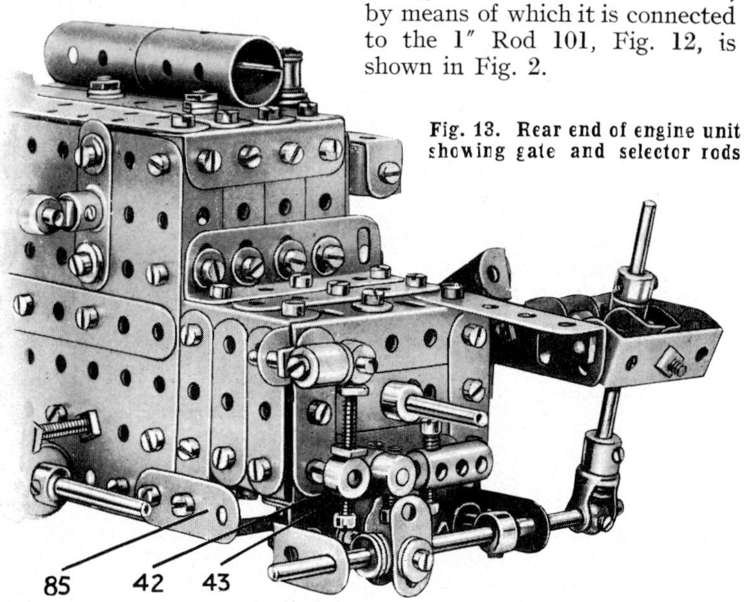

Fig. 13. Rear end of engine unit showing gate and selector rods

PARTS REQUIRED TO BUILD THE MOTOR CHASSIS

5 of No.	1b	2 of No.	14	2 of No.	31	2 of No.	80a	4 of No.	142b		
23 ,,	2	2 ,,	15	2 ,,	32	2 ,,	80b	3 ,,	147		
20 ,,	2a	5 ,,	15a	452 ,,	37	1 ,,	81	3 ,,	147b		
10 ,,	3	4 ,,	16	98 ,,	37a	6 ,,	82	1 ,,	155		
3 ,,	4	3 ,,	16a	200 ,,	38	6 ,,	89	2 ,,	162a		
30 ,,	5	5 ,,	16b	1 ,,	40	12 ,,	90	3 ,,	163		
22 ,,	6	3 ,,	17	2 ,,	43	7 ,,	103	2 ,,	164		
14 ,,	6a	9 ,,	18a	2 ,,	45	4 ,,	103c	1 ,,	165		
2 ,,	8b	3 ,,	18b	4 ,,	48	3 ,,	103d	1 ,,	166		
8 ,,	9	4 ,,	19b	8 ,,	48a	2 ,,	103e				
10 ,,	9a	1 ,,	20a	3 ,,	48b	4 ,,	103h				
3 ,,	9b	1 ,,	23	1 ,,	48c	4 ,,	109				
3 ,,	9c	4 ,,	23a	1 ,,	52	11 ,,	111	1 El Electric			
7 ,,	9d	1 ,,	24	2 ,,	55a	24 ,,	111a	Motor.			
2 ,,	9e	5 ,,	25	5 ft. ,,	58	12 ,,	111c	1 of No. 25			
3 ,,	9f	8 ,,	26	50 ,,	59	6 ,,	115	(not included in			
30 ,,	10	1 ,,	27	6 ,,	62	1 ,,	116a	Outfit).			
12 ,,	11	2 ,,	27a	3 ,,	62b	2 ,,	120a	' 5ft. of 26			
74 ,,	12	1 ,,	28	13 ,,	63	1 ,,	120b	S.W.G. bare			
2 ,,	12a	2 ,,	29	2 ,,	63b	2 ,,	125	copper wire.			
8 ,,	12b	1 ,,	30	4 ,,	64	1 ,,	136				
4 ,,	12c	1 ,,	30a	1 ,,	70	5 ,,	137				
3 ,,	13a	1 ,,	30c	10 ,,	77	2 ,,	140				

An L Outfit Model

Courtesy)   *(Rea Limited*

Giant Ship Coaler at work Coaling a Liner.

The Meccano High-Speed Ship Coaler

A S soon as the steamship had passed the experimental stage and had become a practical proposition, it was natural that engineers should begin to visualise the immense possibilities that were opened up. Short voyages had been carried out with perfect success, and it was realised that the next step should be the crossing of the Atlantic. Among the prominent engineers of that day who turned their attention to this problem was I. K. Brunel. Throughout his career his brilliant mind worked on big lines, and the steamship conquest of the Atlantic must have appealed to him very strongly. We are told that in 1835, at a meeting of the Directors of the Great Western Railway, one of the party remarked upon what he regarded as the enormous length of the proposed railway from London to Bristol. Brunel immediately exclaimed: "Why not make it longer, and have a steamboat to go from Bristol to New York, and call it the '*Great Western*'" Most of those present treated the suggestion as a joke, but Brunel was in grim earnest, and in due course the construction of the "*Great Western*" was commenced.

The crossing of the Atlantic by a steam-propelled vessel obviously involved a very large consumption of coal, and a heated controversy arose as to whether it was possible for any steamship to carry a sufficient supply of coal to enable her to cover the distance. Brunel was quite satisfied in regard to this matter, but his views were strongly opposed by one Dr. Dionysius Lardner, who at that time was a prominent figure in the scientific world. At a meeting of the British Association held at Bristol in 1836, Lardner expressed himself very emphatically regarding the impossibility of a direct crossing of the Atlantic. In the course of his lecture he said :—

Moreover, in no part of the ship is there any escape from the husky din which accompanies the ritual of coaling.

On this occasion the coaling took place at night from great coal-carrying rafts containing gangs of hundreds of coolies. Each raft carries high aloft cressets or iron baskets blazing with fire. The rafts are made fast to the great vessel, planks are run up to the coal bunkers, and then there begins an unceasing procession of gaunt folk carrying yellow baskets full of coal up one plank and returning with them empty along another.

As they pass up and down, their rags dance in the wind, clouds of coal dust and smoke circle round them, while the light from the cressets flashes fitfully upon the file, making their sweating limbs glow as with a fervent heat. The stream of basket carriers might be coming out from the crater of a volcano, and it is a matter of wonder that they are neither charred nor smothered. . . . .

"Hour after hour the dry tramp of feet along the plank continues, hour after hour the same hoarse dirge is screamed forth from a hundred creaking

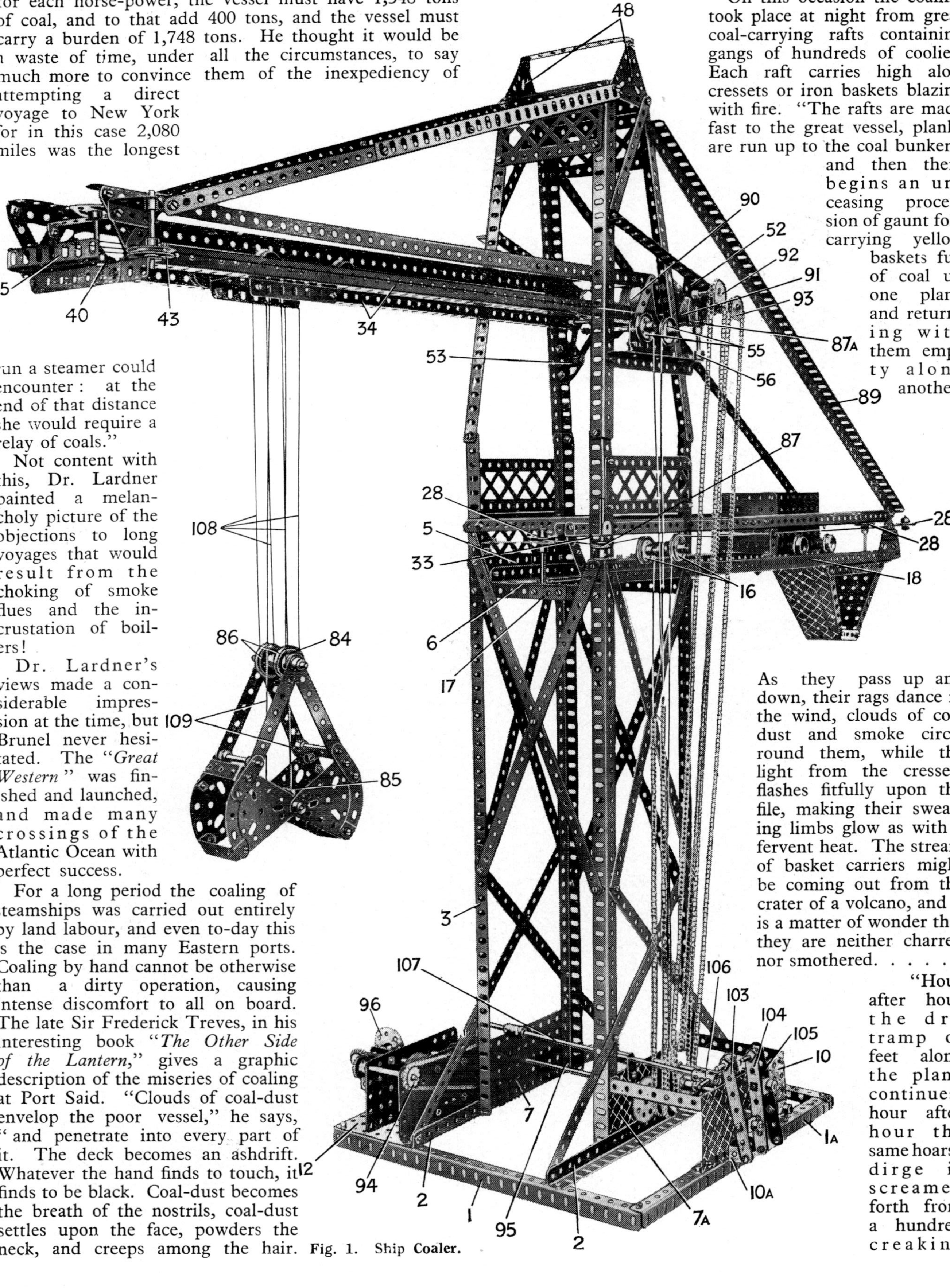

Fig. 1. Ship Coaler.

" Let them take a vessel of 1,600 tons, provided with 400 horse-power engines. They must take 2¼ tons for each horse-power, the vessel must have 1,348 tons of coal, and to that add 400 tons, and the vessel must carry a burden of 1,748 tons. He thought it would be a waste of time, under all the circumstances, to say much more to convince them of the inexpediency of attempting a direct voyage to New York for in this case 2,080 miles was the longest

run a steamer could encounter : at the end of that distance she would require a relay of coals."

Not content with this, Dr. Lardner painted a melancholy picture of the objections to long voyages that would result from the choking of smoke flues and the incrustation of boilers!

Dr. Lardner's views made a considerable impression at the time, but Brunel never hesitated. The "Great Western" was finished and launched, and made many crossings of the Atlantic Ocean with perfect success.

For a long period the coaling of steamships was carried out entirely by hand labour, and even to-day this is the case in many Eastern ports. Coaling by hand cannot be otherwise than a dirty operation, causing intense discomfort to all on board. The late Sir Frederick Treves, in his interesting book "The Other Side of the Lantern," gives a graphic description of the miseries of coaling at Port Said. "Clouds of coal-dust envelop the poor vessel," he says, "and penetrate into every part of it. The deck becomes an ashdrift. Whatever the hand finds to touch, it finds to be black. Coal-dust becomes the breath of the nostrils, coal-dust settles upon the face, powders the neck, and creeps among the hair.

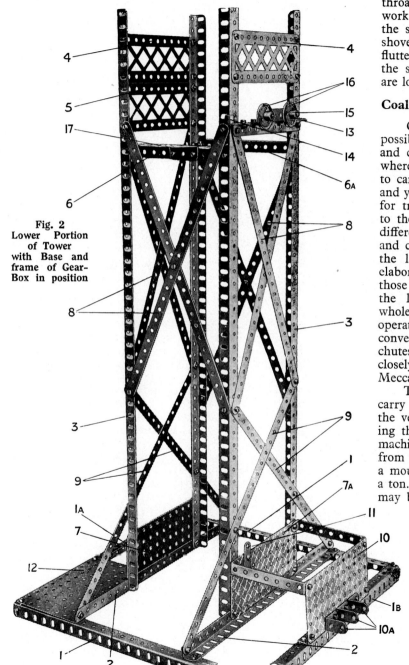

Fig. 2
Lower Portion
of Tower
with Base and
frame of Gear-
Box in position

throats, hour after hour the spades are at work and the baskets come and go. Then the scuffle of feet ceases, the scrape of the shovels dies away, the fire in the cressets flutters out, the barges are empty, and to the same weird chant they glide away and are lost in the gloom."

Coaling by Machinery.

Coaling by hand on these lines is only possible in parts of the world where ample and cheap native labour is available. Elsewhere machinery must be called into play to carry out operations at a sufficient speed, and yet economically. The method employed for transferring the coal from the quayside to the ship's bunkers varies considerably in different ports, according to local conditions and circumstances. The coaling facilities of the larger ports are naturally on a more elaborate and more interesting scale than those at the smaller ports. At several of the larger ports, for instance, there are whole fleets of floating coaling machines operated by grabs in conjunction with belt conveyor, and also by bucket elevators and chutes. These machines correspond very closely in their working principles to the Meccano model shortly to be described.

The grab machines do not themselves carry any coal, but are moored alongside the vessel to be coaled, and barges containing the coal are brought alongside the grab machines. The grab is lowered into the barge, from which it takes up in its great steel jaws a mouthful of coal weighing something over a ton. This coal is raised to whatever height may be required and is then released on to a travelling belt conveyor, by which it is carried across the deck of the vessel to the hatchways. In the Meccano model, the automatic discharging truck corresponds to the belt conveyor.

While the coal is on its journey along the conveyor the grab descends again and takes up another load, and so the process goes on, the loading proceeding at the rate of over 100 tons per hour. As soon as one barge is emptied, another one takes its place, so that the loading continues without interruption until the necessary amount of coal has been taken on board.

The photograph on page 1 shows the giant grab elevator "Pensarn," which belongs to Rea Limited, engaged in coaling a liner in the Liverpool docks. In order to make it possible to coal ships in any part of the dock system, the entire structure is built on a flat barge or pontoon, which may be brought close up to the side of the vessel to

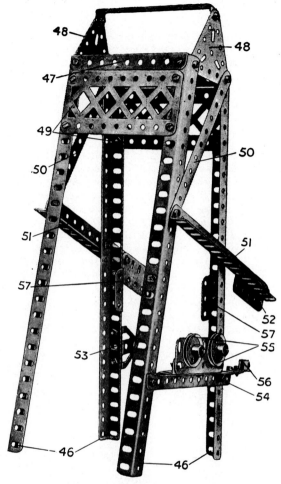

Fig. 3. Upper Portion of Tower

be coaled. The grab, which is suspended from a trolley in the same way as that in the Meccano model, can be seen on the left of the photograph. A hopper, seen in the centre of the structure, receives the coal from the grab and discharges it on to the belt conveyor on the right. The grab bucket of this particular elevator raises 22 cwt. of coal to a height of 60 ft. above the water line. When working at these limits the machine is capable of delivering into a steamer 120 tons of coal per hour. The special barges used in conjunction with the elevator have a capacity of from 500 to 1,500 tons. One of these barges can be seen in the foreground of the photograph.

The machines operated by bucket elevators and chutes differ from the grab machines in that they themselves carry the coal. They are capable of holding from 1,000 to 1,100 tons. The coal is made to fall in regulated quantities through a false bottom on to a travelling chain of buckets, which lift it to the top of the machine and discharge it down chutes directed either over the decks into hatchways, or into side ports. By means of elevator machines coaling can be carried out at the rate of some 300 tons per hour. In addition, the coaling can be delivered overall to a height of more than 50 ft., thus ensuring the speedy coaling of a large liner without any necessity for the vessel to move from her loading or discharging berth.

The High-speed Ship Coaler has been designed specially to illustrate the possibilities of mechanical coaling. It is one of the most interesting of all Meccano models, and if carefully constructed it operates with wonderful precision and in a most realistic manner. The whole of the movements necessary for coaling a miniature ship are controlled from a central gear-box, and are carried out with perfect accuracy. The model is one that makes a particular appeal to Meccano enthusiasts, because, in addition to the enjoyment of building it, it affords endless fun when completed. Moreover, a considerable amount of dexterity is required for its successful manipulation. There are so many movements that the operator has to use his intelligence all the time, and must be quick with his fingers in order to carry out the various stages without a hitch. In other words, it is just as exciting to operate as it is to build.

At first sight the Meccano Ship Coaler may seem to differ considerably

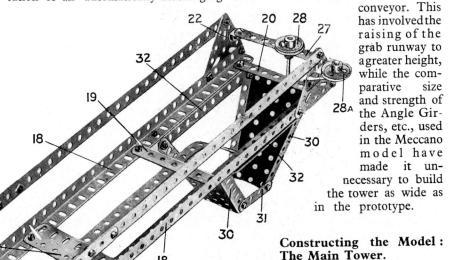

Fig. 4
Truck Runway, with Chute

from the elevators used in actual practice, but a closer inspection will reveal the fact that the only important variation from the usual type is the substitution of an automatically-discharging truck for the more orthodox belt conveyor. This has involved the raising of the grab runway to a greater height, while the comparative size and strength of the Angle Girders, etc., used in the Meccano model have made it unnecessary to build the tower as wide as in the prototype.

Constructing the Model: The Main Tower.

The construction of the model should be commenced by building the main tower. Fig. 2 shows the tower in detail, with superstructure, gearing, etc., removed. The base of the tower consists of four 12½″ Angle Girders 1 bolted in the form of a square and spanned by two similar Girders 2. Four 24½″ Angle Girders 3, forming the chief supports of the tower, are braced at the top by the 5½″ Angle Girders 6, 6a and the 5½″ Braced Girders 4, 5, whilst their lower ends are joined by two 5½×2½″ Flat Plates, 7, 7a. The rigidity of the structure is increased by 12½″ crossed Strips 8, 9.

The framework of the gear-box is formed by erecting a 5½×2½″ Flat Plate 10 edgewise on one of the base Girders 1 and joining it to the Plate 7a by means of two 3½×½″ Double Angle Strips. Three 1×1″ Angle Brackets 10a are secured to the outer side of the Plate 10, and a 1½″ Strip 11 is attached in a vertical position to the Plate 7a. A 5½×3½″ Flat Plate 12, bolted to the base in the position shown forms the bed to which an Electric Motor will later be attached.

A 5½″ Angle Girder 13 bolted near the upper ends of two of the Girders 3, above the gear-box, carries a Crank 14, and a 2″ Angle Girder 15, secured to the Girder 13, carries two 1″ loose Pulley Wheels 16, which are mounted on Threaded Pins and kept in position by Collars and set screws. The addition of a Trunnion 17 to the Girder 6 completes the construction of the main tower unit.

Upper Portion of Tower.

The upper tower (Fig. 3) is built of four 12½″ Angle Girders 46 surmounted by two 4½″ Angle Girders 47 and two 2½″ Triangular Plates 48 joined by a 4½″×½″ Double Angle Strip. The wider sides of the tower are strengthened by 4½″ Braced Girders 49, and the narrow sides by two 5½″ Strips 50. To the ends of these Strips 50 are bolted the 7½″ Angle Girders 51, the projecting ends of which slope downward and carry 2½″ Flat Girders 52. Below the Girders 51, two 1½″ Angle Girders 57 are attached to the uprights 46 as shown, and further down, on one side only, is a Trunnion 53.

The 5½″ Angle Girder 54 carries a 3″ Angle Girder and a 3″ Flat Girder, to which the 1″ loose Pulleys 55 are attached by Threaded Pins in the same way as the Pulleys 16 (Fig. 2). A Crank 56 is bolted as shown (Fig. 3) to the short projecting end of the Girder 54.

The Truck Runway.

The construction of the truck runway, chute, etc., will be followed from Fig. 4. Two 24½″ Angle Girders 18, separated by 3½″ Strips 19, 20 and a pair

A 1″ loose Pulley 28a is free to rotate about a Threaded Pin secured in a Trunnion, which in turn is bolted to one of the Triangular Plates 22. A Collar with grub-screw keeps the Pulley in position. A 1½″×½″ Double Angle Strip 33 is bolted to the end of one of the Strips 24.

The guide rail 29 consists of two 12½″ Strips, one end of each Strip being clamped between two Flat Girders 21; this rail also passes between two 3½″ Strips 19, and its end is curved downward to overhang the chute. The latter consists of two Sector Plates 30 joined by 2″ Strips 31 and bolted to 5½″ Angle Girders 32 on the underside of the rails 18.

The Flanged Wheels of the automatically-discharging truck run on the edges of the outer vertical sides of the Angle Girders 18.

The Grab Runway.

Fig. 5 shows the runway traversed by the trolley from which the grab is suspended. The rails 34 and the strengthening members 35 consist of 24½″

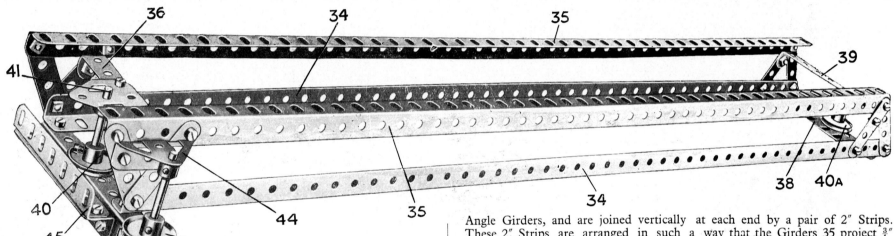

Fig. 5. Grab Trolley Runway

of 3½″ Flat Girders 21, are the rails on which the truck (Fig. 6) runs. At the outer ends of the rails are the 2½″ Triangular Plates 22, and at the inner ends are the 2½″ Strips 23. The latter are joined to the Plates 22 by the Strips 24, which consist of 12½″ Strips connected end to end by overlapping 3″ Strips 25.

Two 3½″ Strips 26, 27 are attached respectively to the Strips 23 and the Triangular Plates 22 by means of Angle Brackets, and short Rods journalled through the middle holes of these Strips carry 1″ fast Pulleys 28, the Rod at the outer end of the runway being also journalled in the 3½″ Strip 20. As will be explained, an additional bearing for the Rod 28 is provided when the runway is attached to the main tower. The Strips 26, 27 are used together with Angle Brackets in preference to 3½″×½″ Double Angle Strips, since they permit the Strips 24 to be spaced exactly at the desired distance apart.

Angle Girders, and are joined vertically at each end by a pair of 2″ Strips. These 2″ Strips are arranged in such a way that the Girders 35 project ¾″ further from the tower than the rails 34. The rails are spaced apart by the 4½″ Angle Girder 37 (the end of which projects 1″) and the 3½″ Flat Girder 38, while two 3½″×½″ Double Angle Strips 36, 39 are bolted between the end 2″ Strips.

A 1″ loose Pulley Wheel 40a is mounted on a Threaded Pin secured to the Flat Girder 38, but is prevented from moving vertically by a Collar and grub-screw. At the outer end of the runway a 1″ Pulley Wheel 40 is fixed to a 2″ Rod 41 journalled in bearings consisting of the Girder 37 and a Flat Trunnion bolted to the Double Angle Strip 36. A second 1″ fast Pulley 43 is similarly secured to a 2″ Rod journalled in the projecting end of the Girder 37 and a Trunnion 44 bolted to one of the pairs of 2″ Strips. The 3½″ Angle Girder 45 is mounted on a similar Girder bolted to the 4½″ Angle Girder 37.

The flanges of the grab trolley wheels ride on the inner edges of the horizontal flanges of the Angle Girders 34. For this reason care must be taken to see that the rails 34 are exactly parallel to one another before they are finally secured in position.

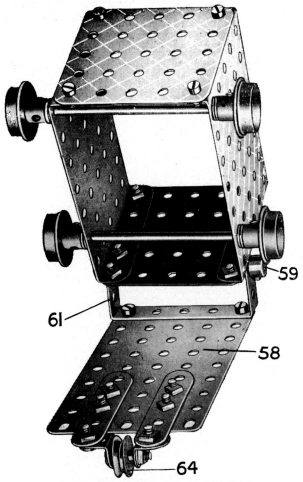

Fig. 6. Automatically-Discharging Truck

truck wheels run on the upturned flanges of the rails 18 (Fig. 4).

Building the Grab Trolley.

The grab trolley traverses the rails 34 (Fig. 5) and from it is suspended the grab.

Two 3½″ Flat Girders form the sides of the trolley (Fig. 7). They are joined by 1½″ × ½″ Double Angle Strips 67, and their end holes form journal-bearings for the 3″ Axle Rods carrying the four ¾″ Flanged Wheels secured to 3″ Axle Rods. Two 2″ Rods 69 journalled in the 3½″ Flat Girders carry two 1½″ Strips 72 and three pairs of ½″ loose Pulley Wheels 73, 74 and 75, which are spaced apart by fixed Collars. Washers should be placed between the Pulleys 73 and 75 and the side Girders.

The Truck

Fig. 6 is a view of the underside of the automatically - discharging truck, which runs on the rails 18 (Fig. 4). Two 3½″ × 2½″ Flanged Plates joined by 2½″ × 2½″ Flat Plates form the walls of the truck, and the hinged bottom consists of a 4½″ × 2½″ Flat Plate 58. A 3″ Rod 59, journalled in Angle Brackets bolted to one of the end plates, is retained in position by Collars, and acts as a pivot for a 2½″ × 1″ Double Angle Strip 61 bolted to the Plate 58.

The truck runs on four ¾″ Flanged Wheels secured to 3½″ Rods, each wheel being spaced away from the sides of the truck by two Washers. The ½″ loose Pulley Wheel 64 turns freely on a Pivot Bolt mounted in two Angle Brackets, which are secured to the ends of two 2½″ Strips bolted to the Plate 58. The

Construction of the Grab.

Each jaw of the grab (Fig. 8) is composed of two 2½″ Triangular Plates pivoted on a 2″ Axle Rod 78 and joined by 1½″ × ½″ Double Angle Strips 79. Four 2½″ Curved Strips (small radius) are bolted to the Triangular Plates, and to these are attached the 1½″ Strips 80, which are mounted pivotally on 2″ Rods 81. Four 3½″ Strips 82 also pivot about Rods 81, and a 2½″ Rod 83 journalled through their upper ends carries two 1″ fast Pulley Wheels 86 and two ½″ loose Pulleys 84. The Rods 81 and 83 are held in position by Collars and grub-screws.

Two ¾″ Flanged Wheels 85 are butted together on the Rod 78 to form a wide grooved Pulley. The Rod 78 is held in place between the Triangular Plates by Collars made fast to its ends.

Assembly of the Main Units.

The two portions of the tower are united by bolting the lower ends of the Angle Girders 46 (Fig. 3) to the tops of the Girders 3 (Fig. 2). The Angle Girders 18 of the Truck runway (Fig. 4) are then bolted to the Girders 6, 6a, and the outer ends of the runway are supported by two 24½″ Angle Girders 89 (Fig. 1) bolted to the Girders 46 of the upper tower.

The grab runway is mounted pivotally on a 4½″ Axle Rod journalled in the lower holes of the 1½″ Angle Girders 57 (Fig. 3) and its outer end is supported by two ties, each consisting of a 12½″ Angle Girder and a 12½″ Strip overlapped nine holes, which connect it to the top of the tower.

The end of the 2″ Rod bearing the 1″ Pulley Wheel 28 at the inner end of the truck runway may now be passed through a hole in the Trunnion 17 (Fig. 2). A ½″ loose Pulley Wheel 87 (Fig. 1) is mounted on a 2″ Axle Rod secured in the boss of the Crank 14 (see also Fig. 2) and passes through the 1½″ × ½″ Double Angle Strip 33. A similar Wheel 87a is supported at the inner end of the grab runway by a Collar on another 2″ Rod that is made fast in the boss of the Crank 56.

The drums on which are wound the cords for operating the grab are formed by Meccano Wood Rollers 90, 91 (part No. 106), which are gripped between Bush Wheels secured to 6½″ Axle Rods that are journalled in the 2½″ Flat Girders 52 (Fig. 3). These Rods are retained in position by means of Collars and grub-screws, and carry on their

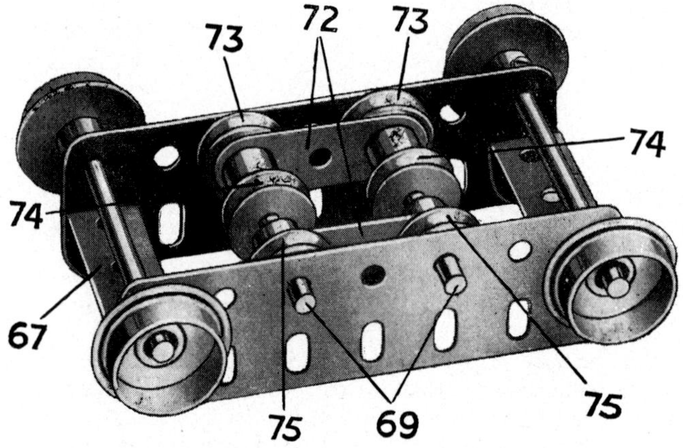

Fig. 7. Grab Trolley, showing guide pulleys for hoisting cords

ends the 1″ Sprocket Wheels 92, 93. Their other ends pass through the loops at the ends of two Springs, which are attached to the Trunnion 53 (Fig. 3) and are constantly under tension. The friction thus set up prevents the weight of the grab from unwinding the cords on the rollers when the latter are disconnected from the driving mechanism.

A Meccano Electric Motor should next be bolted to the Flat Plate 12 in the position shown (see Figs. 1 and 9).

Transmission and Gearing.

The gear-box and various controls are shown in Fig. 9. The arrangement of the mechanism is as follows :—A Worm Wheel secured to the armature spindle of the Electric Motor meshes with a 57-teeth Gear Wheel 96 on a 2″ Rod that is journalled in a Channel Bearing secured to the side of the motor frame. A $\frac{7}{8}$″ Bevel Gear, carried on the opposite end of the 2″ Rod, engages with a similar Bevel Gear, from the Rod of which the drive is led via a $\frac{3}{4}$″ Sprocket Wheel 94 to a 2″ Sprocket Wheel on the end of the 11$\frac{1}{2}$″ Axle Rod 95. This Rod 95 passes through the Flat Plates 7a, 10, and is provided with two $\frac{1}{2}$″ Pinion Wheels 97, 98.

Three 6$\frac{1}{2}$″ Axle Rods 99, 100, 101 are journalled in the side plates 7a and 10 of the gear-box. The first of these carries a 57-teeth Gear Wheel to mesh with the $\frac{1}{2}$″ Pinion 97, and two Sprocket Wheels that engage short Sprocket Chains, to the ends of which are tied lengths of cord.

The cords thus connected to the inner 1″ Sprocket Wheel pass round the 1″ Pulley Wheels 16, 87, 28a, and 28, and are tied to opposite ends of the truck, while those from the outer Sprocket Wheel are led around the Pulleys 55, 43, 40, 87a, 40a, and are tied to the grab trolley. When the Rod 99 revolves, therefore, the truck and the grab trolley are simultaneously drawn inward or outward. Their positions should be adjusted before securing so that the grab trolley will come to rest in the tower immediately above the truck.

The Rod 100 is situated directly above the 11$\frac{1}{2}$″ Rod 95, and carries a 57-teeth Gear Wheel to mesh with the $\frac{1}{2}$″ Pinion 98. It also is provided with a 1″ Sprocket Wheel 102, which is connected by means of an endless Sprocket Chain to a similar wheel 92 on the spindle of the Wood Roller 90. A cord wound on this roller passes over one of the $\frac{1}{2}$″ loose Pulley Wheels 74 in the grab trolley (Fig. 7), and round the $\frac{3}{4}$″ Flanged Wheels 85 of the grab (Fig. 8). It is then carried back and over the second $\frac{1}{2}$″ Pulley 74 in the grab

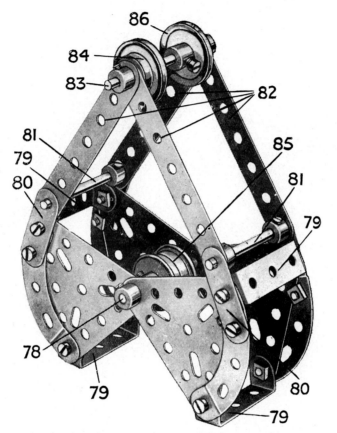

Fig. 8. Grab. The sides should be filled in with cardboard or additional Meccano parts, so that the grab can be put to practical use

trolley and tied to the Angle Girder 45 at the end of the grab runway (Fig. 5.)

The Rod 101 bears a 57-teeth Gear Wheel that can be made to engage with the $\frac{1}{2}$″ Pinion 97. It is also provided with a 1″ Sprocket Wheel, which is connected by another endless Sprocket Chain to the Sprocket Wheel 93 driving the roller 91 (Fig. 1). This roller is provided with two cords for raising and lowering the grab. These cords pass over the $\frac{1}{2}$″ loose Pulley Wheels 73, 75 of the grab trolley, under the 1″ Pulleys 84 of the grab, and back over the second pair of $\frac{1}{2}$″ Pulley Wheels 73, 75, and are finally tied to the Angle Girder 45.

The Axle Rods 99, 100, 101 are all slidable in their bearings, and their movements are controlled by means of the handles 103, 104, 105, consisting of 3$\frac{1}{2}$″ Strips pivotally attached by means of bolts and nuts (S.M.1) to the 1×1″ Angle Brackets 10a (see also Fig. 2). The 3$\frac{1}{2}$″ Strips are connected to the sliding Rods by means of Double Brackets, which are retained in position on the Rods by Collars and pivoted to the Strips by means of bolts and lock-nuts (S.M. 1A). The Gear Wheels on the Rods 99, 100, 101 can thus be brought in or out of engagement with the $\frac{1}{2}$″ Pinion Wheels 97, 98 by operation of their respective handles.

The Electric Motor is controlled by a handle 106, consisting of a 2″ Rod secured in the end transverse hole of a Coupling on the extremity of an 8″ Rod 107, which is extended by a Coupling and a 2″ Rod. The latter is attached to the central starting lever of the motor by means of an End Bearing (part No. 166).

When the handle 105 is pushed inward, the grab closes if the hoisting mechanism is stationary; if the Electric Motor be reversed, the grab will open. Operation of the handle 104 causes it to be raised or lowered, but the handle 105 should be thrown at the same time in order to prevent the cord 107 from becoming slack when the grab is rising, or retarding the progress of the latter if it is descending. Care should be taken that the cords are wound on the rollers 90, 91 in the correct directions, so that all three cords 108, 109, operating the grab are either paid out or hauled in simultaneously when the handles 104, 105 are thrown together.

The handle 103, when thrown, causes both the truck and the grab trolley to travel inward or outward, according to the direction in which the motor is running.

If the sides of the grab and the chute are filled in with stout cardboard, gravel or some similar substance may be used as a substitute for coal, and the model made to function in exactly the same manner as its prototype does in actual practice. The Ship Coaler should be placed with the end of the trolley runway immediately above the heap of coal, while the chute should overhang some receptacle representing the bunkers of a ship. The usual procedure for operating the model is as follows :—The grab and truck are first run out to their farthest extent The grab is then lowered, being opened during the descent, and on reaching the heap of coal to be loaded it is caused to close. Next the motor is reversed and the raising and traversing operations are carried out until the grab arrives in the tower directly above the truck. Operation of the handle 105 causes it to deposit its load, and the original outward movement is then repeated. The dipping centre rail of the truck runway (Fig. 4) presently allows the bottom of the truck to open and drop its load of coal down the chute.

Much additional interest will be obtained by arranging the model to discharge the material through the chute into a train of Hornby open Goods Wagons. If possible the train should be arranged to run on a track elevated on some suitable support, so that the top of the trucks are within an inch or so from the bottom edge of the chute. The elevated track support might be arranged to resemble the side of a quay ; the Meccano Ship Coaler would then appear to be floating on the water alongside. The coal should be collected by means of the grab from the "barges" and delivered via the automatically-discharging truck and chute into the train.

The idea could be extended to practically any extent. For instance, the Ship Coaler could form the nucleus of an extensive dock railway, with goods sidings and marshalling yards, etc. The development of a scheme of this kind would afford any Meccano boy hours of enjoyment and instruction.

Final Adjustments.

A little adjustment to the completed model will probably be necessary to ensure that the different movements are timed correctly. This is effected by altering the positions of the Sprocket Chains and the cords wound on the Wood Rollers 90, 91, for which purpose the Rollers and Sprocket Wheels may be loosened on their axles, the set-screws being made fast again when the mechanism has been adjusted correctly.

To ensure that the model shall work smoothly, the Gears, Sprocket Chains, etc., should be carefully oiled periodically.

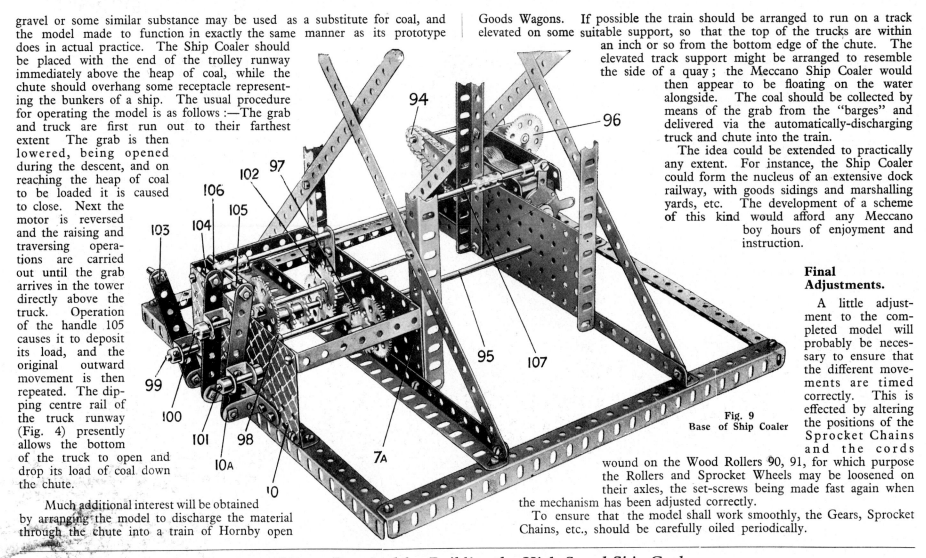

Fig. 9
Base of Ship Coaler

List of Parts Required for Building the High-Speed Ship Coaler

18 of No. 1	2 of No. 8b	3 of No. 12a	12 of No. 17	312 of No. 37	1 of No. 52a	8 of No. 76	5 of No. 103d
2 ,, 2	4 ,, 9	1 ,, 13	2 ,, 18a	6 ,, 37a	2 ,, 53	4 ,, 90a	1 ,, 103e
12 ,, 3	3 ,, 9a	1 ,, 13a	10 ,, 20b	20 ,, 38	1 ,, 53a	15 ,, 94	2 ,, 103f
2 ,, 4	2 ,, 9b	5 ,, 14	4 ,, 24	2 ,, 43	2 ,, 54	1 ,, 95	2 ,, 106
4 ,, 5	2 ,, 9c	1 ,, 15	2 ,, 26	1 ,, 46	38 ,, 59	4 ,, 96	9 ,, 115
10 ,, 6	2 ,, 9f	3 ,, 16	4 ,, 27a	8 ,, 48	2 ,, 62	3 ,, 96a	4 ,, 126
7 ,, 6a	3 ,, 11	2 ,, 16a	2 ,, 30	4 ,, 48b	3 ,, 70	4 ,, 97	1 ,, 126a
12 ,, 7	8 ,, 12	2 ,, 16b	1 ,, 32	1 ,, 48c	2 ,, 72	3 ,, 100	1 ,, 160
14 ,, 8							1 ,, 166

Meccano Electric Motor

(Overseas 3d. Canada &c. Cents.)   Australia 4d.

New Meccano
Motor-Cycle and Sidecar

THE first attempt to construct a cycle to be driven by a petrol engine was made in 1885 by Daimler, the famous engineer who was responsible for so much pioneer work with motor-cars. No really serious effort to produce a practical machine was made until ten years later, however, when a motor bicycle was invented by Colonel Holden, and patented in 1896 and 1897. The original machine is at present in the Science Museum at South Kensington. It has four horizontal air-cooled cylinders, placed two in line on each side of the frame. The carburetter is of the old surface type, the petrol vapour being mixed with a stream of air that passes over a diaphragm of copper gauze that is always wet with petrol. Ignition is by coil and accumulator.

The next noteworthy effort was made by Messrs. Werner in the early years of the present century, and the principal features of their model have been retained to this day. They used a single vertical cylinder set low down in the frame, and the crank case formed an integral part of the frame of the machine. A small pulley on the crank-shaft drove a larger one, fixed to the back wheel by means of a belt; and pedals were retained in order that the rider could assist the engine when necessary.

The carburetter represented a great advance on that used on Holden's machine, the incoming air being charged with petrol vapour by a spray controlled by a float feed, as in modern instruments. Ignition was still by coil and accumulator. The tank was fitted

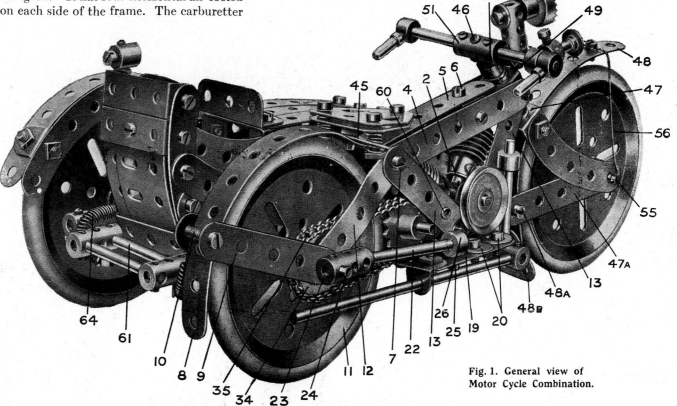

Fig. 1. General view of Motor Cycle Combination.

Published by MECCANO LIMITED, BINNS ROAD, LIVERPOOL.   Printed in England. 628/5.

to the frame above the engine, and was divided into compartments for petrol and oil as on modern machines, except that there was an additional compartment in which the accumulator was carried. The drive to the rear wheel was by belt.

Great improvements have, of course, been made since that time, both in the efficiency of the engines and in the methods of transmission of power to the rear wheel. The use of a magneto for ignition became universal in comparatively early days, but even as late as 1914 belt drive was still fairly common. The machine that won the Senior T.T. Races in that year had a single cylinder set vertically in the frame in the usual fashion, and a magneto was used for ignition. It was chiefly notable for such special features as a variable speed gear that made use of variable belt pulleys on the engine shaft and the rear wheel, and a multiple-plate clutch operated from the handle-bars.

In modern machines the belt has been completely replaced by chains and sprocket wheels, while gear boxes with toothed gear wheels giving various ratios have become universal. In most cases these differ from the average motor-car gear box in that all the gear wheels are always in mesh, and changes are made by means of movable dog clutches.

The model described in this leaflet is an excellent example of Meccano miniature engineering, and offers a remarkable testimonial to the adaptability of the system. Its construction will prove no light tax on the ingenuity of even long-experienced Meccano boys, and it is undoubtedly a task calling for nimble fingers.

Building the Meccano Motor Cycle

The only item included in the model that is not a regular Meccano part consists of a small elastic band; this should be about $1\frac{3}{4}''$ in length when fully extended. The novel use of the Curved Strips in the construction of the sidecar, by which a pleasing streamline effect has been obtained, forms an interesting feature of the model. Both the sidecar and saddle are mounted on springs.

Each engine cylinder consists of a Worm Wheel, secured by its set-screw to the shank of a Bolt passed through a Flat Bracket 2 carried from a Double Bracket 3 (Fig. 2). The tank consists of two $3\frac{1}{2}''$ Strips 4 (Fig. 1) and one $3''$ Strip 5, held together by Double Brackets at 6 and 7. A $5\frac{1}{2}''$ Strip 8 is bolted by its end hole to the end of the Strip 5, and is bent round as shown to form the rear mudguard. It is clamped in position between two $2\frac{1}{2}''$ Strips 9 by means of a $\frac{3}{4}''$ Bolt 10. The driving wheel 11 is carried in the ends of $2\frac{1}{2}''$ Strips 12, which are bent slightly as shown in Fig. 4, as also are the Strips 9.

The V-shaped engine frame is built up from $2\frac{1}{2}''$ Strips 13 converging upon $1''$ Triangular Plates 14 (Figs. 4 and 2). The side $2\frac{1}{2}''$ Strips have been removed in Fig. 2 in order to reveal some of the engine details; normally they are secured by the Bolts 15, 16, 17, and 18. A $2''$ Flat Girder 19 (Fig. 1) is secured to two Angle Brackets 20 bolted to the base of the outer $1''$ Triangular Plate. A similar Flat Girder 21 (Fig. 2) is attached to the first Girder 19 by means of Bolts passed through the elongated holes of both Girders.

A tie-rod provided on the right-hand side of the machine consists of a $2\frac{1}{2}''$ Rod 22 (Fig. 1) nipped in the end of the Coupling 23, in which the back axle 24 is allowed to rotate freely. A set-screw 25, carrying one Washer, is passed through a hole in the Flat Girder 19, and entering the threaded bore of a Collar 26, grips the Rod 22 fast in position. Another tie-rod of different construction is fitted to the left-hand side of the machine. This comprises a $4\frac{1}{2}''$ Axle Rod 27 (Fig. 2) secured to the Flat Girder 21 by means of a Collar and set-screw 28, in a similar manner to that just described. Two Couplings 29 and 30 are mounted on the Rod 27. Coupling 30 forms an additional support for the back axle, and the centre transverse hole of the Coupling 29 is employed as a bearing for a $2''$ Axle Rod 31 (Fig. 4). This Rod 31 carries a $\frac{1}{2}''$ fast Pulley 32 (Fig. 2), and a $\frac{3}{4}''$ Sprocket Wheel 33 (Fig. 4).

The back axle 24 (a $2''$ Rod journalled through the Couplings 23 and 30

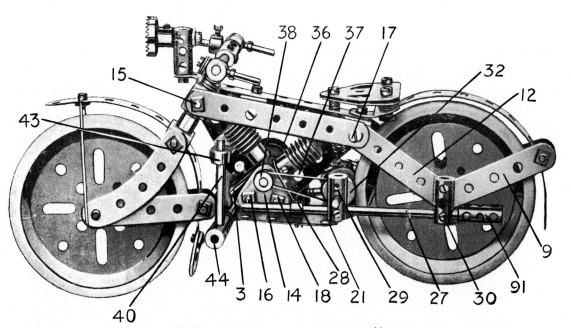

Fig. 2. The Motor Cycle, showing near side.

and Strips 9 and 12) is gripped by the set-screw of the driving wheel 11, and carries a 1″ Sprocket Wheel 34 (Fig. 1) which is caused to engage with the ¾″ Sprocket 33 by means of a Sprocket Chain 35, composed of 39 links. The ½″ Pulley 32 (Fig. 2) is connected to the shaft of the flywheel 36 by means of a small rubber band 37, which passes round the groove of the Pulley and round the flywheel shaft itself, being guided between a Washer and Collar with set-screw 38. Hence, as the machine runs along, the flywheel is caused to revolve at considerable speed.

A 5″ Rod 39 and 2″ Rod 40 (Fig. 4) represent the exhaust pipe. The Rod 39 passes through the Angle Bracket 41, and is secured in the end of the Coupling 42, representing the silencer; the 2″ Rod 40 is secured in the centre transverse hole of the Coupling 42, while its upper end, passing through the Collar 43, is gripped by its set-screw. The latter, carrying a Washer, passes through the centre hole of the Strip 13 before entering the Collar. The short exhaust pipe 40 is duplicated on the other side of the machine (see Fig. 2); it should be noted that the Coupling 44 in this illustration is connected to Coupling 42 (Fig. 4) by means of a 1″ Axle Rod.

The saddle is composed of two Flat Trunnions secured to the framework by means of three ½″ Bolts. A 1½″ Strip 45 (Fig. 1), bolted transversely to the second hole of the 5½″ Strip 8, forms supports for the rear saddle springs. The saddle is mounted on three Compression Springs, placed one on each of the bolts that hold the Flat Trunnions in position.

The steering column, handlebars, etc., are constructed as follows :—a 2″ Rod 46 is passed through the Fork Piece 47 and its end enters the centre hole of the 5½″ Strip 48, which is bent round to form the front mudguard. A Washer is then placed against the boss of the Fork Piece and the Rod 46 is journalled through two Double Brackets 49, which are placed one within the other and bolted to the ends of the Strips 4 and 13. Three Washers, a Collar 50, and Coupling 51 are then placed in position on the steering column as shown. The handlebars are built up from Threaded Pins, Collars, and two 1½″ Rods, carried from the Coupling 51.

The head-lamp is composed of a ¾″ Contrate Wheel 52 (Fig. 4) secured to the shank of a ¾″ Bolt passed completely through the Coupling 53. The latter is secured to a Bolt passed through an Angle Bracket, which in turn is secured

by a set-screw 54 to the Collar 50.

The front wheel forks consist of 2½″ Strips 47a (Fig. 1) and 2½″ Curved Strips, all of which are slightly splayed to allow free movement of the road wheel. The mudguard 48 is clamped between the Strips 47a by means of a ¾″ Bolt 48a passed through their end holes, in a similar manner to the Bolt 10 on the rear mudguard 8. The set-screw of the front road wheel is removed in order that it may revolve independently of the 1½″ Axle Rod 55. The wheel is held in a central position on its axle by means of a Collar and three Washers mounted within the forks on one side of the wheel, to equalise the width of the boss on the other. The mudguard 48 is secured by means of a tie 56. This consists of a Meccano Heald (Part No. 101), the end holes of which are slipped over the axle 55 before the 2½″ Curved Strips are placed in position. The Heald is then doubled beneath the Curved Strip and taken over the Strip 48, and thence down to the opposite end of the axle 55. It is secured to the mudguard by means of a Bolt passed through its centre hole. A 1″ Triangular Plate 48b bolted to the second hole of the Strip 48 forms a "splashguard."

A "Klaxon" horn 57 (Fig. 4) is provided. It is constructed from the "ram" of a Meccano Spring Buffer, the screwed end of which engages the threaded bore of a Collar 58 mounted on the handlebars. A Collar 59 with set-screw added represents the operating handle and completes the realistic effect.

The undercarriage of the sidecar is built up from a Crank Handle 60 (Fig. 3) and 3½″ Rod 61 connected by Couplings and 3½″ Rod 62. Two Couplings and a 2″ Rod 63 serve as a luggage carrier, while

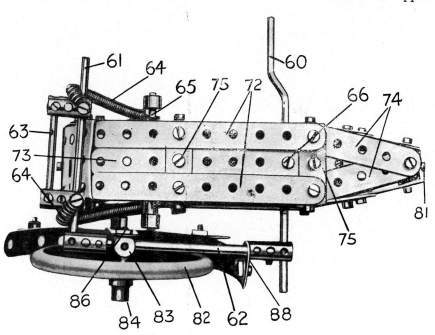

Fig. 3. Underneath view of the Sidecar.

Bolts inserted in the Couplings carry Springs 64, between which the car is suspended. The springs are attached to the car by means of a 2½″ Rod 65. A set-screw 66 passed through the bottom of the car enters the threaded bore of a Collar on the Crank Handle 60, so holding the car in position.

Constructional details of the Sidecar

Each side of the car is composed of the following parts (see Fig. 4) :—
67, 2½″ and 5½″ Curved Strips overlapped two holes and bolted together; 68, 2½″ Curved Strips and 3½″ Strips overlapped two holes and bolted together; 69 and 70, 5½″ Curved Strips. The front ends of all the side

members, with the exception of 68, are bolted to a Corner Bracket 71 in the nose of the car. The floor (Fig. 3) is composed of two $4\frac{1}{2}''$ Strips 72, a $5\frac{1}{2}''$ Strip 73, and two $2\frac{1}{2}''$ Strips 74, bolted to $1\frac{1}{2}'' \times \frac{1}{2}''$ Double Angle Strips 75. The top (Fig. 4) consists of three $3''$ Strips 76, two $2\frac{1}{2}''$ Strips 77, and one $1\frac{1}{2}''$ Strip 78, also secured to $1\frac{1}{2}'' \times \frac{1}{2}''$ Double Angle Strips. The back is built up from three $1\frac{1}{2}''$ Double Angle Strips, bolted between the corner $2\frac{1}{2}''$ Curved Strips 80, and two $2\frac{1}{2}''$ Flat Girders slightly bent as shown, and secured by a Bolt 79. All four sides taper towards the nose of the car and are secured to two Double Brackets bolted together by the Nut and Bolt 81 (Fig. 3).

A seat is provided within the sidecar. This is constructed from two $1\frac{1}{2}''$ Flat Girders secured, by means of a Bolt passed through the elongated hole in the end of each, to a $\frac{1}{2}''$ Reversed Angle Bracket. The latter is bolted to the floor of the car by means of the screw 75 (Fig. 3).

The third road wheel 82 runs freely upon a $1\frac{1}{2}''$ Rod bolted in the top transverse bore of a Coupling 83. Two Washers are placed on the $1\frac{1}{2}''$ Rod between this Coupling and the wheel, while the latter is held in place by the Collar 84. The Coupling 83 is secured to the Rod 62, which passes through its centre. A $2\frac{1}{2}''$ Strip 85 (Fig. 4) is secured to the $\frac{1}{2}''$ Bolt 86 (Fig. 3) passed through the lower end of Coupling 83.

The Strip 85 serves to support the mudguard, which is constructed from $5\frac{1}{2}''$ and $2''$ Strips

overlapped two holes and bolted together. The mudguard is bent round the wheel as shown in Fig. 4 and carries two $2\frac{1}{2}''$ Curved Strips secured by Angle Brackets 87. A Flat Bracket 88 (Fig. 3) is bolted to the end hole of the $2''$ Strip and engages the Rod 62.

The side-lamp 89 consists of a Threaded Boss, screwed to the upturned shank of a Bolt which serves to secure the Angle Bracket 90.

The sidecar may be quickly connected or detached from the motorcycle. The Crank Handle 60 passes through the Strips 13 of the engine-frame (its extreme end is just visible in Figs. 1 and 4), while the Rod 61 enters the end hole of a Coupling 91 (Fig. 2) where it is gripped by the set-screw. It will be seen, therefore, that by loosening this screw the sidecar may be immediately detached, and the motor-cycle used as a solo machine if so desired.

All three wheels are fitted with Meccano Rubber Rings (Part No. 142) to represent pneumatic tyres.

Amongst other features that may be added if desired are a pillion (constructed from two short Flat Girders "sprung" by a method similar to that employed in the saddle) and a rear stand, for attachment if the model is used as a solo outfit. Still further refinements, such as number-plates, etc., would give the finishing touch to the compact and realistic appearance of the model.

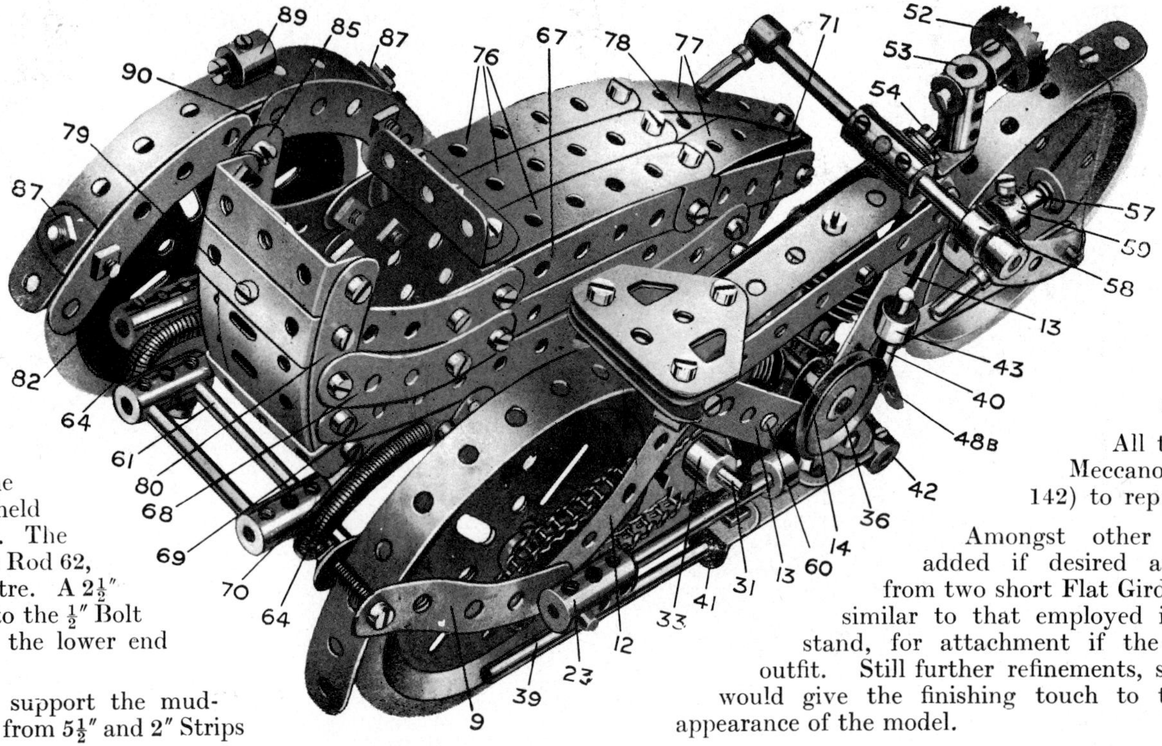

Fig. 4. View from above.

List of Parts Required to Build the Motor-Cycle and Sidecar.

MOTOR-CYCLE.

2 of No. 2	1 of No. 15	1 of No. 23A	2 of No. 90	2 of No. 115				
2 ,, 3	1 ,, 15A	2 ,, 32	$6\frac{1}{2}''$,, 94	1 ,, 116				
1 ,, 4	1 ,, 16	28 ,, 37	1 ,, 96	1 ,, 120A				
10 ,, 5	5 ,, 17	10 ,, 37A	1 ,, 96A	3 ,, 120B				
1 ,, 6A	4 ,, 18A	16 ,, 38	1 ,, 101	2 ,, 126A				
2 ,, 10	1 ,, 18B	11 ,, 59	2 ,, 103G	2 ,, 142				
6 ,, 11	2 ,, 19B	8 ,, 63	3 ,, 111	Small elastic band				
4 ,, 12	1 ,, 22	3 ,, 77	3 ,, 111A					

SIDECAR.

2 of No. 2	3 of No. 12	1 of No. 37A	8 of No. 90				
2 ,, 2A	2 ,, 16	3 ,, 38	2 ,, 103F				
5 ,, 3	1 ,, 16A	2 ,, 43	2 ,, 103H				
5 ,, 5	1 ,, 17	7 ,, 48A	1 ,, 111A				
2 ,, 6A	1 ,, 18A	4 ,, 59	1 ,, 125				
1 ,, 9F	1 ,, 19	5 ,, 63	2 ,, 133				
1 ,, 10	1 ,, 19B	1 ,, 64	1 ,, 142				
2 ,, 11	55 ,, 37	6 ,, 89					

Giant Block-setting Crane

(The Largest Meccano Model)

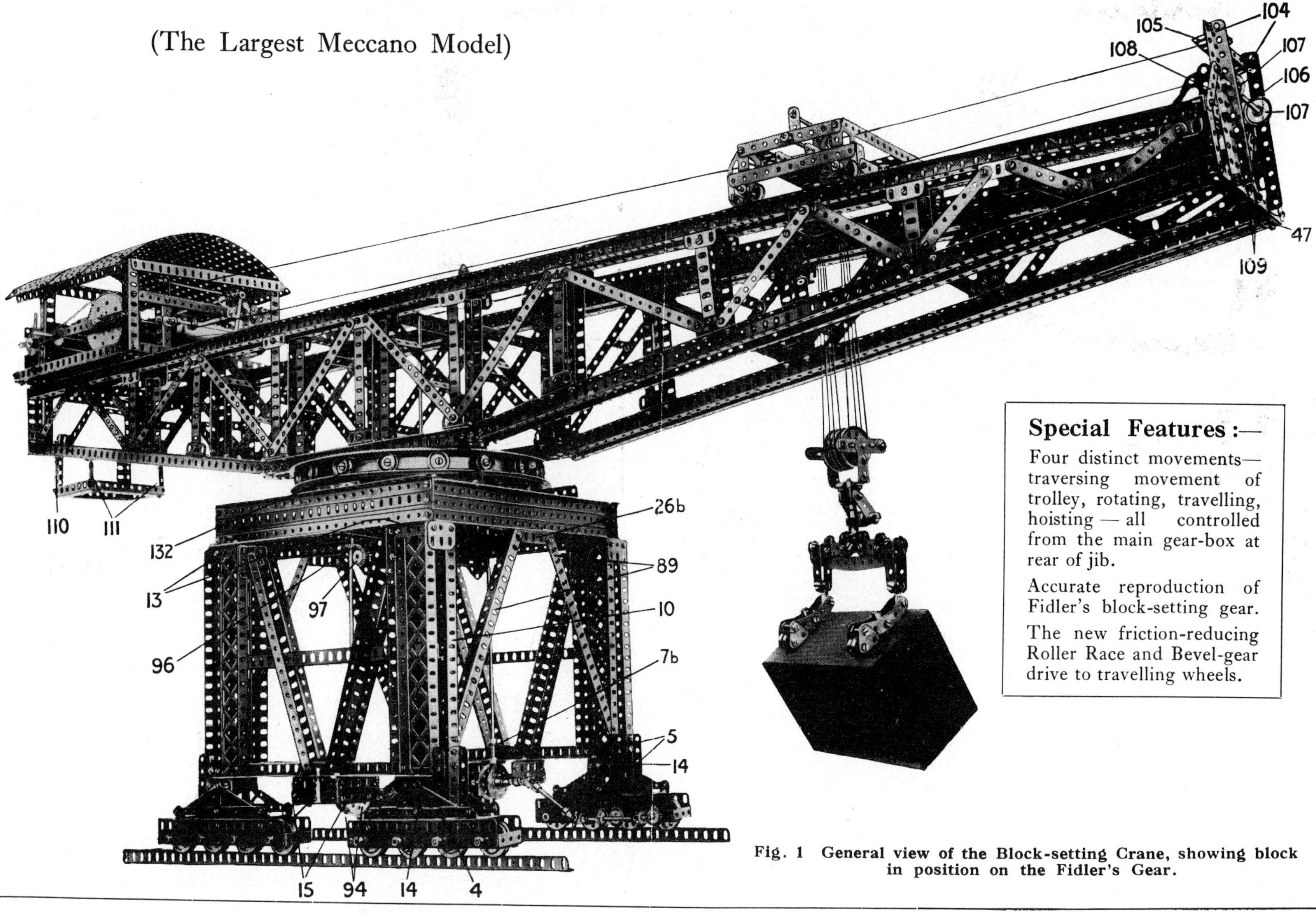

Special Features :—

Four distinct movements—traversing movement of trolley, rotating, travelling, hoisting — all controlled from the main gear-box at rear of jib.

Accurate reproduction of Fidler's block-setting gear.

The new friction-reducing Roller Race and Bevel-gear drive to travelling wheels.

Fig. 1 General view of the Block-setting Crane, showing block in position on the Fidler's Gear.

Published by MECCANO LIMITED, BINNS ROAD, LIVERPOOL

ON every coast line, no matter which one you take, you will always find a few natural harbours. This rule applies equally to the coasts of the British Isles. Good examples are given by Southampton Water on the south coast and Milford Haven on the west, but if we relied solely on natural harbours we should be very badly off. In olden times these natural harbours were sufficient for our small fleets, but as times changed more harbours became necessary. So artificial means had to be brought into use where nature would not oblige. The breakwaters which are constructed must be capable of withstanding an enormous pressure caused by the waves. It is not generally realised what force waves can exert, but when a breakwater weighing 3,300 tons has been moved bodily by the action of the waves we can understand that breakwater construction is by no means an easy task to complete efficiently. Knowing they have to contend with such a great force, engineers have consequently to design their breakwaters on a large scale. Some of the most well-known artificial harbours are those at Portland and Dover, while every boy has heard of the famous Mole at Zeebrugge. We would naturally expect that such huge structures would demand huge machinery to construct them, and this is actually the case. Cranes capable of lifting blocks of concrete and granite weighing anything up to about 50 tons have to be made, and some of the largest cranes in existence are those used in harbour construction.

The magnificent model illustrated on the cover is a reproduction of one of the huge Titan block-setting cranes that have been illustrated and described from time to time in the Meccano Magazine and which, as we have often pointed out in the "M.M.," form one of the most suitable subjects for reproduction in Meccano. This particular crane is one of the finest examples of its type, and has several distinct movements. It is equipped with Fidler's block-setting gear, which depends from a trolley that is drawn along a pair of rails on the upper side of the boom. The boom itself can be swivelled in any direction by means of an Electric Motor, and the entire crane is capable of travelling under its own power on four separately-propelled bogies—every action, in fact, which can be carried out by the actual crane, is reproduced in the Meccano model.

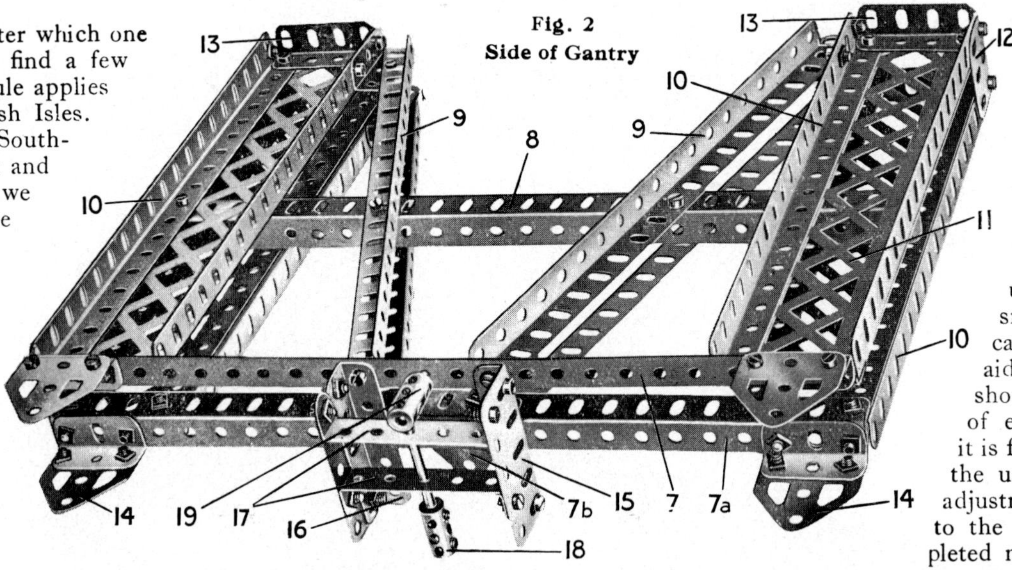

Fig. 2
Side of Gantry

Fig. 3
Frame of
Bogie

Building the Model

This leaflet describes the construction of the model by the unit system, i.e., instead of the whole structure being laboriously erected by the gradual addition of single parts the main portions are first built as separate units. Each unit is as simple to construct as a small model, and the whole model can be finally assembled with the aid of a few nuts and bolts. Care should be taken that the mechanism of each unit works smoothly before it is fitted into the model. In many cases the use of Washers to obtain accurate adjustments will contribute materially to the successful operation of the completed model.

Constructing the Sides of the Gantry

Fig. 2 shows one complete side of the gantry before incorporation in the model. The two upright pillars are connected at their lower ends by two 12½" Angle Girders 7, 7A, and higher up by the cross-piece 8 (another 12½" Angle Girder), and are further supported by the struts 9 (four 9½" Angle Girders). Each of the pillars consists essentially of four 9½" Angle Girders 10 bolted at their lower ends to the Girders 7, 7A, and joined by Braced Girders 11 and Flat Girders 12. At the top of each pillar are the 2" Angle Girders 13, which will serve to connect the pillars to the top of the gantry. The struts 9 are joined to the Girders 10 by 1½" Angle Girders, and to the Girders 7, 7A by nuts and bolts.

The Girders 7, 7A carry on their underside four Flat Trunnions 14 affixed by means of 1½" Angle Girders, and also a small framework consisting of two 2½" Flat Girders 15 bolted to the 2½" Angle Girders 16 and joined by two 2½" Double Angle Strips 17, which form bearings for a 2½" Axle Rod carrying the Coupling 18 on its inner end. This Rod is also secured in the lowest transverse hole of a second Coupling 19, in the end of which is gripped a 1" Rod passing through the centre hole of the Girder 7. A Flat Trunnion 7B is fixed to the Girder 7A by means of a 1½" Flat Girder

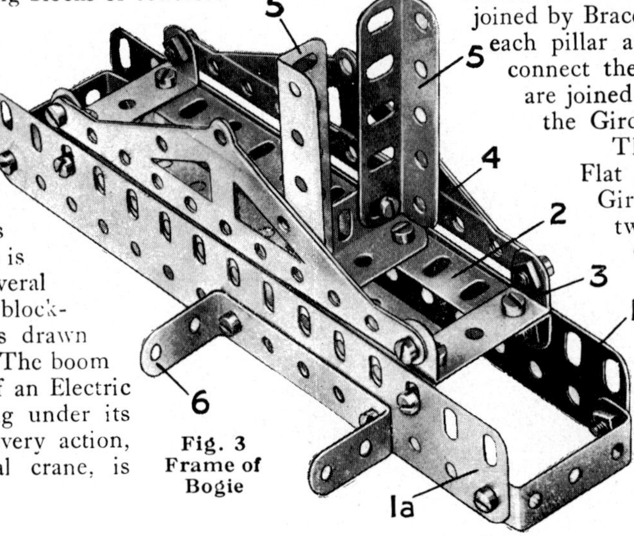

Top of Gantry (Figs. 4 and 5)

Begin this part of the crane by building four composite girders, each consisting of two 12½″ Flat Girders with the round holes of one overlapping the elongated holes of the other throughout their length, four 12½″ Angle Girders being bolted to the two edges to form an H-section joist. The four built-up joists or girders are now bolted together as shown in Fig. 5, making a rectangular framework. Two 12½″ Angle Girders 20, bolted across the top of this framework, carry 1½″ Angle Girders 21, while the 12½″ Angle Girders 22, 23, join the inside middle points of the pairs of Girders 24, 25 respectively. Two 2½″ Angle Girders 26 are attached to similar Girders bolted to the rectangular framework, and two identical Girders 26A are fastened in the same way to the Girder 22. A 2½″ Angle Girder 26B may be seen bolted to the underside of the Girder in the foreground of Fig. 5, and a corresponding part should be fitted to the back of the frame.

Across the bottom of the framework are two 12½″ Angle Girders 27, and two Flat Trunnions bolted to the middle points of these Girders, together with the 1″ by 1″ Angle Bracket 28, form bearings for the 8″ Rod 29, to which three ⅞″ Bevel Gears 97, 98 are secured in the positions shown.

The Bogies

The four bogies on which the crane runs are constructed

as follows : Two Flat Girders, 1 and 1A (Fig. 3) are joined at their ends by 1½″ by ½″ Double Angle Strips. Two 5½″ Angle Girders, 2, bolted to the inner sides of the Flat Girders, are joined by 1½″ by ½″ Double Angle Strips that carry two pairs of Girder Frames bolted flat together. The Girders 2 are also joined by a 1½″ Angle Girder supporting two upright 2½″ Angle Girders 5. A 2½″ by 1″ Double Angle Strip 6 is bolted to the outer side of one of the Girders 1, 1A. Two of the four bogies are built with this Strip 6 on the Girder 1, while in the remaining two it is on the Girder 1A, so that, when finished, one pair of bogies should be exactly the same in appearance as the other pair would look if viewed with the aid of a mirror in the reverse position.

Assembling the Gantry

The top, sides, and bogies of the gantry having now been built as separate units, the gantry itself may be completely assembled.

Fig. 4 is a sectional view of a portion of the gantry, some parts of which have been removed for the sake of clearness. It gives a good view of the mechanism that operates the driving wheels, and also shows quite plainly the means by which the various units are fastened together. The 2″ Angle Girders 13 (Fig. 2) are bolted underneath the main composite girders of the top portion of the gantry (Fig. 4) and the Girders 10, 26B (see general view) are braced by two 9½″ Angle Girders 89 (Figs. 1, 4). The Girders 5 of the bogies (see Fig. 3) are bolted to the outer sides of the Girders 10 on the gantry and the Girder Frames 4 to the Trunnions 14.

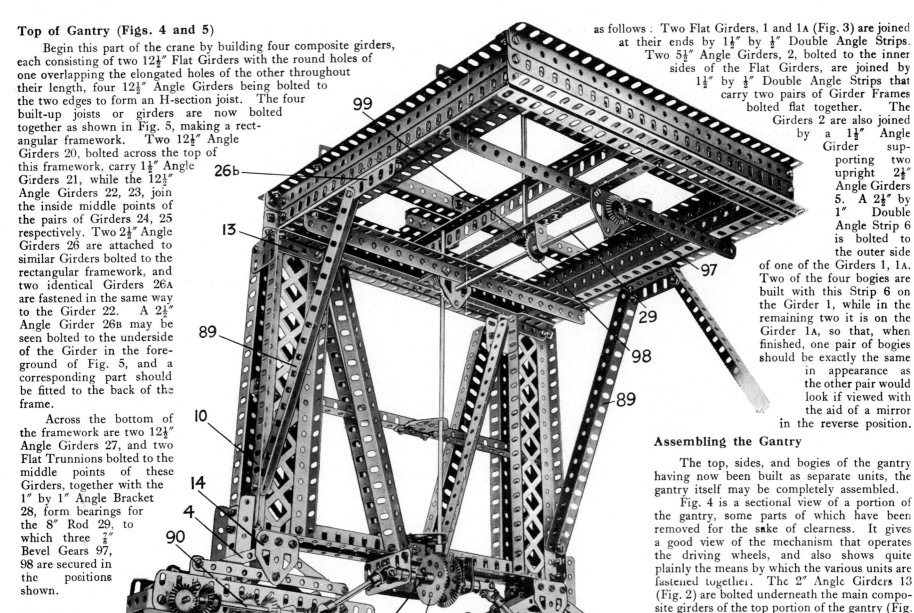

Fig. 4. View of Gantry with one side removed.

Each bogie is provided with two trailing and two driving wheels each made by butting together a Bush Wheel and a Flanged Wheel and securing them to the axle, which in the case of the trailing wheels is a 2″ Rod and in the case of the driving wheels a 2½″ Rod. The driving wheels are operated by ⅞″ Bevel Gears meshing with similar gears on the 3½″ Axle Rods 90, which are journalled in the Double Angle Strips 6 (see Fig. 3). A Washer is placed on each driving axle to keep the ⅞″ Bevel Gears in correct engagement.

Each of the Rods 90 is connected by a 2″ Rod 91 and two Universal Couplings 93 to a 1½″ Bevel Gear 94, secured to a 1½″ Axle Rod 92. The four Rods 92, to which the Bevels 94 are secured, are separate 1½″ Rods entering opposite sides of the Couplings 18 : their other ends are journalled in the Flat Girders 15, and they are held in position by fixed Collars. The four Bevel Gears 94 engage with two ½″ Bevels secured to Rods that are journalled in bearings consisting of the Angle Girders 22, 23 (see Fig. 5) and the Trunnions 7B (see Fig. 2). These Rods carry at their upper ends two ⅞″ Bevel Gears 96 meshing with the ⅞″ Bevel Gears 97 (see Figs. 5, 6) on the Rod 29. The Bevel Gear 98, which is also secured to the Rod 29, takes the drive from the ⅞″ Bevel Gear 99 on a Rod 100 that is journalled in one of the top transverse Girders of the boom and in the centre bosses of the roller-bearing unit, and carries at its upper end a ⅞″ Bevel Gear 101 engaging with a similar wheel on the Rod 102, which is driven from an Electric Motor via the mechanism of the gear-box, and causes the four bogies to travel simultaneously along the rails. Hence the model is actually propelled by eight of its sixteen wheels.

Structural Details of the Boom.

Fig. 7 is a view of one side of the boom : the other side, being exactly similar, has been removed for the sake of clearness. Each side should be built separately in accordance with the instructions given below, and the whole then assembled into the complete unit.

Along the upper edge extend a pair of U-section channel girders 30 and 30A, each composed of four 24½″ and two 12½″ Angle Girders bolted together

in pairs and joined end to end by the 3″ Strips 32. Six 1½″ Strips 31 hold the channel girders 30, 30A side by side about ½″ apart.

The girders forming the lower edge are similarly constructed, the forward end consisting of 12½″ channel girders 33 and 18½″ channel girders 34. The slotted holes of the Girders allow them to be bolted at an angle to the 12½″ centre girders 35 by means of 2″ Strips 36. The Channel Girders 37 are attached in the same manner and are composed of 18½″ Angle Girders.

The upright Angle Girders 38, 39, 40, 41, which are respectively 5½″, 4½″, 3½″ and 2½″ long, are bolted to the upper girders 30, 30A, and to the lower girders 35, 34, 33 and 37 by means of 1½″ Angle Girders 42, and are connected by 1½″ Strips 43, while the oblique struts 44, the different lengths of which are clearly seen in Fig. 7, are bolted to the Girders 42 and joined by 1½″ by ½″ Double Angle Strips 45. It should be noted that the Strips 44 are not in every case fixed to the same point on the short Angle Girders 42, and that, although there is no upright Girder (corresponding to 38, 39, 40, 41) near the extreme end of the boom, the short Girder 42 is included in order that the Strips 44 may be attached to it. The lower channel girders are joined in the same way as the upper girders 30, 30A by 1½″ Strips at the points 46.

On the forward end of the boom are bolted two 7½″ Angle Girders 47 connected by 2½″ Strips 48, while the opposite end of the boom bears two 3½″ Angle Girders 49, to which are attached the 7½″ Angle Girders 50.

The rail 51 is bolted under the Strips 31 to the girder 30, its end hole coinciding with the third hole of the girder, and is provided with stops consisting of a Flanged Bracket and a 1″ Triangular Plate.

The end of a 5½″ Angle Girder 52 is bolted in an inverted position to the inside upper edge of the Girder 30 : two similar girders are attached to the upper edge of the Girder 30, and carry respectively a 1½″ and a 3½″ Flat Girder. Another 1½″ Flat Girder 54A is bolted lengthwise by its slotted holes to the Channel Girder 30. A 5½″ Angle Girder 53A is bolted as shown to one of the vertical Angle Girders 38.

The parts 47, 48, 50, 52, 53, 54, 53A, 54A, should not be duplicated in building the other side of the boom. In all other respects the second portion is constructed in exactly the same manner as the first, but in an inverse

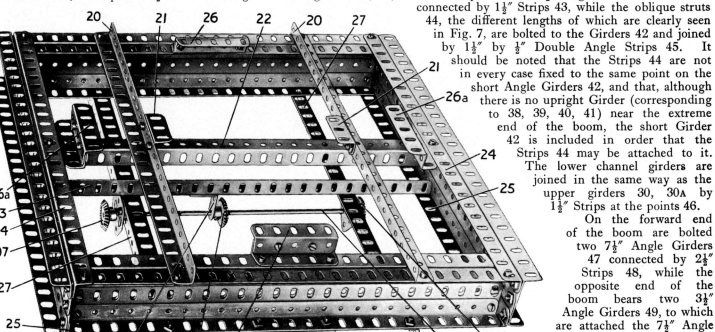

Fig. 5. Top of Gantry, showing short Girders (26, 26a) on which roller race is mounted

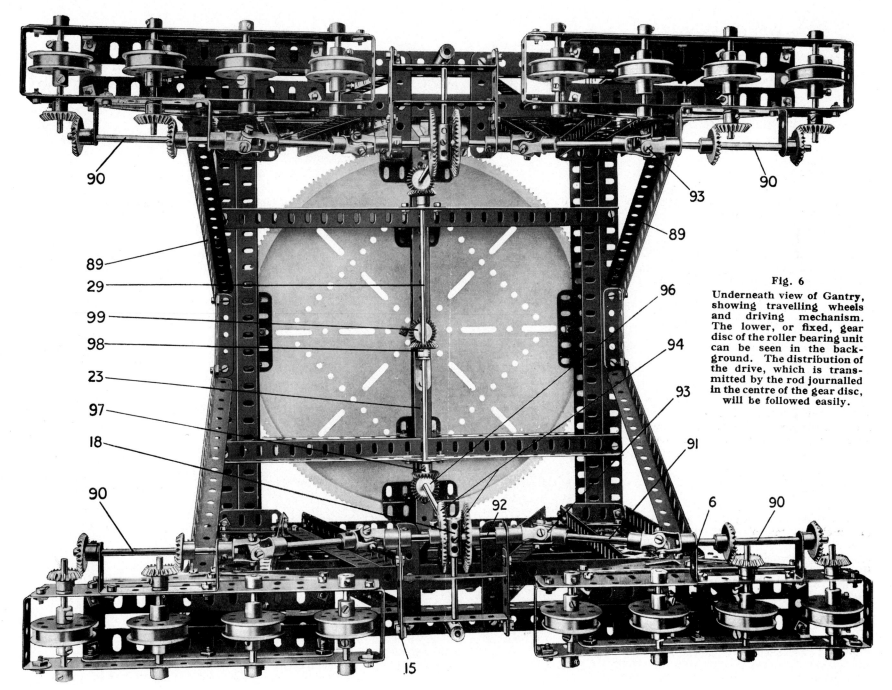

90

90

93

89

89

29

99

98

23

97

18

90

96

94

93

91

92

6

90

.15

Fig. 6

Underneath view of Gantry, showing travelling wheels and driving mechanism. The lower, or fixed, gear disc of the roller bearing unit can be seen in the background. The distribution of the drive, which is transmitted by the rod journalled in the centre of the gear disc, will be followed easily.

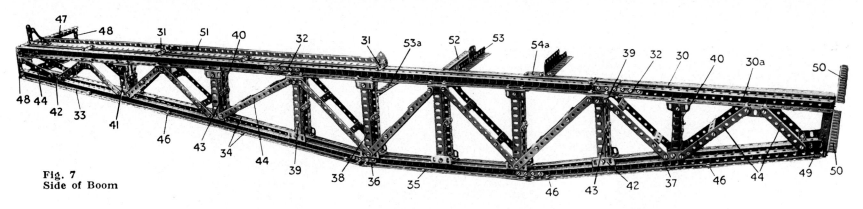

**Fig. 7
Side of Boom**

direction, i.e., the whole unit is reversed to correspond with the first half. The two sections can then be fitted together and secured with nuts and bolts passed through the ends of the transverse members 47, 50, 52, 53, etc. Provided that all the ties and struts shown in the illustrations are reproduced the complete boom will form an extremely rigid unit, capable of withstanding tremendous strain.

Two 5½″ vertical Angle Girders 104, bolted to the Girders 47 (see Figs. 7, 8), carry a 4½″ Angle Girder 105, and form journal bearings for a 4½″ Axle Rod 106, to which are secured two 1″ fast Pulley Wheels 107. Further rigidity is imparted to the structure by two 2½″ Strips 108 and the crossed ½″ Strips 109.

The "cradle" 110, which is designed to accommodate a balance weight for counteracting the weight of the boom, consists of two 3½″ and two 4½″ Angle Girders slung on a pair of 2½″ Angle Girders bolted to the Lower 7½″ Angle Girder 50, and two 1½″ Strips 111, which are attached to the lower channel girder 37 by means of Angle Brackets.

The Roller Bearing (Fig. 9).

The large roller bearing, by means of which the boom of the crane is able to turn smoothly in any direction, may be purchased, together with the small toothed wheel, as a complete unit. The upper Geared Disc, which forms the movable race, is bolted to the Girders 35 of the boom, while the lower Disc is secured to the Girders 26 on the top of the gantry. The Ring Frame 132 is spanned by a 9½″ Strip, through the central hole of which passes the Rod 100. Sixteen ¾″ Flanged Wheels journalled on Pivot Bolts secured around its periphery run smoothly on a shoulder near the edge of the lower Geared Disc,

and the upper Disc, by means of a similar shoulder resting on the ¾″ Flanged Wheels, revolves easily but steadily about the Rod 100. Two Bush Wheels, with set-screws removed, are bolted to the centres of the Geared Discs, and the Rod 100 is free to revolve in their bosses quite independently of the roller bearing.

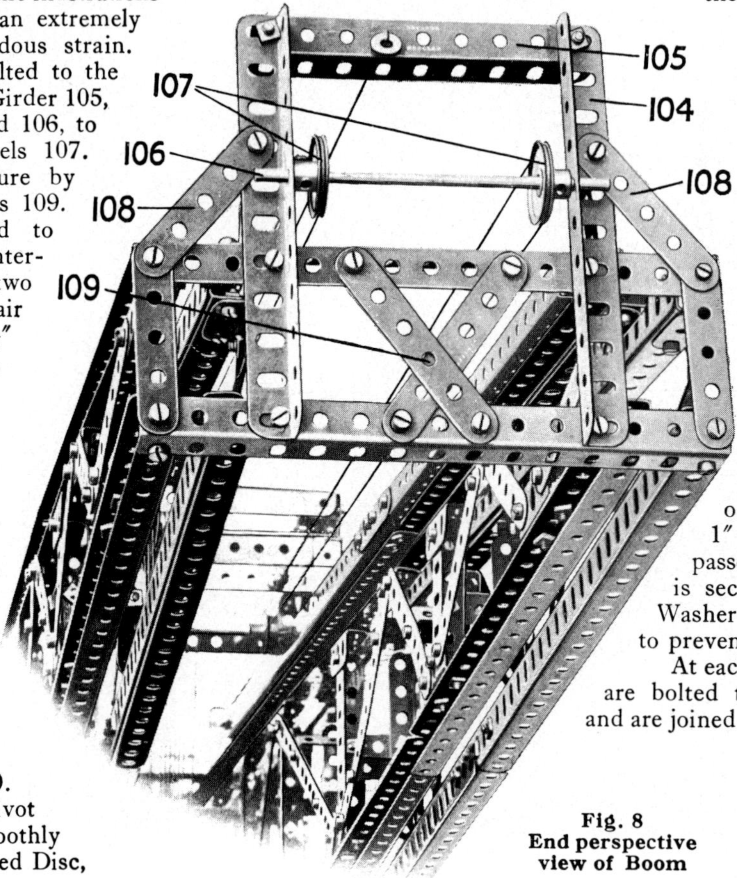

The Crane Trolley

The trolley shown in Fig. 10 is designed to travel on the rails 51 along the top of the boom (Fig. 7). Two 4½″ Angle Girders 55, together with two 5½″ Angle Girders, form a rectangular frame supported by four Trunnions on a lower frame comprising two 5½″ Strips 60 joined by the 5½″ Angle Girders 56. Four inverted Trunnions provide bearings for two 6½″ Axle Rods to which are secured the ¾″ Flanged Wheels on which the trolley runs. A third 6½″ Rod 57, journalled in the Girders 55 and held in place by Collars and set screws, carries five 1″ Pulley Wheels 58 spaced apart by six short Strips 59, and prevented by Collars and set screws from sliding on the Rod 57. A 5″ Rod 57A, journalled in 1″ by ½″ Angle Brackets bolted to the Girders 55, passes through the end holes of the Strips 59, and is secured in place by Collars and set screws. A Washer is placed under the head of each of the bolts 61 to prevent it from touching the Rod 57.

At each end of the trolley, two 1″ by 1″ Angle Brackets are bolted to the underside of the inverted Trunnions, and are joined by a 5½″ Strip 62. Handrail Supports attached to the Strips 62 enable the trolley to be drawn along by cords.

**Fig. 8
End perspective
view of Boom**

The Gear Box

The roof of the gear-box is formed by bolting

six $5\frac{1}{2}''$ by $3\frac{1}{2}''$ Flat Plates together in threes (Fig. 11), and joining them by a middle portion consisting of two $5\frac{1}{2}''$ by $2\frac{1}{2}''$ Flat Plates overlapped three holes. The cover thus formed is then attached to the framework by means of Meccano Hinges 103, which readily conform to the angle of the roof. The framework itself consists of four $9\frac{1}{2}''$ Angle Girders bolted together as shown (Fig. 11).

Fig. 12 shows a view of the gear-box, from which the roof and the greater part of the mechanism have been removed. The square base, composed of four $9\frac{1}{2}''$ Angle Girders, is strengthened by two similar Angle Girders 64. Four vertical $4\frac{1}{2}''$ Angle Girders 65 carry the $7\frac{1}{2}''$ Strips 66 and the $9\frac{1}{2}''$ Angle Girder 67. Two vertical $3''$ Angle Girders bolted to the Girder 67, together with two $2\frac{1}{2}''$ Angle Girders 69 (which are braced by Corner Brackets), form supports for a $7\frac{1}{2}''$ Angle Girder 70 and two $7\frac{1}{2}''$ Strips 71. A $4\frac{1}{2}''$ Flat Girder 72, carrying two $1\frac{1}{2}''$ Flat Girders 73, is bolted to a vertical $2\frac{1}{2}''$ Strip 74 and the upright Girders 69, 65. These Strips and Girders, etc., form the necessary bearings for the shafts of the gear box. Care should be taken to see that they are placed exactly in their correct positions and secured very rigidly.

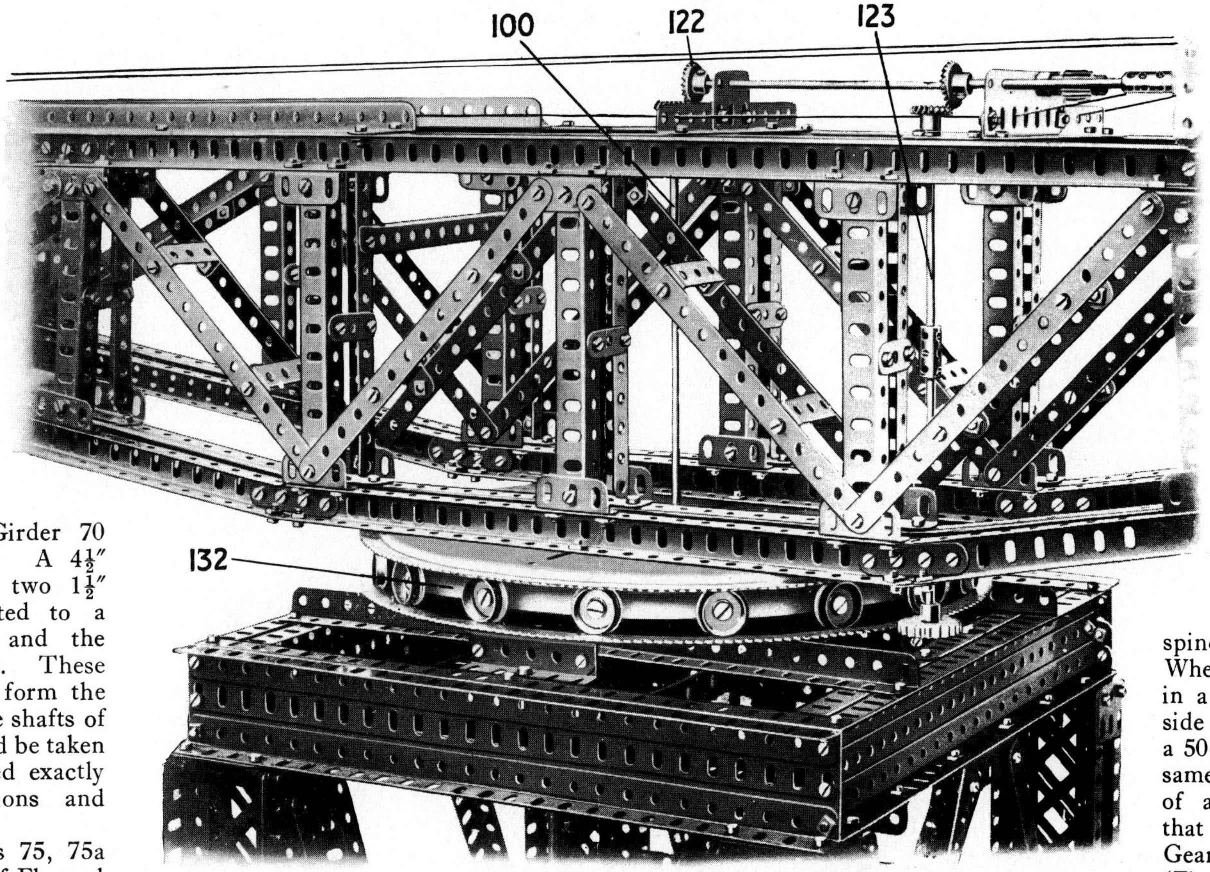

Two $3\frac{1}{2}''$ Axle Rods 75, 75a are journalled in a pair of Flanged Brackets and $7\frac{1}{2}''$ Strips 71, and meet inside the Worm Wheel 77 which is secured to the Rod 75. Two $1''$ Gear Wheels are secured to the Rods 75, 75a and a second Worm Wheel is mounted on the Rod 75a. The Worms are spaced on their respective Rods by means of Collars and set screws. The $5''$ Rod 79, bearing a $\frac{1}{2}''$ Pinion Wheel and a 50-teeth Gear Wheel that meshes with the Worm Wheel 77, is journalled in bearings consisting of a $1\frac{1}{2}''$ Angle Girder and a $3\frac{1}{2}''$ Angle Girder 82: an $8''$ Rod, parallel with the Rod 79, carries a second 50-teeth Gear

Wheel engaging with the Worm 77a: this Rod bears on its outer end a Coupling 83. Washers are placed between the Girder 82 and the Girders 64 in order to bring the 50-teeth Gear Wheels into mesh with the Worms 77, 77a.

A $5\frac{1}{2}''$ Strip 86 is attached by means of a Meccano Hinge to the Girder 67, one end of the Strip being left free inside the gear-box. The manner of attaching the remaining parts of this unit, viz., a $1\frac{1}{2}''$ Flat Girder 84, two $1''$ by $1''$ and one $\frac{1}{2}''$ by $\frac{1}{2}''$ Angle Bracket 85, 85a, a $1''$ Triangular Plate 87, and the $3\frac{1}{2}''$ and $2''$ Angle Girders 88, 88a, may be seen from the illustration (Fig. 12.)

The framework of the gear-box, built as shown in Fig. 12, should be attached to the rear end of the boom by means of nuts and bolts, and the remainder of its mechanism may then be added. The Electric Motor, which is of the high-voltage type, is bolted to the Angle Girders 64, 88, 88a (Figs. 12, 13). A Worm Wheel secured to the armature spindle turns a 57-teeth Gear Wheel on a $2''$ Rod journalled in a Channel Bearing on the side of the motor frame, and a 50-teeth Gear Wheel on the same Rod engages the teeth of a $\frac{3}{4}''$ Pinion Wheel 113 that meshes with a 57-teeth Gear Wheel on the Rod 114 (Fig. 13). This Rod, which is thus in constant rotation, may be caused to transmit the power from the Electric Motor to the Rods 75, 75a (which as already stated, meet inside the Worm Wheel 77) by operating the Threaded Pin 115. By this means a $1''$ Gear Wheel on the Rod 117 can be made to engage simultaneously the $1''$ Gear Wheel 116 and the $1''$ Gear Wheel on the Rod 75. The drive is then led through the gears shown in Fig. 12 to the $\frac{1}{2}''$ Pinion Wheel on the outer end of the Rod 79. A $\frac{1}{2}''$ Pinion on the Rod 118 can be brought into gear with this $\frac{1}{2}''$ Pinion by pulling the handle 119, which thus

Fig. 9 Central portion of model, showing roller bearings supporting the boom causes the double width face ½″ Pinion Wheel 120 to turn a similar Pinion on the Rod 121. Reference to Fig. 9 will show that this Rod actuates the traversing mechanism of the crane by means of the Bevel Gears 122 and the gears already described in the section dealing with the gantry.

The handle 115, which causes the crane to travel on its wheels as described when turned in a clockwise direction, is also used to swivel the crane. For this purpose it is turned in an anti-clockwise direction (i.e., to the left) thus interposing a 1″ Gear Wheel between similar Gear Wheels on the Rods 114, 75A. The latter Rod, which is thus caused to revolve, rotates the Coupling 83 by means of the Worm and 50-teeth Gear Wheel shown in Fig. 12, and a Rod secured in the Coupling turns a vertical Rod 123 by means of two ⅞″ Bevel Gears. The small toothed wheel of the roller bearing unit, which is secured to the lower end of the Rod 123, rolls around the teeth of the upper Geared Disc and swivels the boom bodily about the centre of the roller bearing.

The Rod 114 carries on its ends two 1″ Sprocket Wheels which are connected to a 1″ Sprocket Wheel and a 3″ Sprocket Wheel secured respectively to the Rods 124, 125. The Rods 124, 125 are thus constantly revolving, and operation of the handle 131 interposes ½″ Pinion Wheels secured to a 6½″ Rod between ½″ Pinions on the Rods 124, 125 and 57-teeth Gear Wheels on the spindles of the Wood Rollers 126, 127, causing the latter to rotate. (Only one of the Rollers, of course, can be operated at a time.) The Roller 127 carries two cords, which are each given a few turns round its circumference. One end of each cord is led under one of the ½″ Loose Pulley Wheels 128, and is tied to a Handrail support on the end of the trolley (see Fig. 10). The other ends of the cords are stretched to the forward end of the boom, passed round the 1″ Pulley Wheels 107 (see Figs. 1, 8) and tied to the remaining Handrail Supports on the trolley.

The Wood Roller 126 carries only one cord, which passes in turn round the five 1″ loose Pulley Wheels of the trolley

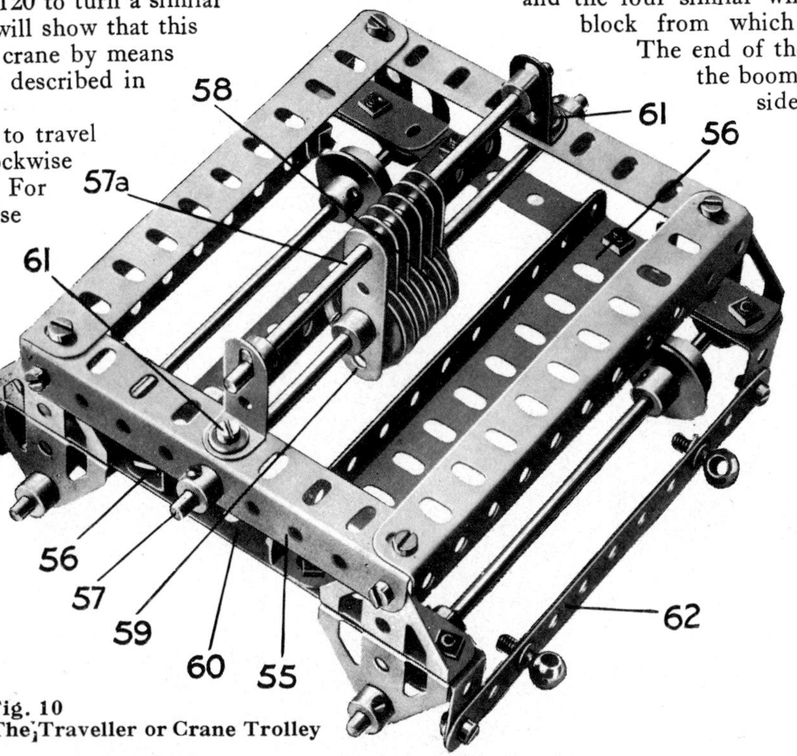

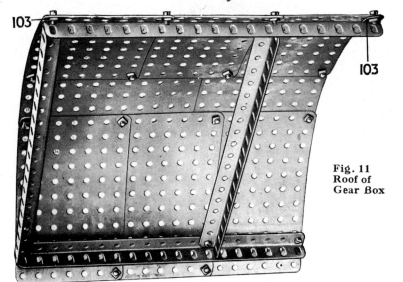

Fig. 10
The Traveller or Crane Trolley

Fig. 11
Roof of Gear Box

and the four similar wheels that form the sheaves of the pulley block from which the block-setting gear is suspended. The end of the cord is then carried to the front end of the boom and is tied to a Washer on the opposite side of the Girder 105.

The block-setting gear is prevented from falling-back by means of a brake operated by the handwheel shown in the back of the gear box between the handles 119, 131. A 2½″ Rod secured in the boss of the Bush Wheel is gripped in the smooth bore of a Threaded Coupling, into the threaded bore of which is screwed a 1″ Screwed Rod. An End Bearing on the opposite end of the Screwed Rod actuates a Crank that is secured to a 6½″ Rod by means of a ⅜″ bolt, so that when the hand wheel is turned to the right, the ⅜″ Bolt causes the Strip 86 to press on the flanges of two Flanged Wheels secured to the same Rod as the Wood Roller 126, thus preventing the cord on the Roller from unwinding. The Strip 86 should be bent slightly to ensure effective contact with the Flanged Wheels.

Fidler's Block-setting Gear

The concrete blocks of which breakwaters and sea-walls are constructed are often laid horizontally in the same way as the bricks of an ordinary wall, but in many cases a more complicated setting is required, and the blocks are set at an angle—or, as it is technically termed, "on the inclined bond." In this way the breakwater is made much more capable of resisting the assaults of the sea than it would be if the blocks were set in the more usual position with their faces vertical.

The problem of slinging the blocks for setting on the inclined bond, however, presents some difficulty, a fact which will be more readily appreciated by anyone who has constructed a model of a crane and attempted to set a small block of wood or stone in the manner described. The problem is difficult even with a model, but in actual practice it is considerably more complicated, for the blocks must be lowered to within an inch or less of their correct position, and the movements controlled to a nicety even though they may be carried out amid heavy seas and stormy weather.

The difficulty is solved by the ingenious tilting mechanism known as Fidler's patent block-setting gear. Photographs of this gear, together with a detailed account of its action, appeared in an article on Giant Block-setting Cranes in the "Meccano Magazine" for May, 1925. The Meccano model of Fidler's Gear differs from the actual mechanism in detail only, and carries out its functions in exactly the same manner as its prototype.

Two pairs of 5½" Curved Strips 1, bearing twelve Flat Brackets 2 and spaced apart by the thickness of two Washers, represent the massive notched beam of the Fidler's Gear (Fig. 16). This beam hangs from a swivelling joint, the whole being suspended from a special four-sheaved pulley block. The swivel bar consists of a 2" Rod 12 bearing at its lower end a small Fork Piece (part No. 116A) on which the beam is pivoted, and is itself supported in the Pulley Block by means of a Collar. The rotating movement of the beam on the central swivel is controlled by a Worm Wheel 15, which meshes with a ½" Pinion 16 secured to the vertical swivel bar.

Two links 3, each formed by a pair of 2" Strips and two ¾" Bolts, are suspended from the outer notches of the beam. The lower ¾" Bolts of these links pass through the smooth bores of Handrail Supports 4 that are screwed into the longitudinal bores of two Threaded Bosses, where they are secured in position by nuts screwed tightly against the tops of the Bosses. Two ¾" Bolts, passed through the transverse holes of these Threaded Bosses, and held in place by lock-nuts (Standard Mechanism No. 263), support the crossheads 5. Each crosshead consists of two 2½" large radius Curved Strips to which two 1" Triangular Plates 6 are rigidly secured by means of a ¾" Bolt and nuts. A roller consisting of two ½" loose Pulley Wheels 7

is mounted on a ¾" Bolt secured between each pair of Triangular Plates.

From the middle point of each crosshead hangs a Lewis Bar. This bar is made by securing a Coupling across the end of a 5" Rod 8, the upper end of the Rod being attached to a Collar. Those who do not possess Collars of the new type, which have two separate threaded bores, will find it necessary to use in their stead the "spiders" or central collars of Universal Couplings. The Collar is pivoted on two ordinary bolts passed through the middle holes of the crosshead 5 and secured by nuts screwed firmly against the sides of the Collar to prevent the bolts from binding on the Rods 8. The upper end of each Lewis bar is fitted with a portion of a Dog Clutch, and the corresponding part of one Clutch should be attached to a Rod 9 to form a key with which the Lewis bars may be turned. The key is provided with a handle consisting of two Threaded Pins screwed into a Collar 10. The same arrangement is used to turn the Worm Wheel 15 that controls the swivelling movement of the beam.

The Fork Piece 11 from which the beam is suspended is secured to a 2" Rod 12 journalled in two Double Brackets bolted one within the other to Angle Brackets, which in turn are secured to the 1" by ½" Angle Brackets 13 in the pulley block. Two 1½" Strips 14, which carry the Worm Wheel 15 on a 1½" Rod, are secured by means of ¾" Bolts to the pulley block, from which they are spaced away by two Washers mounted on the shanks of the bolts.

It will be observed that the pulley block is constructed from two pairs of simple Bell Cranks bolted to the 1" by ½" Angle Brackets 13, their outer arms being spaced apart by means of the 2" Threaded Rods 18. The sheaves consist of four 1½" Pulley Wheels, one of which should be secured to the 2" Axle Rod 19 in order to retain the latter in position.

The concrete blocks which are to be set by Fidler's Gear are specially made with two perpendicular holes running completely through them. The holes are of sufficient width across one of their sections to take the T-shaped

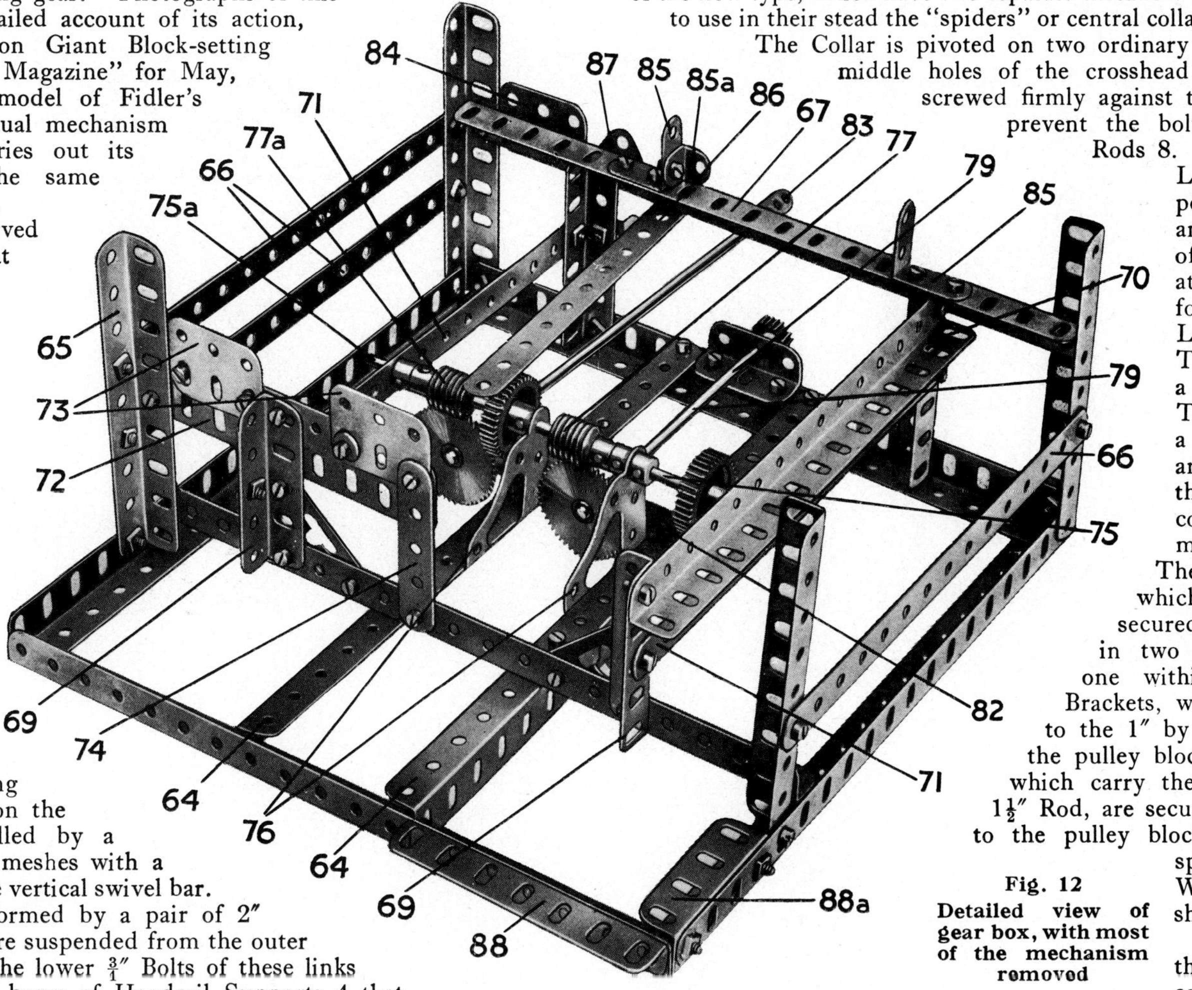

Fig. 12
Detailed view of gear box, with most of the mechanism removed

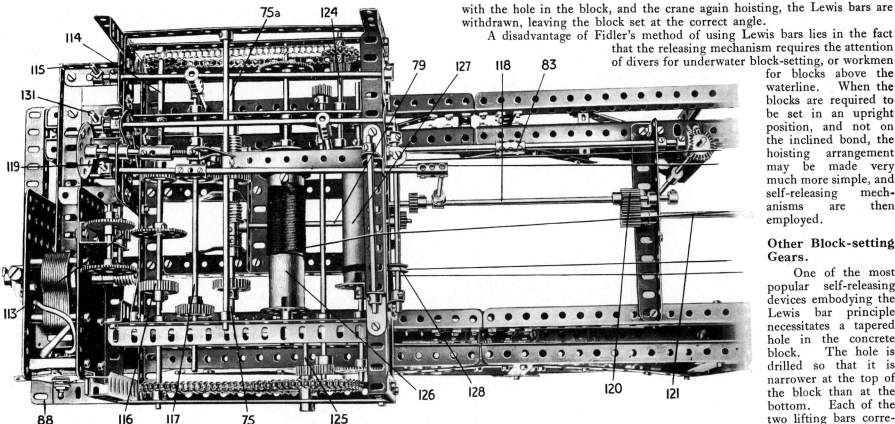

Fig. 13. Bird's-eye view of Gear Box, Motor, and adjacent mechanism.

with the hole in the block, and the crane again hoisting, the Lewis bars are withdrawn, leaving the block set at the correct angle.

A disadvantage of Fidler's method of using Lewis bars lies in the fact that the releasing mechanism requires the attention of divers for underwater block-setting, or workmen for blocks above the waterline. When the blocks are required to be set in an upright position, and not on the inclined bond, the hoisting arrangement may be made very much more simple, and self-releasing mechanisms are then employed.

Other Block-setting Gears.

One of the most popular self-releasing devices embodying the Lewis bar principle necessitates a tapered hole in the concrete block. The hole is drilled so that it is narrower at the top of the block than at the bottom. Each of the two lifting bars corresponding to those illustrated in the

pieces at the ends of the Lewis Bars. The blocks are also recessed at the lower ends of the vertical holes in order to prevent the Lewis Bars from fouling the breakwater while the blocks are being set. The holes and recesses are reproduced in the wooden block used in conjunction with the Meccano model.

The block is brought alongside the crane on a special truck. The Fidler's Gear is then lowered, and the T-shaped Lewis Bars are guided through the vertical holes in the block. When they have penetrated to the full depth of the holes, the bars are given a quarter turn, which throws their T-shaped ends out of register with the holes and prevents them from being withdrawn. Meanwhile the rollers on the crossheads take a bearing on the top of the block and roll across, altering the relative positions of the points of suspension and the Lewis Bars. The block is then lifted at the exact angle at which it is to be set in position. The crane swivels round until the block is directly above its place in the breakwater, and lowers it as necessary. When the block rests in position, the T-shaped rods are again turned until they are in register

Fidler's gear consists of two members coupled together by short connecting links, so that they resemble a parallel ruler. The connecting links are of different lengths, those connecting the lower ends of the two members being longer than those near the upper ends. One member—the outer one—is connected to the lifting beam by means of a simple shackle or loop, and the other member is attached to the beam by a short length of chain.

To raise the block the shackle of the outer member is passed over the lifting beam and the hoisting mechanism set in motion. As the outer member rises, the connecting links force the two members apart so that they become jammed in the tapered hole in the concrete block. The release is effected as follows : when the block is deposited on

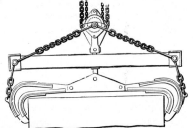

Fig. 14. Friction Grip for setting Concrete Blocks.

the ground, the shackle falls by its own weight away from the lifting beam. The hoisting mechanism is then set in motion, but this time the chain-coupled member only is raised, and owing to the peculiar arrangement of the connecting links it is automatically drawn close to the outer member so that both members may be withdrawn easily from the block.

In order that the mechanism may be perfectly self-acting, it has been found necessary to add a lever and weight to ensure the falling away of the loop or shackle from the lifting beam as soon as the tension is relaxed, which happens when the block rests upon the ground.

Meccano boys may wish to try other forms of block hoisting gear. There are a large number of different types of grips or mechanical jaws for handling blocks that depend for their operation entirely on friction, and any one of these could easily be reproduced in Meccano. The general principle upon which friction grips are designed is that the direction of pressure between the grip jaws and the block shall make an angle with the normal to the surfaces in contact, which angle is less than the angle of friction.

A form of grip embodying this principle that was actually employed in connection with the Madras Harbour works is illustrated in Fig. 14. It consists simply of two hooks spanning the block, the hooks being hinged to a central connecting piece. By using connecting pieces of different lengths, or by varying the distance between the pivots of the hooks, it is easy to arrange for the same grip to handle blocks of various sizes.

The releasing apparatus employed with this type of grip consists of a second barrel on the lifting gear, the chain from which is connected to a stretcher-frame. This is joined to the outer ends of the hooks by short chains. The main hoisting cable or chain acts upon the centre of the connecting piece, so that when the load is suspended by means of this cable, the grappling hooks are brought to bear upon the block. The power of the grip varies of course according to the weight of the block being lifted, but it is always sufficient to hold the block quite firmly and safely.

When it is required to release the block, a brake is applied to the second barrel while the main hoisting cable is lowered. As the latter is paid out the stress is diverted to the chains connected to the stretcher-frame, and this allows the hooks to open. By reversing the crane mechanism the grip may then be raised clear of the block. When the block is being raised or lowered the main hoisting cable and the cable attached to the stretcher-frame must be hauled in or paid out at exactly the same speed and the strain must bear entirely on the pulley block and not on the short chains connected to the stretcher-frame. This method of operation is similar to that employed in controlling the grab in the Meccano Ship Coaler.

Another effective block-setting grab, or grip, illustrated in Fig. 17, was specially designed for placing in position the apron blocks at the Harbour works at Mormugao. In this model the jaws of the grip are in the shape of

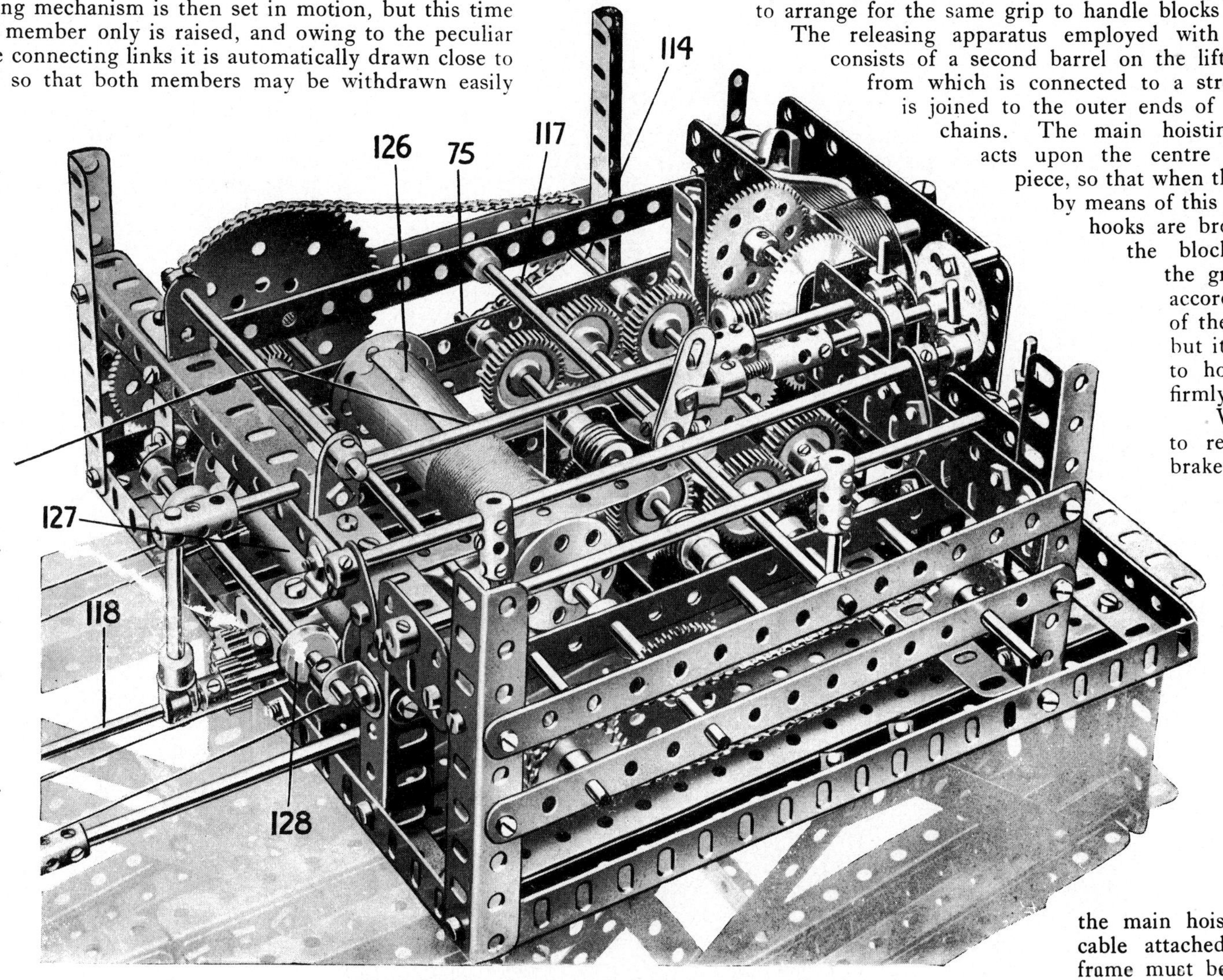

Fig. 15. General view of Gear Box with all mechanical details in position.

bell cranks, the upper arms of which are connected together by short links and a massive ring. This ring is connected to the pulley block by means of a hook (see Fig. 18). When a block is lifted the stress is borne by this hook and the ring, and therefore the upper arms of the clips are drawn together so that the jaws securely grip the block. The

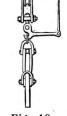

block is released by moving the hook about its pivot on the pulley block, so freeing the ring. This movement is effected by pulling a rope attached to the extended arm of the hook (Fig. 18): the rope may be led back to a convenient operating position on the boom of the crane, or even on the driving platform. Again, it may be led over a pulley attached to the boom and allowed to hang down to the ground, where it may be operated by a man standing near the point where the blocks are being placed.

When the ring is released from the hook, the friction grip mechanism is supported by the two short chains shown attached to the pulley block and to the ends of the distance-piece or stretcher-frame. The length of the distance-piece must be adjusted according

**Fig. 17.
Another type of Friction Grip**

to the size of the block that it is desired to handle.

Meccano boys who are able to refer to the 1928 Meccano Book of New Models will find a simple type of Meccano Friction Grip Tongs illustrated and described on page 21 of that publication. This particular model consists essentially of two levers pivoted towards one end to a connecting bar. The shorter arms of the levers form the grip tongs proper, and the upper ends of the longer arms are connected by links to a bar that is capable of sliding vertically in a guide. The upper end of this sliding bar is attached to the hoisting block, and when the strain is taken by the hoisting cable, the bar rises in the guide and thereby forces outward the upper ends of the grip levers. This has the effect of gripping the block very tightly between the lower ends of the levers. The levers are adjusted to take various sizes of blocks by changing the points of attachment to the connecting bar.

In the Meccano model the blocks may be released when the tension of the hoisting cord is relaxed, by pulling a short length of cord, which draws down the vertical sliding bar.

**Fig. 18.
Detail of Grip shown in Fig. 17.**

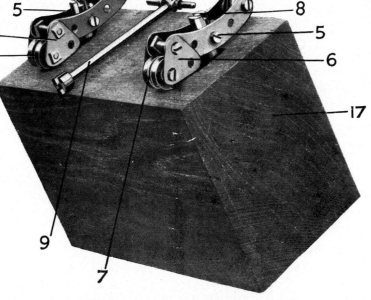

Fig. 16. The Fidler's Block-setting Gear, designed to set the blocks at an angle

Parts required for Building   the Giant Block-setting Crane

2	of No.	1	2	of No.	12b	6	of No.	31	8 ft. of No.	103a
1	,, ,,	1a	4	,, ,,	13	4	,, ,,	32	6 ,, ,,	103b
2	,, ,,	1b	10	,, ,,	13a	683	,, ,,	37	1 ,, ,,	103c
15	,, ,,	2	2	,, ,,	14	30	,, ,,	37a	1 ,, ,,	103d
5	,, ,,	2a	6	,, ,,	15	43	,, ,,	38	4 ,, ,,	103f
8	,, ,,	3	4	,, ,,	15a	1	,, ,,	45	9 ,, ,,	103h
20	,, ,,	4	5	,, ,,	16	4	,, ,,	46	8 ,, ,,	103k
5	,, ,,	5	4	,, ,,	16a	57	,, ,,	48	2 ,, ,,	106
17	,, ,,	6	16	,, ,,	17	4	,, ,,	48a	6 ,, ,,	111
28	,, ,,	6a	7	,, ,,	18a	6	,, ,,	52a	7 ,, ,,	111c
16	,, ,,	7	2	,, ,,	18b	90	,, ,,	59	8 ,, ,,	113
18	,, ,,	7a	18	,, ,,	20	1	,, ,,	62	5 ,, ,,	114
52	,, ,,	8	20	,, ,,	20b	12	,, ,,	63	6 ,, ,,	115
44	,, ,,	8a	4	,, ,,	21	1	,, ,,	63c	8 ,, ,,	126
4	,, ,,	8b	2	,, ,,	22	2	,, ,,	64	12 ,, ,,	126a
32	,, ,,	9	9	,, ,,	22a	2	,, ,,	70	4 ,, ,,	127
16	,, ,,	9a	6	,, ,,	23	2	,, ,,	76	3 ,, ,,	133
13	,, ,,	9b	22	,, ,,	24	8	,, ,,	77	6 ,, ,,	136
2	,, ,,	9c	1	,, ,,	25	2	,, ,,	81	2 ,, ,,	139
29	,, ,,	9d	7	,, ,,	26	1	,, ,,	82	2 ,, ,,	139a
9	,, ,,	9e	2	,, ,,	26a	4	,, ,,	90	8 ,, ,,	140
104	,, ,,	9f	3	,, ,,	27	4	,, ,,	89	3 ,, ,,	144
16	,, ,,	10	4	,, ,,	27a	2 ft. of No.		94	19 ,, ,,	147b
2	,, ,,	11	26	,, ,,	30	1	,, ,,	95b	1 ,, ,,	160
3	,, ,,	12	2	,, ,,	30a	3	,, ,,	96	1 ,, ,,	165
7	,, ,,	12a	4	,, ,,	30c	8	,, ,,	99a	1 ,, ,,	166

Travelling Bucket Dredger, or Conveyor

Special Features.

Three distinct movements, *i.e.* travelling, raising and lowering of Bucket Arm, and operation of Bucket Chain.

A fine working model that can be used in conjunction with Hornby Trains.

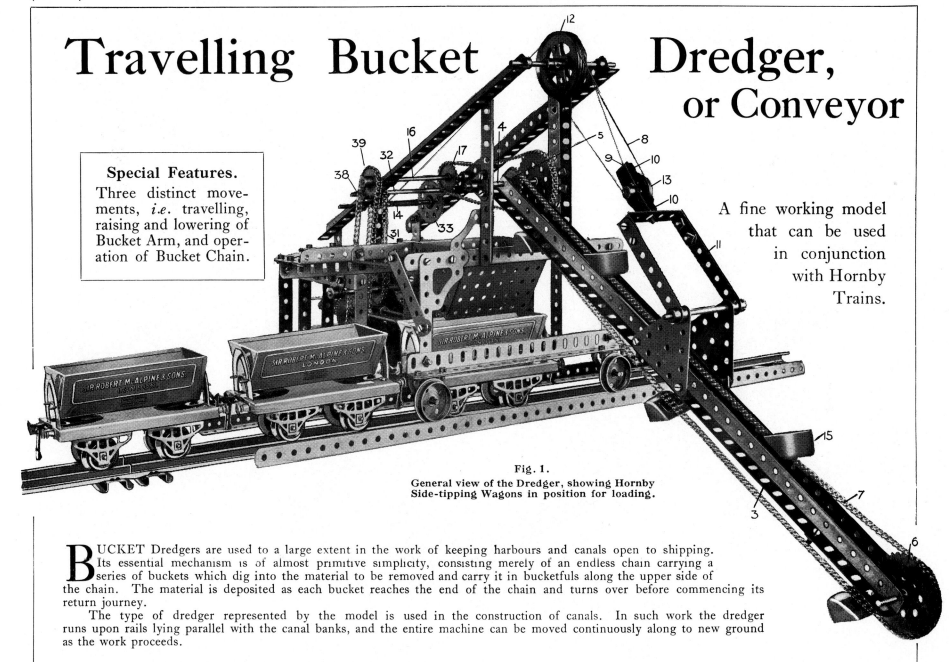

Fig. 1.
General view of the Dredger, showing Hornby Side-tipping Wagons in position for loading.

BUCKET Dredgers are used to a large extent in the work of keeping harbours and canals open to shipping. Its essential mechanism is of almost primitive simplicity, consisting merely of an endless chain carrying a series of buckets which dig into the material to be removed and carry it in bucketfuls along the upper side of the chain. The material is deposited as each bucket reaches the end of the chain and turns over before commencing its return journey.

The type of dredger represented by the model is used in the construction of canals. In such work the dredger runs upon rails lying parallel with the canal banks, and the entire machine can be moved continuously along to new ground as the work proceeds.

In the case of the dredger reproduced in Meccano, a railway line runs through the centre of the machine, and the material removed by the buckets is deposited via a chute into a railway truck placed directly underneath. As each truck is loaded, it is moved on and replaced by another until a complete train is formed, when the material may be removed to any convenient point. From this it will be seen that the model is an ideal one for use in conjunction with Hornby model railways, and for this reason it will appeal to a very large number of boys.

The Meccano Model

In Fig. 1 three Hornby Side-tipping Wagons are shown in use in conjunction with the model, one wagon being in position under the chute to receive its load. In practice the rails that carry the Flanged Wheels on which the dredger runs are laid along the edge of the dock wall or revetment, etc., a standard railway line being laid between these guide rails. The six Flanged Wheels of the Meccano model run on rails formed from Angle Girders, but if desired Hornby Rails may be used for the purpose.

If the chute is lined with cardboard or tin plate the model can be made to convey gravel or sand, etc., from a heap at the side of the track direct to the waiting train.

By operating the various levers (see Fig. 5) and the switch arm of the Electric Motor, the operator can control the several movements of the model. These include (1) raising and lowering the Bucket Arm:

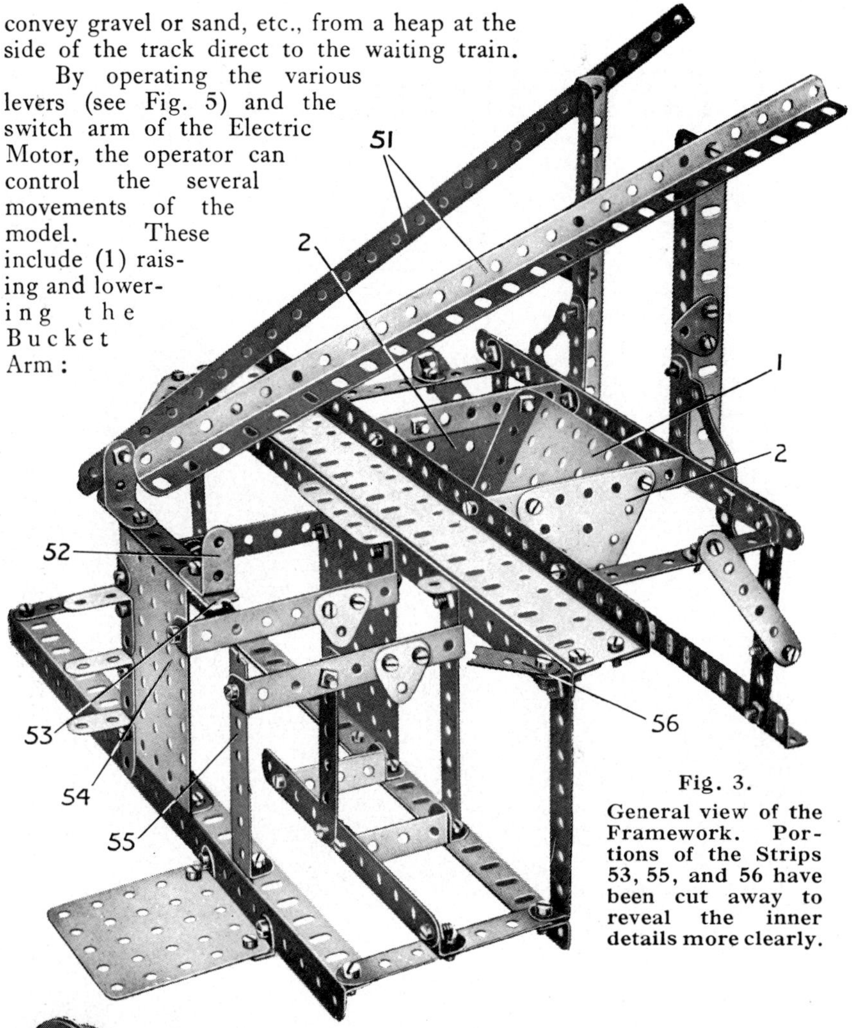

Fig. 3.
General view of the Framework. Portions of the Strips 53, 55, and 56 have been cut away to reveal the inner details more clearly.

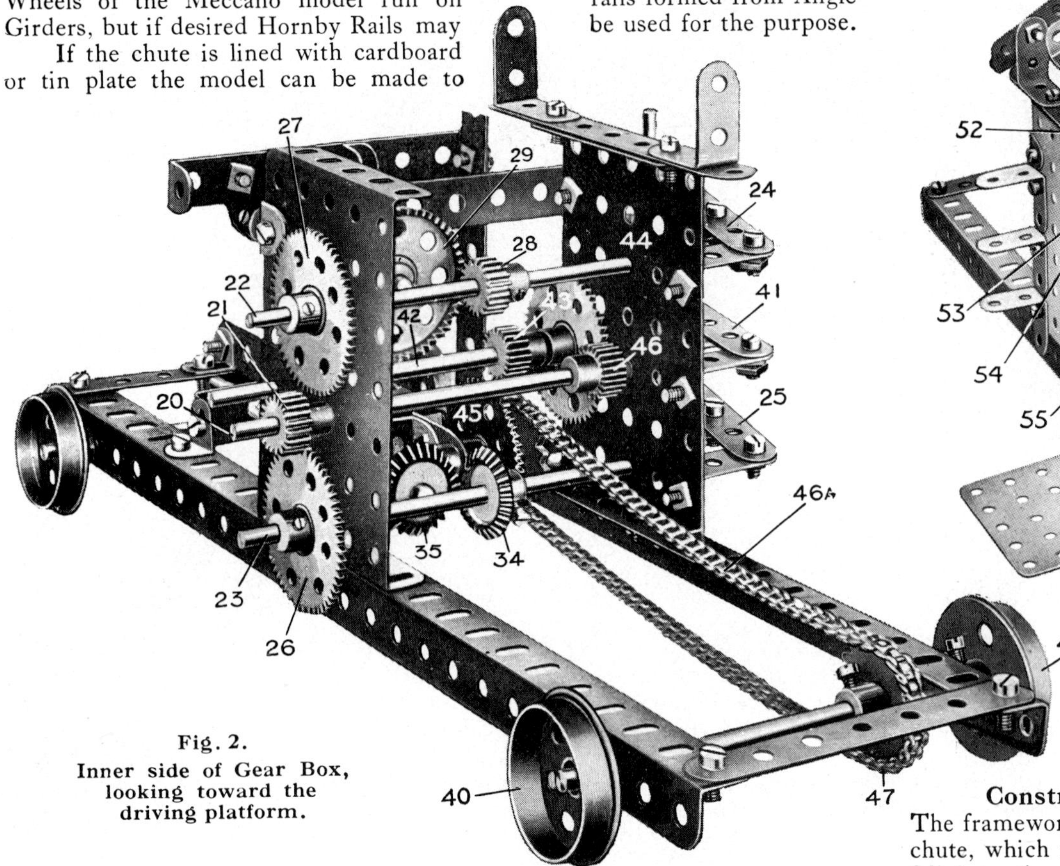

Fig. 2.
Inner side of Gear Box, looking toward the driving platform.

(2) starting and stopping the movement of the Buckets up and down the Bucket Arm: and (3) causing the entire machine to move to and fro on its track. These movements can be obtained separately or simultaneously, and the reverse in each case is effected by moving the Motor control switch.

Construction of the Framework

The framework of the Dredger is shown in Fig. 3. In the centre is seen the chute, which receives the material removed by the Buckets and allows it to fall into the wagon that has been shunted underneath. It consists of a

$3\frac{1}{2}''$ by $2\frac{1}{2}''$ Flanged Plate bolted to a pair of $2\frac{1}{2}''$ Triangular Plates, which are carried on two $3\frac{1}{2}''$ by $\frac{1}{2}''$ Double Angle Strips as shown.

The $12\frac{1}{2}''$ Angle Girders 51 are bolted near their upper ends to two $5\frac{1}{2}''$ Angle Girders and at their lower ends to two $1''$ by $1''$ Angle Brackets 52. These Angle Brackets are bolted to a $5\frac{1}{2}''$ Strip 53 which in turn is fastened to the $3\frac{1}{2}''$ Flanged Plate 54. In Fig. 3 only a small portion of the $5\frac{1}{2}''$ Strip can be seen, part of it having been removed in order to show the other details of the framework more clearly. Actually the end of the $5\frac{1}{2}''$ Strip is fastened to the top of a vertical Double Angle Strip 55 as shown in Fig. 5. The $5\frac{1}{2}''$ Strip 56 (only a portion of which can be seen in Fig. 3) is also bolted to the Strip 53.

The Bucket Arm

The bucket arm, which is shown clearly in Fig. 1, is built up from two $18\frac{1}{2}''$ Angle Girders 3 joined by $2''$ Strips and braced near the centre by diagonally-disposed $3''$ Strips. It is pivoted on a Rod 4, and a $1''$ Sprocket Wheel is placed on this Rod between the Angle Girders 3. A $2''$ Sprocket Wheel 6 is carried on a $2''$ Rod journalled in the lowest holes of the arm, and a length of Sprocket Chain 7 is led over these wheels and five or more Dredger Buckets are attached to the Chain at equal intervals. A $2''$ Sprocket Wheel is also fastened on the Rod 4 and is driven from a $1''$ Sprocket 17 on the Rod 16 by means of a Sprocket Chain.

To the centres of the $18\frac{1}{2}''$ Girders 3 two $2\frac{1}{2}''$ Triangular Plates are attached by means of Angle Brackets, and a yoke consisting of two $3\frac{1}{2}''$ Strips 11 and one $2\frac{1}{2}''$ by $1''$ Double Angle Strip is attached pivotally to these Plates by means of a $3\frac{1}{2}''$ Rod and four Collars. A support for the $1''$ Pulley Wheel 13 is made from two Cranked Bent Strips held together by a $1''$ Rod and two Collars. In the end holes of the $12\frac{1}{2}''$ Girders 51 is journalled a $4\frac{1}{2}''$ Axle Rod carrying two $2''$ Pulley Wheels 12, free on the Rod.

The hoisting cord is fastened to one of the holes of the Cranked Bent Strips 10, and passed over one of the $2''$ Pulleys 12 and round the $1''$ Pulley 13. It is then led over the second $2''$ Pulley Wheel 12 and wound on the Axle Rod 14.

Gear Box and Clutch Mechanisms

The arrangement of the mechanism, operating levers, etc., should be clear on reference to Figs. 2, 4 and 5. The latter illustration is a general view of the gear box, showing the operating levers and driving platform (a $2\frac{1}{2}''$ by $2\frac{1}{2}''$ Flat Plate) in the foreground. Fig. 2 shows the inner side of the gear box, looking towards the driving platform end, while Fig. 4 is a view of the same side taken from the platform end.

The drive from the armature spindle of the Electric Motor is transmitted to the various portions of the model as follows. The $\frac{1}{2}''$ Pinion 48 on the spindle (Fig. 5) meshes with a 57-teeth Gear Wheel secured to a Rod journalled in the side plates of the Motor. This Rod carries a further $\frac{1}{2}''$ Pinion situated inside the Motor. A $2\frac{1}{2}''$ Axle Rod journalled in the end holes of the Motor frame carries a second 57-teeth Gear Wheel engaging the teeth of this $\frac{1}{2}''$ Pinion. It is provided also with a $\frac{3}{4}''$ Pinion that meshes with a 50-teeth Gear Wheel on the Rod 20 (see Figs. 2 and 4). In Figs. 2 and 4 the Electric Motor has been removed, together with the mechanism mounted on it and the 50-teeth Gear Wheel on the Rod 20, in order to show the remaining gears more clearly.

The hoisting movement of the bucket arm is effected from the Rod 22. This Rod carries a 57-teeth Gear Wheel 27, a $\frac{1}{2}''$ Pinion 28, and the clutch mechanism. This mechanism, which is identical on all three sliding Rods 22, 23 and 42, consists of a Double Bracket retained in position on the end of the Rod by two Collars, Washers being placed between the inner Collar and the Flanged Plate. The operating lever consists of a $3\frac{1}{2}''$ Strip with a Threaded Pin attached to one end. It is pivoted to the Double Bracket by means of

Fig. 4.
Inner side of Gear Box, from driving platform end.

a bolt and two nuts (see Standard Mechanism No. 262) and at its other end to a $1''$ by $1''$ Angle Bracket bolted to the side of the gear box. By moving the Threaded Pins the Rods 22, 23 and 42 can be slid in their bearings, and different sets of gears may thereby be brought into operation.

Thus, either of the Gear Wheels 26, 27 (Figs. 2 and 4) can be brought into gear with the $\frac{1}{2}''$ Pinion 21 on the Rod 20 by means of the Clutch levers 24 and 25. The $\frac{1}{2}''$ Pinion 28 on the Rod 22 is in constant engagement with a $1\frac{1}{2}''$ Contrate Wheel 29 and the Rod to which the Contrate is secured also bears a $1''$ Sprocket Wheel 30 (Fig. 5), which is coupled to a similar Sprocket Wheel on the Rod 32 by a Chain 31. The Rod 32 carries a $\frac{1}{2}''$ Pinion 33a that, by means of the 57-teeth Gear Wheel 33, rotates the winding spindle 14, on which is wound the Cord 8 that operates the bucket arm. It will be seen that if the clutch lever 24 is pushed inward, the above-mentioned train of gears comes into operation, so raising or lowering the bucket arm.

The Rod 23 may be moved in its bearings by means of the clutch arm 25, thus engaging the 57-teeth Gear Wheel 26 with the $\frac{1}{2}''$ Pinion 21 (Fig. 2) the $\frac{7}{8}''$ Bevel Gears 34 and 35 being brought into mesh simultaneously. Motion is thus transmitted to the Rod 36 and the Sprocket Wheel 37 (Fig. 4) is rotated. This Sprocket Wheel is coupled by means of the Chain 38 to the Sprocket Wheel 39 on the Rod 16 (Fig. 5). In Fig. 1 can be seen the transmission from the Rod 16 to the Rod 4, a 1″ Sprocket Wheel driving the 2″ Sprocket Wheel on the Rod 4 by means of the Chain 17.

By means of this mechanism, therefore, the drive from the Motor can be used to move the Dredger Buckets 15 up and down the bucket arm.

Traversing Movement

When it is required to move the whole dredger along its rails, the middle clutch lever 41 is pulled out. This causes the Rod 42 to slide in its bearings and brings the 57-teeth Gear Wheel 44 into mesh with one of the $\frac{1}{2}''$ Pinions on the driving shaft 20 ; another $\frac{1}{2}''$ Pinion 43 on the Rod 42 is caused to engage simultaneously with a 57-teeth Gear Wheel 45 (Figs. 2, 4) secured to a short Rod that carries the 1″ Sprocket Wheel 45a (Fig. 5). A 1″ Sprocket Wheel 47 on the axle of the rear travelling wheels 40 (Fig. 2) is connected with the Sprocket Wheel 45a by means of a Sprocket Chain 46a. The clutch lever 41 thus controls the movement of the model along the track.

The track consists of three rails built up from Angle Girders, Strips being used as sleepers to keep the Girders at the correct distance apart. Any length of track can be constructed, of course, on which to run the Dredger. A long stretch of track will increase greatly the pleasure to be derived from operating the model.

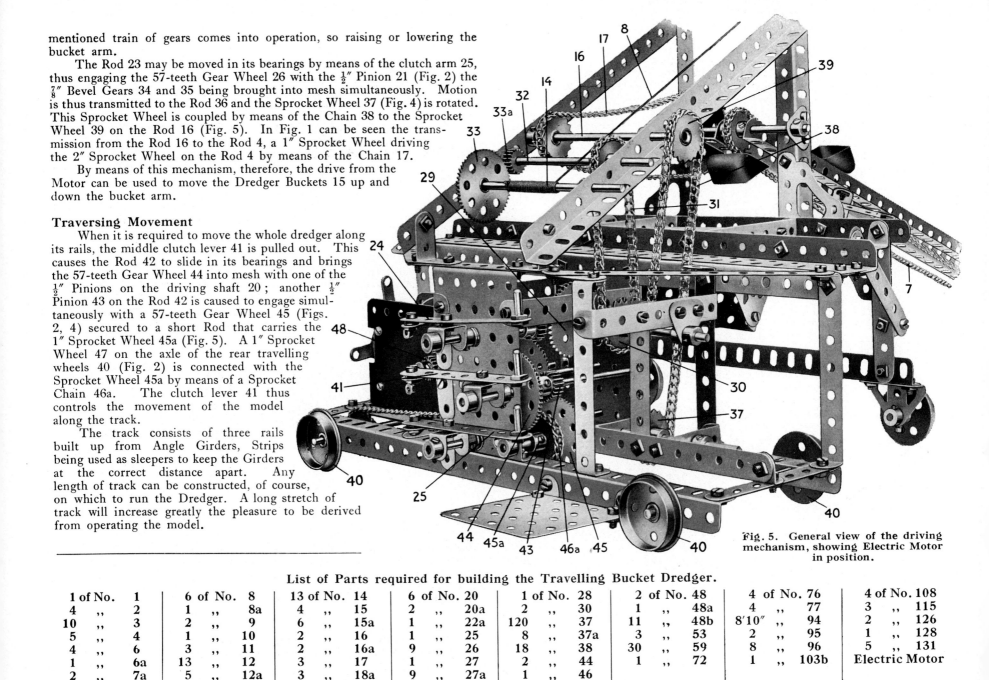

Fig. 5. General view of the driving mechanism, showing Electric Motor in position.

List of Parts required for building the Travelling Bucket Dredger.

1 of No.	1	6 of No.	8	13 of No.	14	6 of No.	20	1 of No.	28	2 of No.	48	4 of No.	76	4 of No.	108
4 ,,	2	1 ,,	8a	4 ,,	15	2 ,,	20a	2 ,,	30	1 ,,	48a	4 ,,	77	3 ,,	115
10 ,,	3	2 ,,	9	6 ,,	15a	1 ,,	22a	120 ,,	37	11 ,,	48b	8′10″ ,,	94	2 ,,	126
5 ,,	4	1 ,,	10	2 ,,	16	1 ,,	25	8 ,,	37a	3 ,,	53	2 ,,	95	1 ,,	128
4 ,,	6	3 ,,	11	2 ,,	16a	9 ,,	26	18 ,,	38	30 ,,	59	8 ,,	96	5 ,,	131
1 ,,	6a	13 ,,	12	3 ,,	17	1 ,,	27	2 ,,	44	1 ,,	72	1 ,,	103b	Electric Motor	
2 ,,	7a	5 ,,	12a	3 ,,	18a	9 ,,	27a	1 ,,	46						

The Meccano Stiff-Leg Derrick

with Radius Indicator

Special Features

The Derrick is built exactly in accordance with real engineering practice. It is strong and very realistic in appearance. The load may be raised or lowered, or the jib luffed or swivelled, by manipulating convenient hand levers.

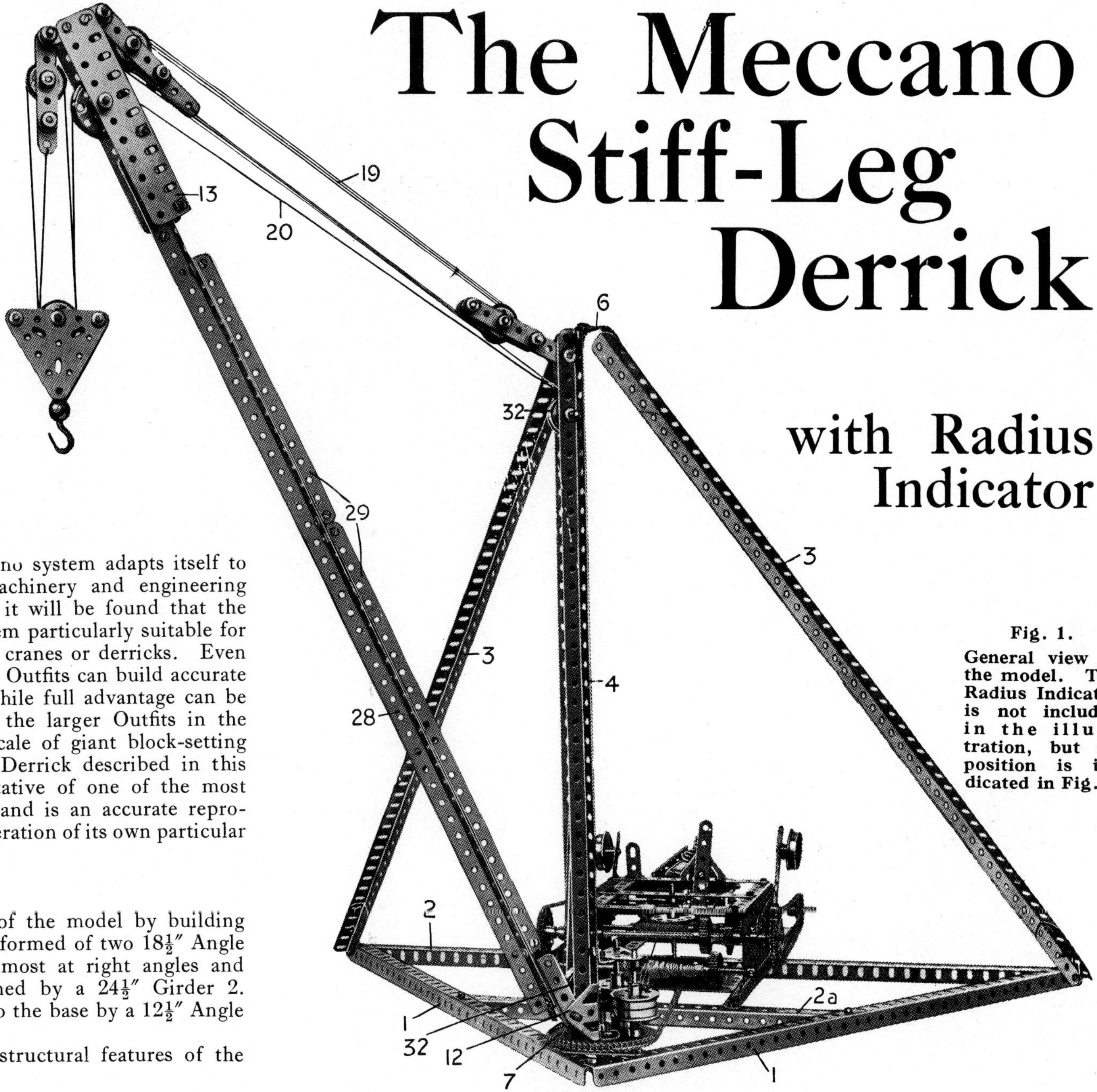

Fig. 1.
General view of the model. The Radius Indicator is not included in the illustration, but its position is indicated in Fig. 7.

ALTHOUGH the Meccano system adapts itself to the reproduction of machinery and engineering structures of all kinds, it will be found that the nature of the parts makes them particularly suitable for building the various types of cranes or derricks. Even the possessors of the smallest Outfits can build accurate working models of cranes, while full advantage can be taken of the possibilities of the larger Outfits in the construction on a reduced scale of giant block-setting cranes, etc. The Stiff-Leg Derrick described in this leaflet is a worthy representative of one of the most useful "families" of cranes, and is an accurate reproduction in appearance and operation of its own particular type.

Structural Details

Begin the construction of the model by building the triangular base. This is formed of two $18\frac{1}{2}''$ Angle Girders 1 bolted together almost at right angles and having their outer ends joined by a $24\frac{1}{2}''$ Girder 2. Further rigidity is imparted to the base by a $12\frac{1}{2}''$ Angle Girder 2a.

In describing the main structural features of the

Published by MECCANO LIMITED, BINNS ROAD, LIVERPOOL Printed in England. 628/5

crane, it would perhaps be well to give some account of their functions, and the reasons for the particular method of construction that has been adopted. Apart from the base, the derrick consists essentially of the following component parts :—the jib, the operating cables 19, the vertical member 4, and the two side members or ties 3. These units combine to absorb all the strains and stresses generated in the crane while it is at work.

The jib, which is the most massive portion of the structure, is designed to receive as much as possible of the load imposed on the derrick. Most of the strain on the jib head is converted into compressive force applied to the jib itself, the remainder being taken by the cables 19.

The jib is built up from two 24½″ Angle Girders 28 bolted together to form a T-girder, and strengthened by pairs of 12½″ and 7½″ Angle Girders bolted together and secured along the upper sides of the Girders 28. The head of the jib (Fig. 2) consists of two 5½″ Flat Girders secured to 2½″ Angle Girders bolted in the first and fourth holes of the Girders 28. A pair of 2″ Strips bolted to the outer ends of the 5½″ Flat Girders provide bearings for two 2″ Rods, to which are pivoted the pulley blocks of the jib head. The outer block, which forms part of the hoisting mechanism, consists of two 2½″ Strips and one 3″ Strip, in which are journalled 1″ Rods. Two 1″ loose Pulley Wheels are mounted on one of these Rods, and the Strips are spaced as required by Washers and Collars. The inner or rear pulley block of the jib is built up of two 2½″ Strips and two 3½″ Strips, and contains three 1″ loose Pulley Wheels mounted on a 1½″ Rod.

Two 2½″ Triangular Plates, joined by 1″ Axle Rods and spaced apart by Washers, form the framework of the three-sheave pulley block to which the Loaded Hook is attached. Three 1″ loose Pulley Wheels are free to revolve on one of the 1″ Rods, and are separated by 2½″ Strips. In each case the Pulley Wheels are spaced by Washers so that they may rotate quite freely.

Vertical Member, Ties, etc.

The tension on the cables 19 is transmitted by the latter to the upper end of the vertical member 4, where the major portion of the strain is borne by the tension members 3. The cables 19 and ties 3 are pulling against each other

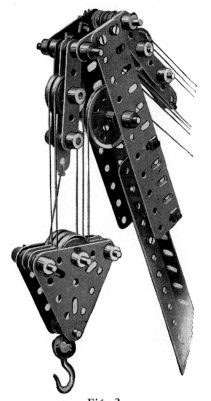

Fig. 2.
Head of Jib, showing movable and fixed pulley blocks.

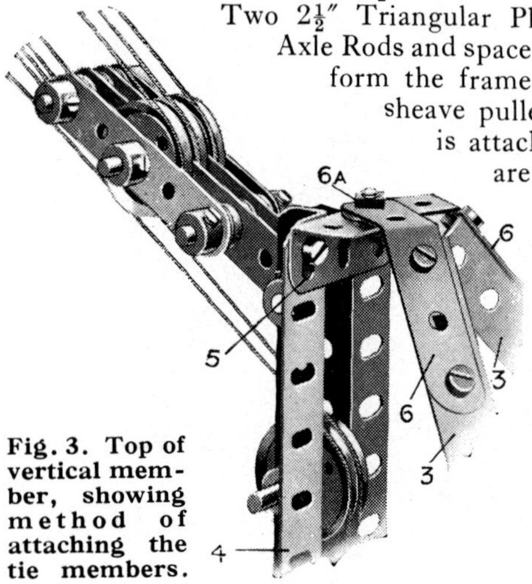

Fig. 4. Swivelling base of Jib.

in directions corresponding to their respective positions, and as the two forces are not in direct opposition they combine in producing a force that tends to depress the upper ends of the tie members 3. This force takes the form of a downward thrust on the vertical member 4. Therefore the latter, like the jib, must be designed to withstand compression. Accordingly it is constructed from a pair of 18½″ Angle Girders bolted together at each extremity, as well as at a point near the lower end, by 1½″ Angle Girders 5 (see Figs. 3 and 4).

The lowest of these 1½″ Girders is secured to a 3″ Sprocket Wheel 7, which forms the swivelling base of the jib. The pivot is a 1½″ Rod, which is passed through the centre hole of the lowest 1½″ Angle Girder 5 and through the boss of the Sprocket Wheel, and is carried in a bearing 8 built up from two 2½″ Strips bolted across the base Girders 1. Two Collars should be placed on this Rod, one above the Sprocket Wheel 7 and one below the 2½″ Strips 8 (Fig. 4).

A Corner Bracket 11 is bolted to one of the 1½″ Angle Girders 5, as shown in Fig. 4, and two vertical 2½″ Rods 10 are journalled in the Bracket and in the 3″ Sprocket Wheel. Two Flanged Wheels butted together and secured to each of the Rods 10 form guide pulleys 9 (Fig. 4). Two 1″ loose Pulley Wheels 32 (Fig. 1), which also act as guide Pulleys, are mounted on horizontal Axle Rods journalled in the Girders of the vertical member 4.

A 2½″ Rod, about which the jib pivots in a vertical plane, is journalled through Trunnions 12 secured to the member 4 (Figs. 1 and 4) and through the end holes of 2″ Angle Girders bolted in the first and third holes of the 24½″ Angle Girders 28 of the jib.

The side members 3 are required to withstand tension only and may be of comparatively light construction, for there is no need for them to be rigid, and steel has a very high tensile strength. They are made of single 24½″ Angle Girders, extended at their lower ends by 2½″ Girders overlapped three holes. The 2½″ Strips 6 (Fig. 3), bolted to the tops of the Girders 3, are bent slightly as shown, and together form a bearing for the bolt 6a. The latter is secured to the Strips by two nuts (see Standard Mechanism No. 262) and its shank forms a pivot about which turns the upper end of the vertical member 4.

The Gear Box

The Meccano Electric Motor, which

Fig. 3. Top of vertical member, showing method of attaching the tie members.

supplies the power for operating the Derrick. may be of either the 4-volt or the high-voltage type. It is bolted to a 5½″ Flat Plate supported on two 12½″ Angle Girders 15, and owing to its position outside the triangular base it helps to counterbalance the weight of the jib and its load.

Three 6½″ Axle Rods 18, 21 and 33, and two 8½″ Rods 16 and 25 are journalled through the 5½″ by 2½″ Flanged Plates that form the sides of the gear box. The 6½″ Rods are retained in position by Collars, but the 8″ Rods are slidable in their bearings. The power from the Motor is led through two 3 : 1 reduction gears, each consisting of a ½″ Pinion Wheel and a 57-teeth Gear Wheel, and then is transmitted via a ¾″ Sprocket Wheel and a length of Sprocket Chain 17 to a 2″ Sprocket Wheel on the Rod 16. A second 2″ Sprocket Wheel on this Rod is connected with a 1″ Sprocket Wheel on the Rod 25.

The lower end of the Strip 26, which serves as a hand lever and is pivoted to a Trunnion on one of the transverse 5½″ Strips of the gear box, engages two Collars secured to the Rod 25. By moving the lever 26 to the right, a ½″ Pinion on the Rod 25 is caused to mesh with the 57-teeth Gear Wheel 22, and thus the power is communicated to the Rod 33. A Worm on this Rod operates a further 57-teeth Gear Wheel on the vertical Rod 27, which, in its turn, carries a 1″ Sprocket Wheel that swivels the jib by means of a Sprocket Chain passing round the 3″ Sprocket Wheel 7.

Luffing and Hoisting Movements

The luffing movement of the jib is brought into operation by moving the Crank 24. The Crank is connected by a 5″ Rod to the Coupling 30, which, by means of a 1″ Rod in its end transverse hole engaging two Collars on the Rod 16, causes the latter to slide in its bearings.

When the Rod 16 is moved as far to the right as possible, the 1″ Gear Wheel 31 engages a similar Wheel on the Rod 18, and the latter winds or unwinds the cord 19 according to the direction in which the Motor is running. This cord 19 passes between the guide pulleys 9 at the base of the upright member 4, round one of the Pulley Wheels 32, and over a similar Pulley Wheel near the top of the member 4. It is then led in turn round each of the sheaves in the pulley blocks on the jib and the vertical member, and is tied finally to the tail of the block on the jib.

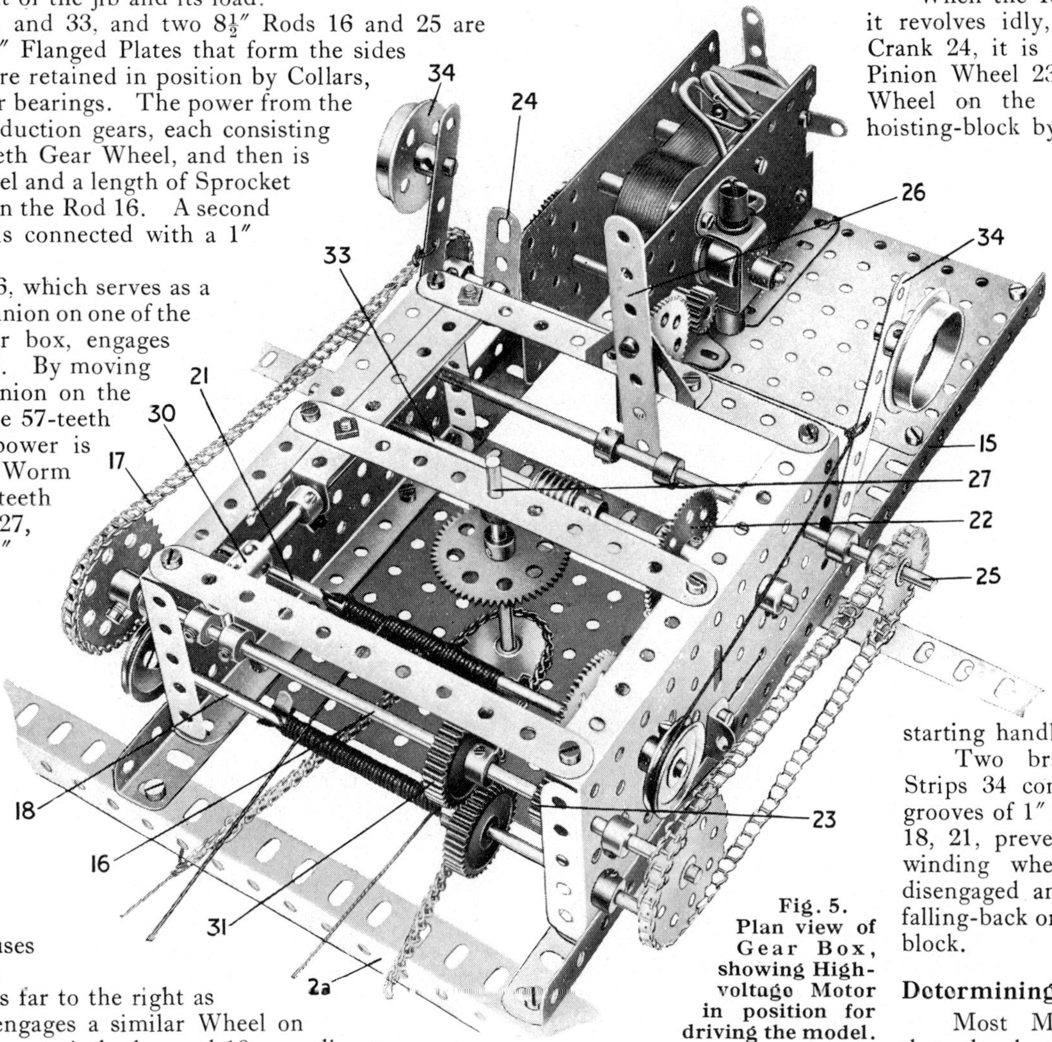

By the use of this arrangement of pulleys a considerable mechanical advantage is obtained, which enables the jib to be luffed by the application of a very small force, even when the load Hook is carrying a considerable weight.

When the Rod 16 is in its central position it revolves idly, but when, by means of the Crank 24, it is moved over to the left the ½″ Pinion Wheel 23 meshes with a 57-teeth Gear Wheel on the Rod 21, which operates the hoisting-block by means of the cord 20. The latter is conducted between the guide pulleys 9, round the lower and upper Pulleys 32, and over a 1½″ Pulley Wheel in the jib head. Next it passes in turn around each of the Pulley Wheels in the hoisting-block and in the outer pulley block of the jib, and finally is tied as shown to the tail of the upper block.

From the above it will be clear that the lever 26 controls the swivelling movement of the crane while the handle 24 controls the raising and lowering of the load on the Hook and the luffing of the jib. Reversing is effected, of course, by means of the starting handle of the Electric Motor.

Two brakes, consisting of weighted Strips 34 connected to cords engaging the grooves of 1″ fast Pulley Wheels on the Rods 18, 21, prevent the cords 19, 20 from unwinding when their respective gears are disengaged and thus obviate any danger of falling-back on the part of the jib or hoisting-block.

Determining the Strength of a Crane.

Most Meccano boys probably know that the load capacity of a crane varies according to the particular angle of the jib, for the nearer the latter approaches the horizontal position the greater will be the strains upon it in proportion to the load.

This statement may be verified quite easily by applying the well-known principle of the Triangle of Forces, which may be summarised as follows :

Fig. 5.
Plan view of Gear Box, showing High-voltage Motor in position for driving the model.

If three forces meet at a point and are in equilibrium, and we know one of the forces, we may determine the other two by drawing a triangle, making each side parallel to the direction of one of the forces, and comparing the dimensions of the three sides. It will be found that these dimensions are in the same proportion as the three forces.

For example, supposing the side corresponding to the known force is four units in length and the others are eight and ten units, and supposing the known force is four tons, then we know that the other two forces must equal eight and ten tons respectively.

In the case of a crane the three forces are (a) the load suspended from the head of the jib, (b) the tension member, or tie, which supports the jib (in luffing cranes the operating cable or chains, etc., with which the jib is raised or lowered correspond to the tie members), and (c) the jib, which acts as a strut to withstand the compressive force, exerted by the combination of (a) and (b). All three forces meet in the head of the jib and counterbalance each other : that is to say, they are in equilibrium.

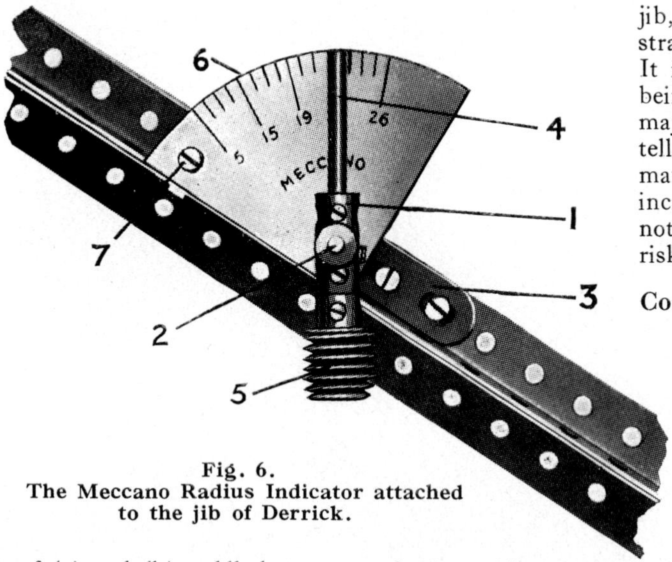

By drawing one or two triangles and showing the side that is parallel to the jib in a different position in each triangle, it will be found that the strains that the crane structure must withstand increase as the jib approaches more nearly the horizontal position, as stated above. It should be noted that the disposition and proportion of the strains or forces vary according to the particular type of crane.

Functions of a Radius Indicator

Fig. 7.
Showing position of Radius Indicator in the Stiff Leg Derrick.

These facts render it impossible for an engineer to build a luffing crane that will lift a specified load with equal facility at any position of the jib. He therefore designs his crane to lift a certain load at a certain radius, the radius being measured from the point about which the crane pivots to a point immediately beneath the load hook. Thus a swivelling and luffing crane that is described in the specification as capable of raising with safety a load of 20 tons at a radius of 20 feet may be able to lift only 10 tons or thereabouts at a radius of 35 feet.

Therefore, when lifting a heavy load with a crane of this type, care must be taken to see that the jib is at the proper angle to cope with that load. A margin of safety is allowed, of course, for each of the various positions of the

---

Fig. 6.
The Meccano Radius Indicator attached to the jib of Derrick.

---

jib, but if this margin is overstepped, excessive strains may be set up in the structure and machinery. It is to minimise the possibility of such a mistake being made that a radius indicator is fitted to the majority of luffing cranes. A glance at this indicator tells the operator the position of the jib and the maximum load that he can handle safely without increasing the angle of the jib. Hence the device not only saves time but also obviates a considerable risk of accidents.

Construction of the Meccano Radius Indicator

Fig. 6 shows the indicator attached to the side of the jib in the Derrick, and the actual position of the device in relation to the remainder of the model is indicated more clearly by the arrow in Fig. 7.

The Coupling 1 is free to turn about the 1½″ Axle Rod 2, which is gripped in the boss of a Crank 3 bolted to the upturned flanges of the jib girders. It carries in its upper end a further 1½″ Rod 4 and in its lower end a 1″ Rod on which is secured the Worm 5. The weight of the latter serves to keep the Rod 4 always vertical, no matter in what position the jib is placed. A dial 6, shaped from a piece of stout cardboard, is bolted at 7 to an Angle Bracket attached to the jib. The Rod 2 passes through a hole in the dial and carries two or three Washers to space the Coupling 1 away from the card so that the Worm 4 will clear the edges of the girders forming the jib. The jib should now be placed in different positions and the radius covered by the load hook for each position should be marked on the card.

An indicator of this type proves very useful when loading, say, a stationary lorry or railway wagon, for the jib-angle required to bring the load directly over the vehicle having once been noted, each succeeding load can be swung round and luffed immediately to the correct position. In addition, interesting experiments may be made by means of the indicator and the load capacity and efficiency of various types of Meccano Cranes tested.

Parts required for building the Stiff-Leg Derrick

2 of No.	2	2 of No.	12	2 of No.	26	50 of No.	59
6 ,,	3	2 ,,	13a	3 ,,	27a	1 ,,	62
2 ,,	4	4 ,,	14	2 ,,	31	1 ,,	63
12 ,,	5	1 ,,	16	1 ,,	32	2 ,,	76
2 ,,	6	3 ,,	16a	3 ,,	35	1 ,,	94
5 ,,	7	4 ,,	17	79 ,,	37	2 ,,	95a
4 ,,	7a	9 ,,	18a	88 ,,	38	1 ,,	95b
5 ,,	8	5 ,,	18b	2 ,,	40	2 ,,	96
2 ,,	8b	6 ,,	20	1 ,,	48b	2 ,,	103
6 ,,	9b	1 ,,	21	2 ,,	52	3 ,,	126
2 ,,	9e	2 ,,	22	2 ,,	52a	1 ,,	133
3 ,,	9f	15 ,,	22a	1 ,,	57b	1 Electric Motor	

Meccano Platform Scales

Built with Meccano Outfit K

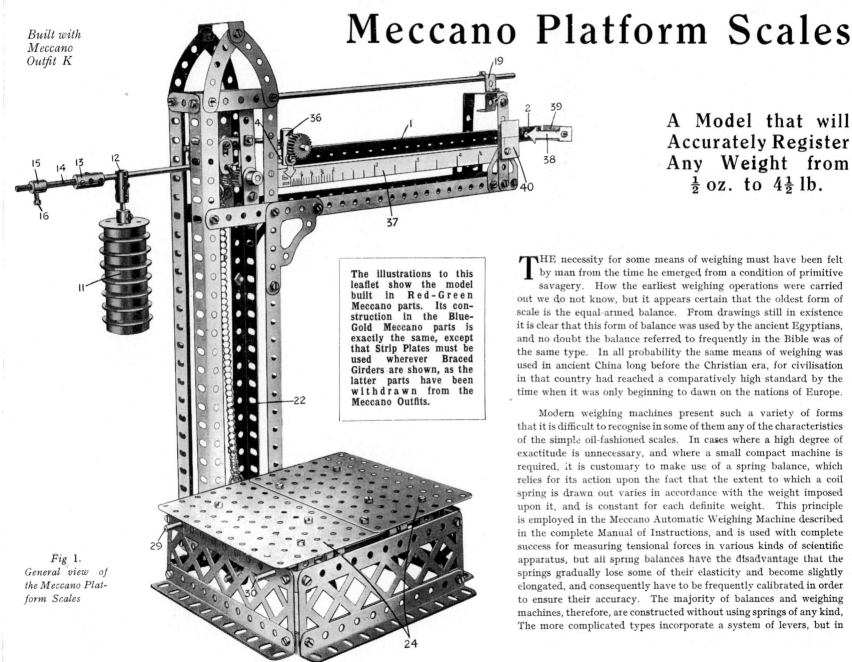

Fig 1.
General view of the Meccano Platform Scales

A Model that will Accurately Register Any Weight from ½ oz. to 4½ lb.

The illustrations to this leaflet show the model built in Red-Green Meccano parts. Its construction in the Blue-Gold Meccano parts is exactly the same, except that Strip Plates must be used wherever Braced Girders are shown, as the latter parts have been withdrawn from the Meccano Outfits.

THE necessity for some means of weighing must have been felt by man from the time he emerged from a condition of primitive savagery. How the earliest weighing operations were carried out we do not know, but it appears certain that the oldest form of scale is the equal-armed balance. From drawings still in existence it is clear that this form of balance was used by the ancient Egyptians, and no doubt the balance referred to frequently in the Bible was of the same type. In all probability the same means of weighing was used in ancient China long before the Christian era, for civilisation in that country had reached a comparatively high standard by the time when it was only beginning to dawn on the nations of Europe.

Modern weighing machines present such a variety of forms that it is difficult to recognise in some of them any of the characteristics of the simple old-fashioned scales. In cases where a high degree of exactitude is unnecessary, and where a small compact machine is required, it is customary to make use of a spring balance, which relies for its action upon the fact that the extent to which a coil spring is drawn out varies in accordance with the weight imposed upon it, and is constant for each definite weight. This principle is employed in the Meccano Automatic Weighing Machine described in the complete Manual of Instructions, and is used with complete success for measuring tensional forces in various kinds of scientific apparatus, but all spring balances have the disadvantage that the springs gradually lose some of their elasticity and become slightly elongated, and consequently have to be frequently calibrated in order to ensure their accuracy. The majority of balances and weighing machines, therefore, are constructed without using springs of any kind. The more complicated types incorporate a system of levers, but in

21/934/4·5   *Published by* MECCANO LIMITED, BINNS ROAD, LIVERPOOL, 13.   Printed in England almost every case the essential mechanism consists of some variation of the original balanced arm.

Importance of the " Knife-edge "

The ordinary balance consists of a lever of the first order called the beam, supported at its centre on a fulcrum. At each end of the beam is hung a scale pan, one of these pans being for the weights and the other for the object that is to be weighed.

It is necessary that the beam should be able to swing quite freely on its support, and in order to ensure this, the fulcrum consists of a steel or agate prism or " knife-edge," with its sharp edge at right angles to the direction of the beam and resting upon a plane of polished steel or agate. This construction reduces friction to the minimum. A pointer fixed to the centre of the beam indicates—by coming to rest in the line of direction from the fulcrum to the centre of gravity of the beam or by swinging evenly on each side of that line—when the balance is horizontal, which occurs when the weights in one scale pan exactly balance the object in the other.

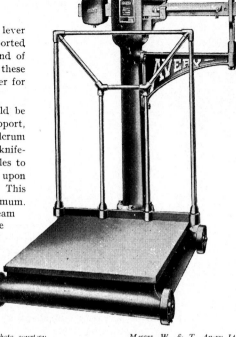

Photo courtesy   *Messrs. W. & T. Avery Ltd.*

Fig. 2. Portable Platform Weigher

The Roman Balance

A very important modification of the equal-armed balance is the steelyard or Roman balance. This consists essentially of a bar of steel suspended near one of its ends from which hangs the object to be weighed. A weight used as a counterpoise moves along the longer arm of the bar. The result of placing the counterpoise on the longer arm is to enable a small weight to balance a very heavy object, thus doing away with the necessity for using heavy weights. The position of the counterpoise when the arm is level indicates the weight of the object balanced on the shorter arm.

A simple model of a Roman Balance, with which the principle of the model about to be described may be demonstrated, is shown in Fig. 3. Before using this little model, a counterpoise should be added to the short arm of the lever so that the longer arm is maintained in a horizontal position when the sliding weight is pushed as closely as possible to the fulcrum. The counterpoise may consist of a series of Strips, etc., and once the correct weight has been ascertained it can be secured in position. The smallest additional weight on the short arm of the balance will then cause the longer arm to rise vertically and the sliding weight must be moved outward to restore it to its original position. The distance through which the sliding weight is moved indicates the weight of the object.

Roman Balance in its Modern Form

From the simple steelyard has developed the modern commercial platform weighing machine, which is a familiar object in the warehouses and factories of our industrial towns.

In this type of balance the object to be weighed is not hung directly from the steelyard, but rests upon a low platform. This arrangement enables heavy and bulky objects, such as sacks full of various materials, to be weighed quickly and with the greatest ease. The whole machine usually is mounted on wheels and thus can be moved easily about a warehouse and operated in any position required.

A typical high-class platform weighing machine is shown in Fig. 2. Such machines are made in various sizes having capacities of from 3 cwt. to 20 cwt. For weighing certain kinds of material the back rail of the platform shown in the photograph is apt to be inconvenient, and therefore machines may be obtained without this rail.

The same type of machine is used in railway stations, and in other places, without the wheels. In many cases the weighing platform is sunk until level with the station platform, so that heavy loads may be moved on to it with the greatest ease. It is generally found arranged in this way in the parcel offices, and larger machines of a similar type are employed in the goods yards and in the yards of mills and factories.

Although differing in outward details from the design of the weigher shown in Fig. 2, the Meccano model nevertheless closely resembles in principle that machine. The Avery weigher is fitted with wheels so that it may be moved about as required, and, if desired, the Meccano model may be made portable by mounting the base on 1″ Pulley Wheels or Flanged Wheels, etc.

The model was perfected only after much experimental work, and it may well be regarded as still another triumph for the Meccano system. Its internal details, although necessarily of a complicated nature, have been designed with a view to reducing friction to a minimum, with the result that the model will weigh objects ranging from $\frac{1}{2}$ oz. to $4\frac{1}{2}$ lbs. with remarkable accuracy provided that it is carefully calibrated.

The Steelyard

The framework of the model requires no detailed explanation, for it is shown clearly in Figs. 1 and 5. The steelyard 1, Fig. 1, consists of a $12\frac{1}{2}$″ Strip, and an $11\frac{1}{2}$″ Rod extending along the back of this Strip is attached to it by means of Couplings. The Coupling at the outer end is in a horizontal position, and is secured to the steelyard by means of an ordinary bolt entering one of its transverse threaded bores, the $11\frac{1}{2}$″ Rod being made fast in the longitudinal bore. The $12\frac{1}{2}$″ Strip is similarly attached to the Coupling 5, Fig. 6, the same bolt serving to attach the Strip and to secure the end of the $11\frac{1}{2}$″ Rod in the lowest transverse hole of the Coupling. The Coupling 5 is carried on the end of a 3″ Rod 6 which passes through further Couplings 7 and 8 and enters another Coupling in which a $3\frac{1}{2}$″ Axle Rod 10 is mounted. This Rod carries the balance weights 11, which may be secured at any point along its length by means of the Coupling 12.

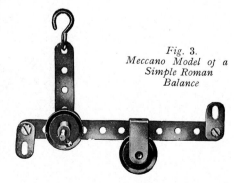

Fig. 3. Meccano Model of a Simple Roman Balance

The Rod 10 is extended at its outer

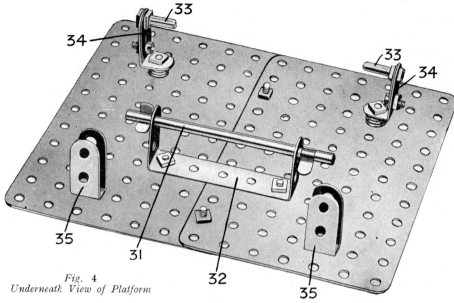

Fig. 4
Underneath View of Platform

another Hook, which passes under a 1″ Rod held in the end holes of the levers 23, Fig. 5.

Platform Mechanism.

The levers 23, Fig. 5, are pivoted on Hooks 24, which are held in position on the 6½″ Rod 30 by means of Collars. A central 3″ Rod 25 journalled in the Strips 23 is also retained in place by Collars, and carries a special suspension link 26 consisting of a Double Bracket and a ¾″ Bolt. This link supports a 5″ Rod 27, to the ends of which two further levers 28, consisting of 2″ Strips, are attached by means of Collars and Spring Clips, the opposite ends of the levers being pivoted to Hooks 28a on the 6½″ Rod 29.

The platform, which is shown inverted in Fig. 4, is composed of two 5½″ × 3½″ Flat Plates overlapped one hole and bolted together. A 2½″ × 1″ Double Angle Strip 32 attached to the underside carries a 3½″ Axle Rod 31, which is retained in position by Clips. When the platform is in position, this Rod rests on the levers 23, Fig. 5, while two Threaded Pins 33, secured to the 1″ × ½″ Angle Brackets 34, rest on the levers 28.

Four Washers are placed between each of the Angle Brackets 34 and the underside of the platform, and two Washers are placed on each of the bolts that secure the Double Angle Strip 32. Single Bent Strips 35 bolted to the 5½″ × 3½″ Flat Plates fit over the Rod 30 in the base, Fig. 5, and form vertical guides for the platform.

end by a Coupling 13 and a 2″ Threaded Rod 14 on which is screwed a Threaded Boss 15. Very accurate balance adjustments can be made by turning this Threaded Boss, and when the steelyard is exactly balanced the Boss is secured in position by the bolt 16.

The Knife-edge Bearing

Almost all accurate balances incorporate some form of knife-edge bearing; in the smaller instruments, as we have already remarked, this usually consists of a triangular prism of agate, an exceedingly hard semi-precious stone, but in the case of large machines this is obviously impracticable owing to the brittle nature of agate and the amount of this material that it would be necessary to use, and steel therefore often takes the place of agate. In the Meccano model a very efficient knife-edge bearing is obtained without any deviation from the standard system of parts.

The Coupling 7, Fig. 6, carries two Centre Forks 17, the points of which rest between the teeth of two ½″ Pinion Wheels. Thus the whole weight of the balance arm, including the load imposed upon it, rests on the six hard steel points of the Centre Forks with the result that an unusually delicate balance is obtainable. The two ½″ Pinions are secured to a 2″ Rod rigidly held in two Cranks, which are attached to a pair of 3½″ Strips pivoted to the ends of a Coupling. The central transverse hole of this Coupling carries an 11½″ Rod 18, which passes through the middle hole of a horizontal 1½″ Strip that forms part of the framework. Collars are secured to the Rod 18 on both sides of this 1½″ Strip, but are spaced sufficiently far apart to allow the Rod a certain amount of freedom to pivot. A stop 19 for the Rod 18 is provided at the outer end of the framework, Fig. 1, and consists of a Reversed Angle Bracket to which a nut and bolt are attached.

Two Flat Brackets 20 suspended from the ends of the Coupling 8 carry in their lower holes a 1″ Rod, which is retained in position by Clips. A Hook suspended from this 1″ Rod is connected with the levers 23 in the base of the model by the Sprocket Chain 22 and

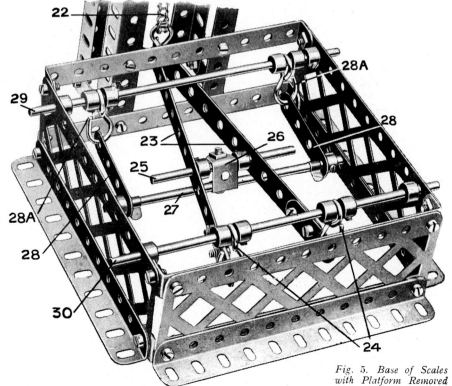

Fig. 5. Base of Scales with Platform Removed

The arrangement of the levers underneath the Platform is specially designed to make the machine respond to the slightest pressure, and to ensure that the same weight placed on any part of the platform (except at the extreme edges) will produce an equal pull on the Chain 22, whether the load is transmitted to the Chain by way of the Rod 31 and the levers 23 or by the Threaded Pins 33 and the levers 28.

Details of Indicator, etc.

A weight 36, Fig. 1, consisting of a Strip Coupling, a short Rod, and a ¾″ Pinion, slides along the steelyard 1 and carries a small pointer cut from cardboard, which indicates the load being weighed by means of the graduated scale 37. A piece of cardboard 38 should be cut in the form of an arrow and bolted to a Reversed Angle Bracket 39 in such a position that it comes to rest opposite a line on the cardboard indicator 40 when the steelyard is exactly horizontal. An upper and lower stop should be provided for the steelyard, consisting of a Reversed Angle Bracket and a 1″ × ½″ Angle Bracket respectively. The upper stop is clearly seen in Fig. 1 immediately below the stop 19.

In building the model, care should be taken that each part is in the exact position shown. When the scales are complete, the steelyard should be balanced carefully by moving the weight 11 and minute adjustment made by means of the Threaded Boss 15 until the arrow 38 is exactly on the line on the indicator 40 when the sliding weight is in its innermost position. The bolt 16 should then be tightened up to secure the Threaded Boss on the Threaded Rod 14.

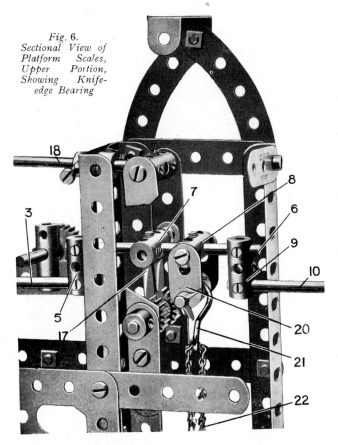

Fig. 6.
Sectional View of Platform Scales, Upper Portion, Showing Knife-edge Bearing

The scale 37 is cut from cardboard, and is provided with extensions at each end by means of which it may be bolted to the 12½″ Strip 1 of the steelyard. To graduate the scale, known weights are placed on the platform, and the sliding weight 36 is moved along the steelyard until the arrow 38 points once more to the line on the indicator 40. The exact position of the pointer attached to the weight should be noted on the scale in each case, and the magnitude of the weight marked against it. The need for exactitude, both in calibrating (*i.e.*, graduating the scale) and in the actual process of weighing, cannot be stressed too greatly, for a slight variation on the scale represents a considerable difference in the weight on the platform.

The steelyard is lifted into weighing position by placing the 11½″ Rod 18 under the stop 19 (see Fig. 1). The object to be weighed is then placed on the platform, and the weight 36 adjusted as explained until the pointer 38 is opposite the line on the indicator 40. The pointer attached to the sliding weight will then be found to indicate on the scale 37 the exact weight of the object. When not in use the

scales should always be put out of action by releasing the Rod 18 from under the stop 19.

Miscellaneous Points

The model should be oiled at frequent interval and all working parts must be kept clean and perfectly free to move. The Coupling 7 of the fulcrum in particular should not be allowed to touch the suspended 3½″ Strips on either side of it.

The appearance of the model may be improved considerably by filling in the sides of the upright member with a number of Strip Plates. The framework enclosing the steelyard may also be covered with either Strips or Flat Girders. This will not only give the model a more solid and workmanlike appearance, but will protect the knife edge and the other working parts from possible disarrangement, and, in addition, will help to eliminate from the bearings dust and other foreign matter which, if allowed to accumulate, would increase friction and impair the efficiency of the Scales.

In addition to affording a very interesting model to build, the Meccano Platform Scales form a really useful household article. To the more studious Meccano boy further interest attaches in that the model illustrates clearly and simply the general principles of the lever when used as a mechanical power and as a means of changing the direction of a force. Although the internal arrangements are perhaps a little complicated, it is a model that any Meccano boy can build. It will amply repay the little extra time and concentration that may be required to make it efficient and accurate.

List of Parts Required for Building the Meccano Platform Scales

Qty		No.	Qty		No.	Qty		No.	Qty		No.
3	of No.	1	1	of No.	12A	2	of No.	26	1	of No.	63B
2	,, ,,	2	3	,, ,,	12B	8	,, ,,	35	1	,, ,,	64
2	,, ,,	3	2	,, ,,	13	78	,, ,,	37	2	,, ,,	65
2	,, ,,	4	2	,, ,,	14	14	,, ,,	38	1	,, ,,	81
3	,, ,,	5	1	,, ,,	15	1	,, ,,	46	4	,, ,,	90
2	,, ,,	6	3	,, ,,	16	3	,, ,,	48	2	,, ,,	102
6	,, ,,	6A	2	,, ,,	16B	4	,, ,,	48D	2	,, ,,	108
4	,, ,,	8	1	,, ,,	17	2	,, ,,	52A	1	,, ,,	111
2	,, ,,	9	2	,, ,,	18A	6	,, ,,	57C	1	,, ,,	111A
4	,, ,,	10	1	,, ,,	18B	20	,, ,,	59	2	,, ,,	115
1	,, ,,	11	8	,, ,,	20	2	,, ,,	62	2	,, ,,	126A
2	,, ,,	12	1	,, ,,	25	8	,, ,,	63	3	,, ,,	195

The Meccano Roundabout

A Mechanical Wonder that will provide hours of Fun

SPECIAL FEATURES

Revolving platform and superstructure, rotating cars, leaping horses, etc. Operation entirely automatic.

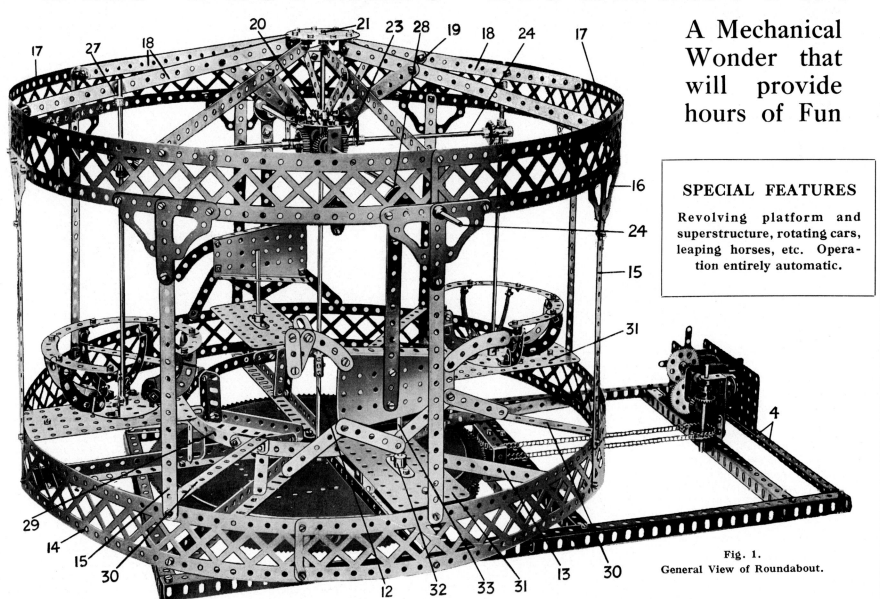

Fig. 1.
General View of Roundabout.

Published by MECCANO LIMITED, BINNS ROAD, LIVERPOOL

Printed in England.   528/10

From times beyond memory the roundabout has been a source of pleasure to young people. The progress of civilisation has changed it, of course, as it has changed almost everything else, and it is difficult to recognise the huge whirling structures of to-day as the direct descendants of the creaking contraption which, at the instance of a perspiring operator, was induced to revolve slowly with its load of half-a-dozen children. Yet from this humble source have sprung all the hurtling dragons, flying boats, and similar ingenious devices with which our modern fairs are provided.

In its original form, however, with a few alterations such as increased size and the use of steam or electric power, the old favourite is as popular as ever, and it is a poor fair that does not boast an old-fashioned roundabout. Young people who, having attained the mature age of sixteen or seventeen, are restrained by an overburdening sense of responsibility from taking part in the general "fun of the fair," often yield to the temptation to bestride a glorified quadruped bearing the somewhat fanciful inscription "Sally" or "Dobbin," and even staid old men who, if they have smiled at all during the last ten years, do not betray the fact by their faces, have been known to cast dignity to the winds and take a ride "for old times' sake." Modern amusement devices cannot completely oust from our fairs the old-fashioned roundabout.

The Meccano Roundabout is an excellent example of the adaptability of the Meccano system. The different movements, which include the rotating superstructure, the revolving cars, and the leaping horses, are all faithfully reproduced as in the prototype of the model, and its appearance when working gives an effect of realism that can only be fully appreciated by those who have actually seen the model in operation.

The base of the roundabout (Fig. 2) is built of two 24½″ Angle Girders joined by nine 12½″ Angle Girders 1, 2, 3, 4. A 5½″ by 2½″ Flat Plate 5, bolted to the Girders 3, carries two Trunnions joined by a 2½″ by 1″ Double Angle Strip 6, which, together with the Plate 5, provides bearings for a short Axle Rod carrying a 1″ Sprocket Wheel 7 and a special toothed wheel 8.

The Roller Bearing (Fig. 2).

The large Geared Roller Bearing on which the whole of the superstructure rotates may be purchased as a complete self-contained unit (part No. 167).

It is suitable for incorporation in many different models, and comprises two large Geared Roller Races (9 in the illustration, Fig. 2), each about a foot in diameter, a Ring Frame, sixteen ¾″ Flanged Wheels 11, sixteen Pivot Bolts with nuts, and a special Pinion. The small Flanged Wheels are journalled on the Pivot Bolts, which are secured round the outer edge of the Ring Frame, and the latter is inserted between the two Roller Races so that the Flanged Wheels run smoothly on a shoulder near the edge of the lower Race 9, which is bolted to the Girders 2, while the upper Roller Race, by means of a similar shoulder resting on the ¾″ Flanged Wheels, revolves easily, yet steadily, about the Axle Rod 12. In this way no points in the

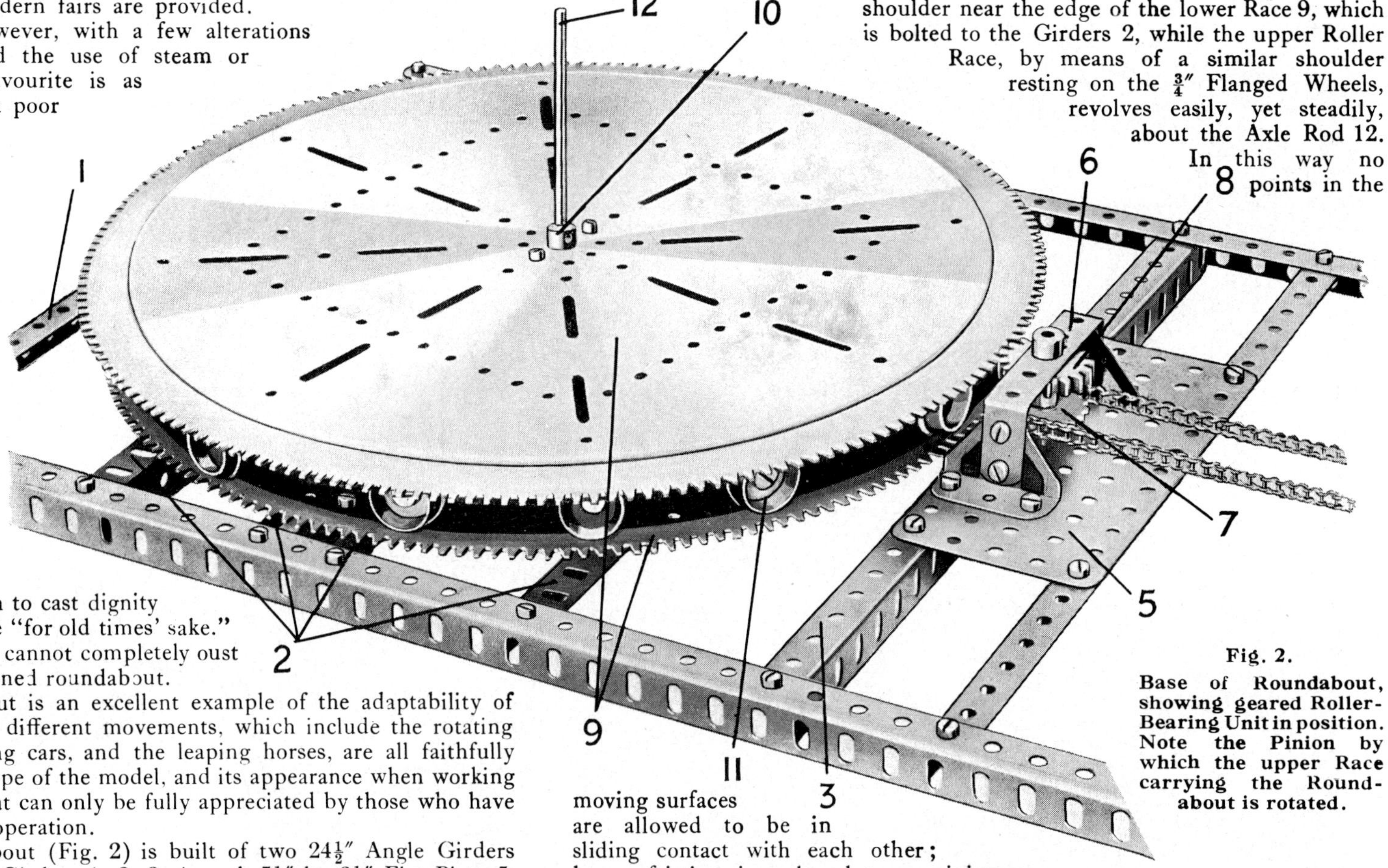

Fig. 2.
Base of Roundabout, showing geared Roller-Bearing Unit in position. Note the Pinion by which the upper Race carrying the Roundabout is rotated.

moving surfaces are allowed to be in sliding contact with each other; hence friction is reduced to a minimum.

The Rod 12 is secured rigidly in the boss of a Bush Wheel that is bolted to the lower Roller Race 9, and passes through another Bush Wheel secured to the centre of the upper Roller Race. The set-screw of the latter Bush Wheel should be removed so that the upper Race is quite free to revolve about the Rod 12. The revolving portion of the model is built on to a base formed of eight 9½″ Angle Girders 13 bolted to the upper Geared Race 9 of the Roller Bearing and having their outer ends secured by means of Angle

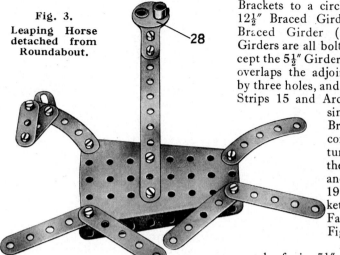

Fig. 3.
Leaping Horse detached from Roundabout.

Brackets to a circle formed of five 12½″ Braced Girders and one 5½″ Braced Girder (Fig. 1). These Girders are all bolted end to end except the 5½″ Girder, one end of which overlaps the adjoining 12½″ Girder by three holes, and are joined by 9½″ Strips 15 and Architraves 16 to a similar circle of Braced Girders 17, connected in their turn by means of the 9½″ Strips 18 and the 3½″ Strips 19 to Angle Brackets bolted to two Face Plates 20 (see Figs. 1, 4).

A circle composed of six 5½″ Strips 29, overlapped as required, is carried on eight vertical 2″ Angle Girders bolted to the Girders 13, and is connected to the Braced Girders 14 by four 5½″ by ½″ Double Angle Strips 30.

The bosses of the Face Plates 20 form journal bearings for an 11½″ Axle Rod 21 to which is secured a Contrate Wheel 22 (Fig. 4) that engages the teeth of the four 1″ Gear Wheels 23 on the Rods 24. The Axle Rod 21 is extended by means of a Coupling 25 and the short Rod 12, which is secured in the boss of the lower Geared Race of the Roller Bearing, so that the Contrate Wheel 22 remains immovable, and the revolving structure causes the Gear Wheels 23 to travel around the Wheel 22, at the same time rotating about their own axes and operating the jumping horses and revolving cars.

Leaping Horses.

The horses on the roundabout are no common hacks : indeed they are rather remarkable creatures, and the fact that they bear only a slight general resemblance to the animals whose name they boast will, unless our experience of roundabouts is at fault, make them all the more suitable for incorporation in this model. The body of each horse, as will be seen from Fig. 3, consists of a Sector Plate, and is provided with a tail (a 2½″ large radius Curved Strip) and four 2½″ Strips representing legs. The passenger is expected to sit astride the horse immediately behind the supporting Strip. During "rush hours" no doubt an extra passenger could be squeezed in between the front of the supporting Strip and the horse's neck. The gracefully arched but rather ill-nourished neck may be distinguished from the tail by the fact that it bears a shapely head (two 1½″ Strips) surmounted by a Flat Bracket with which the poor beast must do his best to hear. Much fun may be obtained by adjusting the angles of the neck, tail, and legs to represent the characteristic trotting and galloping attitudes.

Each of the horses is carried on a 5½″ Strip bolted to a Single Throw Eccentric 28, which, secured to one of the Rods 24, imparts a realistic leaping motion to the horse. One end of the horizontal Rod 24, on which the Eccentric 28 is mounted, is journalled in a 1″ by 1″ Angle Bracket secured to the lower of the Face Plates 20, while the Braced Girders 17 and the Architraves 16 provide a bearing for the opposite end.

A 5½″ by 2½″ Flat Plate 31 is and the Strips 29 by means of ries a Double Arm Crank 32, in secured a 3″ Rod 33 acting as a ing horse. The rod 33 passes

bolted to the Girders 14 Angle Brackets, and car- the boss of which is vertical guide for the leap- through the lower flange

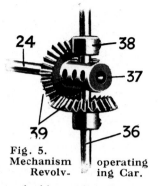

Fig. 5.
Mechanism operating Revolving Car.

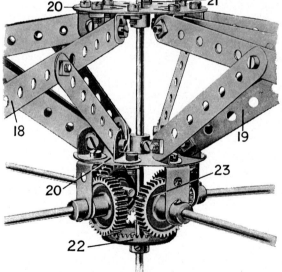

Fig. 4.
Operating Mechanism at top of Main Stem.

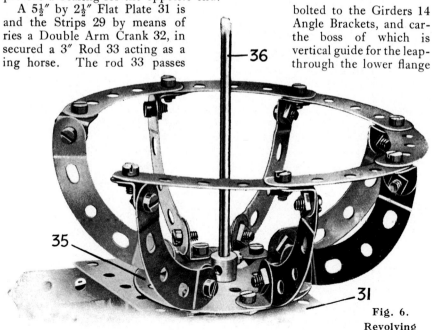

Fig. 6.
Revolving Car.

of the Sector Plate forming the body of the horse. This arrangement is identical for both horses, as can be seen in Fig. 1.

Revolving Cars.

Each revolving car (Fig. 6) comprises a Face Plate 35 to which seven 2½″ small radius Curved Strips are affixed by means of Angle Brackets. Six 2½″ large radius Curved Strips attached to the upper ends of the small radius Strips form an arm rest for the occupants of the car. An 11½″ Axle Rod 36, secured in the boss of the Face Plate, is journalled in bearings consisting of the 5½″ by 2½″ Flat Plate 31 and an Angle Bracket 27 bolted to one of the 9½″ Strips 18. This Rod 36 passes through the central transverse hole of a Coupling 37, in the longitudinal bore of which is journalled one end of the Rod 24. The Rod 36 is supported in the Coupling 37 by a fixed Collar 38, and carries a second fast Collar between the Face Plate 35 and the Flat Plate 31.

The Rods 24, 36 carry ¾″ Bevel Gears 39 that are in continuous engagement with each other. Thus, as the whole upper structure revolves, the 1″ Gear Wheels 23, rolling around the teeth of the Contrate Wheel 22, rotate the Axle Rods 24, and this movement, transmitted via the Bevel Gears 39 to the vertical Rods 36, causes the cars to spin round, while at the same time the horses, actuated by the Eccentrics 28, leap in the most approved roundabout fashion.

The effect produced by the variety of motions embodied in the model is remarkable. For this reason the Meccano Roundabout is an ideal model for attracting attention to window displays or Meccano Club exhibitions, etc.

Arrangement of the Gearing.

A Worm Wheel secured to the armature spindle of the Electric Motor (see Fig. 7) meshes with a 57-teeth Gear Wheel 40 on the Rod 44, to which is also secured a ½″ Pinion 42 that engages a second 57-teeth Gear Wheel on the Rod 43. The drive is then led via a pair of ⅞″ Bevel Gears to a 1″ Sprocket Wheel 41, which is connected by an endless Sprocket Chain to the 1″ Sprocket Wheel 7 (Fig. 2). The special 1″ Pinion 8 is secured to the same Rod as

Fig. 7. Showing Gears mounted on Electric Motor.

the Sprocket Wheel 7, and by turning the upper Geared Race of the large Roller Bearing causes the platform and super-structure of the roundabout to revolve about the Rods 12, 21.

It should be noted that the gearing just described was designed for use with the Meccano high-voltage Electric Motor, and is unsuitable for the 4-volt type. The latter is, however, quite powerful enough to operate the model at a considerable speed, and if it is desired to make use of the smaller Motor it is only necessary to omit the ½″ Pinion 42 and the gears on the Rod 43, adding a ⅞″ Bevel Gear on the end of the Rod 44 to mesh with a similar Bevel Gear on the vertical Rod that carries the Sprocket Wheel 41. By this means the total reduction of the gearing will be diminished to one-third of that afforded by the original arrangement.

The operation of the Roundabout is entirely automatic, and once the Motor has been started the model will work continuously without any attention whatever. The realism of its appearance will be greatly enhanced if the roof, floor and central part are filled in with suitably coloured cardboard.

All gears and bearings in the Roundabout should be oiled at frequent intervals, particular attention being paid in this respect to the Geared Roller Bearing. If this is done, the model should work almost noiselessly and without any sign of shaking or rattling. The gearing has been so arranged that the Roundabout will operate at a speed proportional to that of its prototype, but if a greater speed is required, it is only necessary to make a slight alteration to the gearing similar to that already described, as the Electric Motor has an ample reserve of power.

Those boys who possess a sufficient number of parts will doubtless be able to improve the model considerably. For example, the revolving platform might be filled in with Flat Plates, and steps might be arranged around its sides.

List of Parts Required to Build the Meccano Roundabout.

17 of No.	1a	62 of No.	12	1 of No.	26	2 of No.	54	2 ft. of No.	100
8 ,,	2	6 ,,	12a	2 ,,	27a	12 ,,	59	16 ,,	108
8 ,,	3	5 ,,	13	6 ,,	30	2 ,,	62b	4 ,,	109
8 ,,	5	2 ,,	14	1 ,,	30c	3 ,,	63	2 ,,	126
4 ,,	6a	1 ,,	15a	4 ,,	31	5 ,,	70	4 ,,	126a
2 ,,	7	2 ,,	16	1 ,,	32	16 ,,	90	2 ,,	130
7 ,,	8	1 ,,	16a	288 ,,	37	14 ,,	90a	1 ,,	160
8 ,,	8a	1 ,,	16b	8 ,,	38	2 ft. of No.	94	1 ,,	167
8 ,,	9e	1 ,,	18a	1 ,,	48a	2 ,,	96	1 Electric	
2 ,,	10	2 ,,	24	8 ,,	48d	10 ,,	99	Motor	

Alternative Construction.

If desired Meccano built-up roller bearings may be substituted for the special Geared Roller-Bearing unit. Suitable built-up roller bearings are described in the "Standard Mechanisms Manual" (detail No. 101). If this form of construction is adopted the following alterations are necessary to the list of parts required. For part No. 167 substitute :—

8 of No.	2a	8 of No.	20	3 ft. of No.	94
8 ,,	3	76 ,,	37	2 ,,	109
8 ,,	9a	16 ,,	38	16 ,,	119
16 ,,	12b	8 ,,	48	8 ,,	125
8 ,,	16a	8 ,,	59		

The
Meccano Bagatelle Table

A New Mechanical Game

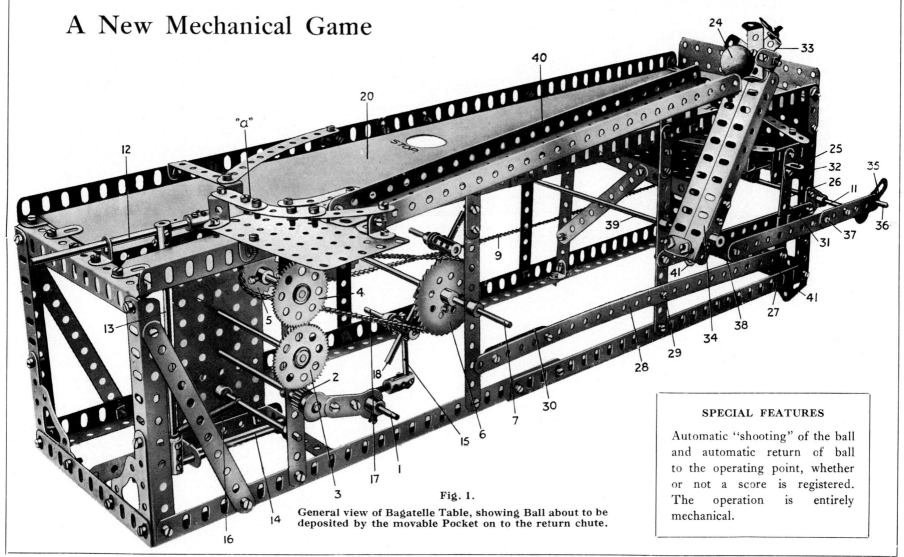

Fig. 1.

General view of Bagatelle Table, showing Ball about to be deposited by the movable Pocket on to the return chute.

SPECIAL FEATURES

Automatic "shooting" of the ball and automatic return of ball to the operating point, whether or not a score is registered. The operation is entirely mechanical.

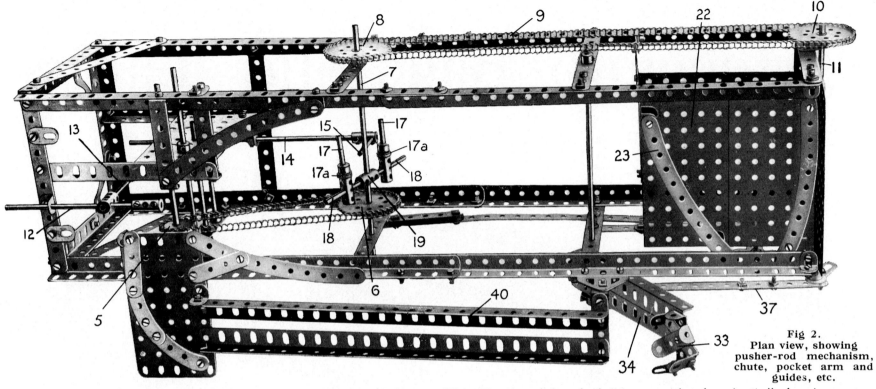

Fig 2.
Plan view, showing
pusher-rod mechanism,
chute, pocket arm and
guides, etc.

B ESIDES forming a very interesting model to build the Bagatelle Table will afford much good fun when used as a game with which to amuse one's friends.

The operation of the model is entirely mechanical. A marble or ball of suitable size is placed on the table at the point marked "a" in Fig. 1. On rotating the operating handle the ball is struck sharply by means of a "pusher-rod" and is sent down the table towards a set of holes cut in the table-top, which consists of a sheet of cardboard. The holes are slightly larger in size than the marble, or ball, and they are marked by various numbers. Should the ball drop into a hole bearing, say, the number 10, that number is the score of the player who operated the "shot."

When the ball falls through any of the holes, it drops on to an inclined plate and rolls towards a trap-door on the one side of the plate. By the operation of the handle, which is turned continuously, this trap-door opens and allows the ball to enter a carrier arm. The latter then rises about its pivot and sends the ball down the inclined chute

(40 in Fig. 1), and thus the ball is returned to the point "a," where it comes to rest in position for a second "shot" to be taken.

Construction of the Frame.

The frame of the model is shown in Fig. 4. Its construction should be commenced by building the base, which is formed from Angle Girders, each long side of the frame being composed of two 12½" Angle Girders 45 over-lapped four holes and bolted together. These are joined at the ends by the 5½" Angle Girders 50 and thus form an oblong base frame.

At the pusher-rod end two 5½" Angle Girders 48 are bolted at vertical right angles to the base frame and spanned at the top by the Angle Girder 56, while to the lower corners of the end so formed two Architraves are bolted in order to give stability. The rear end of the frame is formed from two more Angle Girders corresponding to the Girders 48 secured to the base, but in this case they are spanned by the Flat Plate 44. To complete the

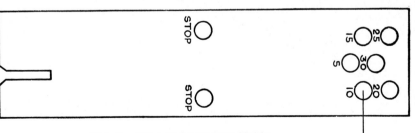

STOP ○

STOP ○

15 25 ○

5 30 ○

10 20 ○

21

Fig. 3.   Plan of Cardboard Table.

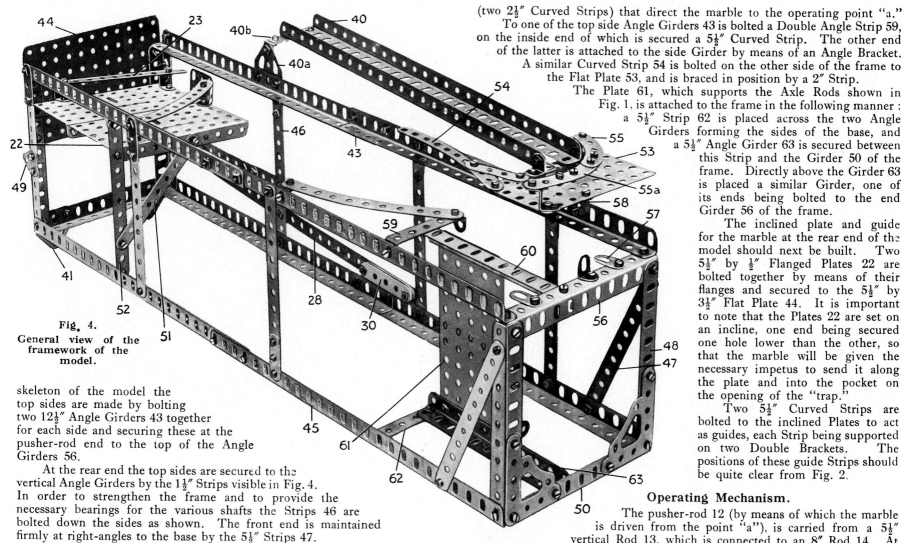

Fig. 4.
General view of the framework of the model.

(two 2½″ Curved Strips) that direct the marble to the operating point "a."

To one of the top side Angle Girders 43 is bolted a Double Angle Strip 59, on the inside end of which is secured a 5½″ Curved Strip. The other end of the latter is attached to the side Girder by means of an Angle Bracket. A similar Curved Strip 54 is bolted on the other side of the frame to the Flat Plate 53, and is braced in position by a 2″ Strip.

The Plate 61, which supports the Axle Rods shown in Fig. 1, is attached to the frame in the following manner : a 5½″ Strip 62 is placed across the two Angle Girders forming the sides of the base, and a 5½″ Angle Girder 63 is secured between this Strip and the Girder 50 of the frame. Directly above the Girder 63 is placed a similar Girder, one of its ends being bolted to the end Girder 56 of the frame.

The inclined plate and guide for the marble at the rear end of the model should next be built. Two 5½″ by ½″ Flanged Plates 22 are bolted together by means of their flanges and secured to the 5½″ by 3½″ Flat Plate 44. It is important to note that the Plates 22 are set on an incline, one end being secured one hole lower than the other, so that the marble will be given the necessary impetus to send it along the plate and into the pocket on the opening of the "trap."

Two 5½″ Curved Strips are bolted to the inclined Plates to act as guides, each Strip being supported on two Double Brackets. The positions of these guide Strips should be quite clear from Fig. 2.

skeleton of the model the top sides are made by bolting two 12½″ Angle Girders 43 together for each side and securing these at the pusher-rod end to the top of the Angle Girders 56.

At the rear end the top sides are secured to the vertical Angle Girders by the 1½″ Strips visible in Fig. 4. In order to strengthen the frame and to provide the necessary bearings for the various shafts the Strips 46 are bolted down the sides as shown. The front end is maintained firmly at right-angles to the base by the 5½″ Strips 47.

The Flat Brackets 57 secured to the Angle Girder 56 at the pusher-rod end are for the purpose of holding the cardboard "table" in position, the cardboard being placed beneath the Brackets and the Angle Girder. A glance at Fig. 1 will give a clear idea of this arrangement.

The chute 40 consists of two 12½″ Angle Girders secured at one end to a 2″ Strip 40b that, in turn, is attached to a Flat Trunnion 40a bolted to the side Girders 43. The other end of the chute is secured to a Flat Plate 53 bolted to the frame by means of Angle Brackets 58. To this Plate are bolted also two ½″ Reversed Angle Brackets carrying the guide Strips

Operating Mechanism.

The pusher-rod 12 (by means of which the marble is driven from the point "a"), is carried from a 5½″ vertical Rod 13, which is connected to an 8″ Rod 14. At the front end of the latter is a 2″ Rod 15 arranged vertically, and a Spring 16 tends to pull the pusher-rod forward to strike the marble. The pusher-rod is depressed against the Spring by the action of two 1″ Rods 17 upon which are mounted ½″ Pulley Wheels 17a carried from two Couplings secured on two 2″ Rods 18 which enter the central Coupling 19. The Axle Rod 7 passes completely through the Coupling 19.

As the Rods 17 rotate, the Pulleys 17a bear against the Rod 15 and depress the pusher-rod rearwardly until released, when the Spring pulls the pusher-rod sharply forward to drive the marble from the point "a" along the table 20 towards the holes 21 (Figs. 1 and 2). If the marble falls into any one of the holes 21 it drops on to the Plate 22, and the guides 23 (Fig. 4) lead it to the end of the Plate, where it is retained by the stop plate 25 (Figs. 1 and 6).

The stop plate consists of a 1½″ Flat Girder bolted to a 3½″ Strip 26. The latter is connected pivotally at 27 by means of a bolt and lock nuts (see Standard Mechanism No. 263), to a 12½″ Strip 28 that is pivoted at 29 and weighted at 30 with five or six 2½″ Strips. The Strip 26 is free to move vertically and slides in an Eye Piece bolted to the frame. The same bolt that secures the trap 25 also secures an Angle Bracket 32.

The Pocket and Arm.

The movable pocket, with its operating arm, is shown in Fig. 5. The pocket consists of three 1½″ by ½″ Double Angle Strips secured to an arm 34 consisting of two 5½″ Angle Girders. The pocket is attached to the arm 34 by a 1″ Triangular Plate, the two base holes of which are bolted to the end holes of the Girders 34—the pocket being secured to the apex hole. Three Washers should be placed on the ½″ Bolt beneath the pocket to raise the latter clear of the bolts securing the Triangular Plates. At the lower ends the Girders 34 are secured together by a Flat Bracket 34a.

The arm 34 is rocked from the Rod 11 (Fig. 1) by a Crank 35, a Threaded Pin 36 on which engages the end holes of a 5½″ and a 3″ Strip 37 overlapped three holes. The other end of the Strip is connected to a Boss Bell Crank 38 bolted to the arm 34 and secured to the Rod 39.

As the Axle Rod 11 rotates, the arm 34 is permitted to fall, and in so doing makes contact with the Angle Bracket 32 and depresses the stop plate 25, thereby permitting the marble to drop from the Plate 22 into the pocket 33. Further rotary movement of the Rod 11 again raises the arm 34 with the marble in the pocket, until the marble is deposited into the chute 40 and thus returned to the point "a"

Meanwhile, on the rising of the arm 34 the Plate 25 is again raised to close the outlet from the inclined Plate 22. The bearings for the Axle Rod 11 are formed by two 1″ Triangular Plates secured to the rear vertical Angle Girders.

Fig. 3 indicates the shape of the cardboard table. The holes 21 should be made only slightly larger than the marble or ball used. (The latter is not supplied in Meccano Outfits). The table is given a slight incline towards the pusher-rod end by forming at the other end two feet with two Flat Trunnions 41 bolted to the lower 5½″ Angle Girder.

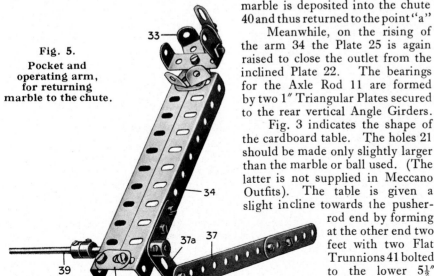

Fig. 5.
Pocket and operating arm, for returning marble to the chute.

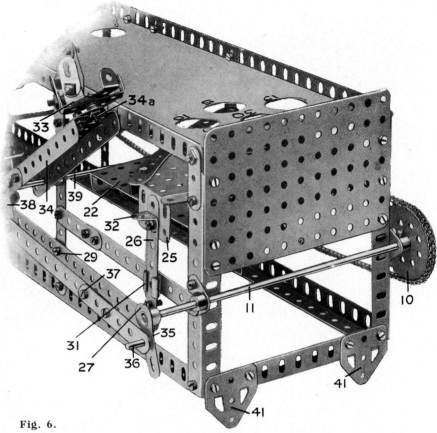

Fig. 6.

End view of the Bagatelle Table, showing stop plate mechanism, etc.

List of Parts required.

1 of No.	1	1 of No.	12b	1 of No.	43	4 of No.	89
10 ,,	2	4 ,,	13a	1 ,,	46	2 ,,	90
2 ,,	2a	2 ,,	14	3 ,,	48	3 ,,	95
1 ,,	3	1 ,,	15	2 ,,	48a	1 ,,	96
1 ,,	4	2 ,,	15a	1 ,,	50	2 ,,	103h
6 ,,	5	1 ,,	16	2 ,,	52	1 ,,	108
21 ,,	6	3 ,,	17	1 ,,	52a	1 ,,	111a
6 ,,	6a	2 ,,	18a	1 ,,	53a	1 ,,	115
10 ,,	8	1 ,,	18b	9 ,,	59	1 ,,	125
11 ,,	9	1 ,,	26	3 ,,	62	3 ,,	126a
6 ,,	10	2 ,,	27a	7 ,,	63	1 ,,	128
5 ,,	11	134 ,,	37	1 ,,	70	1 marble or
9 ,,	12	6 ,,	38	3 ,,	77	small ball

The Meccano Log Saw

Special Features

Saw and feed carriage driven by Electric Motor.

The Saw slides in vertically-adjustable frame, the elevation of which may be altered on operation of hand wheel.

Feed carriage may be thrown out of gear with Motor whenever required, on operation of hand lever.

By substituting a hacksaw blade for the Rack Strips representing the saw, the model can be put to practical use.

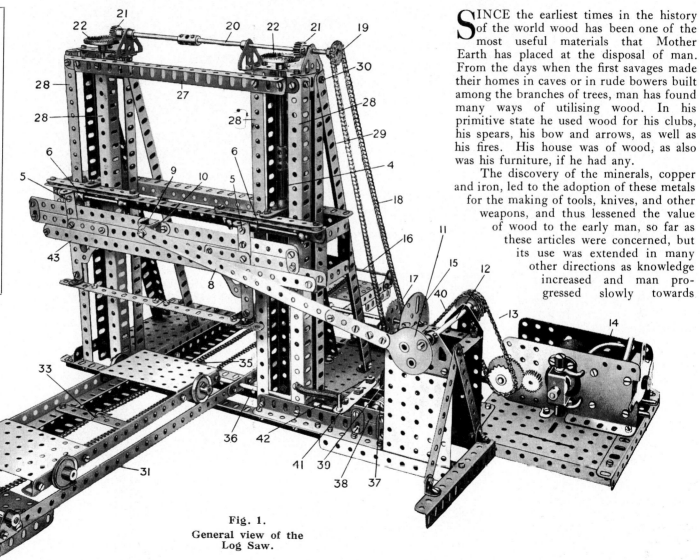

Fig. 1.
General view of the
Log Saw.

SINCE the earliest times in the history of the world wood has been one of the most useful materials that Mother Earth has placed at the disposal of man. From the days when the first savages made their homes in caves or in rude bowers built among the branches of trees, man has found many ways of utilising wood. In his primitive state he used wood for his clubs, his spears, his bow and arrows, as well as his fires. His house was of wood, as also was his furniture, if he had any.

The discovery of the minerals, copper and iron, led to the adoption of these metals for the making of tools, knives, and other weapons, and thus lessened the value of wood to the early man, so far as these articles were concerned, but its use was extended in many other directions as knowledge increased and man progressed slowly towards

Published by MECCANO LIMITED, BINNS ROAD, LIVERPOOL

Printed in England. 528/5

civilisation. For very many centuries wood was used almost exclusively for building habitations, bridges and vessels.

Even in this age of coal and iron, timber is practically indispensable for many purposes. One cannot imagine domestic furniture being made of any other material than wood—certainly stone or metal would not be very satisfactory. Nor would Jack Hobbs be likely to score many centuries if he went out to the pitch carrying an iron bat ! No satisfactory substitute has yet been found for wooden piles for supporting structures built in soft ground, and although the walls of houses and other buildings are now built of brick or stone, an enormous amount of timber is used in the construction of floors, walls, and roofs, etc. Railway sleepers, telegraph poles, wooden road-setting blocks—these are a few of the various ways in which to-day man adapts the product of the forest to serve him in his daily life and to provide for his material comfort.

One of the latest uses for wood is in the production of paper. It might be thought that the number of trees used for this purpose would not be very great, but when it is remembered that quite a number of modern newspapers publish over 1,000,000 copies every day, it will be realised that considerable quantities of timber are necessary. Some of the big newspaper companies own large tracts of forest land in various parts of the world, from which they draw their own supply of wood.

The wood-pulp industry is very extensive in Canada and thousands of men are employed in the numerous processes of paper-making.

Sources of Wood.

Apart from valuable woods such as mahogany, ebony, and cedar, etc., the majority of our timber is imported from countries around the Baltic Sea and from the Western parts of North America, particularly British Columbia. Whole fleets of timber-carrying vessels are engaged in its transportation.

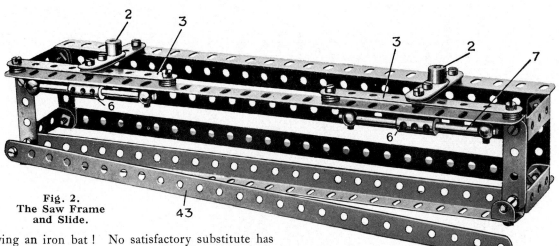

Fig. 2. The Saw Frame and Slide.

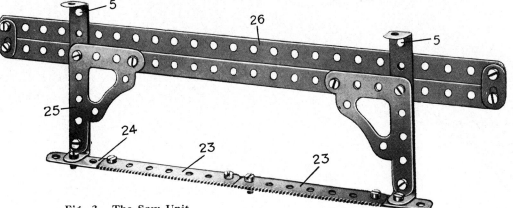

Fig. 3. The Saw Unit.

The magnitude of the logging operations in America is almost incredible. Hundreds of thousands of trees—measuring from six to twenty feet in diameter and growing to great heights—are cut down every year. So great is the demand for wood that the Canadian Government has had to set up a special forestry department, which supervises the logging operations, and by only allowing the mature trees to be cut down prevents unnecessary waste of timber. Meanwhile thousands of young trees are planted year by year to replace those cut down, so that future generations shall be assured of good supplies of this valuable material.

Logging Operations in America.

After the trees have been cut down and deprived of their branches they are dragged to the nearest river—fortunately, rivers are very numerous in Central and Western Canada—and chained together in huge rafts. These are allowed to float downstream until they reach the sawmills, where they are sawn up into beams or planks or prepared for shipping overseas. It is a common practice to trim the sides of the tree trunks into a square form so that they can be stacked together with more economy of space aboard ship.

The Meccano Log Saw illustrated in Fig. 1 is modelled on the actual machines used in sawmills. The cutting edge is represented by Rack Strips, but these may be replaced if desired by a hack saw or similar blade, with two holes drilled in it so that it may be secured to the Meccano framework.

The Meccano Model.

The general layout of the model is shown in Fig. 1, while details of the vertically-adjustable frame and saw slide are shown in Fig. 2 and of the saw unit in Fig. 3.

The construction of the model should be commenced by building the framework, as illustrated in Fig. 4. Each of the rails 31 consists of two 12½″ Angle Girders joined end to end by 2″ Strips. If 24½″ Girders are available they should of course be used here. The frame of the gear box is supported by an Architrave 44 and two 4½″ Strips 45, attached to the gear box by means of Angle Brackets. The 2½″ by 1″ Double Angle Strip 46 is bolted between the two 12½″ Girders 29. The Trunnions at the top of the main vertical members are bolted to 1½″ Angle Girders. The construction of the rest of the frame should be obvious from the illustration.

Construction of the Saw Frame and Slide.

This part of the model is shown in Fig. 2. The box-like portion is made up of four 12½″ Angle Girders connected at the ends by 2″ Strips and 1½″ by ½″ Double Angle Strips. The 12½″ Strip 43 should be secured at one end and the other end left free until the saw unit has been secured in place. The free end of the Strip 43 is then bolted to the Angle Bracket shown.

The Threaded Cranks 2 are bolted to 2½″ Strips and the latter are secured to the frame in the following manner. One end of each Strip is attached by a ¾″ Bolt to one of the Angle Girders at the top of the saw frame, but the Strip is spaced away from the Girder by three or four Washers placed on the shank of the bolt. The other end of each Strip is secured to a 4½″ Strip 3, the ends of which are bolted to the other Girder of the saw frame. It will be noticed that the Strips 3 are spaced away from the Girder by means of Washers: the object of this is to prevent the shanks of the bolts securing the Cranks 2 from fouling the Couplings 6, which must slide freely on the Rods 7.

When completed the saw frame is slipped over the tops of the vertical members 28 (see Fig. 6.) Then the 9½″ Angle Girder 27 is bolted to the upper ends of the Girders 28, and the four 12½″ Angle Girders 29 (Fig. 1) are bolted at 30 to the uprights 28.

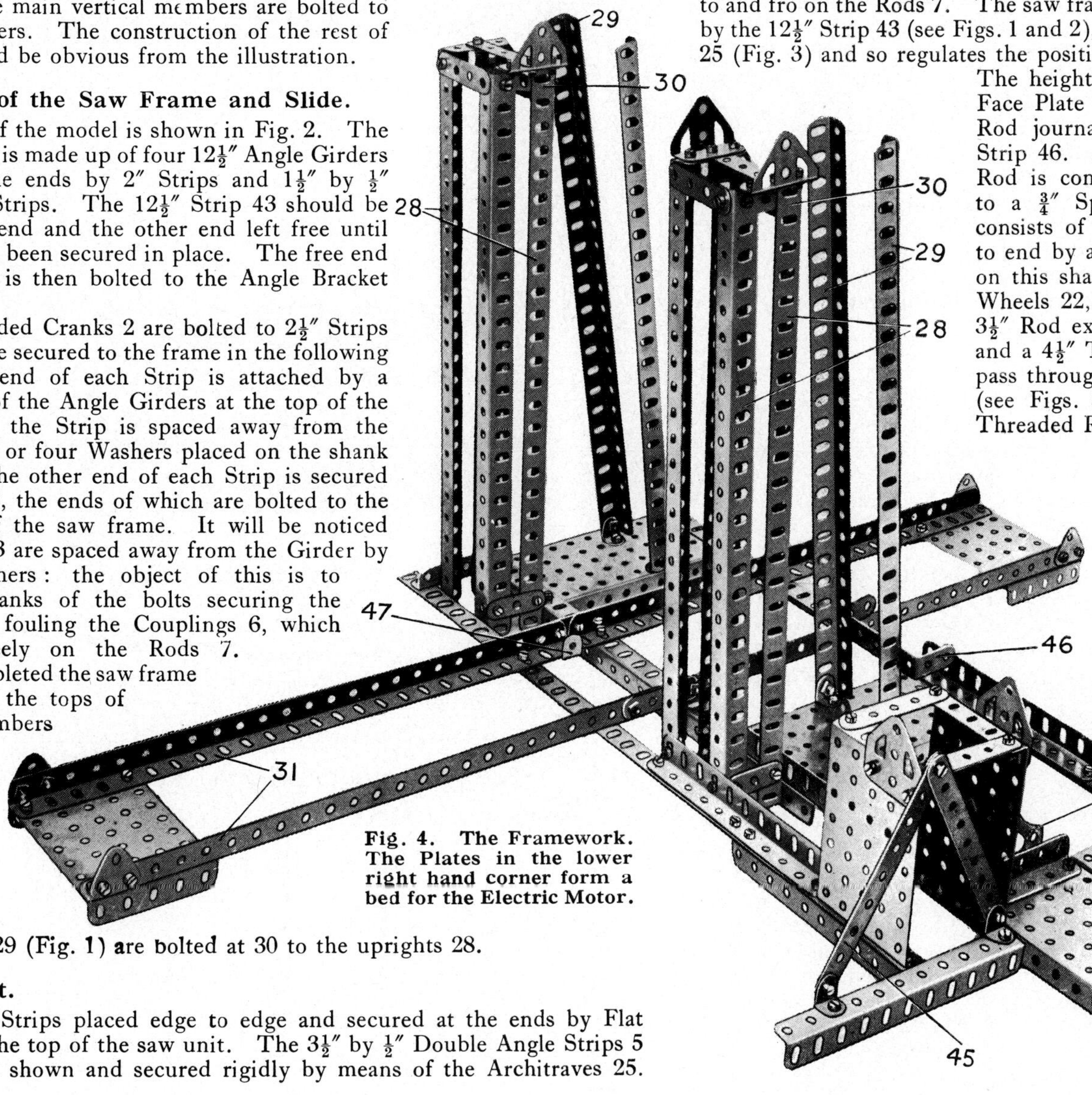

The Saw Unit.

Two 12½″ Strips placed edge to edge and secured at the ends by Flat Brackets form the top of the saw unit. The 3½″ by ½″ Double Angle Strips 5 are mounted as shown and secured rigidly by means of the Architraves 25.

The saw is represented by two Rack Strips 23 bolted to a 9½″ Strip 24 that, in turn, is bolted to the lower ends of the Double Angle Strips 5.

The saw unit is attached to the slide by means of the Double Angle Strips 5, which are bolted to the Couplings 6 of the slide (Fig. 2), but are spaced away from them by Washers so that the Couplings are free to move to and fro on the Rods 7. The saw frame is guided in its transverse movement by the 12½″ Strip 43 (see Figs. 1 and 2), which passes in front of the Architraves 25 (Fig. 3) and so regulates the position of the saw.

The height of the saw is adjusted by turning the Face Plate 15 (Fig. 1), which is secured to a 4½″ Rod journalled in the 2½″ by 1″ Double Angle Strip 46. A 1½″ Sprocket Wheel 17 on the same Rod is connected by an endless Sprocket Chain to a ¾″ Sprocket Wheel on a shaft 20, which consists of a 6½″ Rod and a 3½″ Rod joined end to end by a Coupling. Two ½″ Pinion Wheels 21 on this shaft 20 engage the teeth of 1½″ Contrate Wheels 22, each of which is secured to a vertical 3½″ Rod extended at its lower end by a Coupling and a 4½″ Threaded Rod 4. The Threaded Rods pass through the bosses of the Threaded Cranks 2 (see Figs. 3 and 6). Hence, on rotation of the Threaded Rods the saw slide (Fig. 2) moves up or down as required.

Driving Mechanism.

The Electric Motor may be of either the high-voltage or the low-voltage type. A ½″ Pinion on the armature spindle drives a 57-teeth Gear Wheel on a 2½″ Rod journalled in the Motor frame. A ¾″ Pinion on the opposite end of this Rod meshes with a 50-teeth Gear Wheel on a 3½″ Rod, to which is secured a 1″ Sprocket Wheel that is connected with a similar Wheel on the Rod 12. The reciprocating movement of the saw is caused

Fig. 4. The Framework. The Plates in the lower right hand corner form a bed for the Electric Motor.

by a Triple-throw Eccentric 11, which is made fast to the Rod 12 so as to give its maximum throw of 1″, and joined by a 2½″ Strip and a 9½″ Strip 8 to a Double Bent Strip 10 attached to the saw frame. The bolt that pivots the Strip 8 to the Double Bent Strip is provided with lock-nuts (see Standard Mechanisms Manual, detail No. 263).

A second 1″ Sprocket Wheel on the Rod 12 drives a 2″ Sprocket Wheel on a 2″ Rod 38 (Figs. 1 and 5), which is journalled in two 2½″ Strips attached to the framework by means of Flat Brackets. A Worm secured to this Rod engages a ½″ Pinion on a horizontal 3½″ Rod. When desired, the latter may be connected to an 8″ Rod 36 by means of a Dog Clutch. The Dog Clutch mechanism is shown in detail in Fig. 5. It is controlled by the hand lever 41, which is pivoted at 42 by means of a bolt and lock-nuts. A Single Bent Strip is pivoted to the lever by the same means, and serves to connect it to the 3½″ Rod that carries a section of the Dog Clutch, being retained in position on the Rod by a Collar. The other section of the Clutch is secured to the 8″ Rod 36, and the two Clutch members normally are kept in engagement by a Spring bolted to the lever 41 (Fig. 1). The movement of the feed carriage may be arrested by operating this hand lever.

The Feed Carriage.

The feed carriage, the construction of which is shown clearly in Fig. 1, slowly moves the logs against the saw while they are being cut. It runs on the rails 31, and is actuated by an endless Sprocket Chain 32 attached to the centre of the carriage at 33. The chain passes round a ¾″ Sprocket Wheel 34 at each end of the rail, and is also carried over a 1″ Sprocket Wheel secured to the Rod 36, by which the carriage is driven. The Rod 36 passes through 1½″ Strips in the base of one of the upright members of the framework, its further end being journalled in the Angle Bracket 47 (see Fig. 4).

The procedure to be adopted in operating the model is as follows. The Electric Motor is started, and the saw at once begins to work backward and forward while the feed carriage moves slowly towards it. By disengaging the Dog Clutch, the carriage may be stopped while the material to be sawn is placed in position, but its motion is resumed as soon as the clutch lever is released. The feed carriage is returned

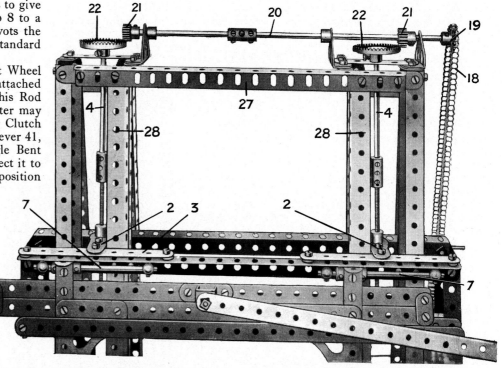

Fig. 6. View showing the elevating mechanism controlling the Saw Frame.

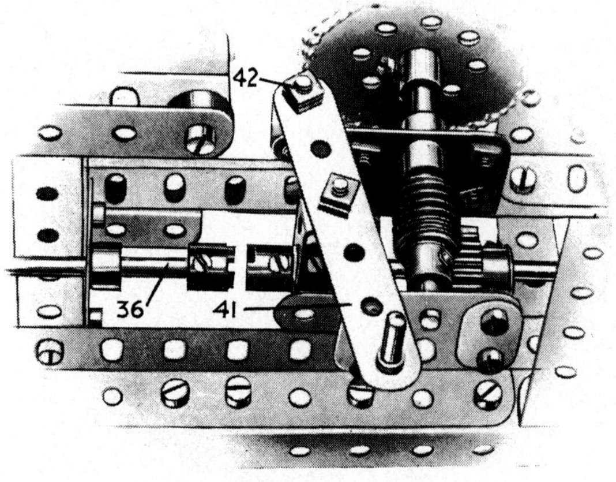

to its original position, of course, by reversing the Electric Motor.

Before the Log Saw is used, the height of the blade should be adjusted to the required position. Planks of any thickness are produced by making several cuts through the same log with the saw at varying heights.

Fig. 5.
Clutch mechanism controlling the Feed Carriage.

Parts required to build the Meccano Log Saw :—

3 of No.	1	14 of No.	12	30 of No.	38	1 of No.	95
2 ,,	1a	1 ,,	12b	1 ,,	43	1 ,,	95a
4 ,,	2a	1 ,,	13	1 ,,	45	4 ,,	96
1 ,,	3	1 ,,	14	4 ,,	48	3 ,,	96a
1 ,,	4	6 ,,	15a	1 ,,	48a	3 ,,	108
8 ,,	5	5 ,,	16	2 ,,	48b	1 ,,	109
10 ,,	6	4 ,,	22	4 ,,	52	2 ,,	110
2 ,,	6a	2 ,,	25	6 ,,	53	2 ,,	115
23 ,,	8	3 ,,	26	13 ,,	59	3 ,,	126
4 ,,	8a	1 ,,	27	2 ,,	62a	2 ,,	126a
7 ,,	9	1 ,,	27a	5 ,,	63	1 ,,	130
2 ,,	9d	2 ,,	28	4 ,,	77	4 ,,	136
4 ,,	9f	1 ,,	32	2 ,,	80b	1 ,,	144
6 ,,	10	146 ,,	37	2 ,,	94	Electric Motor	

Meccano Single-Cylinder Horizontal Steam Engine

The illustrations to this leaflet show the model built in Red-Green Meccano parts. Its construction in the Blue-Gold Meccano parts is exactly the same

Built with Outfit K

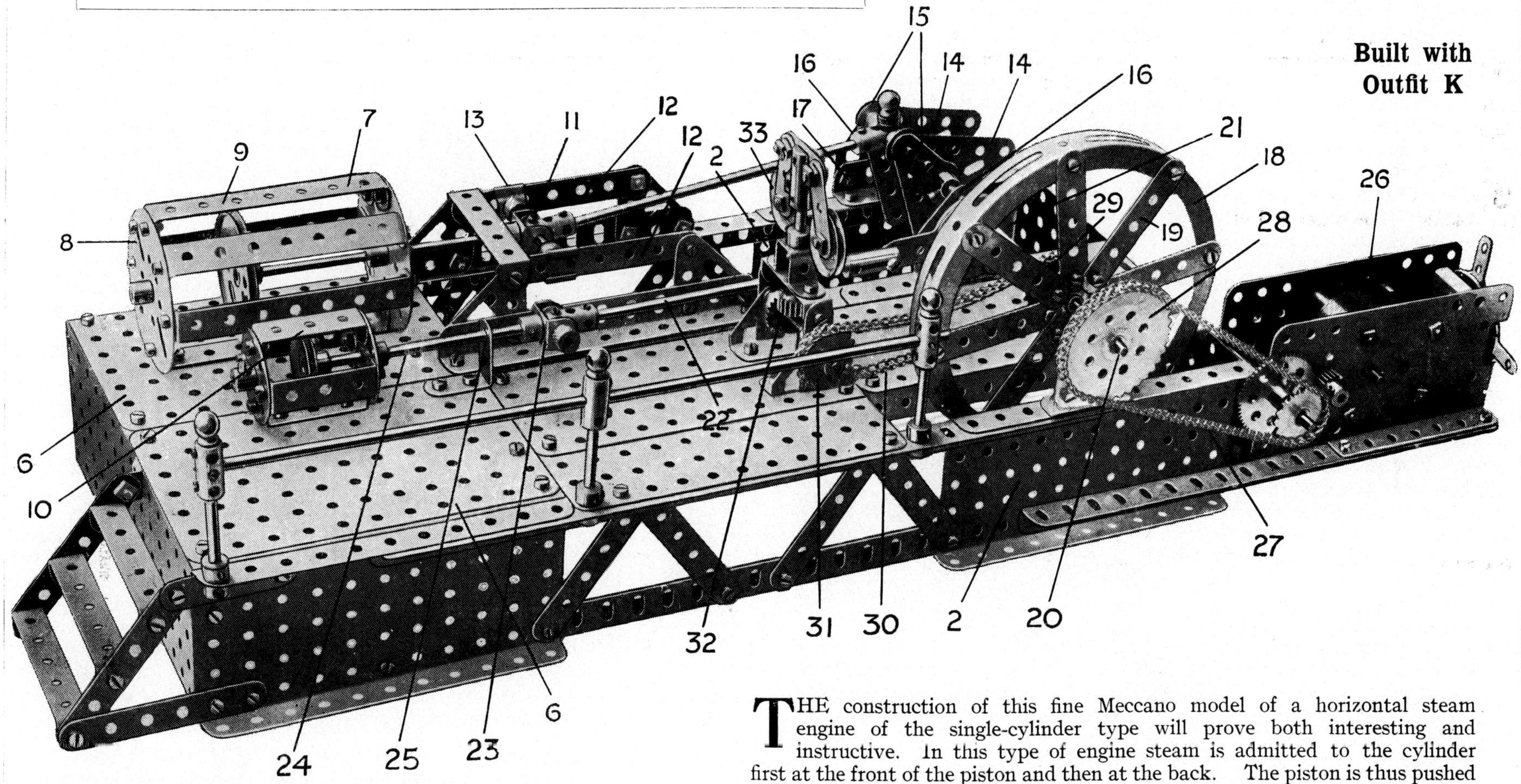

Fig. 1. General view of the Steam Engine, showing the method of coupling the Meccano Electric Motor to the crankshaft

THE construction of this fine Meccano model of a horizontal steam engine of the single-cylinder type will prove both interesting and instructive. In this type of engine steam is admitted to the cylinder first at the front of the piston and then at the back. The piston is thus pushed alternately backwards and forwards, and from this movement such engines are called "reciprocating." The type of reciprocating engine adopted as the prototype of the Meccano model is one of the simplest, and yet in spite of its simplicity the combined efforts of many inventors, spread over a long period, were necessary to produce it.

21/934/4 *Published by* MECCANO LIMITED, BINNS ROAD, LIVERPOOL 13 *Printed in England*

It is interesting to go back to the early days of the steam engine and see how it has developed, step by step, from a mechanical curiosity to a practical working apparatus.

First Practical Steam Engine

James Watt is commonly regarded as the inventor of the steam engine, but as a matter of fact a number of engines using steam had been produced before his time. Watt's great work lay in developing the steam engine from a state of crude inefficiency to what may be described, comparatively, as practical perfection.

The idea of using steam in a cylinder appears to have originated with Denis Papin, a Frenchman, who, about the year 1688, constructed a working model to illustrate his idea. The first really practical engine was erected in 1710 by Thomas Newcomen, an Englishman, and it was used as a pumping engine. It consisted of a vertical steam cylinder, the piston of which was connected to one end of a beam pivoted in the middle. The other end of the beam was attached to rods working the pump. Around the cylinder was a jacket, to which cold water could be supplied.

When the piston in the working cylinder was at the top of its stroke, being raised by the weight of the pump rods, steam was admitted to the cylinder so as to drive out all the air. The steam was then shut off and cold water was admitted to the outer jacket. This condensed the steam in the working cylinder so that a partial vacuum was produced, and atmospheric pressure forced the piston down, thereby raising the pump rods. Each time this occurred one stroke of the pump was made and the operation was then repeated. Newcomen's engine, improved later in some details by its inventor, was used extensively in pumping water from mines. It will be seen that the engine was not a true steam engine, for the forcing down of the piston was done by atmospheric pressure.

James Watt's Great Idea

A model of the Newcomen engine came into the hands of James Watt for repair, and while engaged on this task he hit upon the idea on which the modern steam engine is based.

In the Newcomen engine the working cylinder was first heated by steam and then cooled by water to condense the steam. Watt saw that this alternate

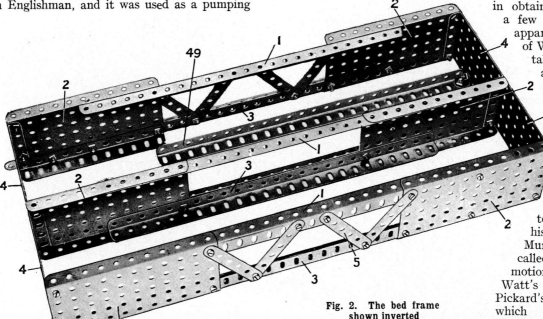

Fig. 2. The bed frame shown inverted

heating and cooling resulted in a great waste of energy, and endeavoured to find some means of keeping the cylinder at an even temperature. It took him a long time to solve the problem, but at last he succeeded by condensing the steam in a separate vessel, instead of in the working cylinder itself.

Talkative Workman Causes Trouble

Watt's improved engine, patented in 1769, was used entirely for pumping, as Newcomen's had been. In 1781 Watt took out another patent for an engine in which the reciprocating motion of the piston was converted into rotary motion, so that ordinary machinery could be driven. Watt had intended to obtain this rotary motion by means of the now familiar crank and flywheel, but he found himself prevented from doing so because a Birmingham button-maker named James Pickard had succeeded in obtaining a patent for this device a few months previously. Pickard apparently got the idea from one of Watt's workmen, who had been talking too freely and bragging about the great things that the rotary engine was going to accomplish. Watt was very angry when he found what had happened, and for a while he was puzzled to overcome the difficulty thus created. He determined not to be beaten, however, and after trying various schemes he decided to use a device invented by his best workman, William Murdock. This device was called the "sun-and-planet" motion, and was utilised on Watt's rotary engines until Pickard's patent expired, after which the simpler and more efficient crank and flywheel were substituted. "Sun-and-planet" mechanism may easily be reproduced in Meccano by means of Gears on Rods held in a frame of strips or cranks.

Watt's Final Improvements

Up to this time Watt's engines were "single acting"—that is to say the cylinder was connected to the condenser only on one side of the piston, so that work was only performed during one stroke of the piston. In 1782 Watt took out a patent for connecting the cylinder to the condenser both back and front of the piston, thus making the engine "double acting," and consequently much more efficient.

In the same year he obtained another patent for a method of securing greater economy in the use of steam. The principle involved in this final improvement was that of shutting off steam from the cylinder when the piston had only travelled part of its journey, and leaving the rest of the thrust to be carried out by the expansion of the steam.

The brilliant inventions we have briefly described were Watt's chief contributions towards the perfecting of the steam engine. Watt found the engine a clumsy mechanism, very inefficient and wasteful of fuel, and only capable of working a pump. Through his inventions it became efficient and economical, and capable of working machinery of almost every kind.

The Meccano Model : The Bed Frame

It will be seen on glancing at the model that no reversing device is fitted to the engine. Usually engines of this kind are equipped with some valve motion that is capable of reversing the direction of rotation of the crankshaft as required. There are instances, however, where an engine is required to run in one direction only and reversing valve motion is therefore unnecessary. By suitably arranging the positions of the main piston in relation to the valve piston the action of a simple steam engine can clearly be understood.

The working portions of the engine are mounted on a raised bed-frame. This frame is shown inverted in Fig. 2, the covering plates 6 having been removed. The construction of the framework is as follows. The 12½″ Angle Girders 1 and 3 are bolted at each end to the 5½″ by 2½″ Flanged Plates 2. Old style Plates are illustrated, and with the new parts the Girders should be mounted outside the flanges. Four 3½″ by 2½″ Flanged Plates 4 are bolted to the Plates 2. Each long side of the framework is braced with four 3″ Strips 5. If desired, these Strips may be replaced by Strip Plates, these giving the base a more solid appearance.

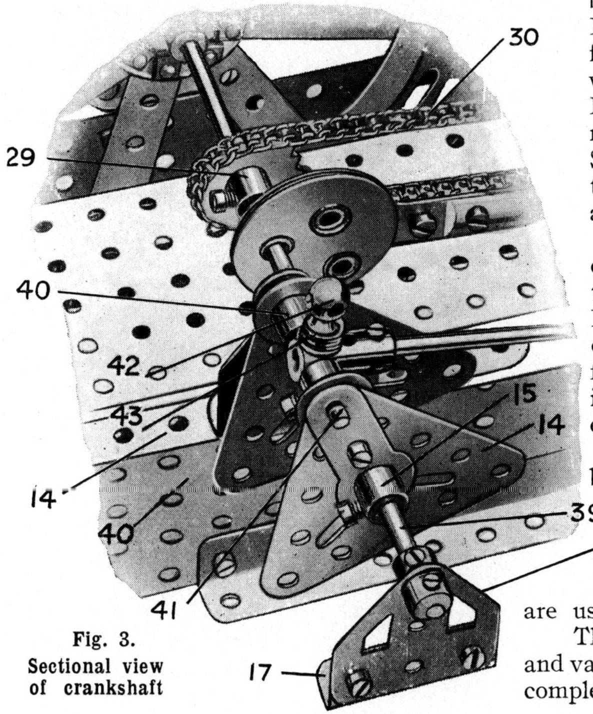

The 12½″ Angle Girder 49 fastened to one of the Plates 4 by an Angle Bracket, forms one side of the slot in which the flywheel 18 turns. It is fastened at its other end to the Flat Plates 6. These Plates 6 should be secured in place as soon as the bed-frame is completed. Three 5½″ by 3½″ and two 5½″ by 2½″ Flat Plates are used, as shown in Fig. 1. The building of cylinder and valve-casing should next be completed. The cylinder 7 is constructed from two Face Plates 8 and 3½″ by ½″ Double Angle Strips 9. The valve-casing 10 consists of two Bush Wheels and four 1½″ by ½″ Double Angle Strips, a 1″ fast Pulley Wheel being placed in the casing prior to fastening the Strips to the Bush Wheels. The casing is secured to the bed plate by nuts and bolts.

Fig. 4.
Sectional view, showing crosshead

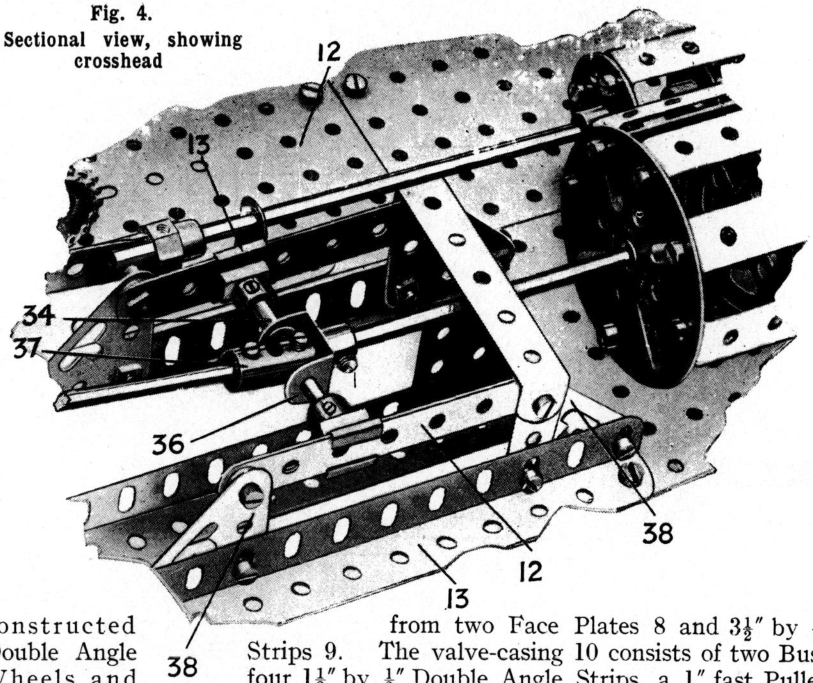

Fig. 3.
Sectional view of crankshaft

The Crosshead

The crosshead 11 should next be built up. It is shown in detail in Fig. 4. The slide-bars are supported at their ends by Corner Brackets 38, which are bolted to 5½″ Angle Girders placed one on each side of the opening in the bed-frame, as can be seen in Fig. 1. The crosshead framework is strengthened at the end nearest the cylinder by means of a 2½″ by ½″ Double Angle Strip bolted to two of the Corner Brackets 38.

To the slide-bars 12 is attached the slidable portion of the crosshead. This consists of a Large Fork Piece 36 fastened to the end of the piston rod, and a Coupling 37 pivoted in the end of the Fork Piece by means of a 2″ Rod 34. When passing the Rod 34 through the Fork Piece and Coupling two Washers should be slipped on each side of the Coupling to retain it in the correct position in the centre of the Fork Piece. Eye Pieces with Bosses 13 are next fitted on to each end of the Rod 34 and arranged to engage the slide-bars 12.

The Crankshaft

The next portion to be assembled is the crankshaft and flywheel. The bearings for the crankshaft consist of Flat Trunnions 16 secured to 1½″ Angle Girders 17, which, in turn, are bolted to the flanges of the Plates 2. The flywheel consists of a Circular Girder 18 connected by means of 2½″ Strips 19 to a Bush Wheel fastened to the shaft 20. A Hub Disc will serve equally well for the flywheel. The Bush Wheel is adjusted so that the edge of the Circular Girder has plenty of room to turn freely in its slot.

A detailed view of the crankshaft is shown in Fig. 3. Each crank arm consists of two Cranks 15 and 40 bolted one on each side of a 2½″ Triangular Plate 14. The inner end of the 2″ Axle Rod 39 is secured in the Crank 15, and the inner end of the 5″ Rod 20 is gripped in the boss of the corresponding Crank 15 on the other crank arm.

The crank pin consists of a 2″ Axle Rod 41 secured in the bosses of Cranks 40. The end bearing of the connecting rod consists of a Coupling that is free to turn about the Rod 41, the set-screw in its end having been removed. A Handrail Support 42 is inserted in place of the set-screw, four Washers 43 being placed on its shank to prevent the latter touching the crank pin 41. By removing the Handrail Support the crank pin may be lubricated. The purpose of balancing the crankshaft by securing the Triangular Plates 14 to the crank arms is to ensure smooth rotary motion of the engine.

It will be realised that every time the crankshaft completes a half revolution the crank arms, connecting rod, and piston rod all come into alignment. Hence in this position, which is known as the "dead centre," there is a tendency for the whole mechanism to come to rest unless some means is devised to carry it round until the piston can again exert its force. The heavy flywheel overcomes the tendency by storing up energy during the piston stroke, which energy is expended in carrying the crankshaft over the "dead centre."

A 1″ Sprocket Wheel 29 on the Axle Rod 20 is connected by an endless Sprocket Chain 30 to the 1″ Sprocket Wheel 31, which drives the governor mechanism. A Triple Throw Eccentric is also fastened to the Rod 20, the ¾″ throw being used. This Eccentric provides the reciprocating motion that actuates the piston valve rod, to which it is joined in the following manner. A Strip Coupling is pivoted on a ⅜″ Bolt passed through the end hole of the Eccentric arm, and a 6½″ Rod 22 is fastened to the Strip Coupling. The Rod 22 has a Coupling attached to its other end and this Coupling is pivoted to a large Fork Piece 23 by means of a 1″ Axle Rod held in place by two Collars. A Washer is placed on each side of the Coupling in order to eliminate side play.

The valve rod 24 is fastened in the boss of the Large Fork Piece 23 and is attached to the 1″ Pulley Wheel which represents the piston valve in the casing 10. The Rod 24 is guided in a 1″ by 1″ Angle Bracket 25 bolted to one of the Flat Plates 6.

The Centrifugal Governor

A separate view of the centrifugal governor is shown in Fig. 5. Its support is built up from Trunnions 48, bolted to one of the base Plates 6, and

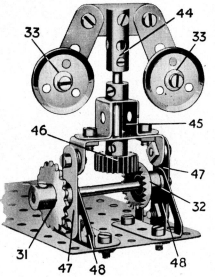

Fig. 5. The Centrifugal Governor

1½″ Strips 47. A 1½″ by ½″ Double Angle Strip is fastened to the Strips 47 by means of ⅜″ bolts, Washers being placed between the Double Angle Strip and the Strips 47 to obtain the correct spacing. A 1″ Sprocket Wheel 31 and ¾″ Contrate Wheel 32 are fastened on a 2″ Rod journalled in the centre holes of the Strips 47, and a ¾″ Pinion 46 meshes with the Contrate 32.

The Pinion 46 is secured to a 2″ Axle Rod journalled in the 1½″ by ½″ Double Angle Strip and also in the Double Bent Strip 45. A Strip Coupling 44 attached to the upper end of the Rod carries in its slot the 1½″ Strip that supports the governor arms. The latter consist of 1½″ Strips pivoted at their upper ends by bolts and lock-nuts and carrying at their lower ends the weights, which consist of 1″ loose Pulley Wheels 33 fastened to the Strips by means of ⅜″ Bolts and nuts. When the 1″ Sprocket Wheel 31 is rotated by means of the Sprocket Chain 30 and the 1″ Sprocket Wheel 29 (Fig. 1), the vertical 2″ Rod carrying the governor arms is set in motion and the weights 33 will rise higher and higher as the speed of the engine increases, owing to centrifugal force.

In the actual engine the weights 33 are coupled to a collar sliding on the vertical shaft of the governor, and the movement of this collar is caused to actuate the valve that controls the supply of steam to the cylinder. If the engine's speed exceeds a certain limit the rising weights commence to close the supply valve, thus diminishing the amount of steam passing through the cylinder, and the speed of the engine drops accordingly.

The model is completed by fixing the Electric Motor in position and coupling it to the crankshaft. The Motor is attached to the engine bed by means of a 9½″ Angle Girder at one side and by an Angle Bracket at the other side. The drive from the armature shaft is led through reduction gearing and a Sprocket Chain drive to the crankshaft. The gear train consists of a ½″ Pinion on the armature shaft engaging with a 57-teeth Gear Wheel on a secondary shaft and another ½″ Pinion on this shaft meshing with a second 57-teeth Gear Wheel, which can be seen in Fig. 1. A 1″ Sprocket Wheel on the shaft of the latter Gear Wheel is connected to the 2″ Sprocket Wheel 28 by means of the endless Chain 27.

This gearing is designed for use with a 6-volt Motor, and if assembled exactly as described the model will work easily at a fair speed. If a 20-volt Motor is used, however, the gearing will have to be adjusted accordingly.

To ensure smooth running of the engine special care should be taken to see that all the bearings are in correct alignment and are kept properly lubricated.

List of Parts Required to Build the Horizontal Engine.

2 of No. 3	1 of No. 8a	2 of No. 12	2 of No. 16	3 of No. 24	4 of No. 48	14 of No. 59	26″ of No. 94	2 of No. 126
11 ,, ,, 4	3 ,, ,, 9	1 ,, ,, 12a	2 ,, ,, 16a	1 ,, ,, 25	4 ,, ,, 48a	4 ,, ,, 62	1 ,, ,, 95	3 ,, ,, 126a
8 ,, ,, 5	1 ,, ,, 9d	1 ,, ,, 13	5 ,, ,, 17	1 ,, ,, 26	6 ,, ,, 48b	6 ,, ,, 63	3 ,, ,, 96	4 ,, ,, 133
1 ,, ,, 6	3 ,, ,, 9f	2 ,, ,, 14	2 ,, ,, 18a	2 ,, ,, 27a	2 ,, ,, 50a	2 ,, ,, 63b	2 ,, ,, 109	3 ,, ,, 136
5 ,, ,, 6a	4 ,, ,, 10	1 ,, ,, 15	1 ,, ,, 20a	1 ,, ,, 29	7 ,, ,, 52	3 ,, ,, 70	2 ,, ,, 116	E6 Electric
7 ,, ,, 8	2 ,, ,, 11	1 ,, ,, 15a	1 ,, ,, 22	160 ,, ,, 37	2 ,, ,, 52a	2 ,, ,, 76	1 ,, ,, 118	Motor
			2 ,, ,, 22a	20 ,, ,, 38	4 ,, ,, 53			
				1 ,, ,, 45				

Meccano Single - Cylinder Horizontal Steam Engine

Fitted with balanced crankshaft, crosshead and centrifugal governor, etc., this model affords an interesting demonstration of the principles of a simple steam engine.

A K Outfit Model

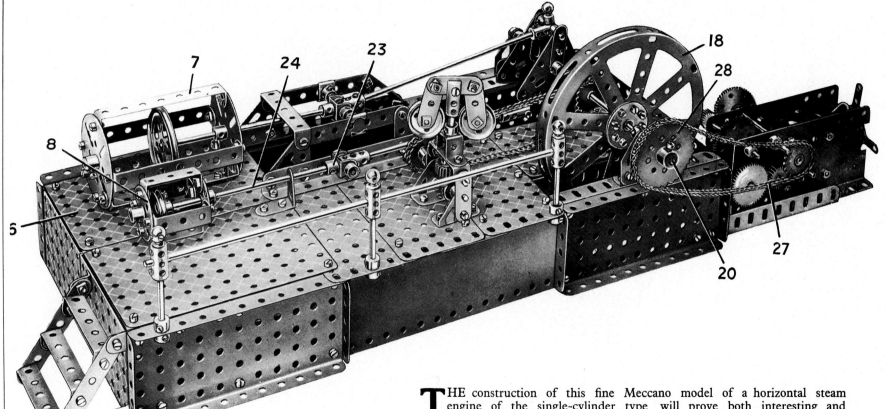

Fig. 1. General view of the Steam Engine, showing the method of coupling the Meccano Electric Motor to the crankshaft.

THE construction of this fine Meccano model of a horizontal steam engine of the single-cylinder type will prove both interesting and instructive. In this type of engine steam is admitted to the cylinder first at the front of the piston and then at the back. The piston is thus pushed alternately backwards and forwards, and from this movement such engines are called "reciprocating." The type of reciprocating engine adopted as the prototype of the Meccano model is one of the simplest, and yet in spite of its simplicity the combined efforts of many inventors, spread over a long period, were necessary to produce it.

It is interesting to go back to the early days of the steam engine and see how it has developed, step by step, from a mechanical curiosity to a practical working apparatus.

First Practical Steam Engine

James Watt is commonly regarded as the inventor of the steam engine, but as a matter of fact a number of engines using steam had been produced before his time. Watt's great work lay in developing the steam engine from a state of crude inefficiency to what may be described, comparatively, as practical perfection.

The idea of using steam in a cylinder appears to have originated with Denis Papin, a Frenchman, who, about the year 1688, constructed a working model to illustrate his idea. The first really practical engine was erected in 1710 by Thomas Newcomen, an Englishman, and it was used as a pumping engine. It consisted of a vertical steam cylinder, the piston of which was connected to one end of a beam pivoted in the middle. The other end of the beam was attached to rods working the pump. Around the cylinder was a jacket, to which cold water could be supplied.

When the piston in the working cylinder was at the top of its stroke, being raised by the weight of the pump rods, steam was admitted to the cylinder so as to drive out all the air. The steam was then shut off and cold water was admitted to the outer jacket. This condensed the steam in the working cylinder so that a partial vacuum was produced, and atmospheric pressure forced the piston down, thereby raising the pump rods. Each time this occurred one stroke of the pump was made and the operation was then repeated. Newcomen's engine, improved later in some details by its inventor, was used extensively in pumping water from mines. It will be seen that the engine was not a true steam engine, for the forcing down of the piston was done by atmospheric pressure.

James Watt's Great Idea

A model of the Newcomen engine came into the hands of James Watt for repair, and while engaged on this task he hit upon the idea on which the modern steam engine is based.

In the Newcomen engine the working cylinder was first heated by steam and then cooled by water to condense the steam. Watt saw that this alternate heating and cooling resulted in a great waste of energy, and endeavoured to find some means of keeping the cylinder at an even temperature. It took him a long time to solve the problem, but at last he succeeded by condensing the steam in a separate vessel, instead of in the working cylinder itself.

Talkative Workman Causes Trouble

Watt's improved engine, patented in 1769, was used entirely for pumping, as Newcomen's had been. In 1781 Watt took out another patent for an engine in which the reciprocating motion of the piston was converted into rotary motion, so that ordinary machinery could be driven. Watt had intended to obtain this rotary motion by means of the now familiar crank and flywheel, but he found himself prevented from doing so because a Birmingham button-maker named James Pickard had succeeded in obtaining a patent for this device a few months previously. Pickard apparently got the idea from one of Watt's workmen, who had been talking too freely and bragging about the great things that the rotary engine was going to accomplish. Watt was very angry when he found what had happened, and for a while he was puzzled to overcome the difficulty thus created. He determined not to be beaten however, and after trying, various schemes he decided to use a device invented by his best workman, William Murdock. This device was called the " sun-and-planet " motion, and was utilised on Watt's rotary engines until Pickard's patent expired, after which the simpler and more efficient crank and flywheel were substituted. " Sun-and-planet " mechanism may easily be reproduced in Meccano by means of Gears on Rods held in a frame of strips or Cranks.

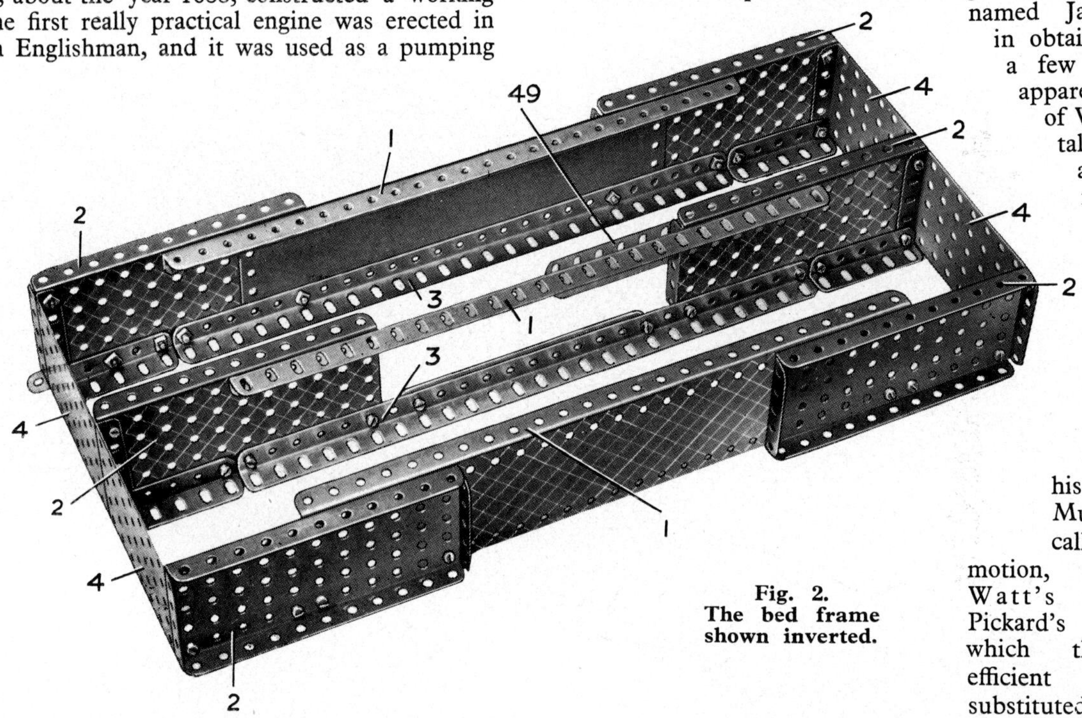

Watt's Final Improvements

Up to this time Watt's engines were " single acting "—that is to say the cylinder was connected to the condenser only on one side of the piston, so that work was performed only during one stroke of the piston. In 1782 Watt took out a patent for connecting the cylinder to the condenser both back and front of the piston, thus making the engine " double acting," and consequently much more efficient.

In the same year he obtained another patent for a method of securing greater

Fig. 2.
The bed frame shown inverted.

economy in the use of steam. The principle involved in this final improvement was that of shutting off steam from the cylinder when the piston had only travelled part of its journey, and leaving the rest of the thrust to be carried out by the expansion of the steam.

The brilliant inventions we have briefly described were Watt's chief contributions towards the perfecting of the steam engine. Watt found the engine a clumsy mechanism, very inefficient and wasteful of fuel, and only capable of working a pump. Through his inventions it became efficient and economical, and capable of working machinery of almost every kind.

The Meccano Model: The Bed Frame

It will be seen on glancing at the model that no reversing device is fitted to the engine. Usually engines of this kind are equipped with some valve motion that is capable of reversing the direction of rotation of the crankshaft as required. There are instances, however, where an engine is required to run in one direction only and reversing valve motion is therefore unnecessary. By suitably arranging the positions of the main piston in relation to the valve piston the action of a simple steam engine can clearly be understood.

The working portions of the engine are mounted on a raised bed-frame. This frame is shown inverted in Fig. 2, the covering plates 6 having been removed. The construction of the framework is as follows. The 12½″ Angle Girders 1 and 3 are bolted at each end to the edges of 5½″ × 2½″ Flanged Plates 2, and four 3½″ × 2½″ Flanged Plates 4 are bolted to the ends of the Plates 2.

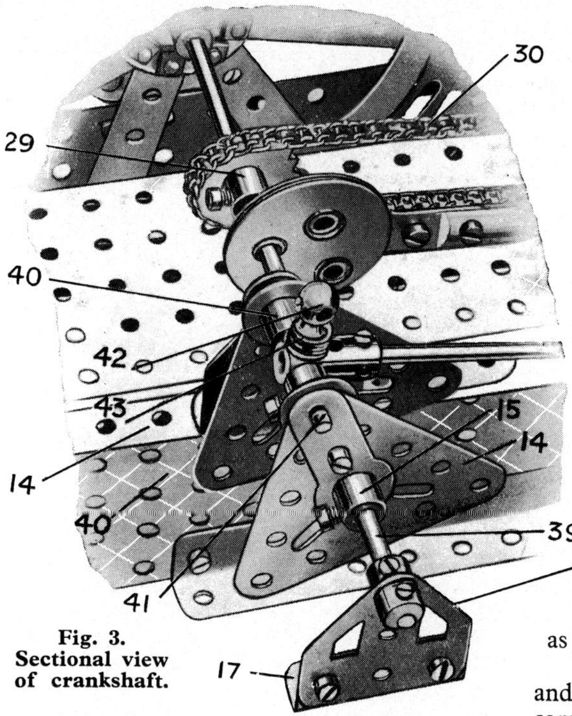

Fig. 3.
Sectional view of crankshaft.

Each long side of the framework is fitted with a 9½″ × 2½″ Strip Plate secured between the 12½″ Angle Girders and the Flanged Plates. The Strip Plates give the base a very solid appearance.

The 7½″ Angle Girder 49 fastened to one of the Plates 4 by an Angle Bracket, forms one side of the slot in which the flywheel 18 turns. It is fastened at its other end to the Flat Plates 6.

These Plates 6 should be secured in place as soon as the bed-frame is completed. Two 5½″ × 3½″, one 5½″ × 2½″. and three 4½″ × 2½″ Flat Plates are used, as shown in Fig. 1.

The building of cylinder and valve-casing should next be completed. The cylinder 7 is

Fig. 4.
Sectional view, showing crosshead.

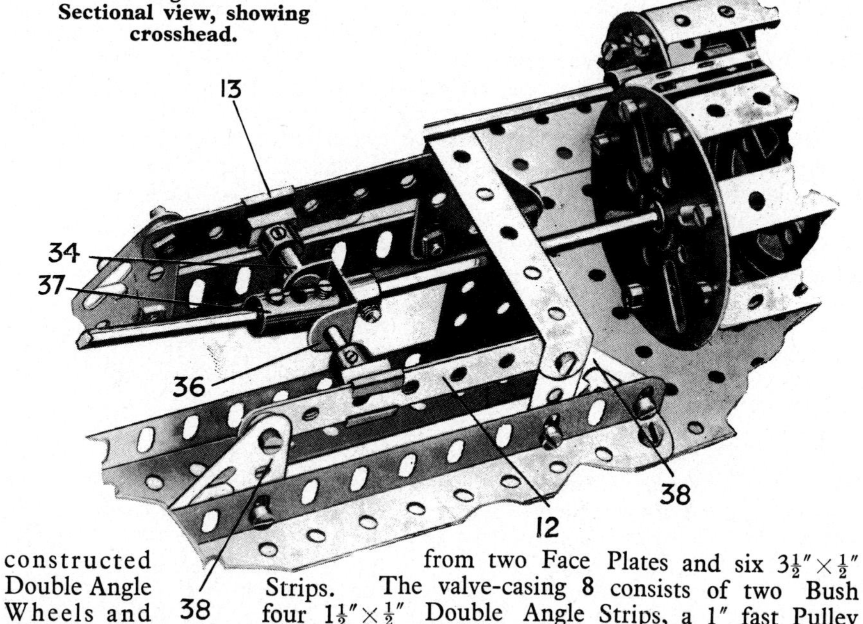

constructed from two Face Plates and six 3½″ × ½″ Double Angle Strips. The valve-casing 8 consists of two Bush Wheels and four 1½″ × ½″ Double Angle Strips, a 1″ fast Pulley Wheel being placed in the casing prior to fastening the Strips to the Bush Wheels. The casing is secured to the bed plate by nuts and bolts.

The Crosshead

The crosshead should next be built up. It is shown in detail in Fig. 4. The slide-bars are supported at their ends by Corner Brackets 38, which are bolted to 5½″ Angle Girders placed one on each side of the opening in the bed-frame, as can be seen in Fig. 1. The crosshead framework is strengthened at the end near the cylinder by means of a 2½″ × ½″ Double Angle Strip bolted to two of the Corner Brackets 38.

To the slide-bars 12 is attached the slidable portion of the crosshead. This consists of a Large Fork Piece 36 fastened to the end of the piston rod, and a Coupling 37 is pivoted in the end of the Fork Piece by means of a 2″ Rod 34. When passing the Rod 34 through the Fork Piece and Coupling two Washers should be slipped on each side of the Coupling to retain it in the correct position in the centre of the Fork Piece. Eye Pieces 13 are next fitted on to each end of the Rod 34 and arranged to engage the slide-bars 12.

The Crankshaft

The next portion to be assembled is the crankshaft and flywheel. The bearings for the crankshaft consist of Flat Trunnions 16 secured to 1½″ Angle Girders 17, which, in turn, are bolted to the Angle Girders. The flywheel consists of a Hub Disc 18, bolted to a Bush Wheel on the shaft 20. The Bush Wheel is adjusted so that the edge of the Hub Disc has plenty of room to turn freely in its slot without touching the sides.

A detailed view of the crankshaft is shown in Fig. 3. Each crank arm consists of two Cranks 15 and 40 bolted one on each side of a 2½″ Triangular Plate 14. The inner end of the 2″ Axle Rod 39 is secured in the Crank 15, and the inner end of the 5″ Rod 20 is gripped in the boss of the corresponding Crank 15 on the other crank arm.

The crank pin consists of a 2″ Axle Rod 41 secured in the bosses of Cranks 40. The end bearing of the connecting rod consists of a Coupling that is free to turn about the Rod 41, the set screw in its end having been removed. A Handrail Support 42 is inserted in place of the set screw, four Washers 43 being placed on its shank to prevent the latter touching the crank pin 41. By removing the Handrail Support the crank pin may be lubricated. The purpose of balancing the crankshaft by securing the Triangular Plates 14 to the crank arms is to ensure smooth rotary motion of the engine.

It will be realised that every time the crankshaft completes a half revolution the crank arms, connecting rod, and piston rod all come into alignment. Hence in this position, which is known as the "dead centre," there is a tendency for the whole mechanism to come to rest unless some means is devised to carry it round until the piston can again exert its force. The heavy flywheel overcomes the tendency by storing up energy during the piston stroke, which energy is expended in carrying the crankshaft over the "dead centre."

A 1″ Sprocket Wheel 29 on the Axle Rod 20 is connected by an endless Sprocket Chain 30 to the 1″ Sprocket Wheel 31, which drives the governor mechanism. A Triple Throw Eccentric is also fastened to the Rod 20, the ¾″ throw being used. This Eccentric provides the reciprocating motion that actuates the piston valve rod, to which it is joined in the following manner. A Strip Coupling is rigidly clamped to the Eccentric stays by means of two bolts, and a 5″ Rod 22 is fastened to the Strip Coupling. The Rod 22 has a Coupling attached to its other end and this Coupling is pivoted to a Large Fork Piece 23 by means of a 1″ Axle Rod held in place by two Collars. A Washer is placed on each side of the Coupling in order to eliminate side play.

The valve rod 24 is fastened in the boss of the large Fork Piece 23 and is attached to the 1″ Pulley Wheel which represents the piston valve in the casing 8. The Rod 24 is guided in a 1″×1″ Angle Bracket, bolted to one of the Flat Plates 6.

The Centrifugal Governor

A separate view of the centrifugal governor is shown in Fig. 5. Its

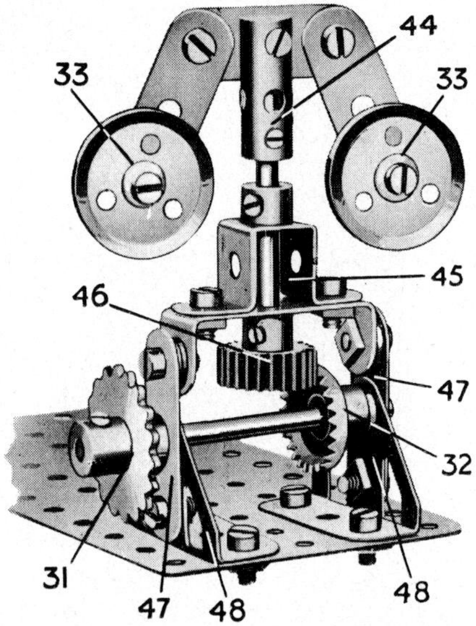

Fig. 5. The Centrifugal Governor

support is built up from Trunnions 48, bolted to one of the base Plates 6, and 1½″ Strips 47. A 1½″×½″ Double Angle Strip is fastened to the Strips 47 by means of ⅜″ Bolts, Washers being placed between the Double Angle Strip and the Strips 47 to obtain the correct spacing. A 1″ Sprocket Wheel 31 and ¾″ Contrate Wheel 32 are fastened on a 2″ Rod journalled in the centre holes of the Strips 47, and a ¾″ Pinion 46 meshes with the Contrate 32.

The Pinion 46 is secured to a 2″ Axle Rod journalled in the 1½″×½″ Double Angle Strip and also in the Double Bent Strip 45. A Strip Coupling 44 attached to the upper end of the Rod carries in its slot the 1½″ Strip that supports the governor arms. The latter consists of 1½″ Strips pivoted at their upper ends by bolts and lock-nuts and carrying at their lower ends the weights, which consist of 1″ loose Pulley Wheels 33 fastened to the Strips by means of ⅜″ Bolts and nuts. When the 1″ Sprocket Wheel 31 is rotated by means of the Sprocket Chain 30 and the 1″ Sprocket Wheel 29 (Fig. 3), the vertical 2″ Rod carrying the governor arms is set in motion and the weights 33 will rise higher and higher as the speed of the engine increases, owing to centrifugal force.

In the actual engine the weights 33 are coupled to a collar sliding on the vertical shaft of the governor, and the movement of this collar is caused to actuate the valve that controls the supply of steam to the cylinder. If the engine's speed exceeds a certain limit the rising weights commence to close the supply valve, thus diminishing the amount of steam passing through the cylinder, and the speed of the engine drops accordingly.

The model is completed by fixing the Electric Motor in position and coupling it to the crankshaft. The Motor is attached to the engine bed by means of a 5½″ Angle Girder at one side and by a 4½″ Girder at the other side. The drive from the armature shaft is led through reduction gearing and a Sprocket Chain drive to the crankshaft. The gear train consists of a ½″ Pinion on the armature shaft engaging with a 57-teeth Gear Wheel on a secondary shaft and a ¾″ Pinion on this shaft meshing with a 50-teeth Gear Wheel, can be seen in Fig. 1. Two more ½″ Pinions and 57-teeth gears drive the Rod of a 1″ Sprocket, connected to the 2″ Sprocket Wheel 28 by the Chain 27.

This gearing is designed for use with a 6-volt or 20-volt Motor, and if assembled exactly as described the model will work easily at a fair speed. The speed can be regulated from the Transformer control or from a Resistance Controller if an accumulator is used.

To ensure smooth running of the engine special care should be taken to see that all the bearings are in correct alignment and that all working parts are kept properly lubricated.

List of Parts Required to Build the Horizontal Steam Engine.

2 of No. 3	1 of No. 9a	4 of No. 15	1 of No. 22	1 of No. 28	6 of No. 48b	4 of No. 62	29″ of No. 94	3 of No. 126
3 ,, 4	6 ,, 9d	1 ,, 16	2 ,, 22a	158 ,, 37	2 ,, 50a	1 ,, 62b	2 ,, 95	1 ,, 130
1 ,, 6	3 ,, 9f	4 ,, 16a	3 ,, 24	5 ,, 37b	6 ,, 52	7 ,, 63	3 ,, 96	4 ,, 133
4 ,, 6a	2 ,, 12	5 ,, 17	2 ,, 25	36 ,, 38	2 ,, 52a	2 ,, 63b	2 ,, 109	4 ,, 136
6 ,, 8	2 ,, 12a	2 ,, 18a	3 ,, 26	1 ,, 45	4 ,, 53	1 ,, 70	2 ,, 116	2 ,, 196
1 ,, 8b	1 ,, 13	2 ,, 18b	1 ,, 27	4 ,, 48	4 ,, 53a	1 ,, 72	1 ,, 118	E6 Electric
4 ,, 9	1 ,, 14	1 ,, 20a	3 ,, 27a	5 ,, 48a	16 ,, 59	2 ,, 76	2 ,, 126a	Motor

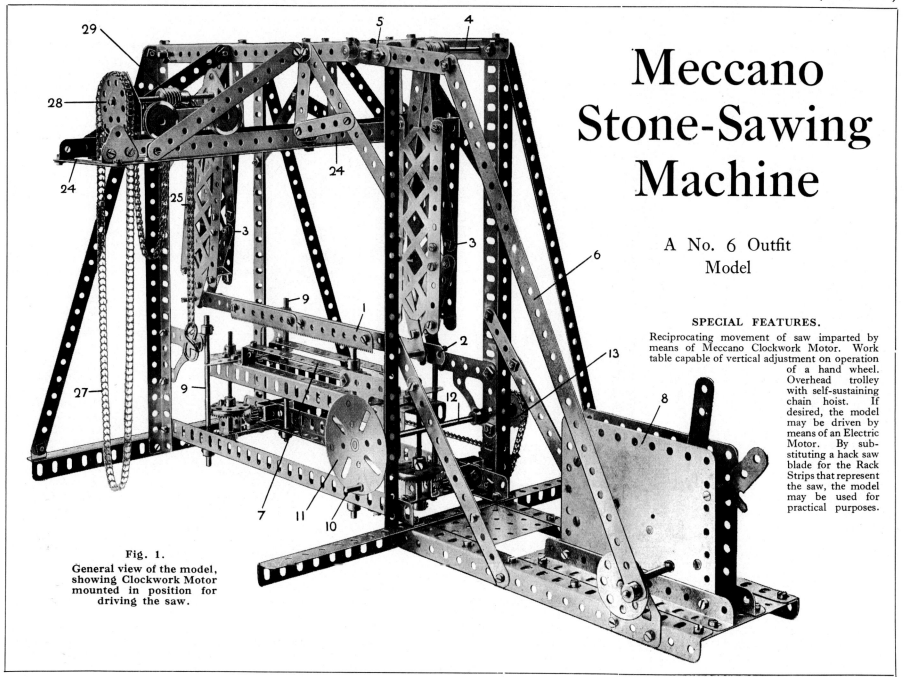

Meccano Stone-Sawing Machine

A No. 6 Outfit
Model

SPECIAL FEATURES.

Reciprocating movement of saw imparted by means of Meccano Clockwork Motor. Work table capable of vertical adjustment on operation of a hand wheel. Overhead trolley with self-sustaining chain hoist. If desired, the model may be driven by means of an Electric Motor. By substituting a hack saw blade for the Rack Strips that represent the saw, the model may be used for practical purposes.

Fig. 1.
General view of the model, showing Clockwork Motor mounted in position for driving the saw.

Published by MECCANO LIMITED, BINNS ROAD, LIVERPOOL   Printed in England. 528/5

ANY Meccano boy who resides near a large stone quarry will be familiar with the wonderful machines that are capable of cutting into large or small blocks the very stone of which large portions of the country are formed. He will be aware of the slow but sure work which these machines perform, gradually cutting their way stroke by stroke through the hardest stone or rock. But all Meccano boys are not so fortunate to be able to study this type of machine at work and doubtless when they have seen large modern buildings in course of construction they have wondered how the blocks of stone—weighing sometimes a ton or more each—were cut into such exact shapes and sizes.

Those wonderful builders, the Romans, must have felt the need of some mechanical means of stone cutting when they were erecting their beautiful palaces and temples. Although their tools were of the crudest type, the work of these early stone-masons was in many respects equal, if not superior, to the work of our modern craftsmen, and it has stood the test of centuries. Some of their pillars and walls are standing to-day, the joints in the stonework fitting as perfectly now as when they were built two thousand or more years ago. Nevertheless, their achievements, although admirable from the artistic point of view, were attained only at the expense of much human suffering.

Practically all the work had to be done by manual labour. Huge blocks had to be hacked out of the solid rock of the quarries, then perhaps dragged for many miles to the place where the building was in progress. On arrival there they were chipped into shape and the surfaces rubbed with pieces of harder stone until they were smooth and flat. They then had to be hauled up into position for setting. As the available knowledge of the mechanical powers was very small, it can be realised how hard and fatiguing the work was. Most of the builders were prisoners of war who were turned into slavery and forced to these heavy and heart-breaking tasks under the lash of an ever-vigilant slave driver. Owing to the crude methods employed in those days, buildings of any size or importance took very many years to construct. When one sees huge buildings now being erected in the course of a few months, the enormous change brought about by modern mechanical methods can be realised. One of the principal aids to the stonemason to-day is the machinery with which the stone blocks are cut and shaped.

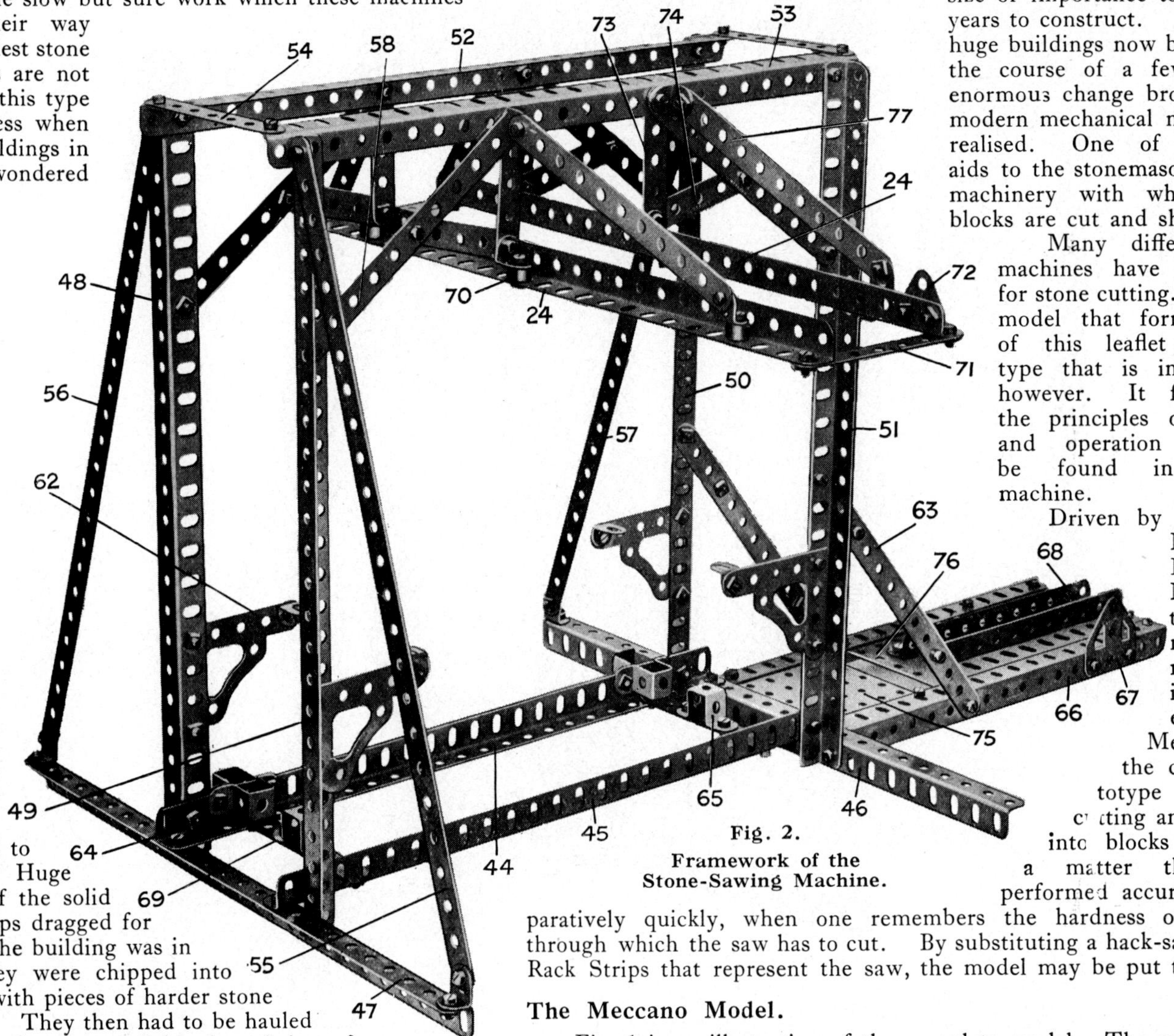

Many different types of machines have been designed for stone cutting. The Meccano model that forms the subject of this leaflet represents a type that is in general use, however. It follows closely the principles of construction and operation that are to be found in the actual machine.

Driven by the Clockwork Motor shown in Fig. 1, or a Meccano Electric Motor, the model will afford many interesting points to enthusiastic Meccano boys. In the case of its prototype the work of cutting and sawing stone into blocks of any size is a matter that can be performed accurately and comparatively quickly, when one remembers the hardness of the material through which the saw has to cut. By substituting a hack-saw blade for the Rack Strips that represent the saw, the model may be put to practical use.

The Meccano Model.

Fig. 1 is an illustration of the complete model. The saw 1 is attached pivotally to the swinging frames 3. One of these frames is pivoted loosely on a Rod carried in the top of the frame and the other is secured by a Crank

Fig. 2.
Framework of the
Stone-Sawing Machine.

to the Rod 4. When the Clockwork Motor is set in motion the swinging cranes are oscillated, thereby imparting a reciprocating or sawing motion to the saw 1.

The stone to be shaped is placed on the support frame 7, and in order to allow for various depths of saw cuts this support frame is constructed so as to permit raising and lowering on operation of the hand wheel 11.

The overhead trolley embodies a self-sustaining hoist, and is used for raising the stone blocks and placing them in position on the support frame 7 for cutting. The trolley runs on the gantry rails 24.

Having obtained some idea of the working arrangements of the model construction may be commenced. The following notes deal with each part of the model in the order in which the building should proceed.

Building the Framework.

The frame of the model is shown in Fig. 2. Its construction should be commenced by forming the base with the Angle Girders 44, 45, 46, and 47. All are 12½″ long and should be bolted together as shown in the illustration. The outside edges of the Girders 44 and 45 should be 3½″ apart.

To form the uprights carrying the gantry rails, 12½″ Angle Girders are bolted at each inside corner of the base. These Girders are shown at 48, 49, 50 and 51. They are joined at the top by the 12½″ Angle Girders 52 and 53, the ends of which are spanned by the 3½″ Strips 54. The upright Girders are braced by the 12½″ Strips 55, 56 and 57. It will be noticed that no corresponding 12½″ Strip is added as a support for the vertical Girder 51, as its presence would hinder the operation of the hand wheel 10.

At the top of the frame the gantry rails 24 are supported by four 2½″ Strips 73. These are bolted directly to the Girders 52 and 53, and attached to the rails 24 by means of Angle Brackets, which are spaced away from the rails by Collars 70. The object of this is to obtain the necessary headway for the trolley, which must be capable of travelling from end to end of the rails. The 5½″ Strips 58, which make the upright frame quite rigid, are secured to the top Girders by the bolt passing through the Strips 73, and on the same bolts are placed Angle Brackets to secure the 5½″ Strips 77. One end of each of the Strips 77 is secured near the outer ends of the gantry rails 24 by means of an Angle Bracket. Collars should also be placed beneath these Angle Brackets. The ends of the gantry rails 24 are

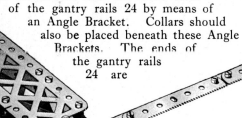

Fig 3.
The saw unit, showing the saw strip attached to the swinging frames.

spanned by 3½″ Strips 71. A 1″ Triangular Plate 72 should be bolted at each end of the rails to act as a stop plate and so prevent the trolley from leaving the rails. An extension for the accommodation of the Motor is made in the base by securing the 9½″ Angle Girders 66 at right angles to the base Girder 46. The Girders 66 are connected together by three 2½″ by ½″ Flanged Plates. The Motor 8 (Fig. 1) is secured in position on the platform thus formed by the two 5½″ Angle Girders 68. A Flat Trunnion 67 bolted to one of the Girders 66 acts as an additional bearing for the Motor shaft.

To take the guides for the vertically-movable work table 7, four Architraves 62 are bolted to the vertical Angle Girders 48, 49, 50 and 51. All that now remains to complete the framework is to bolt the Double Bent Strips 64 and 65 in position to form bearings for the mechanism.

Construction and operation of the Work Table

The work table, with its elevating mechanism, is shown in Fig. 5. The two 5½″ Strips 7, which form the table proper on which the stone is placed for cutting, are mounted on the 9½″ Angle Girders 7a by means of the ½″ Reversed Angle Brackets 23a. A 3½″ Strip is bolted across the Girders 7a near each end of the table, and its outer ends slide on vertical guide Rods 9.

Two horizontal Rods 15 and 18 are journalled in the Double Bent Strips that are secured to the base Girder 44 (see Fig. 2). These Rods carry on their inner ends ½″ Pinion 19 engaging with 1½″ Contrate Wheels 20. The Rods 15 and 18 are caused to rotate simultaneously and in the same direction by means of a Sprocket Chain engaging 1″ Sprocket Wheels on the outer ends of the Rods.

The Contrate Wheels 20 are each secured to a 4½″ Threaded Rod 21, which is journalled in the Double Bent Strip 65 in the base of the model (Fig. 2). The upper ends of the Threaded Rods 21 are inserted in the bosses of Threaded Cranks 22, which are bolted to the Strips 24a of the work table and also to 1½″ Strips that, in turn, are bolted across the 9½″ Angle Girders 7a.

The shaft 15 carrying the Sprocket Wheel 16 is caused to rotate on operation of the hand wheel 11 (Fig. 1) by means of a short Sprocket Chain

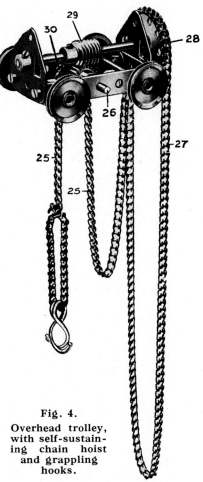

Fig. 4.
Overhead trolley, with self-sustaining chain hoist and grappling hooks.

engaging the Sprockets 13 and 14 (see Figs. 1 and 4). Hence it will be seen that movement of the hand wheel results in a corresponding vertical movement of the table 7.

Swinging Frames.

The swinging frames supporting the saw are shown plainly in Fig. 3. Each frame 3 consists of two 5½″ Braced Girders connected together by Double Brackets at each corner. The four 5½″ Strips 37 are bolted as shown to the sides of the frame to form the swinging support. A 3″ Strip 41 and 2½″ Strip 40 are bolted to each side of the frames and secured together near their other ends. The protruding holes of the 3″ Strips 41 form the bearings for the 1″ Rods that carry the saw Strip 38.

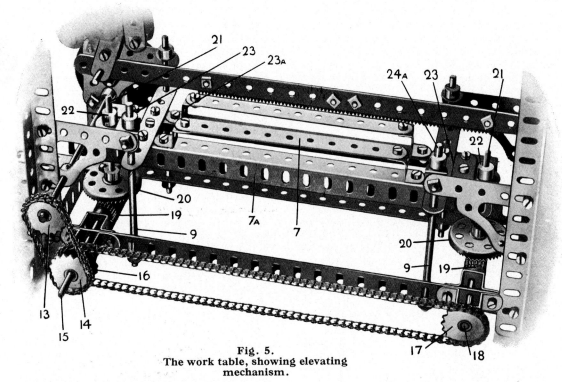

Fig. 5.
The work table, showing elevating mechanism.

Both frames 3 are identical with the exception of the Crank 39, which is used to secure one of the swinging frames to the Rod 4 (Fig. 1).

The Overhead Trolley and Hoist.

The trolley is constructed from two 2½″ by ½″ Double Angle Strips bolted together at each end by Flat Trunnions. The latter form the bearings for the Rod carrying the 1½″ Sprocket Wheel 28 and the Worm 29. The latter engages with a ½″ Pinion secured to the 2″ Rod 26, which carries also a ¾″ Sprocket Wheel 30. One end of the load chain 25 is secured to the trolley framework and the other end is passed over the Sprocket Wheel 30 and attached to the grappling hooks. The Worm 29 is rotated by hauling upon the endless chain 27, which engages with the Sprocket Wheel 28, and the load may thus be raised.

Owing to the arrangement of the Worm and Pinion, the load will remain suspended without overhauling. To lower the load the Chain 27 must be pulled in the opposite direction.

The trolley runs on four 1″ Pulley Wheels, the grooves of which ride on the upturned flanges of the Girders 24 (Figs. 1 and 2).

This type of hand-operated overhead hoist is employed in many factories and workshops to facilitate the movement of heavy loads by hand power.

General Remarks.

When completed, the model may be started, and a little oil applied to the various bearings and gears to ensure quiet and smooth running of the mechanism. It is a wise plan on completing any Meccano model to go over the whole mechanism carefully, to make sure that all shafts carrying Gears or Worms, etc., are in perfect alignment. If this is done, trouble may be avoided, and the machine will operate more easily and freely.

On the actual stone-sawing machine the blade of the saw is made to move easily in the cut, and the heat created by the tremendous friction is counteracted by directing a continual flow of lubricant on the saw blade. Blades of very hard steel are used, of course, and are detachable so as to facilitate regrinding and hardening.

List of Parts Required to Build the Stone-Sawing Machine.

5 of No.	1	15 of No.	12	1 of No.	32	2 of No.	77
19 ,,	2	1 ,,	14	12 ,,	35	2 ,,	80a
1 ,,	2a	1 ,,	15	185 ,,	37	40in. ,,	94
11 ,,	3	5 ,,	15a	32 ,,	38	1 ,,	95a
4 ,,	4	3 ,,	16	6 ,,	45	1 ,,	96a
8 ,,	5	2 ,,	16a	1 ,,	47	4 ,,	100
2 ,,	6a	1 ,,	17	5 ,,	48a	4 ,,	108
12 ,,	7	2 ,,	18a	3 ,,	53	1 ,,	109
4 ,,	8a	4 ,,	22	2 ,,	57	2 ,,	110
2 ,,	9	1 ,,	24	15 ,,	59	2 ,,	115
1 ,,	10	3 ,,	26	2 ,,	62	4 ,,	125
8 ,,	11	2 ,,	28	2 ,,	62a	3 ,,	126a

The Meccanograph

Australia 6d.

(Overseas 4d Canada 8 Cents)

A Wonderful Meccano Model that will draw hundreds of beautiful designs

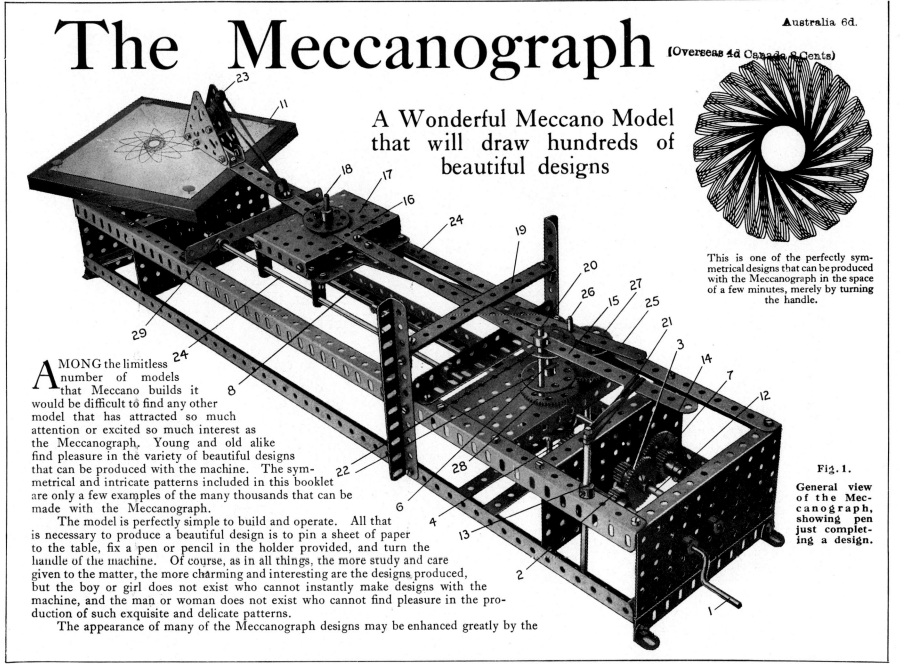

This is one of the perfectly symmetrical designs that can be produced with the Meccanograph in the space of a few minutes, merely by turning the handle.

Fig. 1.

General view of the Meccanograph, showing pen just completing a design.

AMONG the limitless number of models that Meccano builds it would be difficult to find any other model that has attracted so much attention or excited so much interest as the Meccanograph. Young and old alike find pleasure in the variety of beautiful designs that can be produced with the machine. The symmetrical and intricate patterns included in this booklet are only a few examples of the many thousands that can be made with the Meccanograph.

The model is perfectly simple to build and operate. All that is necessary to produce a beautiful design is to pin a sheet of paper to the table, fix a pen or pencil in the holder provided, and turn the handle of the machine. Of course, as in all things, the more study and care given to the matter, the more charming and interesting are the designs produced, but the boy or girl does not exist who cannot instantly make designs with the machine, and the man or woman does not exist who cannot find pleasure in the production of such exquisite and delicate patterns.

The appearance of many of the Meccanograph designs may be enhanced greatly by the

Published by MECCANO LIMITED, BINNS ROAD, LIVERPOOL

Printed in England. 628/10

A few Specimen Designs produced by the Meccanograph

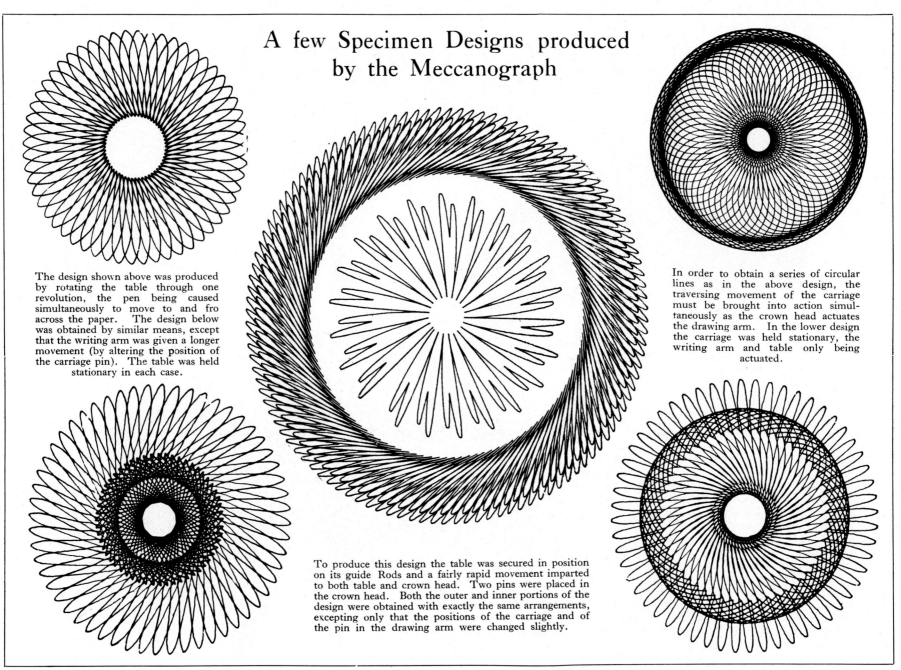

The design shown above was produced by rotating the table through one revolution, the pen being caused simultaneously to move to and fro across the paper. The design below was obtained by similar means, except that the writing arm was given a longer movement (by altering the position of the carriage pin). The table was held stationary in each case.

In order to obtain a series of circular lines as in the above design, the traversing movement of the carriage must be brought into action simultaneously as the crown head actuates the drawing arm. In the lower design the carriage was held stationary, the writing arm and table only being actuated.

To produce this design the table was secured in position on its guide Rods and a fairly rapid movement imparted to both table and crown head. Two pins were placed in the crown head. Both the outer and inner portions of the design were obtained with exactly the same arrangements, excepting only that the positions of the carriage and of the pin in the drawing arm were changed slightly.

use of coloured inks, particularly where combination designs are made, or spaces in the designs may be filled in with water colours.

On the more serious side the machine may be applied to the production of designs suitable for crochet work, decorative glass work, embroidery, etc. In fact the possibilities of the machine are unlimited. It is wonderfully exciting to watch the designs being produced. Unless various adjustments in the machine have been made according to some pre-arranged plan, one has no idea of what the design will be like until it is seen developing under the moving pen or pencil.

This is a model of more than ordinary interest and it is our hope that every Meccano boy will build it. The fascination that it affords can only be appreciated by those who have seen it in operation. There appears to be no limit whatever to the variety and beauty of the designs that may be produced.

How it Works

On turning the handle 1 (Fig. 1) the table 11 is caused to revolve. At the same time the writing arm 16 is actuated by the Rod 20, which functions like a tappet or cam, and the pen is moved to and fro across the table.

With these two movements it is possible to produce an amazing number of different designs merely by varying the relative speed of operation of the table and arm, or by altering the position of the arm, etc.

A further movement may be given to the writing arm by causing the carriage 17 to slide to and fro along the guide Rods 24. This produces almost any number of still more elaborate and intricate designs. There are also many other ways of varying the designs, as will be explained later.

Building the Model : The Framework

The various portions of the model are described in the order in which they should be constructed. The framework should present no special difficulty, but a brief description to supplement the illustrations will no doubt be useful.

The rectangular frame consists principally of four 24½″ Angle Girders bolted at the ends to 5½″ by 2½″ Flanged Plates. The gear box is formed from the front end Plate and another Plate of the same type bolted a short distance away from it. A fourth Plate is bolted in a similar manner near the table end of the machine. The bearings for the tappet mechanism consist of two parallel 5½″ Strips, placed one hole apart and bolted to the two lower 24½″ Angle Girders of the frame, and a 5½″ by 2½″ Flanged Plate bolted directly above them across the two upper 24½″ Angle Girders. The model must stand very firmly on the table, and for this reason a 5½″ Angle Girder, with two Angle

Brackets attached, is bolted flange downward to each end Plate.

The framework is completed by bolting in position the two Girders that carry the guide Rods 24, and the bridge 19, which supports the moving end of the writing arm. The bridge consists of two 5½″ Angle Girders bolted in a vertical position as shown and connected together by two 5½″ Strips. These Strips are spaced apart at each end by Washers, and are bolted to the vertical Girders by means of Angle Brackets.

Care should be taken to see that the writing arm is capable of sliding very smoothly and easily between these Strips. On the other hand, too much play must not be allowed, since this would produce shaky lines in the designs.

The Driving Mechanism

The mechanism operated by the handle 1 may now be placed in position. For most purposes the Crank Handle affords the simplest and most satisfactory method of driving the model, but a Meccano Electric Motor may be used if desired. The speed of the Motor should be reduced considerably by suitable gearing and an efficient means must be provided for stopping the Motor or throwing the model out of gear at the exact instant required, otherwise a design may be spoilt by the pen overstepping the lines.

A ¾″ Pinion 2 secured to the Crank Handle 1 engages with a 50-teeth Gear Wheel on the Rod 12. This same Gear Wheel 3 drives another ¾″ Pinion 7 on the Axle Rod 8, which extends the whole length of the model and drives the table by means of the mechanism to be described later. Secured to the Rod 12 is a ½″ Pinion that meshes with a 1½″ Contrate Wheel 5 (Fig. 5) fastened to the vertical shaft 6. The latter carries the crown head 22 and is caused to transmit motion to another vertical Rod by means of two 57-teeth Gear Wheels 28.

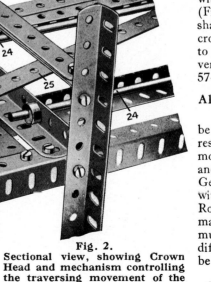

Fig. 2.
Sectional view, showing Crown Head and mechanism controlling the traversing movement of the Carriage.

Alternative Gearing

The speed of the table can be altered without affecting the rest of the mechanism by removing the Pinion 7 (Figs. 1 and 5) and securing the 57-teeth Gear Wheel 14 so that it meshes with the ½″ Pinion 13 on the Rod 12. If this alteration is made the table will then rotate much more slowly and an amazing difference in the designs will be the result.

Of course, there are many other speed ratios that may be

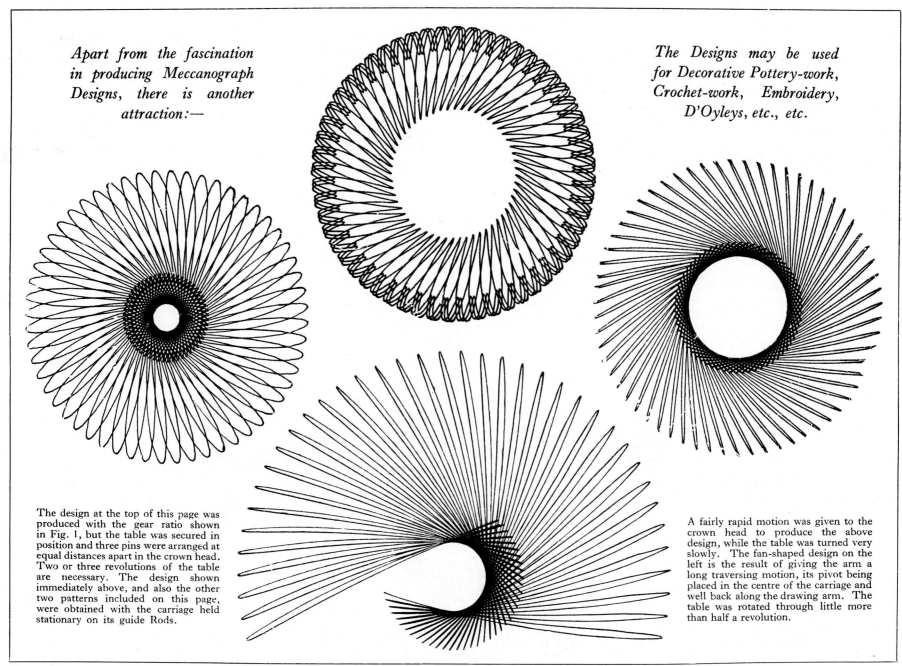

Apart from the fascination in producing Meccanograph Designs, there is another attraction:—

The Designs may be used for Decorative Pottery-work, Crochet-work, Embroidery, D'Oyleys, etc., etc.

The design at the top of this page was produced with the gear ratio shown in Fig. 1, but the table was secured in position and three pins were arranged at equal distances apart in the crown head. Two or three revolutions of the table are necessary. The design shown immediately above, and also the other two patterns included on this page, were obtained with the carriage held stationary on its guide Rods.

A fairly rapid motion was given to the crown head to produce the above design, while the table was turned very slowly. The fan-shaped design on the left is the result of giving the arm a long traversing motion, its pivot being placed in the centre of the carriage and well back along the drawing arm. The table was rotated through little more than half a revolution.

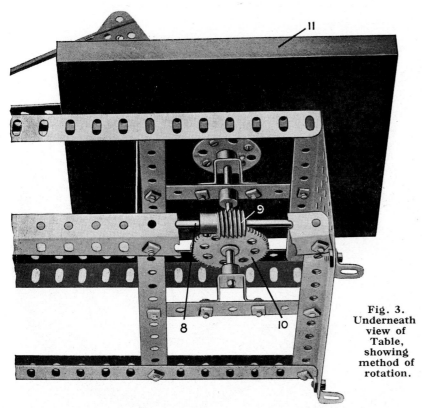

Fig. 3.
Underneath
view of
Table,
showing
method of
rotation.

carriage 17 by means of a short Rod 18 passed through opposite holes in the Flanged Plates forming the carriage. The pin 18 may also be passed through any hole in the pencil arm. An alteration in its position, even by a single hole, will alter the design.

As already explained the Strip 16 is guided between the 5½″ Strips 19. It is caused to bear continuously against the Rod 20 of the crown head by the pulling action of an elastic band 21, which is attached to the upper end of a vertical Rod 13 mounted in the Girders at one side of the frame, as shown in Fig. 1. If desired a piece of Spring Cord may be used instead of the elastic band.

As the crown head rotates the Rod 20 acts as a cam or tappet and causes the writing arm to move to and fro about its pivot 18 on the carriage 17, thereby causing the pen 23 to move across the paper on the table 11.

The pen holder, which is attached to the end of the Strip 16, is formed from two 2½″ Triangular Plates secured together by Double Brackets 31. The pen or pencil is clamped between the foremost Double Bracket at 31 and another Double Bracket bolted at 32. It also rests against a fourth Double Bracket 32 and is held steadily in position by an elastic band 33, one end of which is attached to an Angle Bracket 34 bolted to the arm 16. Spring Cord may be used in place of the elastic, if desired, of course.

The Operation of the Carriage

The carriage 17 is composed of two 3½″ by 2½″ Flanged Plates and two 2½″ by 1″ Double Angle Strips. The end holes of the latter slide on the horizontal 11½″ Rods 24. A 3½″ Strip is bolted to the front of the carriage by means of two Angle Brackets, and at the centre of this Strip the 9½″ Strip 25 is pivoted by a bolt and lock nuts (see Standard Mechanism No. 263).

One of the holes in the Strip 25 is slipped over a Threaded Pin 26 secured to the Bush Wheel 27, the shaft of which is rotated by means of a 57-teeth Gear Wheel meshing

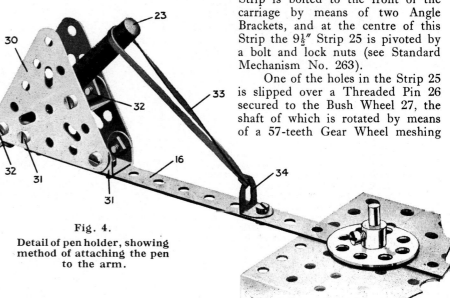

Fig. 4.
Detail of pen holder, showing method of attaching the pen to the arm.

obtained from Meccano gears. A few of them are explained in Section I of the Standard Mechanisms Manual, and any alteration in the speed in one of the driving shafts will produce a whole set of new designs. The relative speeds of the shafts 12 and 6 (Fig. 5) may be varied by using a smaller Contrate Wheel at 5 or by substituting Bevel Gears. The number of possible gear combinations is limitless.

The Crown Head

The crown head 22 is shown clearly in Figs. 1 and 2. It is formed from two Bush Wheels secured one above the other on the Rod 6 and adjusted so that the holes of the uppermost wheel are exactly opposite those of the lower wheel. A 2″ Rod 20 passes through a hole in each Wheel and forms the crown head pin. Its lower end rests on the face of the 57-teeth Gear Wheel 28.

Several pins may be mounted in the Bush Wheels. The addition of a single pin or any alteration in its position will result in an entirely new design.

The Writing Arm

This part of the model is built up from a 12½″ Strip 15 and a 9½″ Strip 16 overlapped three holes and bolted together. The arm is pivoted to the

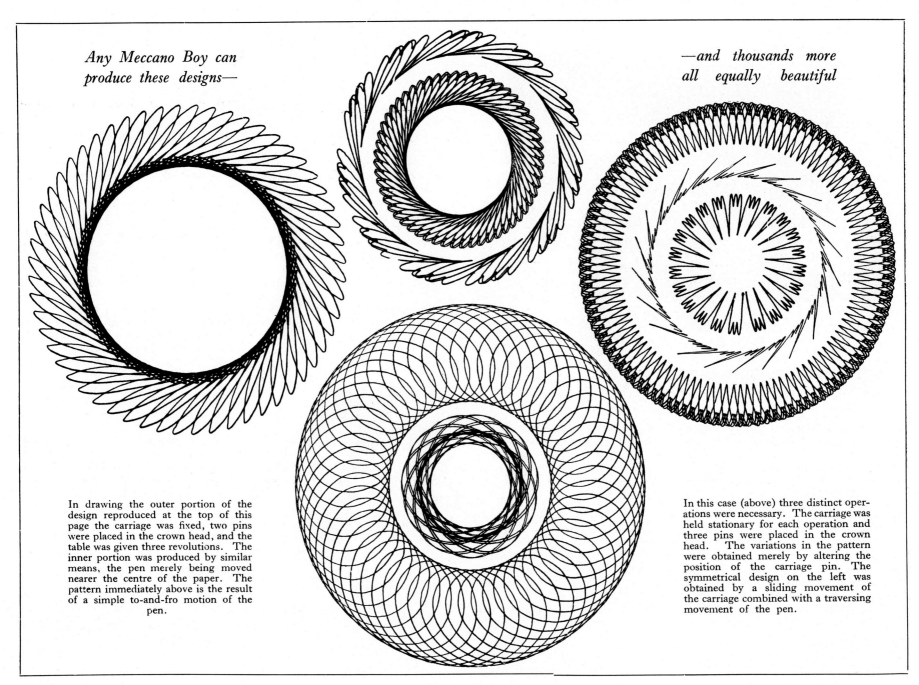

Any Meccano Boy can produce these designs—

—and thousands more all equally beautiful

In drawing the outer portion of the design reproduced at the top of this page the carriage was fixed, two pins were placed in the crown head, and the table was given three revolutions. The inner portion was produced by similar means, the pen merely being moved nearer the centre of the paper. The pattern immediately above is the result of a simple to-and-fro motion of the pen.

In this case (above) three distinct operations were necessary. The carriage was held stationary for each operation and three pins were placed in the crown head. The variations in the pattern were obtained merely by altering the position of the carriage pin. The symmetrical design on the left was obtained by a sliding movement of the carriage combined with a traversing movement of the pen.

Fig. 5. Plan view of Gear Box, showing drive to crown head, etc.

with the similar Gear 28. Hence on rotation of the Bush Wheel 27 the carriage is caused to travel to and fro along the guide Rods 24 and thus a further movement is imparted to the writing arm 16.

Operation of the Table

The mechanism controlling the movement of the table is shown in Fig. 3. The Bush Wheel secured by ordinary wood screws to the underside of the table is mounted on a vertical Rod carrying the 57-teeth Gear Wheel 10. This Gear Wheel is engaged by a Worm 9 fastened to the horizontal Rod 8, which is driven by the Gears 7 or 14 in the gear box (see Fig. 5).

This completes the construction of the Meccanograph. The following are a few general remarks that may be helpful.

First it is important to see that everything works as smoothly as possible. Play in the bearings of the various shafts should be as small as possible. This is specially important in the case of the table operating mechanism (Fig. 3), for if the Rod 8 is capable of longitudinal movement in its bearings, the table may tend to rotate jerkily. All the working parts should be oiled frequently.

If possible a stylo or fountain pen should be mounted on the writing arm when inks of various colours can be employed. Some very fine effects may be obtained if the different portions of a design are drawn in different colours. If the pressure of the pen on the paper is insufficient, small weights should be

attached to the holder or writing arm 16. The weights may consist of a few Meccano Strips or Wheels.

The following notes on how to operate the Meccanograph should enable every Meccano boy to go right ahead and produce hundreds of beautiful designs such as those shown in these pages.

Operating the Meccanograph

After the machine has been completed study it carefully and observe how the different movements are imparted to the writing arm. There is the sliding movement of the carriage 17 and the traversing action that is given to the pen by the crown head. The third movement, i.e., the rotation of the table, does not affect the movement of the arm, but it is nevertheless a very important factor in the production of different designs.

All three movements can be varied in many ways, and the slightest variation in any one will create a vast difference in the designs produced, as will be observed on studying the model closely.

With the model arranged as shown in Fig. 1 the pen is given a single movement across the paper and back again each time the carriage advances and recedes. The traversing movements of the pen can be multiplied if desired, however, by adding to the crown head 22 short Rods similar to the Rod 20.

The traversing movement and the sliding movement can both be employed together if desired, but in the production of certain designs it is essential that the carriage 17 should remain stationary while the traversing movement is given to the arm only. To obtain this result the Strip 25 is removed from the Threaded Pin 26 and Collars 29 on the guide Rods 24 are moved against the legs of the carriage and locked in position to ensure that the carriage remains perfectly firm in position.

As most Meccano boys will know the table 11 is a special Meccano part and can be obtained complete with Bush Wheel secured in position. The drawing paper should be fixed in position by drawing pins so that it can easily be removed when the design is completed.

After a little practice the various adjustments will be found very simple and Meccano boys will know just what to do when it is required to produce certain types of designs. It is a good plan to study carefully exactly what difference a certain adjustment makes to the design, and in this way sufficient data may be collected that will enable one to reproduce again and again any particular design. A pencil note should be added to the corner of each design, indicating the gears employed and the positions of the arms 15 and 25, and of the pins 18, 20 and 26. The operator will then know exactly what to do if he wishes to reproduce a particular design.

Parts required to build the Meccanograph.

1 of No.	1	1 of No.	15	1 of No.	27	1 of No.	48d
2 ,,	1a	2 ,,	15a	4 ,,	27a	5 ,,	52
3 ,,	2	2 ,,	16	1 ,,	28	3 ,,	53
3 ,,	3	2 ,,	17	1 ,,	32	18 ,,	59
4 ,,	7	1 ,,	18a	70 ,,	37	1 ,,	63
6 ,,	9	1 ,,	19	2 ,,	38	2 ,,	76
4 ,,	11	5 ,,	24	2 ,,	45	1 ,,	107
7 ,,	12	2 ,,	25	2 ,,	46	1 ,,	115
4 ,,	13	2 ,,	26				

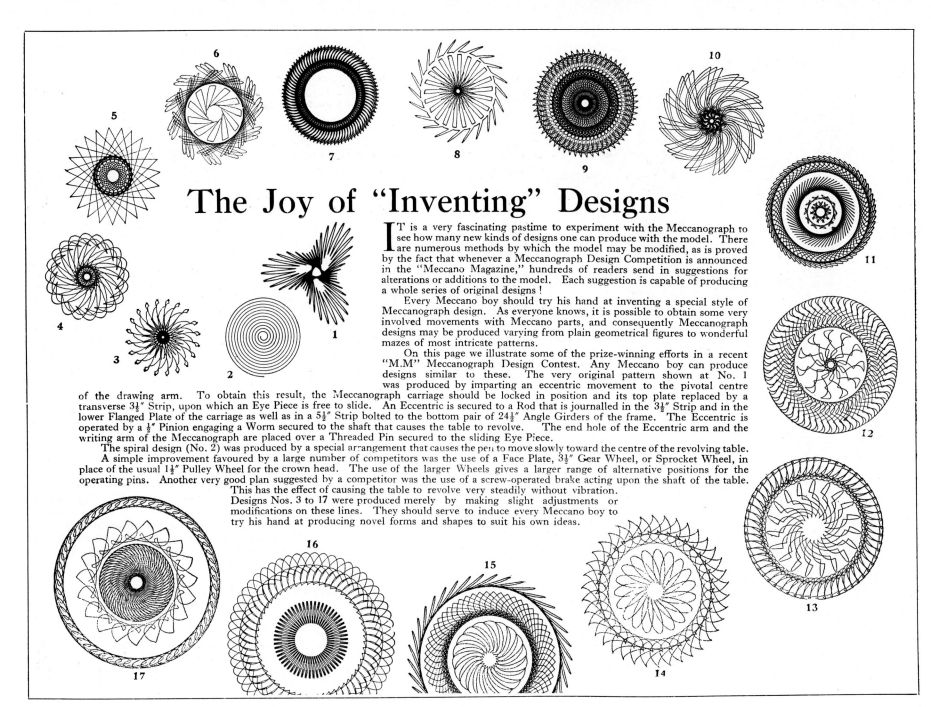

The Joy of "Inventing" Designs

IT is a very fascinating pastime to experiment with the Meccanograph to see how many new kinds of designs one can produce with the model. There are numerous methods by which the model may be modified, as is proved by the fact that whenever a Meccanograph Design Competition is announced in the "Meccano Magazine," hundreds of readers send in suggestions for alterations or additions to the model. Each suggestion is capable of producing a whole series of original designs !

Every Meccano boy should try his hand at inventing a special style of Meccanograph design. As everyone knows, it is possible to obtain some very involved movements with Meccano parts, and consequently Meccanograph designs may be produced varying from plain geometrical figures to wonderful mazes of most intricate patterns.

On this page we illustrate some of the prize-winning efforts in a recent "M.M" Meccanograph Design Contest. Any Meccano boy can produce designs similar to these. The very original pattern shown at No. 1 was produced by imparting an eccentric movement to the pivotal centre of the drawing arm. To obtain this result, the Meccanograph carriage should be locked in position and its top plate replaced by a transverse 3½″ Strip, upon which an Eye Piece is free to slide. An Eccentric is secured to a Rod that is journalled in the 3½″ Strip and in the lower Flanged Plate of the carriage as well as in a 5½″ Strip bolted to the bottom pair of 24½″ Angle Girders of the frame. The Eccentric is operated by a ½″ Pinion engaging a Worm secured to the shaft that causes the table to revolve. The end hole of the Eccentric arm and the writing arm of the Meccanograph are placed over a Threaded Pin secured to the sliding Eye Piece.

The spiral design (No. 2) was produced by a special arrangement that causes the pen to move slowly toward the centre of the revolving table.

A simple improvement favoured by a large number of competitors was the use of a Face Plate, 3½″ Gear Wheel, or Sprocket Wheel, in place of the usual 1½″ Pulley Wheel for the crown head. The use of the larger Wheels gives a larger range of alternative positions for the operating pins. Another very good plan suggested by a competitor was the use of a screw-operated brake acting upon the shaft of the table. This has the effect of causing the table to revolve very steadily without vibration.

Designs Nos. 3 to 17 were produced merely by making slight adjustments or modifications on these lines. They should serve to induce every Meccano boy to try his hand at producing novel forms and shapes to suit his own ideas.

(No. 14)   SPECIAL INSTRUCTION LEAFLETS FOR BUILDING MECCANO SUPER MODELS   (Price 3d.)

(Overseas 4d Canada 8 Cents)

Meccano Grandfather Clock

A Full-size Model that keeps Accurate Time

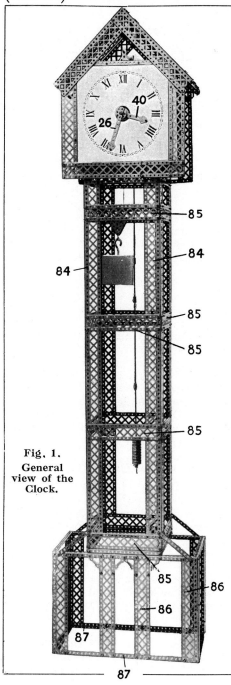

Fig. 1.
General
view of the
Clock.

SPECIAL FEATURES

Accurate time-keeping. Made entirely of Meccano Parts with the exception of the weight, a small flat spring about $1\frac{1}{2}''$ long, and the dial. Special escapement and pallet movement. May be adjusted by altering length of pendulum, etc. Ratchet winding mechanism. Presents a handsome appearance and is suitable for hall or staircase.

IT is doubtful whether many of us appreciate the tremendous amount of work and thought that has been necessary to bring to perfection the mechanism of a clock. In these days clocks and watches are so numerous, and may be purchased for so little, that we forget the wonderful story that lies behind the measuring of time throughout the ages.

How many of us realise, for instance, that the accuracy of our time depends upon the observations of astronomers at Greenwich Observatory? Although it is very interesting to learn about the canals of Mars; about the wonderful clouds of Jupiter, or about the mountains of the Moon, a study of these objects does not comprise the entire duties of the Greenwich astronomers. They are more concerned in checking and keeping correct their master clocks that give the time to all the clocks in the country.

How Astronomers correct our Clocks

Every night the astronomers watch with a large telescope the passage of a star across a particular part of the sky, which passage denotes the correct time. In the telescope are several vertical lines, which are actually portions of a spider's web placed in the eye piece of the instrument. It is possible to calculate the exact instant when a star should pass each of these lines and the observer watches for this to take place. The star enters the field of view from the left and passes each of the lines in turn. When the observer sees that the star is on a vertical line he presses a key, which completes an electric circuit and the exact instant is marked on the cylinder of a recording machine.

The work of the astronomers enables us all to get up punctually: school to start to the minute, and express trains to depart "on the tick." Imagine

Published by MECCANO LIMITED, BINNS ROAD, LIVERPOOL   Printed in England. 428/5.

the chaos that would result if the astronomers set the nation's clocks half-an-hour late! Half the nation would be up late, schools would be late, trains would be all wrong, and every one would be in a bad temper as a result!

Even greater confusion would result at sea, however, for a sailor cannot find the exact position of his ship unless he is provided with the correct time. He obtains this information by wireless, time signals being sent out at stated periods by the Eiffel Tower and other large stations. It is the astronomer who ensures that the radio signals are broadcast at the correct instant. In the case of the Eiffel Tower, for instance, transmissions are actually sent out by a master clock at Paris Observatory, the time of which is checked with the passage of different stars several times during the night.

It is hard to realise how the people of old were able to tell the time before watches and clocks were invented. They did so either by the Sun or the Moon, noting their positions in the heavens by day or night. In those days time was not measured by hours, minutes or seconds, as it is to-day. Instead it was divided into years according to the apparent motion of the Sun among the stars, into months by the revolution of the Moon around the earth, and into days by the alternate light and darkness caused by the rising and setting of the sun.

Later the day was divided into equal portions by watching the movement of a shadow, for as the Sun moves through the sky the position of a shadow continually changes. The different positions were marked by pieces of wood or stone placed on the ground. A development of this early device was the familiar sun-dial, examples of which are still to be seen outside some old churches, or in old-world gardens. The earliest record of a sun-dial is in the Bible, where in the Second Book of Kings, Chap. XX, v. ii, we read of "the dial of Ahaz." The Sun does not always shine, however, and when it is cloudy sun-dials are useless.

As civilisation spread and the lives of people became more ordered and regular there was an increasing demand for some other device for measuring time. This resulted in the introduction of the *Clepsydra*, or water clock, which is of great antiquity.

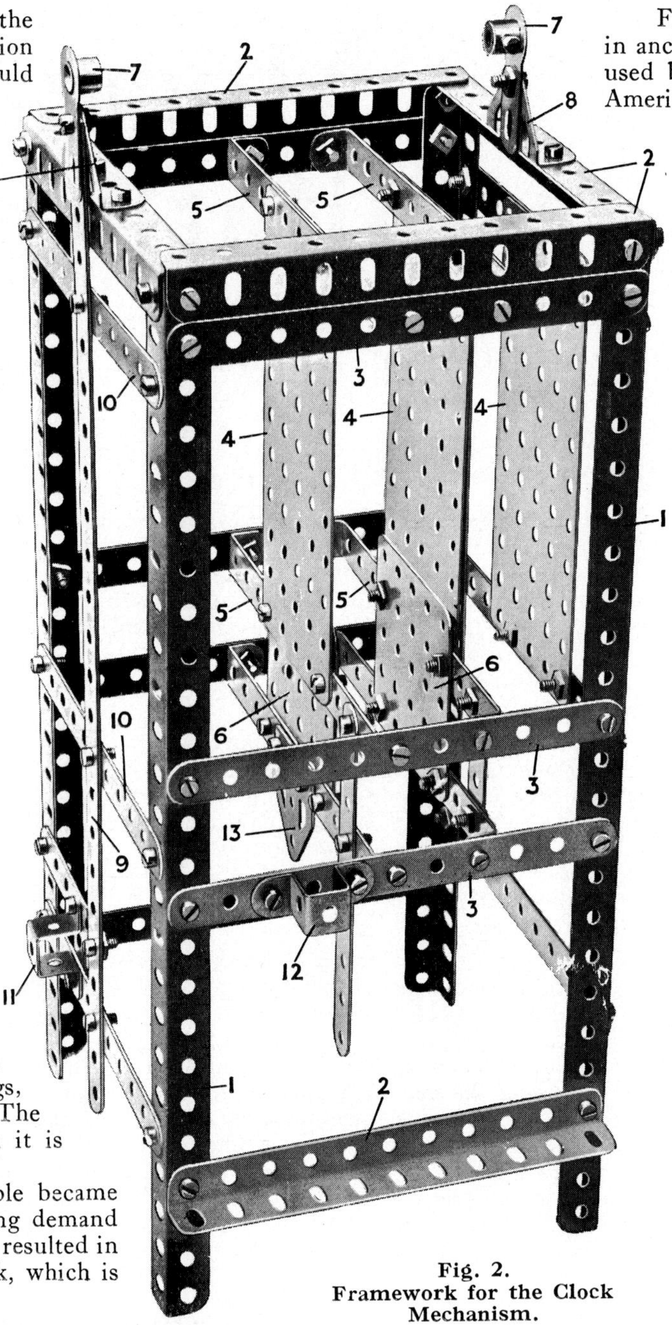

Fig. 2.
Framework for the Clock Mechanism.

From old models discovered, and from references in ancient documents, we know that water clocks were used by the Greeks, and also by the Indian tribes of America. Julius Cæsar, when he invaded Britain in B.C. 55, found water clocks in use among the natives, and with these clocks is said to have observed that the summer nights in Britain were shorter than those in Italy.

The Water Clock

In its original form the water clock consisted of a vessel filled with water, which was allowed to escape through a small hole. By noting how far the level of the water had fallen, it was not difficult to determine the interval of time that had passed since the vessel was filled.

Water clocks—which were superior to sun-dials in that they could, of course, be used day or night—were subsequently improved, and in a later form the water dripped into a second vessel in which a wooden figure was placed. As the level of the water rose in the second vessel the wooden figure floated higher and higher, and the intervals of time were thus more easily noticed.

Soon afterwards hour symbols were painted on the inside of the vessel and a figure with an outstretched arm was used as a float. As the figure rose the arm pointed to the hour on the inner side of the vessel. This movable arm was the forerunner of the hour hand of our present-day clocks.

How the Clock Face Originated

In another type of water clock a dial similar to a clock face was placed over the vessel containing the water. On the water floated a piece of wood attached to which was a string running over a wheel connected to the hands on the dial. The water was allowed to drip from the vessel so that it took exactly a day to empty. As the floating wood sank lower and lower the string pulled the hand around the dial. In this form of water clock the face had 24 figures, but having only one hand could only record the hours.

A considerable amount of skill was exercised in the construction of these water clocks, as is evident from models to be seen in many of our museums. Some of these models are of very beautiful design and clever craftsmanship. One famous example in brass was sent in the year 800 by the King of Persia to the Emperor Charlemagne. In this clock twelve figures of horsemen marched out of twelve windows one by one according to the hour. When twelve hours had passed the figures returned again, closing the windows after them as they marched back.

Measuring Time with Sand

About the year 330 A.D. sand glasses were introduced. These were glass vessels shaped something like a figure 8, the waist of which only allowed the sand placed in the top half of the glass to run through grain by grain. It required an hour to run from the top to the lower half of the glass, after which the glass had to be turned upside down again so that the next hour could be measured by the sand running back again. Although it was not difficult to roughly ascertain how much of the hour had gone by the quantity of sand that had fallen, the great disadvantage of sand-glasses was that people often forgot to turn them back after the hour was run, and so lost the correct time! Then again unless they were attended to continually during the night, the time was lost and the hours could only be counted from the time at which the owner of the glass awakened and started off the sand-glass! Because of these disadvantages it is not surprising to learn that sand-glasses were not in use for very long.

Another early method of measuring time was by burning long candles, made to burn for a certain number of hours. These candles had divisions down their sides, each mark showing when an hour had passed. They were very

unreliable, however, for the slightest draught would alter the rate at which the candles burned, causing them to measure time incorrectly.

Candle Clocks were used at the time of Alfred the Great. Whilst he was a fugitive in his own country the King vowed that if ever he were restored to his kingdom he would devote a third of his time to the service of God. Later when he achieved his desire, he ordered a number of candles to be made so that he might divide his time in accordance with his vow. The candles burned for exactly four hours and were lighted one after another by one of Alfred's Chaplains, who also gave the King due warning of the passing of the hours.

Neither sun-dials, water clocks, sand-glasses nor candles solved the problem of accurately measuring time. This did not become an accomplished fact until the invention of the weight-driven wheel clock.

It is impossible to say exactly when this type of clock commenced to supersede the ancient time measures. Many vague allusions to wheel clocks occur at a very early period, but whether these were some form of water clock or whether they were actually wheel and weight clocks seems doubtful.

To a certain extent wheel clocks were a development of water clocks, in the later models of which a water wheel took the place of the empty vessel and the floating piece of wood. The water dropped on to the paddles of the wheel, driving it round, and every time the wheel made a complete circle a gong was struck. It is believed that the Greeks introduced mechanical movements to take the place of the gong, and also that they connected the wheel with a series of cogs, thereby

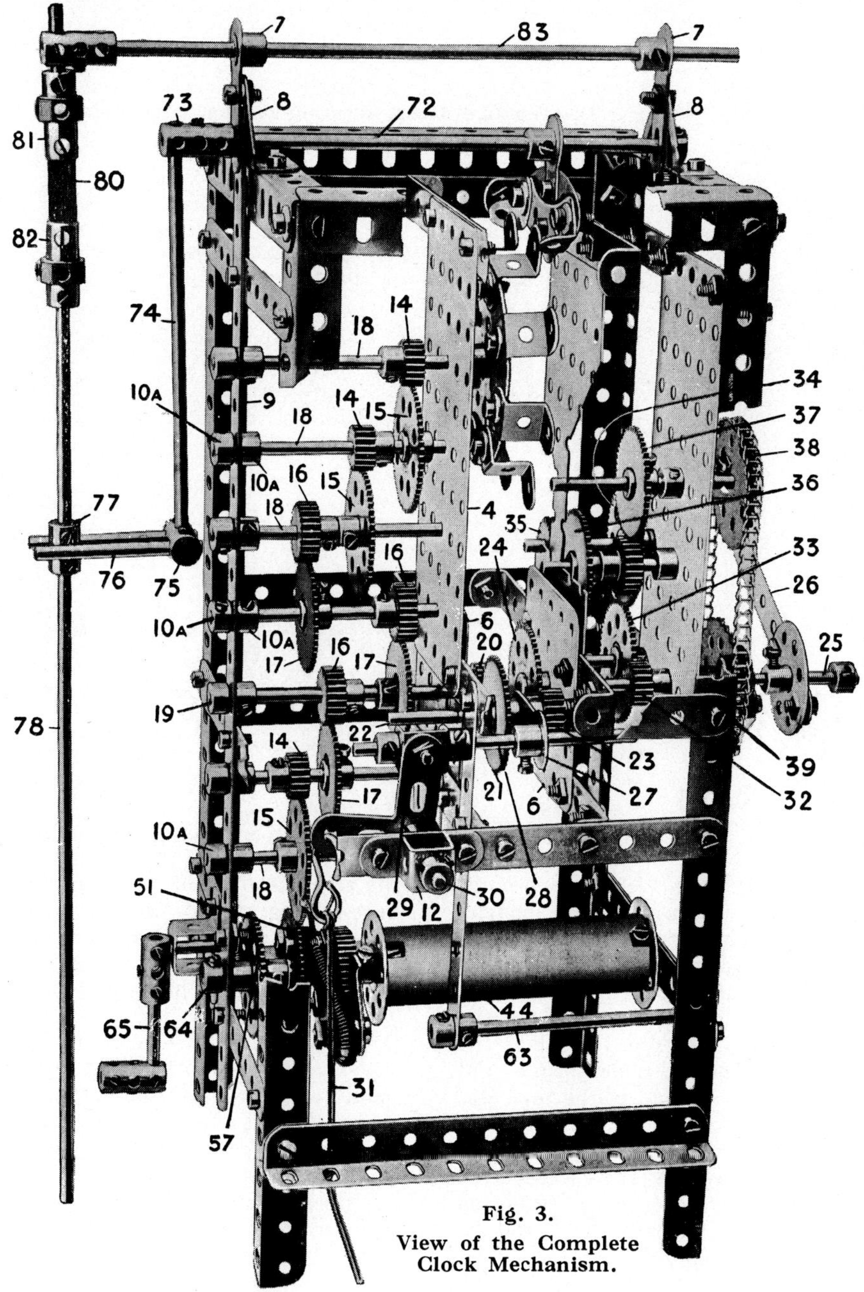

Fig. 3.
View of the Complete Clock Mechanism.

Fig. 4. The Pendulum.

moving an indicator on a dial.

Later a falling weight took the place of the dripping water, so it was in this way that the weight-driven clock first came into existence : some believe that credit for its invention is due to Archimedes, the famous mathematician, who lived in the third century B.C., but whether or not he really did invent the type we do not know.

The First Wheel Clocks

Although there is no record earlier than 1120 A.D. in which a weight-driven clock definitely is described, there seems to be little doubt that weight clocks were used in the monasteries of Europe in the 11th century. Probably these clocks had no dial or hands, but only struck a bell at certain hours to call the monks to prayer. This was an improvement on the previous methods, however, for until then it was necessary for one of the monks to watch the stars in order to know when it was time to waken his brethren for early morning prayers.

The wheel clock was perfected by a German named Henry de Wyck. A rope with a weight attached was wound round a cylinder or barrel which resembled the roller of a household mangle. As the weight dropped, the barrel revolved, moving the clock hand through a train of gear wheels. In his early models de Wyck found that as the weight dropped the speed at which the wheels revolved became faster and faster. When the end of the rope was reached the barrel was actually thrown off its spindle ! He persevered in his experiments, however, and succeeded in overcoming the difficulty. He did so by fitting a series of spikes to a small wheel, and by means of a mechanism that resembled a pawl and ratchet, he checked the revolutions of the barrel. The King of France, Charles V, heard of de Wyck's wonderful clock and asked for one to be made for his palace. Thus it was that the first mechanical clock constructed

Fig. 5.
The Winding Gear, showing ratchet mechanism.

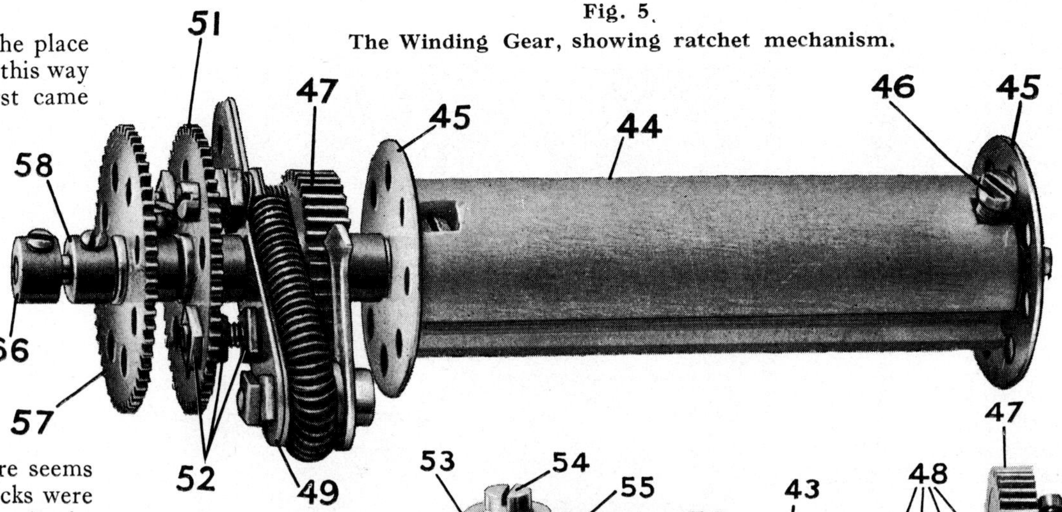

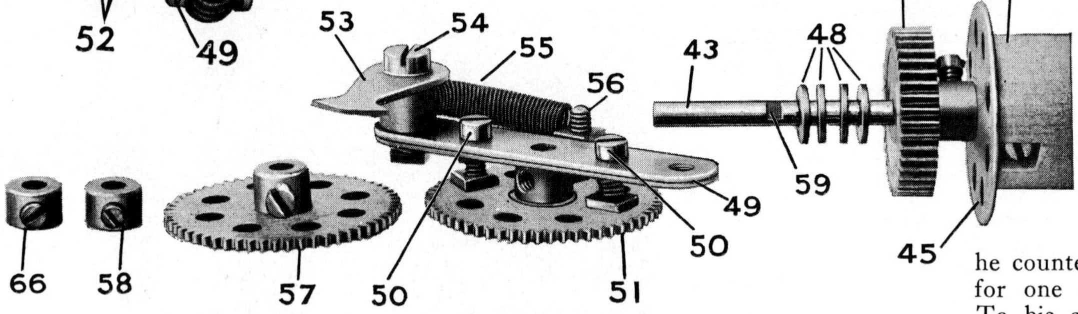

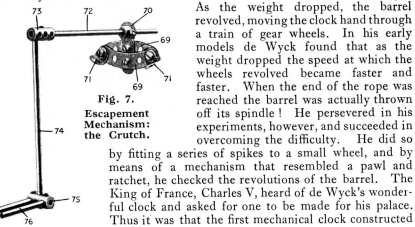

Fig. 6. Component parts of Ratchet Winding Mechanism.

Fig. 7.
Escapement Mechanism: the Crutch.

in France was made by a German citizen.

Discovery of the Pendulum

Shortly after de Wyck's success the whole principle of clock-making was revolutionised by the discovery of the pendulum by the famous Italian, Galilei Galileo, then a youth of 18 years. One day in the Cathedral at Pisa, he noticed the regular movements of a hanging lamp that had been set moving while being lighted. Galileo was struck by the fact that the motion of the lamp never seemed to vary and he decided to test its accuracy. Watches were unknown then, so holding his pulse he counted the time required for one swing of the lamp. To his amazement he found that the lamp always required the same amount of time to complete one swing although the swings were becoming gradually of less extent each moment.

Convinced of the value of his discovery Galileo soon completed a model of the lamp by fixing a weight to the end of a long bar of metal, and it was not long before he had adopted this pendulum to work an astronomical clock.

Solving a Mystery

Once the principle had been established, pendulum clocks became common, and at last the world had a fairly accurate means of keeping time. The next step was to improve the clocks so that they were even more accurate.

In this connection there was one particular trouble to be overcome, which was to understand why the clocks always went faster in winter than in summer. In these days very little was known about the various properties and peculiarities of metal, and it was a long time before the mystery was solved.

Fig. 8. Escapement Mechanism: the Pallet.

Popular opinion had it that in some unknown manner the sun affected the clocks in summer. In the main this idea was quite correct, of course, for the difference in the clock's speed was actually due to the expansion or contraction of the metal of which it was constructed. In the hot days of summer the metal expanded, the pendulum rod became longer and the pendulum required longer to make its beat. In the winter the reverse was the case, and then the clocks always ran a little fast. When more knowledge was obtained about metals, and when their different rates of expansion and contraction were discovered, the mystery was solved.

The difficulty was overcome in a most ingenious manner. The heavy metal weight of the pendulum was replaced with a vessel filled with mercury. Although the pendulum rod continued to expand and lengthen during the summer the mercury in the jar also expanded, rising higher and higher in its containing vessel. This rising of the mercury had exactly the same effect as raising the weight further up the pendulum rod, a procedure that, as everyone knows, causes the pendulum to beat more quickly. The mercury therefore automatically compensated for the alteration in the length of the pendulum rod and the clock was able to keep perfect time without attention at any season of the year.

So accurate is this method of compensation by mercury that it is used at the present time in astronomical clocks. It may also be seen sometimes in the clocks that register Greenwich time at large watch-makers and jewellers' shops. By the invention of the mercury compensating device, pendulum clocks were more or less perfected, though several minor improvements were afterwards made in the gearing and the method of indicating the hour.

The first pendulum clocks were of the "grandfather" type. It is interesting

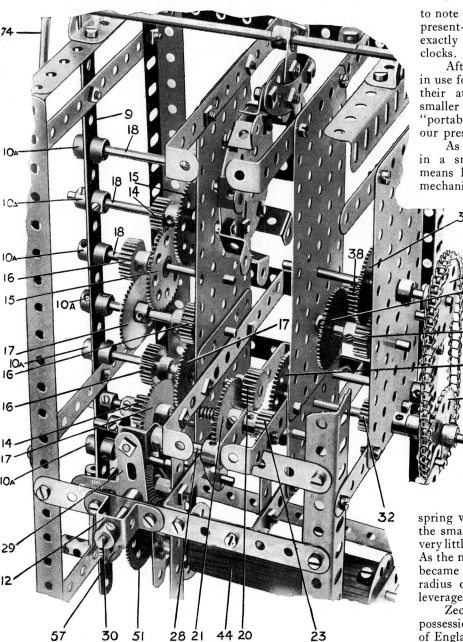

Fig. 9. Section of main Gear Train.

to note that the Meccano Clock and other present-day clocks are constructed on exactly the same principle as the early clocks.

After "Grandfather" clocks had been in use for some time, clock-makers turned their attention to the construction of smaller clocks. These were called "portable clocks," and it is from them that our present day watches originated.

As it is impossible to use a pendulum in a small portable clock some other means had to be found for driving the mechanism. About 1500 Peter Hele of Nuremberg found that a coiled spring might be used instead of a weight, for both store up energy of a similar nature. Trouble was soon met, however, as it was found that as the spring uncoiled it lost its tension and the speed of the wheels became slower and slower.

In 1525 Jacob Zech, of Prague, brought forward a solution to this difficulty. He placed the mainspring in a drum, which revolved as the spring uncoiled. To the drum was attached one end of a string of cat-gut, which was wound on to a conical roller called the "fusee." When the spring was fully wound, the chain lay at the small end of the fusee, where it had very little leverage on the clock mechanism. As the mainspring unwound, and its force became less, the chain came off a larger radius of the fusee, and thus a greater leverage was obtained by the spring.

Zech's first clock is now in the possession of the Society of Antiquaries of England. It is inscribed in Bohemian "Made in Prague by Jacob Zech in 1525," has a spring as motive power with barrel and fusee, and is the oldest portable clock in existence.

In these portable clocks, or watches as they afterwards became, a small flywheel, actuated by a hair-spring, was used in place of a pendulum. Its regular movement allowed the main spring to unwind a little at equal intervals in exactly the same manner as the pendulum allows the weight to fall a little at each swing in the heavier types of clock. The differences in temperature were overcome by Thomas Earnshaw, who invented the compensating balance. This uses the unequal expansion of different metals so as to keep the leverage of the rim of the wheel constant.

There must have been hundreds of disappointments before all the difficulties of clock-making were solved and many years of patient study and careful work had to be expended over each new problem as it arose. Unfortunately, space will not allow any description of the many famous clocks in existence, but we hope that this rough outline of the history of clock-making will add further interest to the construction of the Meccano model Grandfather Clock.

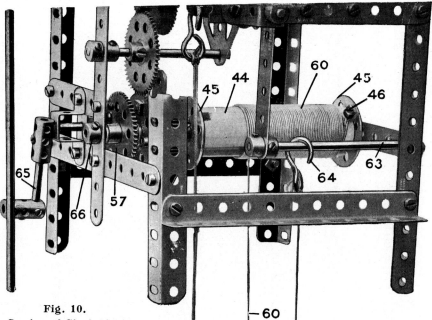

Fig. 10.
Section of Clock Mechanism showing winding gear and weight pulley

The Meccano Model

The following instructions will enable any Meccano boy to build a real Grandfather Clock with Meccano. When finished the clock stands over 6 ft. in height, and if carefully adjusted it will keep accurate time. With the exception of an 18 lb. weight, the dial, and a small piece of flat spring with which to suspend the pendulum, the clock is made entirely of Meccano parts.

This splendid Meccano model should have a wide appeal not only on account of its mechanical interest, but also because it will render real service in the home. It also affords an excellent demonstration of the principles governing clock mechanism, etc.

It is quite certain that among the hundreds of models that can be constructed with Meccano, very few, if any, excel the Meccano Clock from the point of view of general interest and excellence of construction.

Any clock mechanism is a wonderful piece of work, but we are so familiar with clocks of all kinds and descriptions that we seldom appreciate them properly. The principles involved are perfectly simple, however, and as soon as the Meccano boy

commences to build the model he will find that clock-making is not nearly so difficult as he had imagined.

Frame of Mechanism

The construction of the model should be commenced by building the frame that carries the gear trains. This frame is shown in Fig. 2, and as will be seen it consists of four $12\frac{1}{2}''$ Angle Girders 1, connected by $5\frac{1}{2}''$ Angle Girders 2 and $5\frac{1}{2}''$ Strips 3.

Three $5\frac{1}{2}''$ by $2\frac{1}{2}''$ Flat Plates 4 are bolted at their ends to $5\frac{1}{2}''$ by $\frac{1}{2}''$ Double Angle Strips 5, and are extended at their lower ends by $2\frac{1}{2}''$ by $2\frac{1}{2}''$ Flat Plates 6. It will be noted that the lower Double Angle Strips 5 are inserted between the Plates 4 and 6, and that the Plates 6 overlap Plates 4 by two holes. Two Cranks 7 are bolted to Trunnions 8 on the top of the frame and form the bearings for a Rod that supports the pendulum.

A $12\frac{1}{2}''$ Strip 9 is bolted vertically to one of the Trunnions 8 and to $5\frac{1}{2}''$ Strips 10 to form bearings for the main gear train. A Double Bent Strip 11 is bolted on the left side of the frame to form a bearing for the winding handle 65 (Fig. 3), and a second Double Bent Strip 12 forms a bearing for the shift gear that disconnects the driving train from the gearing of the hands so as to allow the fingers of the clock to be re-set when desired. A Flat Trunnion 13 (Fig. 2) is bolted below the left Flat Plate 6 so as to form the bearing for the lowest 3'' Rod of the Clock train 18 (Fig. 3).

No difficulty should be experienced in completing the frame, for the positions of the other Strips, etc., are shown clearly in Fig. 2.

The Main Gear Train

After the frame has been constructed the next part for attention should be the main gear train, which is shown in Fig. 3. This consists of three $\frac{1}{2}''$ Pinions 14 that are in engagement with the 57-teeth Gear Wheels 15. Three $\frac{3}{4}''$ Pinions 16 are secured on the Rods 18 and engage the 50-teeth Gear Wheels 17. The top Rod 18 is $3\frac{1}{2}''$ long and one of its ends is journalled in the Flat Plate 4 while the other end is carried by the Strip 9, Fig. 2. The remainder of the Rods 18 are each 3'' long. They pass through holes in the left hand plates 4 and 6 and the $12\frac{1}{2}''$ Strip 9 (Fig. 2) and are held in position by Collars 10a that are secured to the Rods on each side of the Strip 9. No Collars are necessary, therefore, at the other ends of the Rods.

On the end of the $3\frac{1}{2}''$ Rod 19 is a $\frac{3}{4}''$ Pinion 20, which is shown more clearly in Fig. 9. This Pinion gears with a 50-teeth Gear Wheel 21 fixed on the $2''$ Rod 22, which Rod is so placed as to be free to slide in the vertical Plates 6 (Fig. 2).

Carried on the $2''$ Rod 22 is also a $\frac{1}{2}''$ Pinion 23 geared with a 57-teeth Wheel 24 on a $4\frac{1}{2}''$ Rod 25. The minute hand of the Clock is carried on the end of the $4\frac{1}{2}''$ Rod 25, as is clearly shown at 26 (Fig. 3). The web of a Crank 27 (Fig. 3) engages the $2''$ Rod 22, the Crank being bolted to a $3\frac{1}{2}''$ Rod 28 that carries a Double Bracket bolted to a Bell Crank 29 and pivoted on a Rod 30. The latter is carried in the Double Bent Strip 12.

This part of the mechanism is very intricate and it will well repay the builder to study carefully the illustrations before proceeding with the construction, and so obtain a clear idea as to the general layout of the gear trains and the purpose that is served by each wheel. Great care should also be taken to see that each shaft and wheel is in perfect alignment, as much depends on the free running of the gear trains.

Adjusting the Hands

The reference numbers given here refer to Fig. 3, which clearly shows the gear trains. A cord 31 is connected to the Bell Crank 29 and by pulling on this cord, the Rod 28 is caused to slide and move the gear 21 in or out of engagement with the Pinion 20. This releases the driving train from the Clock hands and thus enables the hands to be adjusted freely.

In order to drive the hour hand from the minute hand Rod 25, a $\frac{1}{2}''$ Pinion 32 on the Rod 25 drives a 57-teeth Gear 33 mounted on a $2''$ Rod.

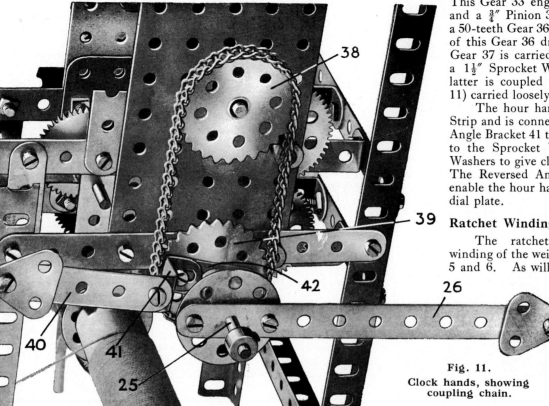

Fig. 11.
Clock hands, showing coupling chain.

This Gear 33 engages a second 57-teeth Gear 34 and a $\frac{3}{4}''$ Pinion 35 on the Rod of Gear 34 drives a 50-teeth Gear 36. Another $\frac{3}{4}''$ Pinion on the Rod of this Gear 36 drives a 50-teeth Gear 37. The Gear 37 is carried on a $2\frac{1}{2}''$ Rod on which also is a $1\frac{1}{2}''$ Sprocket Wheel 38 (Figs. 3 and 9). The latter is coupled to a similar Sprocket 39 (Fig. 11) carried loosely on the Rod 25.

The hour hand 40 (Fig. 11) consists of a $2\frac{1}{2}''$ Strip and is connected by means of a $\frac{1}{2}''$ Reversed Angle Bracket 41 to a $1\frac{1}{2}''$ Strip 42. This is bolted to the Sprocket Wheel 39 and spaced by two Washers to give clearance for the Sprocket Chain. The Reversed Angle Bracket 41 is necessary to enable the hour hand 40 to be brought clear of the dial plate.

Ratchet Winding Mechanism

The ratchet mechanism permitting the winding of the weight is built up as shown in Figs. 5 and 6. As will be seen from the diagrams the complete ratchet element is made by passing a $6''$ Rod 43 (Fig. 6) through a Wood Roller 44, the ends of which are clamped between Bush Wheels 45 secured on the Rod. The bosses of the Bush Wheels are inserted in the ends of the Wood Roller and the bolts 46 engage in the end notches of the roller to key the latter to the Bush Wheels.

A $1''$ Gear Wheel 47 is bolted on the Rod 43 with its boss close against the end Bush Wheel 45. Four Washers 48 are then placed on the Rod. After this the element shown in the centre of Fig. 6 is passed over the Rod 43. This element is made up as follows. Two $2\frac{1}{2}''$ Strips 49 are bolted by $\frac{3}{4}''$ Bolts 50 to a 57-teeth Gear Wheel 51, lock nuts 52 being fitted on the bolts on each side of the Gear Wheel 51 and also beneath the Strips 49. A Pawl 53 is pivoted at 54 in the end hole of the Strips 49 and a Spring 55 is connected to the Pawl boss by a screw and also to a $\frac{3}{4}''$ Bolt 56 carried on the Gear Wheel 51.

After assembly, the complete element is slipped over the Rod 43. It is loose thereon, and the Pawl engages with the teeth of the Gear Wheel 47 (see Fig 5). It will be noticed that the old style Meccano Pawl is used in conjunction with a $1''$ Gear Wheel, but the new Pawl and Ratchet Gear (part Nos. 147 and 148) may be used equally well in their place.

Non-slipping Device

A 57-teeth Gear Wheel 57 (Fig. 5) is passed over the Rod of the Roller and secured thereon, and a Collar 58 (Fig. 5) is fastened against the outside of the Wheel 57. In order that the latter may not slip on the Rod 43 when taking the whole of the strain in winding the heavy weight, a flat surface 59 (Fig. 11) is filed on the Rod in the correct position for engagement by the screw of the Gear Wheel 57. This gives the Gear Wheel 57 a secure grip on the Rod.

A Meccano Wire Line 60 (Fig. 10) is wound on the Wood Roller 44 and passed round a Pulley 61 carried in the pulley block 62. This is made up of two 2½″ Triangular Plates bolted together with Double Brackets.

The other end of the Line 60 is hooked at 64 over the Rod 63. After the Wood Roller 44 has been inserted in its place, another Collar 66 is secured on the extreme end of Rod 43 (Fig. 5).

The winding of the Clock is effected by a Handle 65 (Figs. 3 and 10) provided with a ½″ Pinion (not visible in the photograph) that engages the Gear Wheel 57. The Roller 44 drives the main gear train by reason of its Gear Wheel 51, which engages the first Gear 15 of the train.

The Escapement Wheel and Pallet

Next proceed to construct the escapement. This consists of an escapement wheel or pallet and crutch mechanism. The former (Fig. 8) consists of a Face Plate 66a to which are attached eight ½″ Reversed Angle Brackets 67. To make these quite rigid they must be pressed hard up against the circular edge of the Plate and then bolted tightly in position. Washers 68 should be placed beneath the bolt heads.

The pallet mechanism (Fig. 7) should be constructed from two 2½″ reversed Curved Strips 69 bolted one on each side of the web of a Crank 70. Angle Brackets 71 are bolted in the end holes of the Curved Strips that form the crutch.

The Crank 70 is bolted on a 6″ Rod 72 (Fig. 3) and a 5″ Rod 74 is secured to a Coupling 73 carried on the end of the Rod 72. At the lower end of this is a Coupling 75 carrying two 2″ Rods 76, which engage against two Collars 77 on the pendulum Rod 78.

The Pendulum

As shown in Fig 4, the pendulum consists of three 11½″ Rods 78a, 78c,

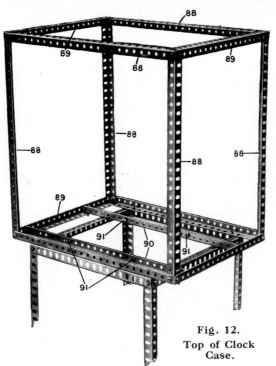

**Fig. 12.
Top of Clock
Case.**

and 78d and a 5″ Rod 78b connected by Couplings. The complete pendulum is connected to the lower end of the 11½″ Rod 78 (see Fig. 3). The pendulum weight 79 is made up of ten Flanged Wheels. A light spring 80 connects the Strip Couplings 81 and 82, the Coupling 81 being connected to the 8″ Rod 83 which is secured in the bosses of the Cranks 7. This spring is not a Meccano part : a strip of thin brass, or part of an old clockwork spring, about 1½″ long and ¼″ wide, will serve admirably for the purpose. The spring is necessary in order to provide for a perfectly easy swinging movement of the pendulum.

Constructing the Clock Case.

The clock case may now be built. It consists of two vertical 24½″ Angle Girders at each corner, overlapped three holes. To these are secured 12½″ Braced Girders 84 (Fig. 1) connected by 9½″ horizontal Braced Girders 85. The base consists of 12½″ vertical Braced Girders 86 and horizontal 18½″ Angle Girders 87.

We now come to the construction of the head of the clock. The frame for this is shown very clearly in Fig. 12. It is built up of 12½″ Angle Girders 88 at the front and back and connected by 9½″ Angle Girders 89. The lower ends of the vertical Angle Girders (Fig. 2) of the works casing are secured by bolts 91 to the 12½″ Angle Girders 90. These rest on the top of the side Angle Girders of the main frame.

The dial should be secured by bolts to the Braced Girders, as indicated in Fig. 1 and then the works casing should be placed in position from the rear.

The hour and minute hands next are secured in place at the front of the dial and the model is complete. After the final assembly of the Clock parts, the mechanism may be wound up and the Clock set in motion.

It will perhaps be found necessary to make several little adjustments before smooth operation of the different parts is secured. Special attention should be paid to the pendulum and probably experiments will have to be made in order to ascertain the exact position required for the weight 79, for any slight alteration to the position of this weight will make a great difference in the timing of the clock and until the right position is found the clock will either gain or lose time.

Parts Required for Clockwork Movement.

1 of No.	1	4 of No.	12	2 of No.	18b	20 of No.	38	2 of No.	72	2 of No.	126		
15 ,,	2	4 ,,	13	10 ,,	20	1 ,,	43	2 ,,	76	1 ,,	126a		
1 ,,	2a	1 ,,	13a	1 ,,	21	2 ,,	45	2 ,,	77	1 ,,	128		
2 ,,	4	2 ,,	14	3 ,,	24	5 ,,	48d	2 ,,	90	1 ,,	141		
1 ,,	5	3 ,,	15a	5 ,,	25	3 ,,	57	10 ,,	94	1 ,,	147a		
1 ,,	6	9 ,,	16	6 ,,	26	35 ,,	59	2 ,,	95a				
2 ,,	6a	1 ,,	16b	5 ,,	27	4 ,,	62	1 ,,	106				
4 ,,	8	1 ,,	16a	8 ,,	27a	9 ,,	63	1 ,,	109				
6 ,,	9	8 ,,	17	1 ,,	31	2 ,,	63b	2 ,,	111				
3 ,,	11	2 ,,	18a	108 ,,	37	3 ,,	70	9 ,,	125				

Parts required in addition to Outfit No. 7 :—1 18-lb. weight, 1 dial, 1 piece flat spring (about 1½″ long).

Parts Required for Clock Case and Frame

4 of No.	2	341 of No.	37
2 ,,	3	8 ,,	38
8 ,,	7	4 ,,	97
4 ,,	7a	8 ,,	98
14 ,,	8	51 ,,	99
12 ,,	8a	24 ,,	99a
4 ,,	9	4 ,,	108
10 ,,	12		

Of the above parts, 33 of No. 99 and 22 of No. 99a are required in addition to Outfit No. 7. These are merely for ornamental purposes.

The Meccano Grandfather Clock

An Accurate Instrument Using Standard Parts

SPECIAL FEATURES

The Clock described in this leaflet is an improvement upon any Meccano Clock yet produced. It keeps accurate time, and runs for eighteen hours on one winding. With the exception of the weight, and the dial (which may easily be fashioned from a piece of cardboard), the model is made entirely from standard Meccano parts. It may be adjusted by altering the length of pendulum, and it incorporates ratchet winding mechanism. The model presents a handsome appearance, and is particularly suitable for a hall or a staircase.

WHEEL clocks of almost every conceivable shape and size have been constructed, but it is doubtful whether there has ever been a more popular type than the weight-driven "Grandfather" pattern. For over 400 years the Grandfather clock maintained its place as the standard time-piece for the home, and it was only with the introduction of mass-produced clocks of relatively small size, during the middle of the last century, that the "Grandfather" was ousted from its proud position. These ingenious clocks were the products of skilled craftsmen, and the excellence of their construction may be gauged by the fact that many that were built more than 100 years ago are still keeping perfect time.

The "Grandfather" type of clock undoubtedly provides one of the clearest examples of the principle of operation of a clock mechanism. The Meccano model that is described in this leaflet therefore fulfils two distinct functions, for besides being a perfect working mechanism that may be put to practical use in the home, it also enables the constructor to gain a thorough knowledge of the principles underlying clock construction.

The Meccano model stands 6 ft. high and runs for 18 hours without rewinding. With the exception of a lead weight and a cardboard dial, which may easily be made at home, the model is composed entirely of standard Meccano parts. When carefully adjusted the model will keep perfect time over long periods, the effective length of the pendulum being capable of adjustment or "compensation" for varying conditions.

The model consists of two main units, the Mechanism and the Clockcase. It is best to construct the clock mechanism first, so that this may be adjusted to operate correctly after which the case may be built up, and the top of the clockcase, and dial, etc., secured in place around the mechanism.

Construction of the Model : The Mechanism Frame

The frame or "skeleton" in which the various Gears and Rods forming the mechanism are accommodated, is shown in Fig. 2. The frame is composed of four 12½" Angle Girders 1 bolted at their lower ends to 9½" Girders 4 and at the top to 5½" Girders 3. Other 5½" Girders 2 and a number of 5½" Strips are secured between the vertical members. Two 5½" Angle Girders are also secured between the Girders 3 to provide supports for the 7½" Strips 7 and 9, the lower ends of these Strips being bolted to 5½" × ½" Double Angle Strips 5 and 8, secured between two pairs of horizontal 5½" Strips. A 9½" Strip 10 is secured to the back of the frame as shown, and a 5½" × 3½" Flat Plate is bolted to the two 12½" Girders forming the front of the frame. A Flat Trunnion 6 is attached to the Double Angle Strips 5, and Double Bent Strips 11 and 12 are secured to the frame in the positions shown to provide bearings for the clutch gear operating shaft and winding crank spindle respectively.

To complete the frame unit, supports for holding an 8" Axle Rod must be secured in place. The front support consists of a Crank 13 bolted to a Flat Trunnion which, in turn, is secured to a 1½" Angle Girder bolted to the top of the frame. The rear support incorporates also a Crank, which is secured to a 2" Strip and a Trunnion bolted to the top of the frame. The pallet pivot Rod 56 (see Figs. 3 and 6) is journalled in the centre holes of the Trunnions and also in the slotted holes in the Cranks 13.

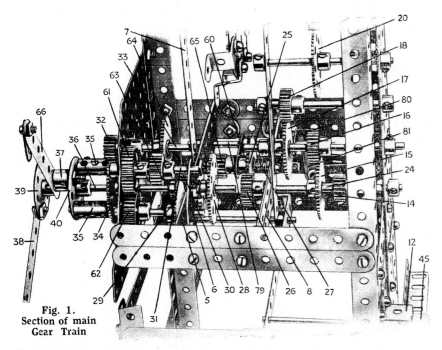

**Fig. 1.
Section of main
Gear Train**

The Main Gear Train

In fitting the various gears in position, it will materially assist the constructor in understanding the operations of the model if he assembles the gears in the order in which they transmit the motion from the prime mover.

The primary gears are the 3½″ Gear Wheels 43 (see Figs. 3 and 5), one of which meshes with a ½″ Pinion 14 on the 3″ Axle Rod 24 (see Fig. 1). This Axle should therefore be pushed into place, and the ¾″ Pinion 26 and the 50-teeth Gear 15 secured in the positions shown in Figs. 1 and 3; the Rod 24 is held in place at its outer end by means of a Collar.

From the ¾″ Pinion 26, the drive is taken to the 50-teeth Gear Wheel 25. This last-mentioned Gear is mounted on a 3″ Axle Rod that is slideable in the holes in the Double Angle Strips 5 and 8 in which it is journalled. It carries in addition to the 50-teeth Gear a ½″ Pinion 65, a Crank 60, and a Compression Spring 27. Three Washers are placed on the Rod between the Pinion 65 and the Double Angle Strips 5 (Fig. 2).

The aim of providing a sliding action for this Rod is to enable the gear train from the clock hands to the winding drum to be "broken" when it is required to adjust the hands of the clock, the action of "declutching" being achieved by the aid of the mechanism now to be described.

The boss of the Crank 60 is slipped on to a 3″ Axle Rod 79 (Fig. 3), journalled in the Double Angle Strips 5 and 8; and the boss is then locked to the shaft by means of its setscrew. A Double Bracket 80 (Fig. 1) is slipped on to the Rod 79 and held in place by means of Collars secured on each side. The Bracket is pivotally connected, by means of the lock-nut device, S.M.262, to a Bell Crank 81, the boss of which is secured to a 2″ Rod journalled in the Double Bent Strip 11 that is secured to the frame of the mechanism (Fig. 2).

To the free arm of the Bell Crank 81, a length of cord is attached, and by pulling on this the Crank 60 will draw the 50-teeth Gear Wheel 25 (Fig. 1), out of engagement with the ¾″ Pinion 26, thus "breaking" the main gear train, and enabling either of the clock hands to be turned freely.

The next step in the construction of the main gear train is to place the Rod 36 (Fig. 1) in position and mount on it the 57-teeth Gear Wheel 28 and the ¾″ Pinion 30, these Gears being secured one on each side of the Double Angle Strips 5.

The Rod 36 carries at its outer end the minute hand, but as we are dealing only with the internal gears at this stage, the minute hand unit should not yet be fitted.

A 2″ Rod is journalled in one of the Double Angle Strips 5 and the Flat Plate forming the front of the frame, and carries a 50-teeth Gear Wheel 29 that meshes with the ¾″ Pinion on the minute hand shaft 36, and a 1″ Gear 62. Two Washers should be placed between the Gear 62 and the Flat Plate in order to allow the Gear to rotate freely.

The Gear 62 engages with a further 1″ Gear 61 mounted on a 2″ Rod 31, which carries also a ¾″ Pinion 63.

To complete the drive to the hour hand, a Rod 33 is journalled in the Strip 7 (Fig. 2) and the 5½″ × 3½″ Plate, and carries a 50-teeth Gear Wheel 64 (Fig. 1), which meshes with the Pinion 63. The Rod 33 carries also a ½″ Pinion 32 mounted on the Rod against the outside face of the Flat Plate.

The hour arm unit may now be built up and secured in position on the Rod 36. The unit consists of a 57-teeth Gear Wheel 34, to the face of which are secured two Couplings 35 by means of bolts. A Bush Wheel 40, with its boss turned inward, rests on the Couplings and is held to them by further bolts, the shanks of the bolts being nipped by the setscrews in the Couplings. A 3½″ Strip 66, fitted with a 1″ Triangular Plate forms the hour hand, and is held to the Bush Wheel 40 by means of a ¾″ Bolt passed through the Strip and a Threaded Boss 37. The hour hand unit is quite free to rotate on the Rod 36, but is spaced away from the face of the Flat Plate by the Wheel boss and Washers. The minute hand unit consists of a 5½″ Strip 38 fitted with a 1″ Triangular Plate, the Strip being bolted to a Bush Wheel 39, which is secured rigidly to the Rod 36.

The Main Gear Train Ratios

After the main gear train has been placed in position, it is interesting to follow the manner in which the drive has been reduced before being taken to the minute hand shaft; and the method employed to provide an auxiliary reduction ratio of 12:1 for the hour hand shaft.

The drive is first taken from one of the Gear Wheels 43 (Fig. 5) to the Pinion 14 (Fig. 1), thus providing a reduction of 7:1. It then passes to the Gear 25 via the Pinion 26, the resulting 2:1 ratio providing a total reduction of 14:1. From the shaft carrying the Gear 25, the drive passes to the minute hand shaft, a reduction of 3:1 being employed here in the form of the ½″ Pinion 65 and the Gear Wheel 28. The total reduction is thus 42:1, and the minute hand will consequently rotate at 1/42 of the speed of the winding drum.

The hour hand drive is composed of a 2:1 ratio between Pinion 30 and the Gear 29; a 1:1 ratio from Gear 62 to Gear 61, and a 2:1 ratio from the Pinion 63 to the Gear 64 on the shaft of which is mounted the Pinion 32 meshing with the 57-teeth Gear 34; the latter Gears giving a final drive of 3:1. The product of this compound gear train is exactly 12:1, so that the hour hand rotates at 1/12 of the speed of the minute hand, and at 1/504 the speed of the winding drum.

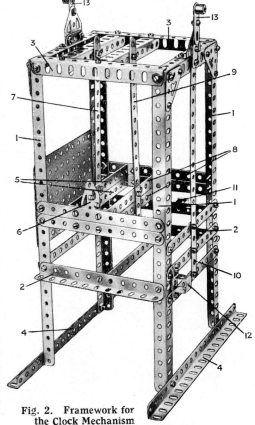

**Fig. 2. Framework for
the Clock Mechanism**

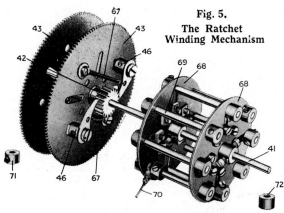

Fig. 5.
The Ratchet
Winding Mechanism

The Wire Line, after being secured to the winding drum, is passed round the groove of a 1½″ Pulley mounted on a 1″ Rod journalled in two Triangular Plates that form the weight pulley block. The Triangular Plates are held apart from each other by means of Double Brackets, and the weight itself is secured to the block by passing a 1″ Axle through the holes in the Plate and also through a ring on the weight. Any form of weight may be used here, provided it is not less than 18 lb. and of such dimensions as not to foul the sides of the clockcase. A suitable shaped weight is shown in the general view.

The other end of the Wire Line, after passing round the 1½″ Pulley, is secured to a Hook attached to the lower 5½″×1½″ Double Angle Strip in the lower portion of the mechanism frame. (See Figs. 1 & 2)

Building and Inserting the Mechanism

It now remains to build the clock case, as shown in the General View of the completed model.

The base of the case consists of two rectangular frames composed of 12½″ and 9½″ Angle Girders spaced apart by means of vertical 12½″ Angle Girders ; 12½″ Braced Girders and extra Angle Girders also being secured as shown to give added strength and to improve the appearance of this portion of the case.

The main body of the case consists of four vertical compound 46″ Angle Girders, each built up from two 24½″ Angle Girders overlapped three holes and bolted together. The vertical members are secured together at top and bottom by 9½″ and 12½″ Angle Girders, and Braced Girders are affixed as shown to provide an artistic finish. The framework is securely bolted to the base of the case, and four 4½″ Strips are attached as shown to ensure rigidity.

The complete mechanism may next be secured rigidly in place by passing bolts through the end holes in the Angle Girders 4 (Fig. 2), and the 12½″ Girders forming the upper portion of the case. The mechanism frame is enclosed in a casing that carries the dial. This casing consists of 12½″ and 9½″ Girders, and four vertical members each consisting of a 12½″ and a 3″ Girder, the latter being overlapped two holes. The frame surrounding the dial is composed of 12½″ Braced Girders and Architraves bolted together in rectangular formation as shown in the view of the completed Clock on page 1.

The dial or clock-face consists of a sheet of white smooth-surface cardboard having a centre hole to admit the hand units. It is fastened in place by boring holes in the card to correspond with those in the Braced Girders in which the securing bolts are placed. Roman numerals or Arabic figures should be drawn on the card in Indian ink. It should be noted that it is not essential to employ all the Braced Girders in order to maintain the required degree of rigidity, as several of these parts are included simply to enhance the appearance of the model.

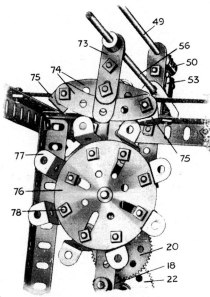

Fig. 6.   The Escapement Mechanism

LIST OF PARTS REQUIRED TO BUILD THE GRANDFATHER CLOCK

9	of No. 1a	25	of No. 8	5	of No. 16	5	of No. 26	1	of No. 57	24	of No. 99a	2	of No. 125
2	„ 1b	12	„ 8a	1	„ 16a	5	„ 27	39	„ 59	1	„ 99b	1	„ 126
11	„ 2	6	„ 9	3	„ 16b	4	„ 27a	6	„ 62	8	„ 100	2	„ 126a
4	„ 2a	1	„ 9f	10	„ 17	2	„ 27b	11	„ 63	1	„ 103a	1	„ 128
2	„ 3	3	„ 11	3	„ 18a	2	„ 31	2	„ 63b	6	„ 108	6	„ 133
1	„ 4	6	„ 12	2	„ 18b	422	„ 37	1	„ 64	3	„ 109	1	„ 141
1	„ 5	4	„ 13	10	„ 20	42	„ 38	2	„ 76	1	„ 111a	2	„ 147
2	„ 6a	4	„ 14	1	„ 21	2	„ 45	2	„ 77	3	„ 111c	1	„ 148
8	„ 7	1	„ 15	2	„ 24	5	„ 48d	2	„ 90	1	„ 113	1	„ 172
4	„ 7a	1	„ 15a	5	„ 25	2	„ 52a	38	„ 99	1	„ 120b	1	18lb. Weight

The Escapement Gearing

After the main gear train has been assembled, the gearing connecting the escapement with it may be secured in place.

The drive from the shaft 24 (Fig. 1) is taken to a ¾" Pinion 16 mounted on a 3" Axle,, by means of the 50-teeth Gear 15 (Fig. 1). The Rod of Pinion 16 also carries a 50-teeth Gear Wheel 17, which meshes with a ¾" Pinion 18 on a further 3" Axle, that is journalled as shown. A 57-teeth Gear Wheel 22 is also mounted on this Axle (see Fig. 3), and this gears with a ½" Pinion 19. The drive is finally transmitted to the pallet wheel shaft 23 (Fig. 3), by means of a further 57-teeth Wheel 20 (Fig.1),meshing with a ½" Pinion secured to the shaft 23.

The Pallet Mechanism

The pallet and pallet wheel are illustrated in Figs. 3 and 6, 7, the latter view showing the details of the construction of these parts very clearly.

The pallet wheel consists of a Face Plate 76 (Fig. 6) mounted on the Axle 23 (Fig. 3). The Plate carries eight Reversed Angle Brackets 77 secured to the Plate by Bolts placed in their slotted holes. Washers should be placed under the heads of these Bolts to ensure a firm grip.

The Pallet itself is built up from two Cranks 73 secured back to back. A 1½" Strip is secured to these, and also two Curved Strips 74. Angle Brackets 75 are also attached to the ends of the Strips 74. The complete Pallet is mounted on a 6½" Axle Rod 56 (Fig. 3), journalled in the supports 13 ; and is held in place at the front end by a Collar and at the rear by means of a Coupling. This Coupling carries a 6½" Axle Rod 55, to the lower end of which a further Coupling 58 is attached, as shown. This Coupling in turn carries two 1" Rods 59 placed in its lateral bores, thus forming a "fork" that enables connection to be made between the Pallet and Pendulum.

The Pendulum

Fig. 4. shows the lower portion of the pendulum and the weight, while the upper part, and the pivot and pivot support, may be seen in Fig. 3.

The complete pendulum rod is built up from four 11½" Axle Rods (Fig. 4), one each for 78a, 78c, 78d and one 6½" Axle 78b. These Rods are connected together by means of Couplings, and a Strip Coupling 54 (Fig. 3) is secured to the end of the Rod 78a. The lower end of the pendulum carries a weight composed of ten 1⅛" Flanged Wheels, the position of the latter being adjusted when setting the clock in operation, to provide the correct movement of the crutch.

The pendulum swings about a pendulum connection 51 (Fig. 3) which is secured tightly in the slots of the Strip Couplings 54 and 53 by means of bolts. A 1" Rod is secured in the vertical bore of the Strip Coupling 53. This Rod is also gripped in the end lateral bore of the Coupling 50 that is mounted on the 6½" Rod 49, the Rod being held rigidly in the bosses of the Cranks 13.

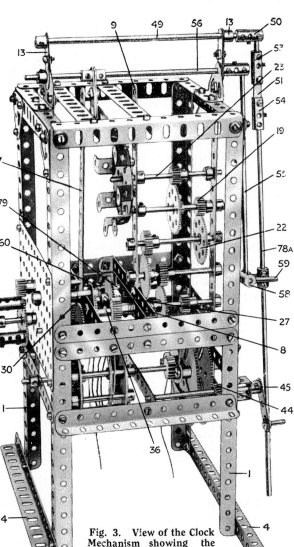

Fig. 3. View of the Clock Mechanism showing the Winding Gear in position.

Ratchet Winding Mechanism

The ratchet winding gear and winding drum are seen incorporated in the mechanism frame in Fig. 3, while Fig. 5 shows the unit disassembled.

The drum, ratchet and gears are mounted upon a 6½" Axle Rod 41. The drum consists of four Face Plates 68, bolted together in pairs and securely locked to the shaft 41 by two set screws placed in each boss. Eight 3" Axle Rods 69 are then passed through the holes in the Plates and held in position by Collars. The loop in the end of the Wire Line 70 is passed over one of the Axles 69, and held in place against one of the Face Plates by means of an additional Collar.

The Ratchet Wheel 42 should next be secured rigidly to the Axle by means of two set-screws, and a 3½" Gear Wheel 43 slipped on to the Rod. As the Gear Wheel must rotate freely on the shaft 41 in one direction, its set-screw should be removed. This Wheel 43 carries two Pawls 46 secured to its face by Pivot Bolts. The Pawls are held in engagement with the teeth of the Ratchet 42 by means of short lengths of Spring Cord 67, one end of each length being secured under the head of an ordinary bolt fixed in one of the holes in the face of the Gear Wheel, and the other end passed through the hole in the Pawl and twisted back to form a strong loop. The length and tension of the springs should be adjusted so as to keep the Pawls in firm contact with the Ratchet, and thus prevent any possibility of slipping. The Gear 43, complete with Pawls and springs, is held in position against the boss of the Ratchet Wheel 42 by means of a Collar.

The complete winding drum axle is journalled in two 5½" Strips forming part of the frame (Fig. 3), and is prevented from moving lengthwise by means of two Collars 71 and 72, secured on each end. The position of the 3½" Gear Wheel carrying the Pawls of the ratchet mechanism must be adjusted so that it engages with the Pinion 14 (See Fig. 1). The second 3½" Gear 43 meshes with a ½" Pinion 44 (Fig. 3), mounted on a 4½" Rod journalled in the Double Bent Strip 12 (Fig. 2) and a 5½" × ½" Double Angle Strip secured between the mechanism frame. This Rod carries also a Crank 45 (Fig. 3), fitted with a Threaded Pin, thus forming a convenient winding handle by which the Wire Line (part No. 141) may be wound round the winding barrel to raise the Clock Weight. The reduction gearing of 7:1 fitted between the winding handle and the drum shaft makes quite easy the operation of lifting the heavy Weight.

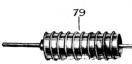

Fig. 4. The Pendulum

Baltic Tank Locomotive

A new Meccano Model of a typical 4-6-4 Passenger Express Engine

> The model is designed to a scale of 1 in. to 1 ft. and is 44 ins. long over all. It is driven by a 4-volt Electric Motor mounted between the main frames and connected by gearing to the centre coupled wheels. The Accumulator may be carried in the coal bunker. Special features include Walschaerts' Valve Gear and brakes on all coupled wheels. The more important parts of the locomotive may be built as separate units, as in actual engineering practice.

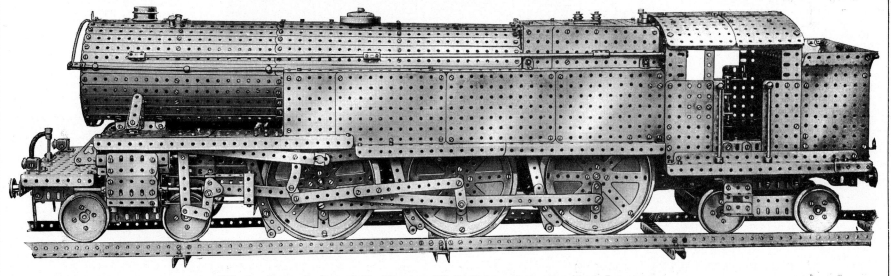

Fig. 1. General view of the Meccano "Baltic" type Passenger Tank Locomotive.

PERHAPS there is nothing that arouses such a thrill of admiration—almost of awe—as a modern locomotive travelling at a speed of 70 m.p.h. or over, and apparently hauling its four or five hundred-ton train with the greatest ease over the shining metals !

What a tremendous difference there is between the locomotive giant of to-day and the first practical locomotive, Stephenson's "Rocket" of a century ago. Great alterations have been made in design and yet the basic principles, such as the fire tube boiler, blast pipe in the chimney, and connecting rods attached direct to the driving wheels, remain unaltered.

A type of locomotive that has come into its own within late years, especially for passenger working of all descriptions, is the tank engine, so called because it has the water tanks—and also the coal bunker—built into the main frames, instead of being contained in a separate vehicle as is the case with the ordinary type of locomotive with tender.

A fine and typical express tank locomotive of the "Baltic" type, designed by Col. Billinton, for the Brighton Section of the Southern Railway, is shown in Fig. 2. It ranks amongst the most powerful of the express tank engines in this country, having a tractive effort of 24,176 lbs. The cylinders are 22″ bore by 28″ stroke (the largest fitted to any two-cylinder locomotive in the British Isles, with the exception of the similarly dimensioned 4-6-0 "Urie" engines of the S.W. Section), and the engine weighs 98 tons. The locomotive illustrated is one of a batch of six used to haul the 350-400 ton expresses between London and Brighton, and often attains a speed in the neighbourhood of 80 m.p.h. The L.M.S. Railway possesses many fine examples of express tank engines, notably the Horwich "Baltics," which can doubtless put up just as excellent a performance as their Southern sisters.

Although the Meccano model tank locomotive described in this leaflet was not built to resemble any particular prototype, the model reproduces the general design of the Baltic class very closely. In common with the large Meccano models, it is constructed entirely on the unit principle, which considerably simplifies the work of assembling the model—besides following actual railway practice.

Construction of the Model ; The Main Frames

As in the case of a real locomotive, so in the model the assembly of the main frames (Figs. 3 and 4) should be made the starting point of the construction. Fig. 3 shows the left main frame (looking towards the front of the model), whilst Fig. 4 gives a very clear idea of the appearance of the inside of the right-hand main frame, with the various connecting Girders and the Meccano 4-volt Electric Motor in the positions they will occupy in the complete unit.

Each main frame (Fig. 3) consists of three $5\frac{1}{2}'' \times 2\frac{1}{2}''$ Flat Plates 1 with one $4\frac{1}{2}'' \times 2\frac{1}{2}''$ Flat Plate 2 at each end. One $24\frac{1}{2}''$ and one $18\frac{1}{2}''$ Angle Girder 3—overlapping one another nine holes—are bolted to the top edges of the Plates 1 and 2 and a further $24\frac{1}{2}''$ Angle Girder (Fig. 4) is attached to the lower edges of the Plates. A $9\frac{1}{2}''$ Angle Girder 4 (Fig. 3) is bolted to the end hole of the $4\frac{1}{2}'' \times 2\frac{1}{2}''$ Plate 2 and to a $5\frac{1}{2}''$ Flat Girder 5. A $2''$ Flat Girder 6 is attached to the $9\frac{1}{2}''$ Girder 4 by means of a $1\frac{1}{2}''$ Angle Girder 7 and also by a $1\frac{1}{2}''$ Strip which is secured to the other end of the $2''$ Flat Girder and to the Girder 4. A $2\frac{1}{2}''$ small radius Curved Strip 8 is attached to the $2''$ Flat Girder 6 as indicated in both Figs. 3 and 4, its other end being secured by a bolt passing through the bottom hole of the $2\frac{1}{2}''$ Strip 9 and the $3\frac{1}{2}''$ Flat Girder 10 (Fig. 3). A corresponding $2\frac{1}{2}''$ Strip 9 and Curved Strip 8 are bolted to the other end of the Flat Girder 10, the other end of the Curved Strip being attached to a Flat Bracket bolted to the end hole of the $4\frac{1}{2}'' \times 2\frac{1}{2}''$ Flat Plate 2. The two $2\frac{1}{2}''$ Strips 9 serve as connecting pieces to hold the various parts firmly together. A $2\frac{1}{2}''$ Strip 26 attached to the $1\frac{1}{2}''$ Angle Girder 7 represents the "guard iron."

The rear end of the main frame is built up in a somewhat similar manner to the front portion. A $9\frac{1}{2}''$ Flat Girder 11 (Figs. 3 and 4) is bolted to the end of the Plate 2, its other extremity being attached to a $2\frac{1}{2}''$ Angle Girder 17a to which is bolted a $1\frac{1}{2}''$ Flat Girder 12. A $2\frac{1}{2}''$ small radius Curved Strip 13 is attached to the Flat Girder 12. As will be gathered from the illustrations both the small radius Curved Strips 13 are secured to a $3\frac{1}{2}''$ Flat Girder which is attached to the rest of the frame in a similar manner to that employed in fixing the Flat Girder 10 at the front end. When both main frames have been completed, the various cross Girders 17 and 18 should be attached to one of the main frames as shown. The front and rear "bogie pin stretchers" 14 and 15 each consist of two $4\frac{1}{2}''$ Angle Girders

bolted together so as to form a channel section girder, being attached to the main frame by means of $\frac{1}{2}'' \times \frac{1}{2}''$ Angle Brackets 16.

The Motor supports consist of two $4\frac{1}{2}''$ Angle Girders 18 secured both to the Motor and to the $24\frac{1}{2}''$ Angle Girders that are bolted to the bottom of the main frame. A $7\frac{1}{2}''$ Angle Girder 28 is bolted to the lower Girder, a Washer being placed between them on the shank of the retaining bolts.

Each half of the smoke-box saddle consists of a $3''$ Angle Girder 19 (Figs. 4 and 8) bolted to the Angle Girders 3. A $2\frac{1}{2}''$ Flat Girder is secured to the Girder 19, flush with the rear end of the latter, and a $\frac{1}{2}'' \times \frac{1}{2}''$ Angle Bracket 20 (Fig. 8) is bolted in the front end hole of the Angle Girder. Two Flat Brackets 21 fixed to the $2\frac{1}{2}''$ Flat Girder will be used eventually to form a connection between the smoke-box and the smoke-box saddle. The $3\frac{1}{2}'' \times 2\frac{1}{2}''$ Flanged Plate 22 is secured to the $3''$ Angle Girders 19, and also to the $9\frac{1}{2}''$ Angle Girder 4 by a $\frac{1}{2}'' \times \frac{1}{2}''$ Angle Bracket.

Before bolting the two main frames together the Motor should have its gearing inserted. The gearing is arranged as follows : a $\frac{1}{2}''$ Pinion secured to the armature spindle of the Motor meshes with a 57-teeth Gear Wheel that is fixed to one end of a $2\frac{1}{2}''$ Rod, to which the $\frac{1}{2}''$ Pinion 23 (Fig. 4) is attached. The Pinion 23 meshes with the Gear 24, which is secured on a $2''$ Rod journalled in the Motor side plates. This Rod carries a $\frac{3}{4}''$ Pinion that engages with the $3\frac{1}{2}''$ Gear 25 on the driving wheel axle 46b.

The two halves of the main frames may now be bolted together.

The Cylinder Block and Crosshead, etc.

The close-up view (Fig. 6) of the left-hand cylinder block and crosshead, etc., gives a very good idea of the details of these parts. The "cylinder" consists of five $2\frac{1}{2}'' \times \frac{1}{2}''$ Double Angle Strips 27 bolted between two Bush Wheels 26 which form the front and back "cylinder covers." Two $\frac{1}{2}'' \times \frac{1}{2}''$ Angle Brackets 29 are secured to the back cylinder cover (see Fig. 8) by the bolts which hold the Double Angle Strips 27 in place ; these Angle Brackets must be diametrically opposite one another in a vertical plane. The $4\frac{1}{2}''$ Strips 30, which represent the "crosshead guide bars," are attached to the Angle Brackets 29 by nuts and bolts, a Washer being placed between each Angle Bracket and guide bar.

The "crosshead" consists of a Strip Coupling 32 (Fig. 6) which is secured on the end of the $6\frac{1}{2}''$ Rod 31 representing the "piston rod." In the transverse tapped bore of the Strip Coupling a $1''$ Screwed Rod is inserted and an Eye Piece 33 secured to each end. A Washer is placed on the Screwed Rod before putting on each Eye Piece, in order to increase the overall distance between the two Eye Pieces. These are termed "crosshead shoes" or "slippers."

Fig. 2. Southern Railway "Baltic" type Tank Engine "Remembrance" employed on the heaviest trains between London and Brighton, including the Southern Belle Pullman. This engine was named in memory of the employees of the Brighton Section who fell in the Great War.

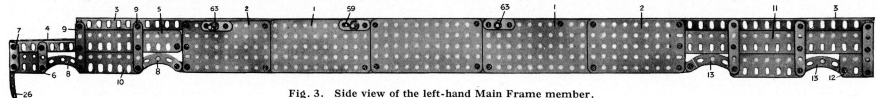

Fig. 3. Side view of the left-hand Main Frame member.

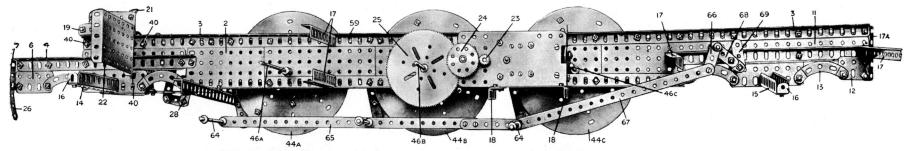

Fig. 4. Main Frame, with left-hand side removed to show Motor and Gearing, etc.

A 1″ Triangular Plate is now attached to a 2″ Strip 34 by a nut and bolt, a Washer being placed under the head of the latter. A bolt 35 is now passed through one of the holes of the Triangular Plate and the top hole of the Strip 34. Two Washers are placed on the shank of the bolt, which is then screwed into the tapped boss hole of the upper crosshead slipper 33. A ⅜″ Bolt 36 is passed through the remaining hole of the Triangular Plate and inserted partially in the end tapped bore of the Strip Coupling 32. Two Washers are placed on the shank of the ⅜″ Bolt between the Triangular Plate and the Coupling.

The valve chest consists of three 3½″ Double Angle Strips 37 bolted between two Bush Wheels. The "valve spindle" 38 is a 4½″ Rod and carries two 1″ fast Pulleys spaced apart by a Coupling, to represent the "slide valve," which is of the piston type.

The cylinder and the valve chest are now mounted on the 2½″ × 2½″ Flat Plate 39 at a distance of 2″ apart, by the four ¾″ bolts 40, which have a Collar and two Washers on each for spacing the cylinder block the correct distance from the main frames.

The "lagging" plate 41, which consists of two 2½″ Flat Girders held together by 2″ Strips, is bolted to one of the 2½″ Double Angle Strips 27 and also to one of the 3½″ Double Angle Strips 37. It will be noticed that the 2½″ Double Angle Strip 27a is attached to an adjacent Double Angle Strip (at the back end only) by a Flat Bracket (see Figs. 6 and 8). This is due to the fact that the bolt normally holding the Double Angle Strip 27a in position on the back cylinder cover has had to be omitted in order to clear the "combining" lever 54.

The 1½″ Double Angle Strip 42 is attached at this stage to the top guide bar only, by a nut and bolt, a Washer being placed on the shank of the bolt between the guide bar and the Double Angle Strip. Two Collars 43 secured to ⅜″ Bolts passed through holes at each end of the bottom 2½″ × ½″ Double Angle Strip 27, represent the "cylinder drain cocks" (see Figs. 1 and 8).

The right hand cylinder block may now be made. It is constructed in a precisely similar manner to the left-hand one.

When completed the cylinder blocks may be mounted in position on the main frames by means of the ¾″ Bolts 40 (see Figs. 4, 6 and 8). In Fig. 4 the shanks of three of the four ¾″ Bolts holding the right-hand cylinder block to the main frame are indicated by their numbers. This should enable the positions of the cylinder blocks to be located correctly on the main frames.

The bottom guide bar 30 together with the 1½″ × ½″ Double Angle Strip 42 secured to the top guide bar, are now bolted to the end of the 7½″ Angle Girder 28 (Fig. 8) the guide bar being placed underneath the flange of the Girder, between the latter and the ½″ portion of the Double Angle Strip 42, It is very important that the crossheads move quite freely in the guides. To this end the guide bars must be carefully adjusted, and kept well oiled.

Driving Wheels and Axles

The next job is to construct the "driving wheels" 44a, 44b, 44c (Figs. 4 and 8). Each consists of a Circular Plate bolted to a Hub Disc, and a Bush Wheel secured to the centre by nuts and bolts. A Double Arm Crank 45a, 45b, 45c, is bolted to each driving wheel so that its centre is 1″ from that

of the wheel. Six driving wheels in all will be required and when they are completed, they may be secured to the driving wheel axles 46a, 46b, 46c (Fig. 4). Each of the latter consists of a 4½″ Rod joined to a 1″ Rod by means of a Coupling. A 25 gramme Weight is bolted to the centre driving wheel 45b in the position shown. This is to balance the reciprocating masses of the connecting and coupling rods, etc. The driving wheels are secured to their respective axles by two set-screws inserted in each of the set-screw holes of the new style Bush Wheels that are bolted to the wheel centres.

The 3½″ Gear 25 is secured to the centre driving wheel axle 46b as shown in Fig. 4. This Gear—as was mentioned previously—meshes with the ¾″ Pinion secured to the 2½″ Rod that carries the 57-teeth Gear 24.

Each pair of driving wheels on any one axle must have their crank pins *exactly at 90 degrees to one another*. This is very important, for if the pins are not exactly at right angles the coupling rods will bind and so prevent the model working satisfactorily. The cranks in a two cylinder steam locomotive are set in the same way.

The Motion (Valve-Gear, Connecting Rods, etc.)

The leading and trailing driving wheel crank pins consist of Pivot Bolts 47a, 47c (Fig. 8) which are held in the bosses of the Double Arm Cranks 45a and 45c by set-screws. One end of each of the "coupling rods" 48a, 48b, which consist of two 7½″ Strips, is journalled on the Crank Pins 47a, 47c, and spaced away from the boss of each of the Double Arm Cranks by means of a Collar on each crank pin. This is to enable the coupling rods to clear the flanges of the driving wheels.

The crank pin 47b consists of a 1½″ Rod held rigidly in the bore of the Double Arm Crank 45b by the latter's set-screws. A Collar is placed first on the crank pin, and then the coupling rods 48a and 48b, after which the connecting rod 49, consisting of a 12½″ Strip, is slipped into place. Care should be taken to see that two Washers are placed on the crank pin between the connecting rod 49 and the ends of the two coupling rods. Lastly the "return crank" 50 is secured in place. This Crank must be set at a slight angle so that its end describes a circular path about the driving wheel centre.

The end of the connecting rod may now be inserted between the jaws of the Strip Coupling 32 forming the crosshead, and the ⅜″ Bolt 36 by which the connecting rod is attached to the crosshead, screwed home.

The "expansion link" 51 consists of two 2½″ large radius Curved Strips connected together by ⅜″ Bolts and spaced apart by four Washers on each of the bolts, a Flat Bracket being secured rigidly to the expansion link by the lower ⅜″ Bolt. The expansion link will eventually be attached pivotally by means of a lock-nutted bolt (Standard Mechanism No. 262) to the Architrave 52 that is bolted to the footplating (see Fig. 7). An Eye Piece 56 slides freely on the front 2½″ Curved Strip of the expansion link.

The motion of the return crank 50 is transmitted to the expansion link by means of the Strips 53, which are attached pivotally to both the return crank and the Flat Bracket on the expansion link by lock-nutted bolts.

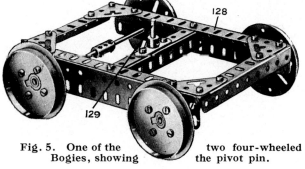

Fig. 5. One of the Bogies, showing the pivot pin. two four-wheeled

The "combining lever" 54 comprises a $3\frac{1}{2}''$ Strip pivoted n the second hole from its top end on a set-screw which is inserted in the tapped hole of a Collar. This Collar is secured on the end of the valve spindle 38. The end of the combining lever is connected to the $2''$ Strip 34 by a short pivoted link, consisting of a $1\frac{1}{2}''$ Strip attached to the Strips 34 and 54 by lock-nutted bolts. The "radius rod" 55—a $7\frac{1}{2}''$ Strip—is attached pivotally to the top end hole of the combining lever by a lock-nutted bolt. The other end of the radius rod is attached to the Eye Piece 56 by a $\frac{3}{8}''$ Bolt held in the bore of the Eye Piece by the latter's set screw. The radius rod must be bent slightly, for the points of attachment to the combining lever and the Eye Piece 56 are not in a straight line.

The end of the radius rod projecting beyond the Eye Piece 56, or "die block," slides in an Eye Piece 57 that is attached pivotally to the $3\frac{1}{2}''$ Strip 58. This latter Strip is bolted rigidly to a Crank secured on the end of the weigh shaft (a $6\frac{1}{2}''$ Rod), journalled in the holes 59 of the main frames (Figs. 3, 4, 8). A second Crank to which a $2\frac{1}{2}''$ Strip 60 is bolted, is also secured to the weigh shaft in the position indicated, close to the main frame. The Strip 60 will be connected to the Threaded Boss 120 (Fig. 9) by the $12\frac{1}{2}''$ Strip 61 when the model is assembled.

The right-hand motion is exactly similar in every respect to that shown in the illustrations except that the Crank to which the Strip 61 is secured is not duplicated on the other end of the weigh shaft. The cranks 58 on each end of the weigh shaft are parallel.

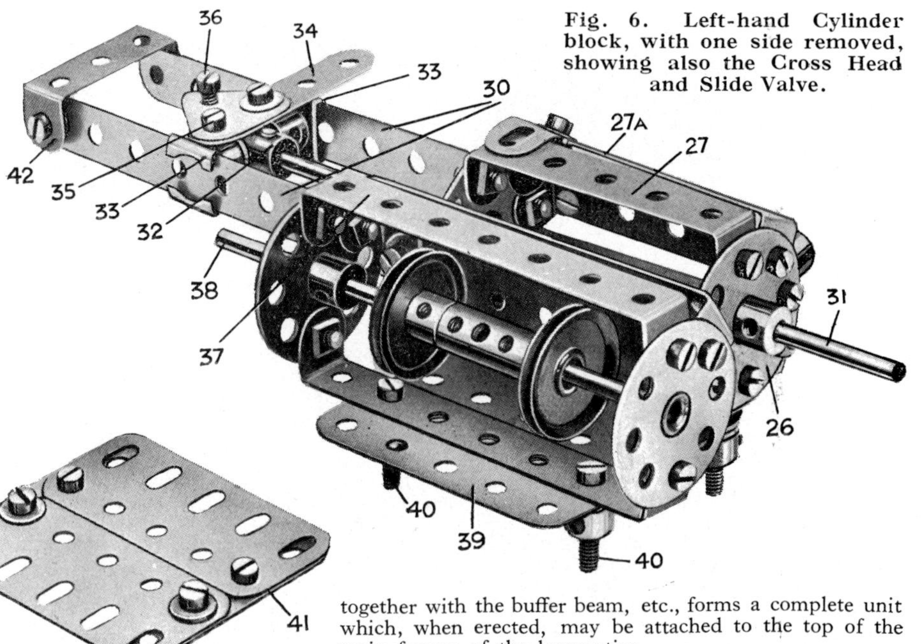

Fig. 6. Left-hand Cylinder block, with one side removed, showing also the Cross Head and Slide Valve.

The Brake Rigging

Each of the "brake blocks" consists of a $2\frac{1}{2}''$ large radius Curved Strip bolted to a $4\frac{1}{2}''$ Strip 62 (Fig. 8); a Washer is placed beneath the head of the bolt securing the brake block to the $4\frac{1}{2}''$ Strip. Each of the Strips 62 is hung from a pivot composed of a $1''$ Rod secured in a Double Arm Crank 63 that is attached to the main frames in the position indicated in Fig. 3. The Strips are retained on the $1''$ Rods by means of Collars. Each pair of "brake hangers" (as the Strips 62 are usually termed) are connected together by a $6\frac{1}{2}''$ Rod 64 (Fig. 4) which is inserted in the bottom hole of the brake hangers, being retained thereon by Collars. A Strip 65 $14''$ long (obtained by bolting a $12\frac{1}{2}''$ and a $3''$ Strip together) connects all the brakes.

The Crank 66 is secured on a $5''$ Rod journalled in holes in the main frames, and is connected to the $6\frac{1}{2}''$ Rod 54 by a $9\frac{1}{2}''$ Strip 67. The latter is attached pivotally to the Crank 66 by means of a lock-nutted bolt. On the same Rod carrying the Crank 66 is secured a second Crank 68

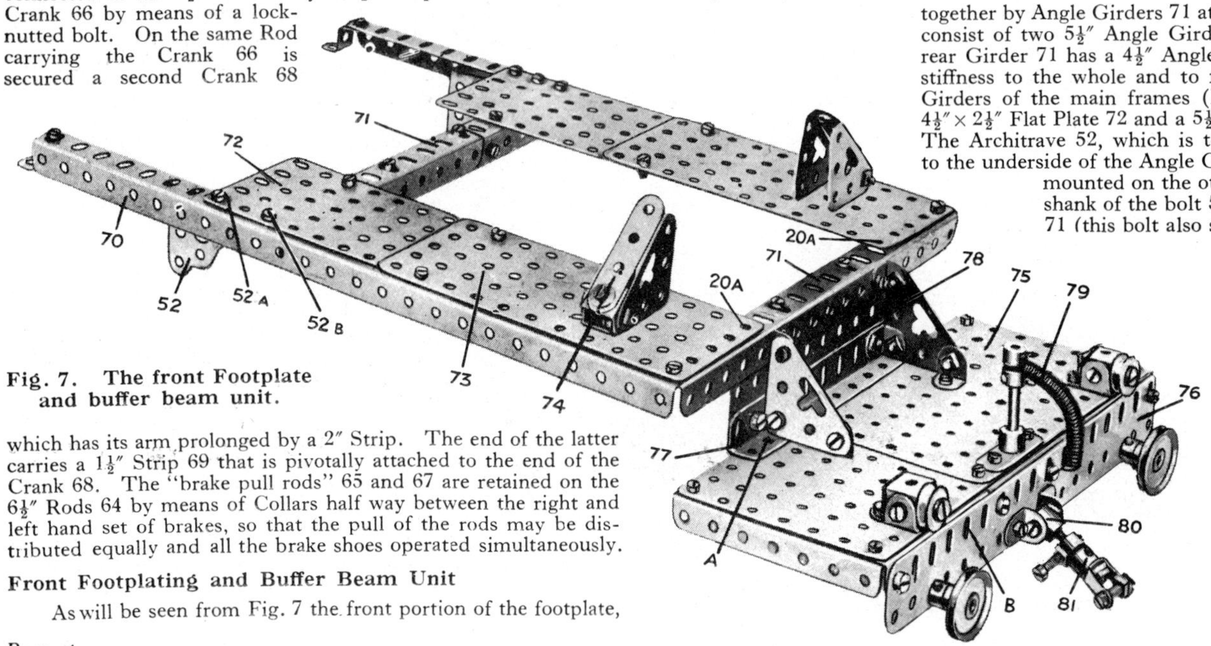

Fig. 7. The front Footplate and buffer beam unit.

which has its arm prolonged by a $2''$ Strip. The end of the latter carries a $1\frac{1}{2}''$ Strip 69 that is pivotally attached to the end of the Crank 68. The "brake pull rods" 65 and 67 are retained on the $6\frac{1}{2}''$ Rods 64 by means of Collars half way between the right and left hand set of brakes, so that the pull of the rods may be distributed equally and all the brake shoes operated simultaneously.

Front Footplating and Buffer Beam Unit

As will be seen from Fig. 7 the front portion of the footplate, together with the buffer beam, etc., forms a complete unit which, when erected, may be attached to the top of the main frames of the locomotive.

The longitudinal $12\frac{1}{2}''$ Angle Girders 70 are connected together by Angle Girders 71 at the points shown in the Figure. The Angle Girders 71 each consist of two $5\frac{1}{2}''$ Angle Girders overlapped five holes and bolted together rigidly. The rear Girder 71 has a $4\frac{1}{2}''$ Angle Girder bolted midway along its bottom edge to give added stiffness to the whole and to form a convenient bracket by which to attach it to the top Girders of the main frames (Fig. 8). Each half of the footplating, which consists of a $4\frac{1}{2}'' \times 2\frac{1}{2}''$ Flat Plate 72 and a $5\frac{1}{2}'' \times 2\frac{1}{2}''$ Plate 73, is bolted to the Girders 70 and 71 as shown. The Architrave 52, which is termed the "expansion link bracket" in practice, is attached to the underside of the Angle Girders 70 and 71 by the Bolts 52a, 52b. A similar bracket is mounted on the other side of the unit, of course. One Washer is placed on the shank of the bolt 52b between the expansion link bracket and the Angle Girder 71 (this bolt also secures the Angle Girder 70 to the Angle Girder 71). Two Washers are placed on the remaining bolt 52a.

The outside steam pipes 74 each consist of a Double Bracket, bolted to the $5\frac{1}{2}'' \times 2\frac{1}{2}''$ Flat Plate 73, through which is passed a $1''$ Screwed Rod. A second Double Bracket is also mounted on the Screwed Rod, on the ends of which are placed two Corner Brackets. A $2''$ Strip secured to this latter Double Bracket finishes off this fitting effectively.

The front portion of the footplate unit carrying the buffer beam consists of two $5\frac{1}{2}'' \times 3\frac{1}{2}''$ Flat Plates 75 overlapped five holes, along the front edge of which are bolted two $5\frac{1}{2}''$ Angle Girders. To the latter are secured the two $5\frac{1}{2}''$ Flat Girders 76 that represent the buffer beam. A $5\frac{1}{2}''$ Angle Girder 77 is bolted to the rear edge of the Plates 75 midway between the ends of the latter. To the $5\frac{1}{2}'' \times 3\frac{1}{2}''$ Flat Plates 75, and the Angle Girders 71, 77, are secured two Corner Brackets 78 which are secured to the parts mentioned by means of $\frac{1}{2}'' \times \frac{1}{2}''$ Angle Brackets. These may be seen clearly in the illustration, where it may also be ascertained that the correct location for the Corner Brackets 78 is $2\frac{1}{2}''$ from the edges of the Plates. A Flat Girder is bolted to the $5\frac{1}{2}''$ Girder 77 to fill up the space between the latter and the Girders 71.

The brake pipe 79 consists of a Spring, one end of which is secured to the buffer beam 76, the other end being mounted on the end of a $1\frac{1}{2}''$ Rod. The latter is mounted in a Double Arm Crank that is secured to the Plates 75. The "buffers" are $1''$ fast Pulleys secured to Threaded Pins that are bolted to the buffer beam. A Collar is placed on each Threaded Pin to represent the buffer stock.

The "screw coupling" comprises a Threaded Boss 80 that is mounted between two $\frac{1}{2}'' \times \frac{1}{2}''$ Angle Brackets bolted to the buffer beam. The bolts by which the Threaded Boss is attached to the Angle Brackets are inserted in the transverse tapped holes of the Threaded Boss, nuts on the shanks of the bolts being locked against the side of the Threaded Boss to prevent the bolts working loose. A $1''$ Screwed Rod has a Collar secured to it, and a $\frac{3}{8}''$ Bolt is inserted in the set-screw hole of this Collar and locked in position by a nut on the shank of the Bolt. A Small Fork Piece 81 is now placed on the end of the Screwed Rod and retained on the latter by means of lock nuts. The addition of a $\frac{1}{2}''$ Bolt between the jaws of the Small Fork Piece completes the coupling.

Each lamp consists of an Eye Piece with two Double Brackets secured to its boss by two bolts that are inserted in the set screw holes on each side of the boss. The front of the

to the edges of the two rearmost cab side Plates 104, and to the Angle Girders 102. Four $5\frac{1}{2}''$ Flat Girders 105 are secured to the Plates 104 in the positions indicated, whilst $4\frac{1}{2}''$ Angle Girders 106 are secured to the front edges of the foremost Flat Girders 105, a $2''$ Slotted Strip 107 being secured to the top of each of these. Four $3\frac{1}{2}''$ Strips 108 are attached to the cab side Plates 104 in the positions shown. Two $4\frac{1}{2}''$ Angle Girders bolted to the rearmost Flat Girders 105 form a convenient means of attaching the back of the cab to the sides. The back of the cab consists of three $4\frac{1}{2}'' \times 2\frac{1}{2}''$ Flat Plates, their bottom edges being bolted to a $7\frac{1}{2}''$ Flat Girder. A $5\frac{1}{2}''$ Flat Girder is secured midway along the top edge of the back of the cab, and a $5\frac{1}{2}''$ Curved Strip is, in turn, bolted to it.

The back of the bunker consists of two $3\frac{1}{2}'' \times 5\frac{1}{2}''$ Flat Plates 109 which are connected together by a $5\frac{1}{2}'' \times 2\frac{1}{2}''$ Flat Plate that overlaps each of the Plates by two holes. The back is now secured in position by being bolted to the $5\frac{1}{2}''$ Angle Girders 110. The extreme lower ends of the latter carry the rear buffer beam, which consists of a $7\frac{1}{2}''$ Flat Girder. The steps 111 each consist of two $1\frac{1}{2}''$ Angle Girders bolted to a pair of $3\frac{1}{2}''$ Strips that are attached to the Angle Girder 102.

It should be noted that the front cab side plates 104 have $4\frac{1}{2}''$ Flat Girders attached to their rear edges, the Handrail Supports carrying the handrails being attached to these Flat Girders. The bottom ends of the handrails rest on $9\frac{1}{2}''$ Angle Girders, to the front end of which $1''$ Reversed Angle Brackets 112 are attached. This Girder forms part of the

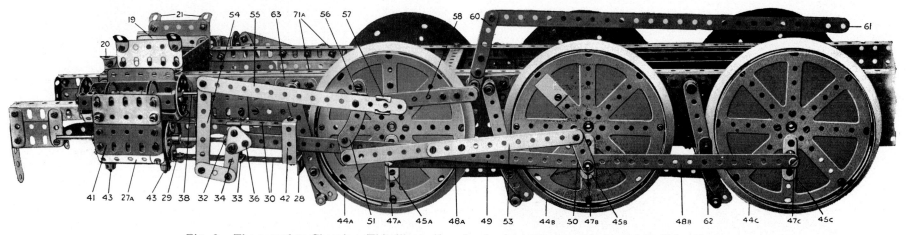

Fig. 8. The complete Chassis. This illustration clearly shows the arrangement of the Valve Gear.

lamp is represented by a $\frac{1}{2}''$ loose Pulley that is mounted on a Pivot Bolt held in the longitudinal bore of the Eye Piece. The head of the Pivot bolt makes a realistic representation of the "bull's eye" lens of the real lamp.

The "lamp irons" are $\frac{1}{2}'' \times \frac{1}{2}''$ Angle Brackets bolted to the Plates 75 in the positions indicated, and the Eye Pieces of the lamps slide down on them. The lamps are thus readily detachable. A lamp iron should also be secured to the smoke-box in front of the chimney and three others—$\frac{1}{2}''$ Reversed Angle Brackets—should be attached to the rear of the coal bunker, one over each buffer and the other at the top centre of the Plate.

Construction of the Cab, Bunker, etc.

The floor of the cab (Figs. 9 and 10) is composed of six $3\frac{1}{2}'' \times 5\frac{1}{2}''$ Flat Plates, each pair of Plates overlapping seven holes in the direction of the width of the cab. In the direction of the cab's length the Plates are placed edge to edge or "butted together," as it is termed. Each side of the floor is bolted to a $9\frac{1}{2}''$ Angle Girder 102 (Fig. 10) extended $1''$ by a $2''$ Angle Girder that is secured to it. A $7\frac{1}{2}''$ Angle Girder 103 is bolted across the front edge of the floor as indicated in both illustrations. The $4\frac{1}{2}'' \times 2\frac{1}{2}''$ Flat Plates 104, which form the sides of the cab, are bolted rigidly to the Angle Girders 102.

The bunker sides, which consist of $5\frac{1}{2}'' \times 3\frac{1}{2}''$ Flat Plates bent over at the top, are bolted

running board and is secured to a similar Girder bolted to the second line of holes from the bottom of the cab side Plates 104. The top ends of the Flat Girders 105 on each side are connected together by a $5\frac{1}{2}''$ and a $2\frac{1}{2}''$ Strip, overlapped two holes.

The cab roof (Fig. 1) consists of four $5\frac{1}{2}'' \times 3\frac{1}{2}''$ Flat Plates, each pair being overlapped four holes in the direction of the width of the cab. The two pairs of Plates are placed edge to edge and connected together by $5\frac{1}{2}''$ Strips bolted across both sets of Plates. The cab roof is attached to the hinges 113 (Fig. 9) which permits of easy access to the cab's interior. When the roof is closed, the shanks of the bolts 114 project through holes in the cab roof, and nuts are placed on the ends of the bolts to keep the cab roof in place.

Brake Control and Reversing Gear

The hand brake consists of a $2''$ Screwed Rod 115 journalled in a Bush Wheel 116 (Fig. 9) that is fixed to the floor of the cab. A Threaded Coupling is attached to the upper end of the screwed Rod, whilst a Threaded Boss 117 is free to move on the lower extremity of the Rod, its travel only being limited by Collars secured on the Rod in the positions shown in Fig. 10. A $2''$ Rod is held in the plain bore of the Threaded Coupling (Fig. 9) and a second $2''$ Rod connected at right angles to the top of the former Rod by means of a Coupling, forms the handle. A Threaded Pin is secured to a Collar and fastened to one end of the handle.

A 3½" Rod 118 (Fig. 9) is journalled in a 1"×1" Angle Bracket secured to the cab side plate 104 by two ⅜" Bolts, three Washers on each of the ⅜" Bolts serving to space the 1"×1" Angle Bracket from the cab side. The other end of the 3½" Rod carries a Threaded Coupling and is journalled in a 3½" Flat Girder bolted to the Angle Girder 106. A 3½" Screwed Rod 119, secured in the tapped bore of the Threaded Coupling, carries a Threaded Boss 120, the travel of which is limited by two stops consisting of Collars which are secured to the Rod. The Rods 118 and 119 are rotated by means of the Double Arm Crank 122 that is fastened on the end of the former Rod. End play of the Rod 118 is prevented by a Collar 121 that is secured on the Rod 118 behind the Flat Girder in which the Rod is journalled.

The driver's brake valve 123 simply consists of a Threaded Pin that is inserted in the set-screw hole of a Collar secured to a 3" Rod. The upper end of this Rod is retained in position by a ½"×½" Angle Bracket bolted to the 1"×1" Angle Bracket in which the Rod 118 is journalled, the other end of the Rod passing through a hole in the cab floor. This completes the construction of the cab unit.

Details of the Side Tanks

The construction of the side tanks is shown well in the general view and in Fig. 12, the latter view showing the inside construction of the right-hand tank.

The top edges of the four 3½"×5½" Flat Plates forming the tank sides are bolted to an 18½" Angle Girder 124 to which the tank top (a 12½" and a 7½" Flat Girder) is secured. The running board 125 which consists of a 9½" and a 7½" Angle Girder overlapped three holes is bolted to the bottom edge of the tank sides. The front edges of the Flat Girders forming the tank tops should project beyond the tank sides to form a beading. To this end the Flat Girders are secured by their slotted holes to the Angle Girders 124. The ½"×½" Angle Brackets 126 and 127 are for the purpose of securing the side tank to the side of the fire-box and front foot-plating respectively, as will be seen on reference to the general view (Fig. 1).

The Construction of the Bogies

Each of the leading and trailing bogies is exactly similar in construction; therefore one description should suffice for both. The construction of the bogies is shown clearly in Fig. 5. The sides of the frame consist of 7½" Flat Girders that are bolted to 7½" Angle Girders 128. The latter are connected together by 4½" Angle Girders at each end and the corners strengthened by means of Corner Brackets. The "bogie pin" 129 consists of a 1" Rod held in a Double Arm Crank that is bolted to two 4½" Angle Girders which are placed together to form a channel-section girder and bolted, in turn, to the 7½" Angle Girders forming the bogie sides.

Each of the bogie wheel axles consists of two 3" Rods connected together by a Coupling. They are journalled in the slotted holes of the 7½" Flat Girders, to allow the wheels to rise and fall independently when traversing uneven ground. The wheels themselves consist of Face Plates to which are bolted Wheel Flanges, and they are secured rigidly to the ends of their axles.

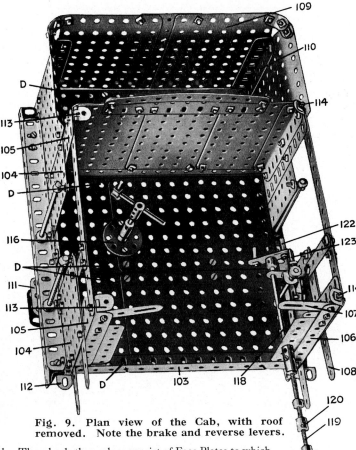

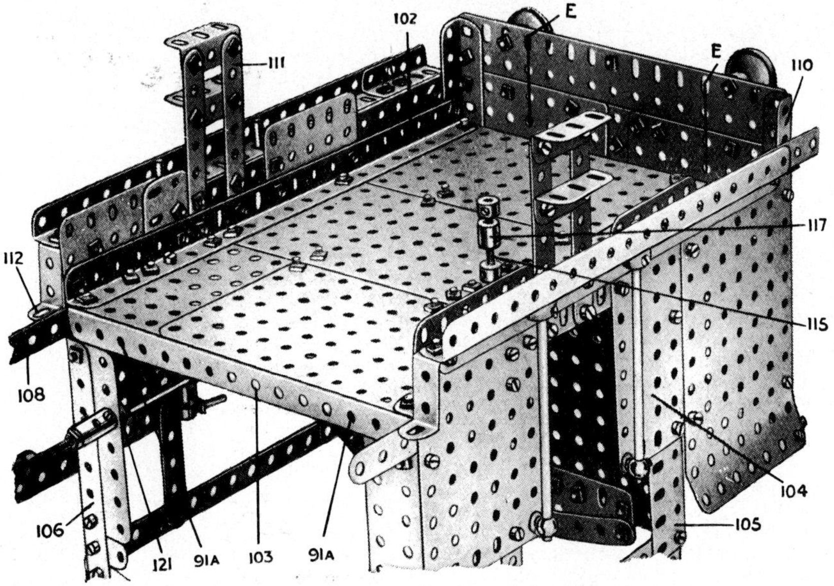

Fig. 9. **Plan view of the Cab, with roof removed. Note the brake and reverse levers.**

The Boiler and Fire-box

The details of the construction of the boiler and fire-box are shown clearly in Fig. 13 and also in the general view (Fig. 1). The "boiler shell" is composed of a number of lengths of 12½" Strips, each length consisting of two 12½" Strips overlapped six holes, and bolted to Hub Discs 83. The three 12½" Strips 84, however, are overlapped four holes, so that the rearward projection portions may be bolted to the fire-box.

The Strip 85 is 9½" in length, a continuation of it being formed by a 2½" Strip 86 bolted to the Hub Disc representing the smoke-box door. Thus there is a gap between the ends of the Strips 85 and 86 in which is placed the boss of the lower Flanged Wheel forming the chimney. The latter is secured in place by a bolt that passes through the end hole of the 2½" Strip 86 and one of the holes of the lower Flanged Wheel. A short Rod is secured in the boss of the Flanged Wheel; and a second Flanged Wheel secured thereon boss downward, completes the chimney.

The steam dome consists of a 1½" Contrate Wheel placed on the top of a Wheel Flange, a short Rod which is held in the boss of the Contrate, secures the steam dome to the boiler top by means of a Collar placed in the Rod beneath the boiler. The Double Brackets 87 are for the purpose of securing the outside steam pipes 74 to the sides of the smoke-box. The front Hub Disc that represents the smoke-box door is filled in by a number of 2½" Triangular Plates.

Fig. 10. **Underneath view of the Cab.**

The side handrails (8″ Rods) are carried by Handrail Supports secured to the front portion of the boiler shell, the front rail (an 8″ Rod) being curved over the smoke-box front and secured to the side handrails by Couplings.

The top of the fire-box is composed of two $5\frac{1}{2}''\times 3\frac{1}{2}''$ Flat Plates, and each side of the two $5\frac{1}{2}''\times 3\frac{1}{2}''$ Flat Plates overlapped eight holes in the direction of their length. Each side is joined to the top of the fire-box by means of the $4\frac{1}{2}''$ Angle Girder 88 and the $2\frac{1}{2}''$ Angle Girder 89. The back plate (Figs. 11 and 13) is composed of two $5\frac{1}{2}''\times 3\frac{1}{2}''$ Flat Plates that overlap one another by three holes ; it is secured to $3\frac{1}{2}''$ Angle Girders which are bolted to the rear edges of the sides of the fire-box. Two $\frac{3}{8}''$ Bolts 90 (shanks outward) take the place of ordinary bolts at the two top corners of the back plate (Fig. 11). Two similar Bolts 91 are attached to the two lower corners of the back plate (Figs. 11 and 13).

The fire-box is attached to the boiler shell by the projecting portions of the three $12\frac{1}{2}''$ Strips 84, only two of which are shown in Fig. 13, the other being on the opposite side of the fire-box.

Boiler Fittings

Most of the boiler fittings are shown clearly in Fig. 11. The "injector" 92 consists of an Octagonal Coupling that is attached by an ordinary bolt to the fire-box back plate. The bolt is passed through a hole in the Plate and inserted in the tapped centre hole of the Coupling. A Threaded Pin is inserted in the remaining tapped centre hole of the Coupling and a $\frac{1}{2}''$ fast Pulley secured to its shank. A $3\frac{1}{2}''$ Crank Handle represents the intake pipe to the injector from the tanks.

The water gauges 93 are represented by $1\frac{1}{2}''$ Rods held in Handrail Supports that are secured to the back plate. Between the two water gauges is placed the "regulator" 94. This consists of a Crank with a $2\frac{1}{2}''$ Strip bolted to it, a Threaded Pin forming a handle. The Crank is secured to the end of a $6\frac{1}{2}''$ Rod 95 (Fig. 13) that is journalled both in the back plate and in a $5\frac{1}{2}''\times\frac{1}{2}''$ Double Angle Strip which is placed across the fire-box near the front end. A Crank 96 is secured to the Rod 95 in a position vertically above the Motor switch, to which it is connected pivotally by means of two $2\frac{1}{2}''$ Strips overlapped two holes. (The bottom of one of these Strips may be seen below the back plate in Fig. 11).

The fire-hole door 97 is represented by a $1\frac{1}{2}''$ Flat Girder which is mounted on two Hinges secured to the back plate. The Hinges are spaced away from the back plate by means of two Washers on the shanks of each of the retaining bolts.

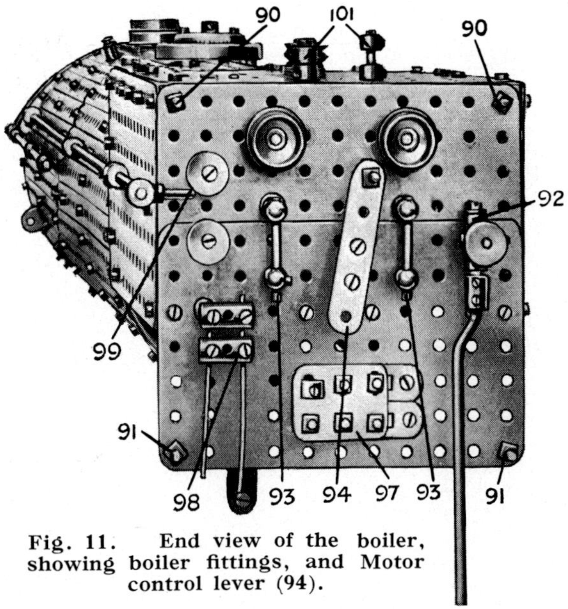

Fig. 11. End view of the boiler, showing boiler fittings, and Motor control lever (94).

The "sight feed lubricator" 98 consists essentially of two Couplings that are secured to the back plate by ordinary bolts inserted in the tapped holes of the Couplings. Short lengths of Spring Cord—to represent the pipes that convey oil to the working parts of the engine—are inserted in the end transverse holes of the Couplings, and retained therein by bolts.

The "blower valve handle" 99 consists of a Threaded Pin, which is inserted in the set-screw holes of a Collar and secured on the end of a $4\frac{1}{2}''$ Rod. This $4\frac{1}{2}''$ Rod is joined to the Coupling 100 that represents the blower valve by means of two $11\frac{1}{2}''$ Rods running along the side of the boiler.

The whistles 101 (low and high note) are represented by Collars ; the high note whistle consists of two Collars on a $\frac{3}{4}''$ Bolt, which is secured to the top of the fire-box by two nuts, whilst the low note whistle is represented by two Collars fixed a short distance apart on a $1\frac{1}{2}''$ Rod ; the Rod is held in place by a Collar beneath the fire-box top. The two Ross pop safety valves are represented by two pairs of $\frac{1}{2}''$ loose Pulleys mounted at each end of a base composed of three $1\frac{1}{2}''$ Strips laid one on top of each other ; $\frac{3}{4}''$ Bolts are passed through the Pulleys and $1\frac{1}{2}''$ Strips and secured to the fire-box top by nuts placed underneath the plate.

The two Spring Buffers that may be seen mounted on the smoke-box just behind the funnel are intended to represent the header vacuum release valves.

All the separate units of the model have now been described and it only remains to do what is perhaps the most interesting part of the job—viz., to erect the various units in their relative positions, and so complete the model.

Assembly of the Model Units ; Attaching the Footplating.

The first part to be attached to the chassis (Fig. 8) is the front footplating and buffer beam unit (Fig. 7).

First remove the Flat Brackets 21 from the smoke-box saddle (Fig. 8) and secure the footplate unit in place so that the holes 71a in the Angle Girders 4 register with those in the $4\frac{1}{2}''$ Angle Girder that is bolted to the underside of the Angle Girder 71 (Fig. 7). The Angle Brackets 20 (Fig. 8) must coincide also with the holes 20a (Fig. 7) so that bolts may be inserted in them. Bolts are also inserted in the holes A, B, and passed through corresponding holes in the Angle Girders beneath. The unit will now be found to be rigidly secured to the main frames, and the Flat Brackets may be replaced on the smoke-box saddle.

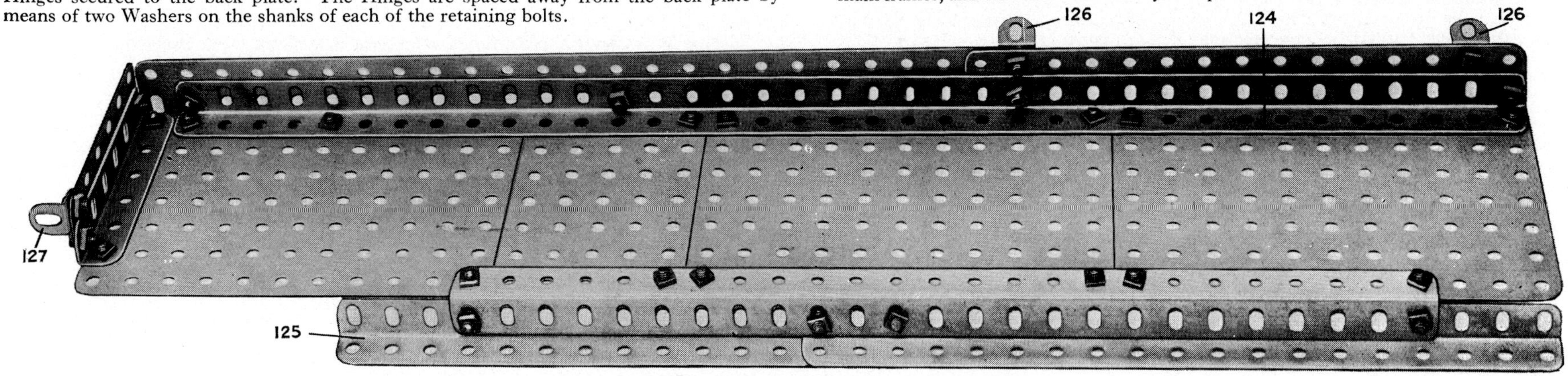

Fig. 12. The right-hand side Tank, inside view.

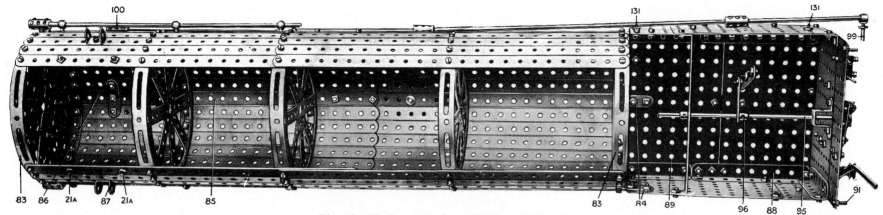

Fig. 13. Underneath view of Boiler and Fire-box.

Each expansion link 51 (Fig. 8) may be now attached to the lowest hole of the expansion link bracket 52 by means of the lock-nutted bolt that forms the pivot of the link. The expansion links are now able to rock about their pivots by the motion of the return crank 50.

Erecting the Cab Unit on the Main Frames

The cab unit (Figs. 9 and 10) is attached to the rear end of the main frame by means of bolts that are passed through the holes D (Fig. 9) on each side to the Angle Girders 3 beneath. The rear buffer beam is secured to the 2½″ Angle Girders 17a (Fig. 4), by four bolts that are inserted through each of the lines of holes E (Fig. 10).

The 1½″ Strip 69 on the Crank 68 (Fig. 4) is attached to the Threaded Boss 117 (Fig. 10) by means of a Bolt that is prevented from working loose by a nut locked against the boss. In inserting the bolt in the transverse tapped hole of the Threaded Boss, care must be taken to see that the Bolt does not nip the Screwed Rod 115, for the Threaded Boss must be quite free on the latter, of course.

The 12½″ Strip 61 (Fig. 8) is connected to the Threaded Boss 120 on the screwed Rod 119 (Fig. 9) in a similar manner.

Placing the Boiler on the Main Frames

The boiler and fire-box (Fig. 13) may now be lowered into position on to the main frames, being attached to the Angle Girder 103 (Fig. 10) by means of the ⅜″ Bolts 91 projecting from the fire-box back plate. The shanks of the bolts are passed through the holes 91a in the Angle Girder 103, nuts securing them in position.

The smoke-box end of the boiler is secured to the saddle by means of the four bolts 21a (Fig. 13), the shanks of which project through the holes of the Flat Brackets 21 (Fig. 8);

nuts on the shanks of the bolts retain the smoke-box in position. The ends of the steam pipes 74 (Fig. 7) are attached to the Double Brackets 87 (Fig. 13) by 1″ Threaded Rods and are held in place by nuts on the ends of the latter.

The ⅜″ Bolts 90 (Fig. 11) pass through the slots in the Slotted Strips 107 (Fig. 9). A 5½″ Curved Strip is now placed on the bolts 90 and nuts on the shanks of the latter serve to retain the Curved Strip. The cab roof—bent to a radius to conform with that of the Curved Strips—may now be attached to the Hinges 113.

The leading and trailing bogies may be attached to their respective bogie pin stretchers 14 and 15. The bogie pins 129 (Fig. 5) are inserted in the centre hole of the stretcher and retained in position by means of Collars.

Two springs (part No. 43) should be attached by means of a ⅜″ Bolt to one of the 4½″ Angle Girders forming the ends of the bogie frames, their other ends being attached to the main frames on each side. The object of this arrangement is to control the swivelling movement of the bogies.

The side tanks are secured to the 3½″ Strips 108 (Figs. 9 and 10) by means of nuts and bolts. The 1″ Reversed Angle Brackets 112 and the ½″ Reversed Angle Brackets on the ends of the Girders 70 (Fig. 7) are then bolted to the running boards. The tanks are further secured by the Angle Brackets 126 being attached to the Bolts 131 (Fig. 13) on the sides of the fire-box. The front ends of the tanks are secured to the Plates 72 (Fig. 7) by the ½″ × ½″ Angle Bracket 127.

The model is now complete and if everything is working freely it should be capable of propelling itself along rails or even a smooth surfaced floor. The Meccano 4-volt 20 amp. Accumulator may be placed in the bunker, thus making the model entirely self contained.

———— List of Parts Required to Build this Model ————

55 of No.	1	8 of No.	8b	6 of No.	14	1 of No.	23a	6 of No.	48b	2 of No.	63c	2 of No.	103a	2 of No.	116a
2 ,,	1a	9 ,,	9	1 ,,	15	15 ,,	24	1 ,,	48d	4 ,,	64	2 ,,	103b	11 ,,	118
6 ,,	1b	25 ,,	9a	10 ,,	15a	1 ,,	25	10 ,,	50a	2 ,,	67	2 ,,	103c	2 ,,	120
9 ,,	2	4 ,,	9b	1 ,,	16	2 ,,	26	28 ,,	52a	9 ,,	70	6 ,,	103d	2 ,,	124
16 ,,	2a	4 ,,	9c	1 ,,	16a	2 ,,	27a	1 ,,	53	2 ,,	72	2 ,,	103e	5 ,,	125
8 ,,	3	4 ,,	9d	9 ,,	16b	1 ,,	27b	13 ,,	53a	9 ,,	76	6 ,,	103f	16 ,,	133
1 ,,	4	4 ,,	9e	3 ,,	17	1 ,,	28	2 ,,	55a	2 ,,	77	2 ,,	103g	14 ,,	136
17 ,,	5	6 ,,	9f	11 ,,	18a	903 ,,	37	8 ,,	58	1 ,,	80a	5 ,,	103h	9 ,,	137
7 ,,	6	24 ,,	10	7 ,,	18b	22 ,,	37a	73 ,,	59	1 ,,	81	6 ,,	103k	1 ,,	139
12 ,,	6a	10 ,,	11	1 ,,	19s	56 ,,	38	9 ,,	62	8 ,,	82	8 ,,	109	1 ,,	139a
4 ,,	7	29 ,,	12	2 ,,	20	6 ,,	43	16 ,,	62b	2 ,,	89	11 ,,	111	6 ,,	146
4 ,,	7a	1 ,,	12a	2 ,,	20b	1 ,,	45	17 ,,	63	10 ,,	90	18 ,,	111c	6 ,,	147b
4 ,,	8	2 ,,	13	8 ,,	22	2 ,,	48	1 ,,	63a	8 ,,	90a	4 ,,	114	1 Electric	
12 ,,	8a	4 ,,	13a	8 ,,	23	12 ,,	48a	2 ,,	63b	8 ,,	103	6 ,,	115	Motor	

The Meccano Loom

A Wonderful Model that Weaves Real Hatbands, Neckties, etc., etc.

SPECIAL FEATURES

The process of weaving is entirely mechanical. The shedding movement of the Heald Frames, the rocking of the Slay and Reed, the to and fro movement of the Shuttle, and the take-up motion by which the woven material is wound on to a roller, are all brought into operation on rotation of the Crank Handle. The material produced by the model is of wonderful quality and can be used for practical purposes.

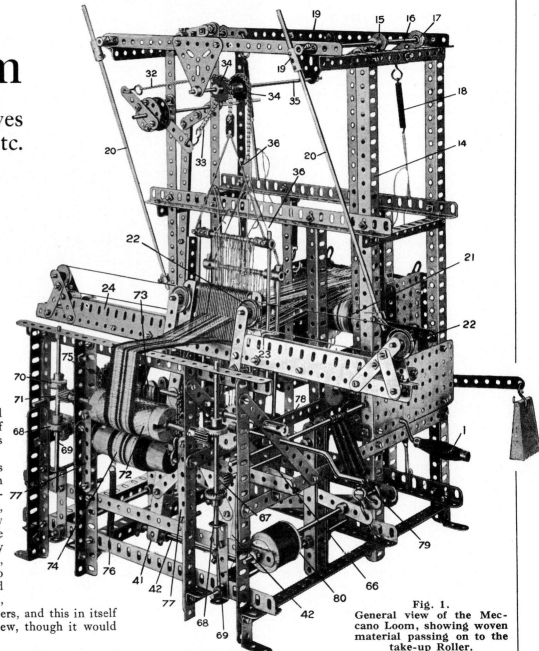

Fig. 1.
General view of the Meccano Loom, showing woven material passing on to the take-up Roller.

MAN is the only creature that has to make clothes, and certainly a good deal of trouble would be saved if our bodies were covered with feathers or fur, thus making clothes unnecessary !

Animals and birds undoubtedly may be regarded as fortunate because they have not to provide themselves with clothes. Yet, on the other hand, there would be many drawbacks if we were subject to the same conditions. For instance, we should not be able to change our clothes to suit any particular climate when we wish to travel abroad : nor could we wrap ourselves in extra heavy overcoats to brave the stormy days of winter. There would be many other disadvantages, too, for we could not change into flannels for cricket nor into "shorts" for footer. There would be no school colours, and no special caps for those boys in the school XI's ! Then again, our mothers and sisters could not have pretty hats nor jumpers, and this in itself would be a terrible calamity indeed, from their point of view, though it would certainly save our fathers a good deal of expense !

Published by MECCANO LIMITED, BINNS ROAD, LIVERPOOL   Printed in England.   928/5

Clothes the Result of Progress

Clothes are the result of civilisation. We read in our history books that, thousands of years ago, before man was civilised, when his battle axes were made of stone and his tools and weapons of flint, he was clothed in the skins of wild animals. Before he thus thought of robbing the animals of their "clothes," primitive man was himself clothed only by a hairy skin. Indeed in those days he probably more closely resembled an animal than a man. As his intelligence developed, however, and as he pushed further and further into the cold regions, he found the necessity for a covering for his body. Thus it came about that he thought of using the skins of the animals that he hunted for food.

As time went on and man rose higher in intelligence, weaving was invented, and fabrics made of flax and similar materials took the place of skins. Some of these fabrics were dyed different colours, and others were decorated with bright patterns, giving a pleasing effect. In this respect we imitate the ancients even to-day, for we like to wear clothes of different patterns, and to have in our homes curtains and carpets in which colours play an important part.

But spinning and weaving are of great antiquity, and as is the case with most arts and crafts, they were first practised in the East. Even at the time when Britain was covered with forests, and its inhabitants were uncivilised and clothed in skins, the people of Eastern nations were wearing woven cloth.

In accounts of the late Lord Carnarvon's wonderful discoveries we read of the fabrics found in the tomb of Tut-ankh-amen, the mighty Pharaoh who lived over 4,000 years ago. Linen was known in Egypt in very early times, for in the Bible we read of Joseph being arrayed in fine linen.

In India, cotton cloth was the ordinary wear of the inhabitants at least five hundred years B.C. The historian, Strabo, speaks of flowered cottons or chintzes, and he particularly refers to the lustre and vivid quality of the dyes with which the Hindus figured their cloths. In early times, the ports beyond the Red Sea did a large trade in cotton cloth. We are reminded of this fact by the names of calico and muslin, for they are called after the towns, Calicut and Mosul respectively, in which they originated.

Vegetable and Animal Materials Make Clothes.

To-day our clothes are generally made either from cotton or from wool,

Fig. 2.
The above illustration shows some of the beautiful material that may be made with the Meccano Loom. Unfortunately, it is not possible to reproduce the finished product in colours, so that the illustration gives but a poor idea of the attractive appearance of the finished fabric, the patterns of which are worked in blue, orange, gold, red, etc.

and it is wonderful to think that these raw materials can be changed so that in their finished form they bear not the slightest resemblance to their original state.

Cotton comes from the pods of the cotton plant, and in this state its appearance resembles cotton wool. It is picked in the fields and packed into great bales, large quantities being pressed into small compass by powerful hydraulic presses. Any readers who have visited Liverpool will have seen heavy loads of these cotton bales passing through the streets from the docks to the warehouse.

Cotton grows in all tropical countries, and is obtained largely from Egpyt and other parts of Africa, from certain parts of Central and Southern America, and from India and China. In these countries the climate is particularly suitable for its growth.

Before it is possible to use the raw cotton and wool they must be converted into thread, or "yarn," as it is called. This work is accomplished by spinning machines, of which there are several types. The yarn is then supplied to the weaver who, with the aid of a loom, weaves it into cloth. This must then be bleached and sized, and dyed and finished, before it is ready for delivery to the shops where we buy it by the yard.

Included in these processes are "picking" and "carding," which respectively clean the cotton of impurities, and arrange the fibres so that they all lie in the same direction.

Drawing and Twisting Cotton.

These fibres are only 1/2000th inch in diameter, and under the microscope are seen to resemble a flat ribbon, twisted like a stick of barley sugar. It seems almost impossible that these tiny fibres could by any process be disciplined into a long and continuous thread, yet the feat is accomplished by the process called "drawing." Here the fibres are drawn out into long strands, called "sliver," and in this form they resemble a thick tape. They then pass through a machine called a "slubber," where they are given a twist and wound on to bobbins. From here they pass to the "roving frame" and then to the spinning machine, which further twists the thread and tightens it up until it reaches the requisite quality and strength. It is not until the cotton fibres reach this stage that they are ready for the final process of weaving into cotton cloth.

Making Woollen Yarn.

Wool, of course, is obtained from the fleece of sheep. As in the case of cotton, the raw wool must first be treated by several processes before it is suitable for weaving, one process being that which extracts the grease. The wool is first picked and cleaned, and then carded and twisted into yarn of varying thicknesses. It has also to be dyed before the cloth is made if a pattern is desired in the finished cloth, but if the finished article is to be of a uniform colour, the fabric may be dyed after weaving.

The Hand-Loom

All weaving was done on hand-looms until 1785, when the power-loom was invented. Hand-looms are still in use in many parts of Scotland and Ireland, for instance, and also in France. Nearly every farm-house in Lancashire in the early days was an independent little factory, and hand-looms were to be found in most of the cottages and houses in the towns and villages. The weaver himself generally bought the raw cotton. This was picked by his children, spun into thread by his wife or his elder girls, and then woven at the loom by his sons, whilst he carried it to the merchant for sale.

There were very few hand-looms in England until about the second half of the 16th century, however, when religious persecutions drove the Protestant weavers from Holland, Flanders and France to this country. These refugees established themselves here, and many of the Flemish weavers settled in the neighbourhood of Manchester, now the centre of the cotton industry.

Warp and Weft

The earliest improvements in the ancient hand-loom were those made in connection with that part known as the shuttle. To understand exactly the functions of the shuttle we must remember that a woven fabric is composed of two elements, the "warp" or longitudinal threads, and the "weft," or cross-threads. If you examine your handkerchief or a tablecloth, you will see exactly what is meant by this. Notice how a woven fabric differs from one of another texture, such as a stocking, jumper, or crochet pattern.

The interweaving of the warp by the weft, called the "picking motion," is effected by passing a thread from the shuttle between some of the threads of the warp. The shuttle moves from one side of the loom to the other, and each time it passes between the threads of the warp, it leaves behind a thread of weft.

There are three distinct operations necessary to enable the shuttle to accomplish this movement. The first is the opening of the warp, when some of the threads are raised for the second operation of picking. The third operation, which is called "beating up" the weft, consists of pressing the weft into position by the reed.

These three primary operations must be carried out on every loom, no matter whether it be the hand-loom of a cottage or the largest power-loom used in a modern spinning factory.

Up to the early part of the 18th century, the shuttle had to be "thrown" backwards and forwards by hand. This was accomplished by two persons, who stood one on either side of the loom. As the shuttle was heavy, throwing the shuttle was very hard work, as well as being a very laborious and slow process. In 1750, however, John Kay, of Bolton, invented the "flying" shuttle. This consisted of a "picking stick" that drove the shuttle and saved the weavers from throwing it with their hands.

Not only did the invention halve the necessary labour, but it also increased the production of the

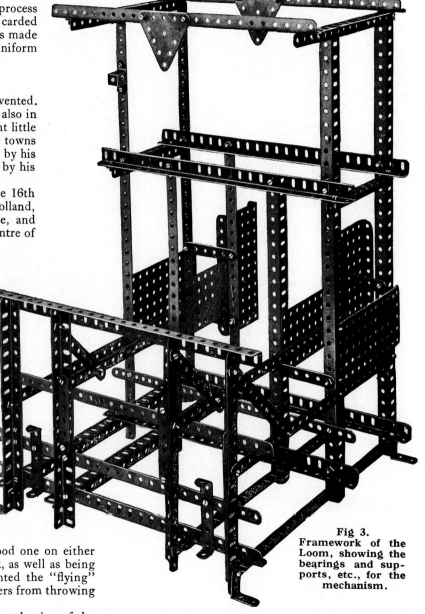

Fig 3.
Framework of the Loom, showing the bearings and supports, etc., for the mechanism.

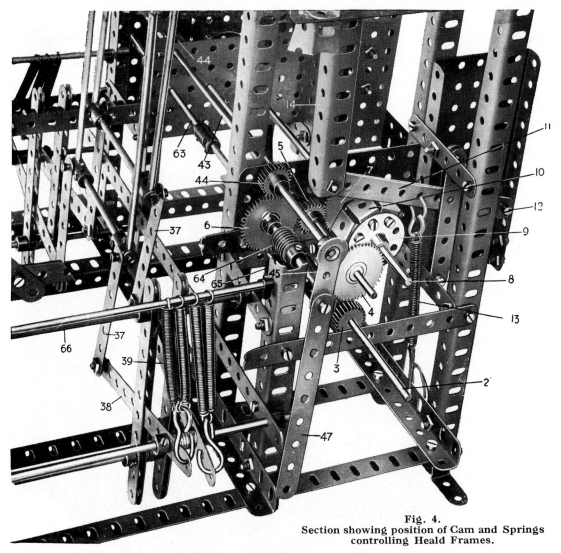

Fig. 4.
**Section showing position of Cam and Springs
controlling Heald Frames.**

discoveries in such days of golden opportunity, and many British families to-day owe their prosperity to the inventions of this period.

James Hargreaves, of Blackburn, and Richard Arkwright, a Preston barber, both produced inventions that improved the output of yarn. Crompton in 1787 invented his spinning "mule," which combined the features of Hargreaves' and Arkwright's inventions. The steam engine, then lately perfected by Watt, was harnessed to drive the spinning mule, and a great increase in cotton production followed.

In 1785 Edmund Cartwright, an English clergyman, invented the power-loom, which enabled cloth of more uniform texture to be produced at a lower cost and in greater quantities.

Strange though it may seem, yet it is a fact that the power-loom was only slowly taken up. It was first used in Glasgow about the end of the 18th century, but about a century ago it was rapidly adopted, especially after it was made so that the cloth was taken up mechanically, instead of it having to be continually pulled forward by the weaver.

In those early days the power that was available was limited, and often advantage had to be taken of a waterfall to drive the mill by means of a water-wheel. The alternative method was to drive the mill by a horse attached to a rotating capstan in the centre of a circle, around which the horse continuously walked.

It is a far cry from the hand-looms of the Ancient Egyptians to the giant power-looms of our modern factories, in some of which there are over 8,000 looms installed and the weekly output is 600 miles of cloth! Nevertheless, the story of the intervening centuries is one of the greatest interest, and not the least extraordinary is the fact that all the changes and improvements have taken place in the last two hundred years.

The Meccano Loom is designed exactly on the lines of the large power looms used in the cotton industry in Lancashire, and is capable of weaving excellent cloth, samples of which are illustrated in Fig. 2. While the three pieces of cloth shown at the top of the illustration were produced on the model Loom as described in the booklet, the other patterns, which are more intricate, require three or more heald frames operating at different times. So far as the texture of the cloth is concerned looms having only two heald frames will produce excellent work. The additional heald frames are only for the purpose of introducing variety of pattern into the finished material.

looms. Thus more yarn was required and attention was turned to improving the method of spinning, to keep pace with these increased demands.

The Inventors' Opportunity

These were, indeed, wonderful times for inventors, and many are the romantic stories that could be written about this period. Men who were in lowly walks of life were able to amass great fortunes from their inventions and

Building the Meccano Loom

The main framework of the loom should be built up carefully as shown in Fig. 3, both sides being exactly similar in construction. When the frame is completed the driving mechanism illustrated in Figs. 1 and 4 may be inserted. In Fig. 4 portions of the framework have been removed in order to reveal the mechanism.

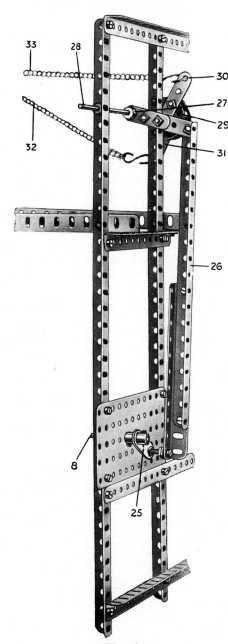

The shaft 2 of the main operating Crank Handle 1, which, if desired, may be fitted with a wooden handle as shown in Fig. 1, carries a ¾″ Pinion Wheel 3 meshing with a 50-teeth Gear Wheel 4. A ¾″ Pinion 5 on the same Rod as the Wheel 4 engages two 50-teeth Gear Wheels 6 and 7 secured to 11½″ Axle Rods that extend through the entire width of the framework.

Picking Motion

The Rod 8 on which the Gear Wheel 7 is mounted also carries at opposite sides of the model two cams 9 of the type shown in Fig. 9. It will be noticed that Bush Wheels are shown in Fig. 4 and 1½″ Pulleys in Fig. 9. Either of these are suitable for the construction of the cams and may be used as preferred.

Each of the cams embodies three Double Brackets 2 (Fig. 9) bolted between the Pulleys or Bush Wheels 1, and the latter are secured to the 11½″ Axle Rods 8 (Fig. 4). The 5½″ Strips 11, which ride on the tops of the cams 9, are pivoted at 12 to Double Bent Strips bolted to the 5½″ by 2½″ Flanged Plates at the rear of the loom. The Strips 11 slide between vertical 3½″ Strips spaced apart by the thickness of two Washers, and are held down by Springs that cause them to follow the cams 9 and impart an up and down movement to vertical 12½″ Angle Girders pivoted to the composite Cranks 15, each of which consists of two Cranks butted together with a 2″ Strip between them. The Rods 16, to which these Cranks are secured, are assisted in responding to the movements of the cams 9 by Springs 18, which are attached to ordinary Cranks 17 by means of Hooks. To the outer end of the Rod 16, by means of a Threaded Pin and ½″ Bolt, is attached the picking stick 20 formed by an 11½″ Rod, the lower end of which is connected to a cord 21 passing roun two 1″ Pulleys 22. This cord is connected

to a Double Bent Strip 23, which engages the Shuttle and flicks it across the slay 24.

The cams 9 are oppositely disposed, that is, the three Double Brackets of one cam are on top while those of the other cam are underneath, so that the picking sticks work alternately, throwing the Shuttle first to one side of the slay and then to the other.

Take Up Motion

This is shown in Fig. 4. On the Rod 63 of the Gear Wheel 6 are mounted also two Worms 64, which engage and drive 57-teeth Gear Wheels 65 on Rods 66. The ½″ Pinions 67 (Fig. 1) drive ¾″ Contrate Wheels 68 on the vertical Rods 69. It will be noted that the Contrate Wheels 68 are reversed. Other ¾″ Contrate Wheels 70 on the Rods 69 engage and drive ½″ Pinions 71 on the Sand Roller 72. Owing to the gearing of the Worm 64 and Gear Wheels 65 the necessary slow "take up" motion is imparted to the Sand Roller, and the woven material, after passing beneath the Sand Roller, passes over the Rod 73 to the lower Roller 74, on which the fabric is wound. The lower Roller 74 is driven frictionally from the Sand Roller and is kept in frictional contact with that Roller by means of the Sprocket Chains 75 at either side, which are hooked on the Rod of the Roller 74 and are kept taut by Springs 76. The Rod of the lower Roller 74 is enabled to move away from the Sand Roller 72 (so as to allow for the increasing diameter of the roll of woven fabric) by causing the ends of its Rod to engage between 2½″ Strips 77 and the frame of the machine at each side.

The Heald Frames

The construction of the heald frames will be clear from the detail given in Fig. 6. The lower ends of the heald frames, as shown in Fig. 4, are connected to 3½″ Strips 37 coupled to 5½″ Strips 38. The latter are controlled by the Springs 39, which tend always to draw the heald frames down.

To adjust the healds correctly set them so that the eyes of both heald frame sets are level when the Cranks 45 are vertical and the Strips 47 (Fig. 4) are horizontal.

As in actual practice, the healds are assembled vertically. In the Meccano Loom there are two frames, but there may be many more frames in actual looms. The healds serve to lift and depress the warp, so that the shuttle may be passed between the threads.

The healds consist of a number of wires, called "leaches," each having in its centre an eye, or "mail," which to a certain extent resembles the eye of a needle. The depression of the warp, referred to above, is made possible by passing the warp threads through these mails.

The warp is the thread that runs longitudinally, from the back to the front of the loom. The thread at right-angles to it is the "weft," which is introduced by the passing of the shuttle between the warp threads and pressed into position by the reed.

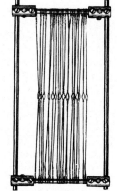

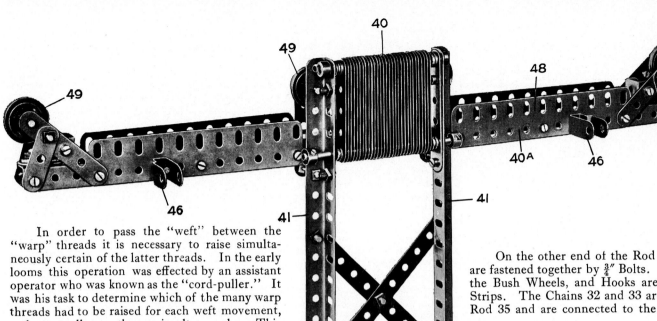

Fig. 7.
The Slay and Reed Frame.

Heald Motion

This is brought out in Fig. 5. On the far end of the Rod 8 is a Crank 25 (two Cranks butted together), the outer end of which is connected to 9½" and 5½" Angle Girders, overlapped nine holes and forming a connection 26, the top of which is coupled to an extended Crank 27 fixed to a Rod 28. The element 27 is made up of a 2½" Strip, the end hole being on the Rod 28, and with two Cranks reversed and bolted through the Strip. On the other end of the Rod 28 are secured two Bush Wheels 29, which are fastened together by ¾" Bolts. A 2½" Strip 30 and 3" Strip 31 are bolted to the Bush Wheels, and Hooks are connected to the outer ends of these two Strips. The Chains 32 and 33 are passed over 1" Sprocket Wheels 34 on the Rod 35 and are connected to the heald frames 36.

Slay

The construction of the slay 40a is shown in Fig. 7, the reed consisting of thirty 2½" Strips 40 (spaced with Washers), mounted on upper and lower Rods and carried on the Angle Girder 41 pivoted on the Rod 42. The slay is rocked to and fro from a Rod 43 (Fig. 4), which is driven from the Gear Wheel 6, a ¾" Pinion 44 on the Rod 43 meshing with the Gear Wheel 6.

On both ends of the Rod 43 are fixed Cranks 45, which are connected to the Cranked Bent Strips 46 (Fig. 4) on the slay by means of 4½" Strips 47. In Fig. 4 the near Strip is shown hanging down disconnected.

The sides of the slay consist of 5½" Flat Girders 48, and the Pulley Wheels 49, round which the picking cords run, are carried as shown in Fig. 1.

The Shuttle moves along the "slay" which supports and guides it as it is jerked from one side of the loom to the other by means of the "picking sticks," suspended from above. Attached to the slay is the "reed" which moves forward with the slay after every crossing of the warp by the weft.

The bed of the slay may be improved by covering its upper surface with a strip of sheet tin, upon which the shuttle can slide more freely.

Warp Thread Tension Mechanism

In order to compensate for the slacking of the warp threads which develops when the shed is formed by the motion of the healds, the warps are passed from the beam 50 (Fig. 10) under the Rod 51 and over another Rod 52 and thence through the eyes of the healds to the reed.

Fig. 8.
The Meccano Shuttle.

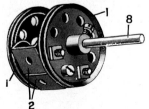

Fig. 9.
Cam for operation of Picking Sticks.

In order to pass the "weft" between the "warp" threads it is necessary to raise simultaneously certain of the latter threads. In the early looms this operation was effected by an assistant operator who was known as the "cord-puller." It was his task to determine which of the many warp threads had to be raised for each weft movement, and to pull on them simultaneously. This process was, of course, very slow and laborious.

During the eighteenth century many different methods were devised to render weaving both easier and speedier. Of these, the "heald-frame" method is one that has proved eminently successful in practice.

Pattern and Texture

It may here be remarked, perhaps, that the pattern depends upon the number of healds : the greater the number employed, the more complex is the resulting pattern. For the weaving of very complex figures the warp must be divided among a large number of healds.

When the Loom has been built, it is necessary to determine what pattern you will weave. Whether it be a tie or a hat-band that is your first effort, the choice of colours for the warp, and the colour of the weft will call into play your artistic qualities to no little extent, in addition to your manipulative abilities in the actual process of weaving.

The pattern, which as we have seen depends on the number of healds employed, does not have any bearing on the texture of the woven fabrics. The closeness of the texture of any material depends upon the number of warp and weft threads to the inch. In actual manufacturing, fine cloth may have 125, or even more, threads to the inch both in warp and in weft.

Thus in addition to the colour and the pattern, you will have to decide of what texture your fabric is to be.

A suitable material for use in this model is No. 8 Star Sylko for warp and No. 40 Sylko thread for weft. No thicker material should be used. Any drapery establishment will supply you.

The beam 50 is braked by means of cords 57 passing over 2″ Pulleys 58 and secured to the frame of the loom, the other ends being connected to Hooks 59, engaging a hole in the Strip 60 pivoted at 61, weights 62 on the outer ends of the Strip 60 putting the required frictional resistance on the beam 50.

Preparing to Weave

In preparing to weave, the first thing to be done is to pass the ends of the warp from the beam (situated at the back of the loom) through the mails of the healds and then through the reed. One or more threads are passed through each division of the reed, and attached to the taking-off roller.

By turning the Crank Handle, the Shuttle is jerked across the slay and passes over the threads held down by the lower heald frame and beneath those raised by the upper heald frame, at the same time leaving in its wake a loose thread of weft. The slay then moves forward and brings up the reed, which drives before it this thread or "first pick" of the weft. By continuing to turn the handle the same process is repeated, the shuttle being again jerked back and across the loom, this time from the other side. The reed again moves forward and presses up the second pick against the first. The taking-off Roller in the meantime slowly rotates, and as the weaving proceeds it rolls around itself the woven fabric.

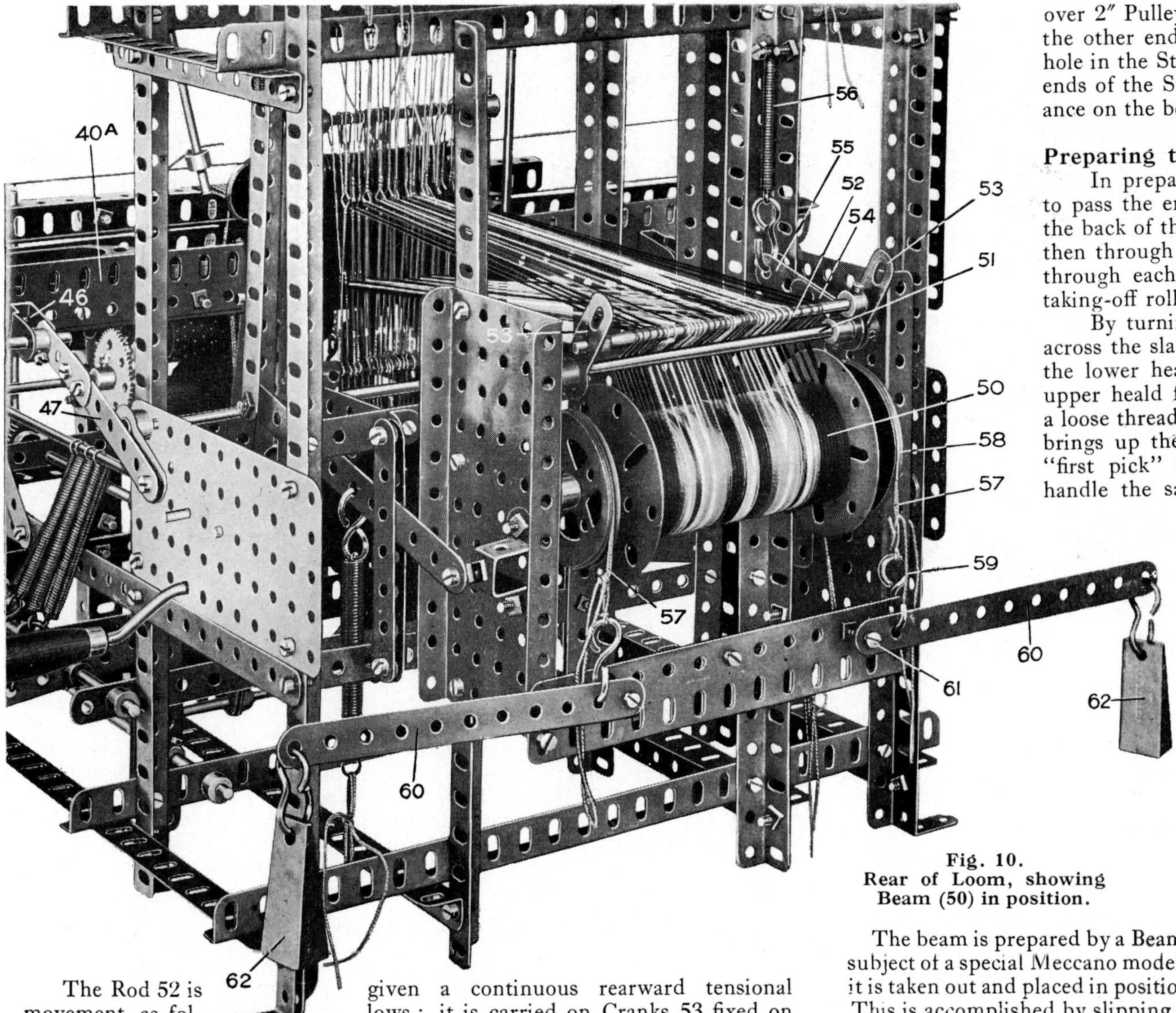

Fig. 10.
Rear of Loom, showing Beam (50) in position.

Preparing the Beam.

The beam is prepared by a Beaming Frame, which is the subject of a special Meccano model. After being prepared it is taken out and placed in position at the rear of the loom. This is accomplished by slipping the 2″ Wheels 58 on the beam spindle, before inserting the latter in the holes of the side Flanged Plates. After doing this the Pulley Wheels are secured to the spindle at each end to hold the beam in position.

All the ends of the threads are drawn under Rod 51 and

Fig. 11.
Weaver's Knot.

The Rod 52 is given a continuous rearward tensional movement as follows: it is carried on Cranks 53 fixed on the lower Rod 51: another Crank 54, to which is connected a 2½″ Strip 55 (the end holes being threaded on the Rod 51) is connected on its outer hole by a Hook coupled to a Spring 56. The Spring 56 therefore rocks the upper Rod rearwardly, and takes up the slacking formed by the shedding action of the healds.

over **52**, and each thread is passed through the healds in the following manner: the first warp thread is passed through the eye of the first heald in the near frame, and thence through the first aperture of the reed : the next thread is passed between the first two healds in the near frame and through the eye of the far frame and thence through the next aperture of the reed. The warp threads may be threaded through the reed spaces in pairs. This process is continued until all the ends are threaded through the reed. They are then carried over the front Angle Girder, under the Sand Roller **72**, over the Rod **73** and on to the take-up Roller **74**,

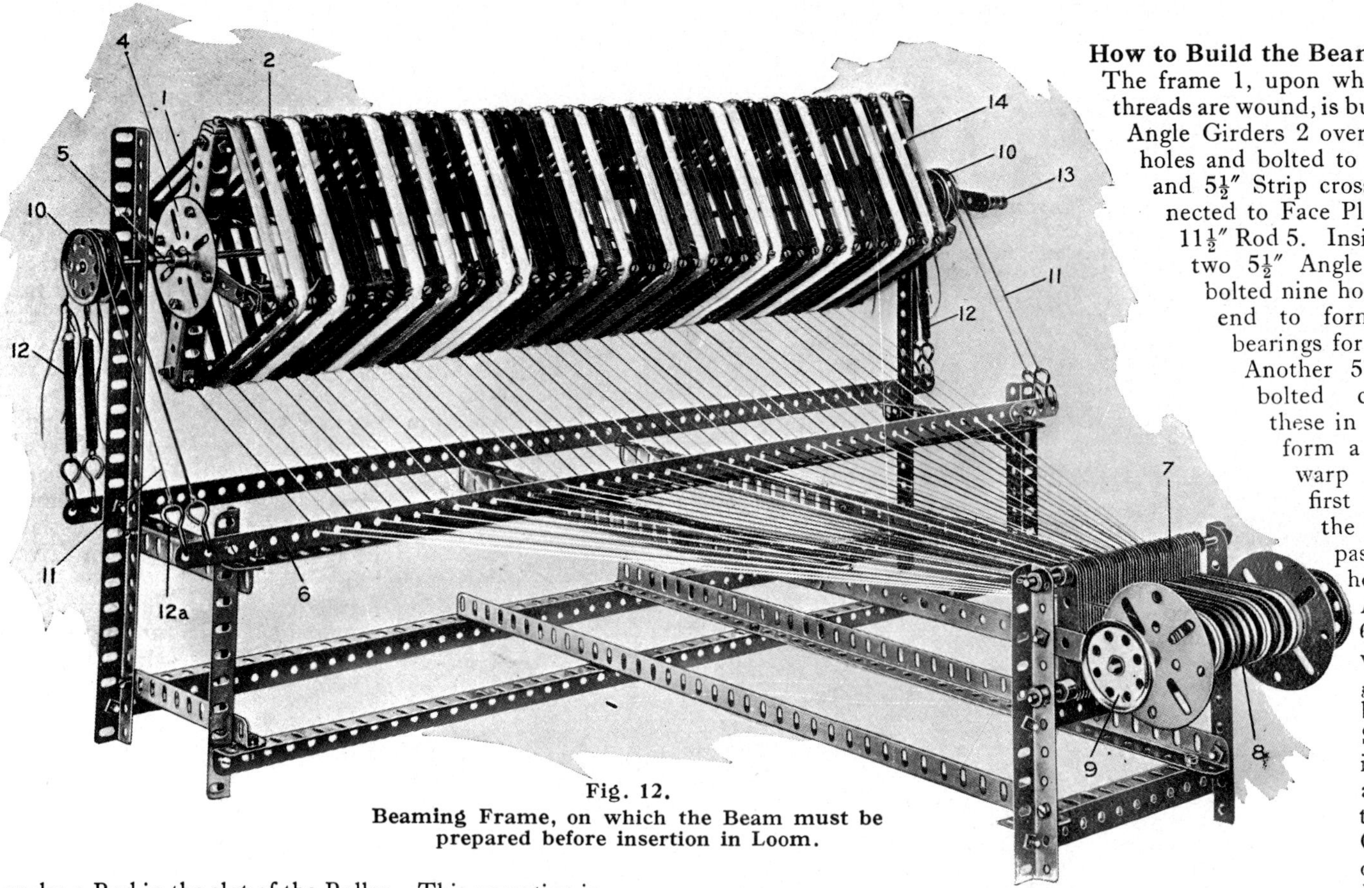

Fig. 12.
Beaming Frame, on which the Beam must be prepared before insertion in Loom.

How to Build the Beaming Frame

The frame 1, upon which the warp threads are wound, is built up of 12½″ Angle Girders 2 overlapped seven holes and bolted to a 5½″ Girder and 5½″ Strip crossed and connected to Face Plates 4 on the 11½″ Rod 5. Inside the frame, two 5½″ Angle Girders are bolted nine holes from each end to form the inner bearings for the Rods 5. Another 5½″ Girder is bolted crosswise to these in the centre to form a stay. The warp threads are first wound upon the frame 1, and pass through the holes in a 24½″ Angle Girder 6, and, converging together, pass between 2½″ Strips 7 forming the reed, and so on to the beam 8. On the far side of the beam Rod is a ½″

where they are gripped under a Rod in the slot of the Roller. This operation is performed more conveniently by two persons with the aid of a Reed Hook.

For winding the weft thread on the spindle forming the cop the spindle should be removed from the Shuttle, and one end inserted in the Coupling **78**. The thread from the bobbin **80** may then be wound round it by turning the Crank Handle **79**.

Fig. 11 illustrates a weaver's slip-knot, which is used when adjustment or tension is necessary.

Pinion engaged by a Pawl (not shown on the photograph) which prevents backward rotation of the beam as the warp threads are wound thereon by turning the 1½″ Pulley Wheels 9. A brake mechanism for tensioning the frame 2 is provided by securing two 1″ Pulley Wheels 10 at each end of the frame Rod 5, cords 11, secured by Hooks 12, passing over the Pulleys 10 and being kept taut by the Springs 12. A handle 13 is provided on the Rod 5 by means of which the warp threads 14 originally are wound on the frame 2.

Parts required for Loom

6 of No.	1	15 of No.	9	6 of No.	16	5 of No.	27	5 of No.	45	4 of No.	82				
22 ,,	2	2 ,,	10	8 ,,	18a	3 ,,	27a	2 ,,	48a	12″ ,,	94				
8 ,,	3	8 ,,	11	2 ,,	19	4 ,,	29	2 ,,	52	4 ,,	96				
9 ,,	4	4 ,,	12	2 ,,	20a	2 ,,	32	17 ,,	57	42 ,,	101				
39 ,,	5	4 ,,	12a	4 ,,	21	6 ,,	35	55 ,,	59	6 ,,	103				
4 ,,	6	4 ,,	13	4 ,,	22	195 ,,	37	15 ,,	62	1 ,,	104				
4 ,,	6a	13 ,,	13a	2 ,,	24	33 ,,	37a	13 ,,	63	1 ,,	106				
6 ,,	7a	10 ,,	14	5 ,,	25	198 ,,	38	4 ,,	67	1 ,,	106a				
17 ,,	8	1 ,,	15	2 ,,	25a	15 ,,	43	4 ,,	70	2 ,,	109				
3 ,,	8a	1 ,,	15a	5 ,,	26	2 ,,	44	2 ,,	76	7 ,,	111				

Parts required for Beaming Frame

2 of No.	1	3 of No.	14	1 of No.	147a
4 ,,	2	6 ,,	21	1 ,,	147b
44 ,,	5	253 ,,	37	1 ,,	148
4 ,,	6	88 ,,	38		
4 ,,	7	4 ,,	43		
2 ,,	7a	8 ,,	57		
12 ,,	8	10 ,,	59		
10 ,,	9	1 ,,	63		
8 ,,	12	1 ,,	103		
2 ,,	13	4 ,,	109		

Ask your dealer for a complete illustrated list of Meccano parts.

The New Meccano Loom

A WONDERFUL MODEL THAT WEAVES REAL HATBANDS, NECKTIES, ETC., ETC.

SPECIAL FEATURES

The process of weaving is entirely mechanical. The shedding movement of the Heald Frames, the rocking of the Slay and Reed, the to and fro movement of the Shuttle, and the take-up motion by which the woven material is wound on to a roller, are all brought into operation on rotation of the Crank Handle. The material produced by the model is of excellent quality and can be used for practical purposes.

Fig. 1. General view of the new Meccano Loom, showing woven material passing on to the take-up Roller

THE art of spinning and weaving is of great antiquity. Even at the time when Britain was covered with forest and its inhabitants were uncivilised and clothed in skins, the people of Eastern nations were wearing woven clothes.

Up to the year 1785 all weaving was done on hand-looms and indeed many of these machines are still in use in parts of Scotland and Ireland, and also in France. In the early days nearly every farmhouse in Lancashire was an independent little factory and hand-looms were to be found in most of the cottages and houses in the towns and villages. The weaver himself generally bought the raw cotton. This was picked by his children, spun into thread by his wife or his elder girls and then woven at the loom by his sons, whilst he carried it to the merchants to sell.

The earliest improvements in the hand-loom were those made in connection with that part known as the shuttle. To understand exactly the functions of the shuttle we must remember that a woven fabric is composed of two elements, the "warp" or longitudinal

Published by MECCANO LIMITED, OLD SWAN, LIVERPOOL, ENGLAND

Printed in England

threads, and the "weft," or cross-threads. If you examine your handkerchief or a tablecloth, you will see exactly what is meant by this. Notice how a woven fabric differs from one of another texture, such as a stocking, jumper, or crochet pattern.

The interweaving of the warp by the weft, called the "picking motion," is effected by passing a thread from the shuttle between some of the threads of the warp. The shuttle moves from one side of the loom to the other, and each time it passes between the threads of the warp, it leaves behind a thread of weft.

There are three distinct operations necessary to enable the shuttle to accomplish this movement. The first is the opening of the warp, when some of the threads are raised for the second operation of picking. The third operation, which is called "beating up" the weft, consists of pressing the weft into position by the reed.

These three primary operations must be carried out on every loom, no matter whether it be the hand-loom of a cottage or the largest power-loom used in a modern spinning factory.

Up to the early part of the 18th century, the shuttle had to be "thrown" backward and forward by hand. This was accomplished by two persons, who stood one on each side of the loom. As the shuttle was heavy, throwing it was very hard work, as well as being a very laborious and slow process. In 1750, however, John Kay, of Bolton, invented the "flying" shuttle. This consisted of a "picking stick" that drove the shuttle and saved the weavers from throwing it with their hands.

Not only did the invention halve the necessary labour, but it also increased the production of the looms. Thus more yarn was required and attention was turned to improving the method of spinning, to keep pace with these increased demands.

In 1785 Edmund Cartwright, an English clergyman, invented the power-loom, which enabled cloth of more uniform texture to be produced at a lower cost and in greater quantities.

Fig. 2. The Loom framework showing bearings and supports, etc., for the mechanism

Strange though it may seem, yet it is a fact that the power-loom was only slowly taken up. It was first used in Glasgow about the end of the 18th century, but about a century ago it was rapidly adopted, especially after it was made so that the cloth was taken up mechanically, instead of having to be continually pulled forward by the weaver.

The Meccano Loom is designed exactly on the lines of the large power looms used in the cotton industry in Lancashire, and is capable of weaving excellent cloth.

Building the Meccano Loom

The construction of the Meccano model Loom is commenced by building up the main framework, which is shown in detail in Fig. 2. Four 18½″ Angle Girders 1 and 6 are secured in a vertical position at one end of the base Girders 2, and two 9½″ Girders 7 are bolted in position at their other ends, as indicated in the illustration. A 9½″ Angle Girder 4 bridges the tops of the Girders 7, and two further 9½″ Angle Girders bolted to it carry 4½″ Angle Girders 11. The remainder of the framework may be successfully completed by studying carefully the illustrations.

The next step in the construction of the model is the assembling of the gearing, which is shown in Fig. 6. To make matters quite clear it must be mentioned that the gearing, as shown in the foreground, is duplicated, with the exception of the operating handle, at the other side of the model.

The operating handle (see Fig. 1), which consists of a Circular Plate with a 3″ Rod attached to its face by a Double Arm Crank, is secured to a Rod carrying a ¾″ Pinion that meshes with two 50-teeth Gears 62 and 63 fixed on separate Rods that run from side to side of the Loom. The first Rod has secured to it a cam 52 and the second Rod carries a Worm 56. Two cams are required, one at each end of the Rod, and they should be built up as shown in Fig. 8 and then secured rigidly to the Rod by duplicate set-screws in the bosses of the Bush Wheels, to prevent their rotation on the Rod.

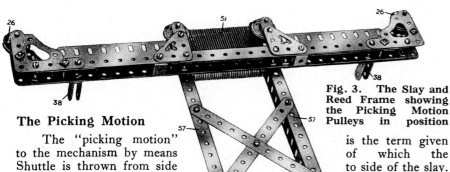

Fig. 3. The Slay and Reed Frame showing the Picking Motion Pulleys in position

The Picking Motion

The "picking motion" is the term given to the mechanism by means of which the Shuttle is thrown from side to side of the slay.

The 5½" Strips 23 (Fig. 6) that ride on the cams are mounted on Pivot Bolts bolted to the 5½" × 2½" Flat Plates seen in Fig. 5, and they slide between guides formed from vertically disposed 3½" Strips.

The free end of each Strip is connected by an End Bearing and a lock-nutted bolt to an 11½" Axle Rod 50 (Fig. 6), the upper end of which is attached in a similar manner to a built-up crank 1½" long that consists of two ordinary Cranks bolted together in such a manner that their bosses are at opposite ends. The composite crank is secured by double grub-screws to a Rod 22 (Fig. 5) in the upper part of the loom, which carries also a Crank 36. A Spring attached to the Crank serves the purpose of maintaining the Strips 23 in intimate contact with the cam.

A Coupling is secured on the end of each of the Rods 22, a Pivot Bolt being passed through its end transverse bore and inserted in the tapped bore of a Coupling on the upper extremity of a rod forming a "picking-stick." The bottom end of the picking-stick is later to be attached to a length of Spring Cord 25. The cams 52 are secured on their Rod in such a manner that the three Double Brackets forming the working face of one cam are diametrically opposite those of the other cam, so that the picking-sticks work alternately, and throw the Shuttle first to one end of the slay and then to the other.

The Take-Up Motion

The arrangement of the "take-up" motion that draws the woven cloth through the loom is indicated in Fig. 6. On the Rod of the 50-teeth Gear 63 is secured a Worm 56 that meshes with a ½" Pinion on a Rod 53. This Rod is duplicated on the far side of the model, and the ends of both Rods terminate in ½" Bevel Wheels that are in mesh with 1½" Bevels on the Rod of the upper take-up roller (Sand Roller, part No. 106a). Owing to the gearing employed, a slow "take-up" is imparted to the Sand Roller, and the woven material, after passing beneath it, is wound on to a lower roller (Wood Roller, part No. 106). The lower roller is rotated by frictional contact with the Sand Roller, and both Rollers are kept together by means of a spring tension device. The lower ends of two Tension Springs are hooked on to the frame of the model, and their upper ends are fitted with short lengths of Sprocket Chain which, after passing over 1" guide Sprockets above the Rollers, are attached to the lower Roller spindle by Hooks. The spindle of the lower Roller slides in a pair of guides 12 so that it is free to move vertically (Fig. 2).

The Heald Frames

As in actual practice, the healds are assembled vertically. In the Meccano Loom there are two frames, but there may be many more in actual looms. The healds serve to lift and depress alternate threads of the warp, so that the shuttle may be passed between the threads.

The healds consist of a number of wires called "leaches," each having in its centre an eye, or "mail," which resembles the eye of a needle. The depression of the warp, already referred to, is made possible by passing the warp threads through these mails.

The warp is the thread that runs longitudinally from the back to the front of the loom. The thread at right-angles to it is the "weft."

The construction of the Heald frames should be quite clear from Fig. 4 (which shows one of the frames removed from the Loom), and therefore we may pass on to their insertion into the Loom. Hooks on the ends of the Springs 59 (Fig. 4), depending from the lower extremity of the Heald frames, are attached to the Girders 20 (Fig. 2). The Flat Brackets 60 at the tops of the frames are bolted to lengths of Sprocket Chain 42 and 44 (Fig. 5) respectively. These Chains pass over 1" Sprocket Wheels 41 and 43, and are attached finally by Hooks to 2½" Strips 45 and 47 that are affixed by ¾" Bolts and Nuts to two Bush Wheels secured rigidly to the Rod 49. The Rod carries an ordinary Crank, which is connected by a Rod 39 to a Crank 31 on one end of the camshaft. The attachment of the Rod 39 to the lower crank 31 is effected by means of a Swivel Bearing 30, and to the upper crank by an End Bearing 48.

Construction of the Slay

The main features of the slay will be clear by referring to Fig. 3. The portion of the slay upon which the Shuttle slides is a girder of channel section, consisting of two 12½" and two 2½" Angle Girders butted together. The Shuttle is prevented from leaving the slay by 5½" Flat Girders, which are bolted to the sides of the channel girder. Architraves at each end serve as bearings for the Rods of 1" loose Pulleys 26.

The Reed 51 consists of thirty-two 2½" Strips mounted on two Rods, each Strip being spaced apart the thickness of one Washer. The Reed is attached to the slay by passing the ends of the Rods carrying the 2½" Strips through the flanges of the 9½" Angle Girders 57. A length of Spring Cord 25 (Fig. 5) passes round each pair of 1" Pulleys and its ends are fixed to the lugs of a Double Bent Strip 27, which slides freely on the bed of the slay. The lower ends

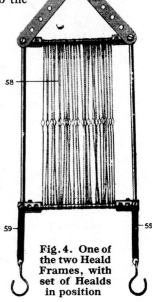

Fig. 4. One of the two Heald Frames, with set of Healds in position

of the picking-sticks will eventually be attached to the Spring Cord and in this manner the Double Bent Strips are made to flick backward and forward, so that when the shuttle is placed at one end of the slay, one of the Double Bent Strips will engage with the pointed end of the Shuttle and throw it to the opposite end of the slay. The other picking-stick and Double Bent Strip then return it.

The slay is mounted in place in the Loom by passing a Rod through the top holes of the Flat Trunnions 19 (Fig. 2) and through the bottom holes in the Girders 57 of the slay. The slay is rocked about its pivot by means of two Cranks 29 (Fig. 5) secured on the ends of the Rod carrying the $\frac{3}{4}''$ Pinions that mesh with the 50-teeth Gears 63 (Fig. 6). Connection between the Cranks and the slay is formed by means of Strips 28, which are attached to the slay by means of the Single Bent Strips 38 (Fig. 5).

The picking action of the model may be greatly improved by lining the bed of the slay with a narrow strip of tin. This improvement enables the Shuttle to slide with considerably greater freedom.

Warp Tensioning Mechanism

When the heald frames descend after forming the "shed," the threads of the warp naturally fall slack, unless special mechanism is provided to remedy the matter. Slacking of the warp would, of course, prevent satisfactory work being turned out by the model, and in order to compensate for any sag of the threads, a particularly ingenious device

known as a "warp tensioner" is incorporated in the model. This mechanism and its arrangement may be seen in the rear view of the model (Fig. 5), and a study of this illustration in conjunction with the following description will make the matter quite clear. It consists of a Rod journalled in the Plates 14 and carrying two Bush Wheels, to one of which a $2\frac{1}{2}''$ Strip 33 is bolted. Two Cranks are bolted to the Bush Wheels as indicated in the illustration, and a Rod is secured in the bosses of the Cranks. The warp threads from the "beam" (a Wood Roller with a Face Plate 24 at each end) are first passed over the fixed Rod, then round the movable Rod, and again over the fixed Rod, to the Healds. The necessary tension is supplied by means of a Spring 34 attached to the Strip 33 as shown in fig. 5.

The beam is restrained from free rotation by a band brake consisting of a 2″ Pulley secured to the beam spindle, and round which passes a cord. One end of the cord is attached to the frame of the model, and the other end is tied to a Spring that keeps the cord in a constant state of tension round the Pulley and thus supplies the required retarding effect.

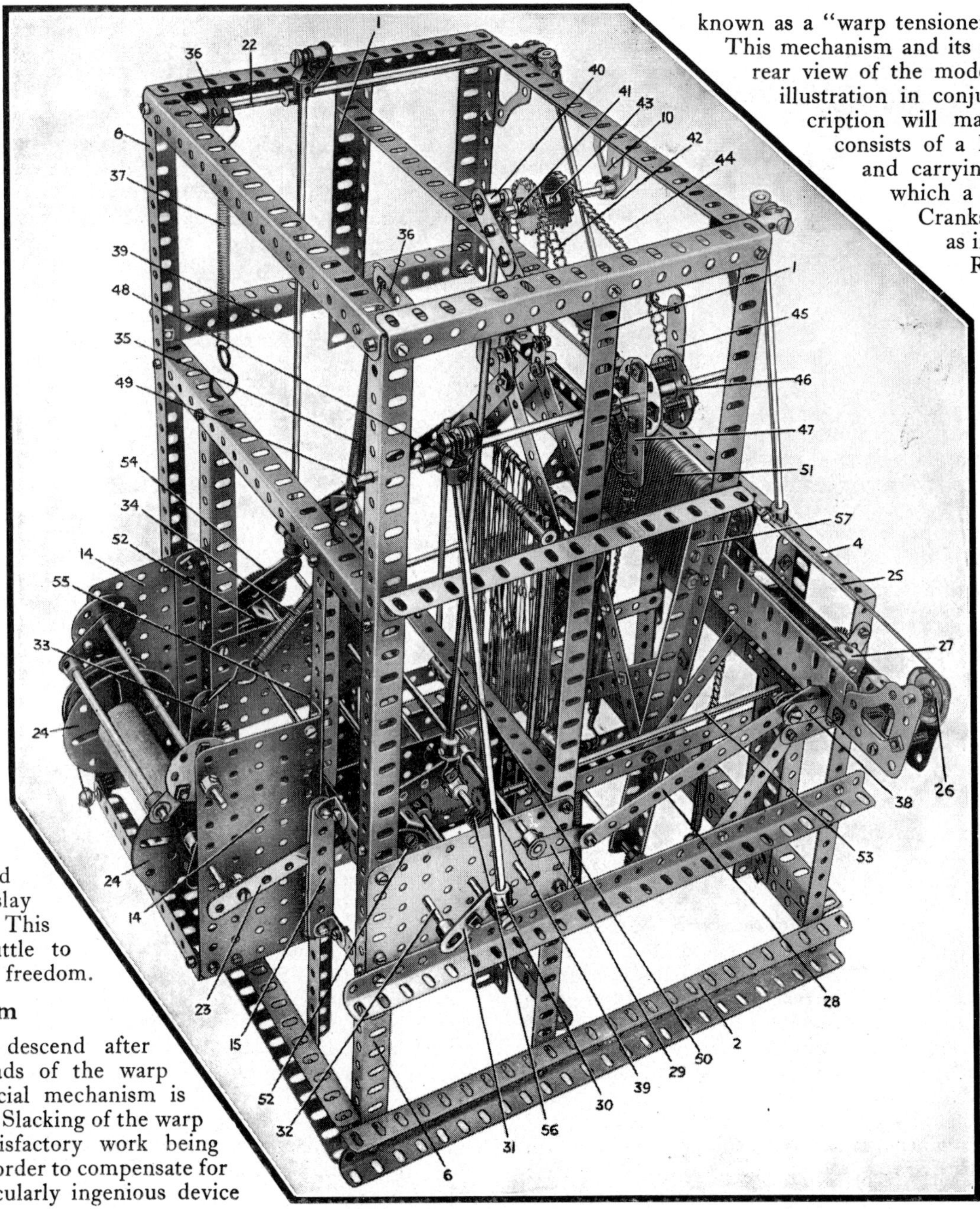

The Beaming Frame

In order to turn out good work with the Loom, it is highly important that the threads of the warp should be wound on the beam evenly. and each individual thread must be laid on under exactly the same tension. For this purpose a beaming frame is employed. A Meccano model beaming frame is shown in Fig. 9. After a little study of

Fig. 5. View of the Loom mechanism from the rear

the illustration no difficulty should be experienced in building the framework, so we may devote our attention to the more obscure points in the construction of the model and its manipulation.

The rotating frame 1 on which the various skeins of silk are wound, consists of four $24\frac{1}{2}''$ Angle Girders, bolts being inserted in the holes of each Girder throughout their length in order that the skeins may be kept separated from each other. A Face Plate 2, attached to each end of the frame, is secured to a Rod 3, which is journalled in the end holes of the vertical girders, and has brake drums in the shape of $3''$ Pulleys 4 fixed at each end. Cords are passed round the Pulleys under tension, which is supplied by Springs.

Each of the warp threads is led behind the Rod 5, through the top hole of each weight 8, and in front of the Rod 7. After leaving the Rod 7 the thread passes behind the Rod 6, and is taken through a hole in the front Girder as shown before it is inserted in the reed 9. This process is repeated with each warp thread in turn. All the warps are then fastened to the beam 11 by clamping them with a Rod 10 in the groove of the Wood Roller. This Rod is held in position by a $\frac{5}{8}''$ Rubber Ring, which is placed over each end of the Rod and the bosses of the Face Plates forming the end of the beam. A Pawl and Ratchet mechanism 12 is fitted to the beam spindle to prevent it from unwinding.

Each of the weights 8 is composed of a $5\frac{1}{2}''$ Strip to which three $2\frac{1}{2}''$ Strips are attached by five nuts and bolts. If the builder does not possess sufficient $2\frac{1}{2}''$ Strips, it will be necessary to construct some of the weights with other Strips to an equivalent weight.

One or two precautions must be observed before attempting to remove the beam from the beaming frame for insertion in the Loom. If all the silk has not been wound off the frame 1, the threads must be cut. Prior to this, a Rod should be clamped over the threads on the beam in a similar manner to the Rod 10 (Fig. 9) in order to prevent the threads from becoming loose and deranged; and a pair of Strips should also be clamped above and below the warp, just in front of the reed. This is to prevent the

Fig. 6. A close-up view of the Picking Motion mechanism

warp threads from pulling out of the reed when the warp is severed. The beam may then be removed from the machine.

Care should be taken to replace the Rod holding in place the turns of warp on the beam, and it should be removed only when the warp is secure on the take-up rollers.

Preparing to Weave

When the Loom has been completed, it becomes necessary to take into consideration the pattern to be woven. Whether it be a hat band or a tie that is to be the first effort, the choice of colours for the warp and the weft—particularly the former—will call upon the artistic ability of the user to no little extent, in addition to manipulative ability in the actual process of weaving.

The best material for use as the warp threads in the Meccano Loom is No. 8 "Star Sylko"; and for the weft No. 40.

Before threading the Healds, etc., it is of the utmost importance to see that the various movements of the model take place in their correct order. First, the Heald frames should both be arranged so that the mails or eyes of the respective groups of healds coincide when the Crank 31 (Fig. 5) is set vertically. Then, with one of the Heald frames raised and the other lowered to their greatest extent, the Cranks 29 should be turned so that the slay is as close as possible to the front heald frame. The Cranks are then secured on the Rod. At the same time the picking motion must throw the Shuttle across the slay, and this cycle of operations must take place with unfailing regularity. Having made quite sure that everything is correctly adjusted attention may be paid to the actual threading of the Healds.

A single warp thread is passed through each mail of the Healds, the threads passing through the mails of the two Heald frames alternately. Care should be taken to see that none of the threads cross. One or more threads may be passed through each division of the reed, and attached to the take-up Rollers. The Meccano Reed Hook will be found useful for passing the threads through the reed.

Sufficient warp thread should be unwound from the beam to allow the

Healds to be easily threaded, and the ends of the threads then clamped to the lower take-off roller, an operation that is accomplished in a similar manner to that adopted with the beam.

The Meccano Shuttle is illustrated in Fig. 7, from which it can be seen that it consists mainly of two parts, a shell and a "cop" on which the weft thread is wound. The latter may be quite easily removed from the shell, and may be wound with thread on the winding machine that is incorporated in the Loom. The winding machine consists of a Crank Handle (seen projecting from the right-hand side of the model in Fig. 1), on which is a 57-teeth Gear Wheel in mesh with a ½" Pinion on a secondary Rod. This Rod has also secured to its outer end a Coupling in which the cop is held during winding. The reel of thread is accommodated on a Rod 18, which is carried in a 2½"×1" Double Angle Strip bolted to the base Girders of the Frame. After winding, the loaded cop is inserted in its shell, the free end of the thread being passed through one of the holes in the side of the shell and allowed to trail freely alongside when the Shuttle is placed in the slay.

When the operating handle is turned, one of the Heald Frames rises and the other falls simultaneously, thus "shedding" the warp. The slay moves up to the Heald frames, and as it pauses before commencing its return journey the Shuttle is thrown across the slay between the parted warp threads, leaving in its wake a trail of weft thread. On the return of the slay the reed drives before it loose thread left by the Shuttle, so forming what is termed the "first pick" of the weft. By continuing to turn the handle the process is repeated, but this time the Shuttle is thrown from the opposite end of the slay. The reed then presses the second pick into place against the first.

The taking-off rollers in the meantime revolve slowly and draw in the woven fabric as weaving proceeds.

Getting the Best from the Loom

Fig. 7. The Meccano Loom Shuttle

Providing that the instructions given in this Leaflet are closely followed, the actual construction of the Loom should offer little difficulty to the average Meccano model-builder ; but there are one or two matters connected with the adjustment and working of the model on which some advice may be given to enable the builder to turn

out really good material that may be put to some useful purpose.

First of all, it should be understood that adjustments to the finished model will be necessary to ensure that the different movements are timed correctly. For example, it is quite probable that in a newly-completed model some difficulty will be experienced in getting the Shuttle to work properly and regularly, and this, of course, is one of the most important movements of the whole machine. Careful attention, therefore, should be paid to this matter.

We have already mentioned that any trouble arising through the Shuttle sticking in the slay may usually be overcome by the simple expedient of lining the floor of the slay with a strip of cardboard, or better still a strip of tin. This will provide a smooth, even surface on which the Shuttle may slide easily to and fro. The next operation is to carefully adjust the springs controlling the picking motion, taking pains to ensure that the tension of both springs is equal. Several experiments may be necessary before the springs are in correct adjustment, but any trouble taken at this point will be amply repaid by the better quality of the woven cloth.

Another important point is the timing of the motion of the slay with that of the Shuttle. Here it may be mentioned that the Shuttle must shoot between the threads of the warp just at the moment when the latter are separated to their greatest extent, which coincides with the instant when the slay is nearest to the Heald Frame. This adjustment is best carried out by arranging matters so that the cams operating the picking-sticks are set in such a manner that the picking-sticks are released when the slay has completed two-thirds of its travel towards the Heald Frames. Thus the effect of the time-lag is counteracted, and the Shuttle passes across the warp at the correct moment.

It should be noted that the bottom set of warp threads, which are depressed by the appropriate Heald Frame during one cycle of operations, must lie closely on the floor of the slay, otherwise the Shuttle may foul them in its passage across the slay. The upper set of threads also should receive attention in order to ensure that the Shuttle has a clear path between the two sets of threads. The adjustments necessary to effect this may be carried out simply by varying the lengths of Sprocket Chain 42 and 44 that connect the Heald Frames to the arms 47 and 45.

In order to obtain the sudden jerk of the picking-

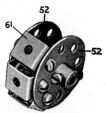

Fig. 8. Cam for operation of Picking Sticks

2 of No.	1b	7 of No.	13a	102 of No.	38	2 of No.	102
12 ,,	2	6 ,,	14	10 ,,	43	4 ,,	103c
8 ,,	3	5 ,,	15	3 ,,	45	1 ,,	104
2 ,,	4	6 ,,	16	2 ,,	46	2 ,,	106
42 ,,	5	3 ,,	16a	1 ,,	47	1 ,,	106a
4 ,,	6	1 ,,	16b	4 ,,	53a	6 ,,	108
2 ,,	6a	4 ,,	18b	14 ,,	57	2 ,,	109
4 ,,	7a	1 ,,	20a	30" ,,	58	2 ,,	111
10 ,,	8	4 ,,	22a	24 ,,	59	2 ,,	111a
17 ,,	8a	9 ,,	24	13 ,,	62	12 ,,	111c
8 ,,	8b	5 ,,	25	1 ,,	62b	1 ,,	126
5 ,,	9	4 ,,	26	13 ,,	63	3 ,,	126a
2 ,,	9a	5 ,,	27	2 ,,	64	2 ,,	133
2 ,,	9d	1 ,,	27a	2 ,,	70	1 ,,	136
4 ,,	10	2 ,,	30a	8 ,,	82	1 ,,	146
8 ,,	11	2 ,,	30c	28" ,,	94	6 ,,	147b
6 ,,	12	2 ,,	32	4 ,,	96	2 ,,	155
2 ,,	12b	202 ,,	37	60 ,,	101	6 ,,	166
6 ,,	13	28 ,,	37a				

Parts required to build the Meccano Loom

sticks that is necessary to throw the Shuttle from end to end of the slay, the operating handle should be turned quickly at the point where the cam releases the picking-sticks. After a little practice the amateur weaver will find this quite easy.

An alternative method of accentuating this motion is to bolt a 2″ Flat Girder against the face of each of the Strips 23 (Fig. 5), so that it projects below the bottom edge of the Strip. This modification will enable the Flat Girder to drop with extreme suddenness off the receding face of the cam, and will thus speed up the motion to a greater extent than would be possible by the Strip merely riding on the cam. In order to cause the Flat Girder to follow closely the contour of the cam, the Spring 37 may be duplicated.

Removing the Cop from the Shuttle

We have not yet explained how the cop may be removed from the Shuttle. This is accomplished by extracting the grub-screw seen at the left-hand end of the Shuttle in Fig. 7. The cop will then move to the left under the action of the spring, and the left-hand end of the cop will drop clear of the Shuttle. It is advisable to mention that the purpose of the spring is to prevent too free rotation of the cop, which would lead to uneven edges in the woven material. If the spring is too strong, on the other hand, the Shuttle will not travel completely across the slay, owing to the braking effect produced. The spring should press quite lightly on the end of the cop, and if it is judged to be too strong, a turn or two may be cut off.

It will be realised that considerable strain is placed upon some of the Gears and Rods of the mechanism, and in order to prevent the Gears slipping on their shafts, all set-screws must be secured very tightly. If any parts are still found to slip on their Rods, especially in connection with the picking motion mechanism, the set-screws should be duplicated, thereby doubling their powers of resistance.

Where considerable trouble is experienced from this cause, it is a good

plan to file a small flat in the Axle Rods immediately beneath the set-screws, thus providing a better gripping surface.

Threading the Heald Frames

There are one or two matters in connection with the threading of the warp threads through the Heald Frames on which some advice may be useful.

Before the warp threads are passed through the Healds, they must first be wound on to the Wood Roller forming the beam, in the manner already described, and this is work that requires a great deal of patience. It is useless to try to rush the operation to completion, for this will lead only to unsatisfactory working of the loom, with consequent deterioration in the quality of the woven material produced. It should be borne in mind that much of the success of the model depends upon the warp threads being wound perfectly evenly upon the beam, and in carrying out this work care must be taken to see that the tension weights do not drop so far that they touch the floor, as the sudden release of tension causes uneven patches to occur on the beam.

It is perhaps scarcely necessary to add that all the working parts of the Loom are to be lubricated thoroughly at regular intervals.

Fig. 9. View of the complete Beaming Frame, on which the Beam must be prepared before insertion in the Loom

Parts required to build the Beaming Frame

4 of No.	1a	15 of No.	9	594 of No.	37	8 of No.	63
62 ,,	2	7 ,,	9b	6 ,,	37a	3 ,,	103
10 ,,	3	8 ,,	13	90 ,,	38	2 ,,	109
2 ,,	4	2 ,,	14	1 ,,	40	6 ,,	111c
224 ,,	5	1 ,,	15	3 ,,	43	1 ,,	147a
12 ,,	7	3 ,,	16	2 ,,	48b	8 ,,	147b
2 ,,	7a	2 ,,	19b	21 ,,	59	1 ,,	148
6 ,,	8						

THE MECCANO SUPER MODEL LEAFLETS

The range of Meccano Super-Models now embraces no less than 38 superb examples of miniature engineering construction. A special instruction leaflet has been published for each of these super models and a selection of the leaflets is illustrated on this page.

A brief description of each model in the series is given below, while the prices of the leaflets are indicated at the foot of this page. Copies of any of the leaflets may be obtained from your dealer or direct from Head Office, post free, at the prices indicated.

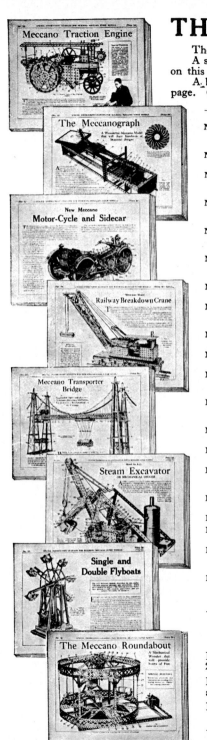

No. 1 MOTOR CHASSIS. This model runs perfectly under its own power. It has Ackermann Steering, Differential, Gear Box and Clutch, etc.

No. 2 SHIP COALER. All the movements of a real ship-coaler are reproduced in this model.

No. 3 MOTOR CYCLE AND SIDECAR. The sidecar is of streamline design and is mounted on springs. The motor-cycle is complete with lamps, horn, exhaust pipes, etc.

No. 4 GIANT BLOCK-SETTING CRANE. This realistic model is fitted with an accurate reproduction of Fidler's block-setting gear.

No. 5 TRAVELLING BUCKET DREDGER. In this model trucks and wagons can run underneath the chute through which falls the material raised by the dredger buckets.

No. 6 STIFF-LEG DERRICK. This model has many interesting movements, including hoisting, luffing and swivelling, which are controlled by suitable levers.

No. 7 PLATFORM SCALES. This model will weigh articles up to 4½ lb. with remarkable accuracy.

No. 8 ROUNDABOUT. This model is most attractive when in motion. As the roundabout rotates the cars spin round and the horses rise and fall.

No. 9 BAGATELLE TABLE. This is an interesting model that will give hours of fun to the players.

No. 10 LOG SAW. In this model the saw is driven rapidly to and fro while the work table travels beneath it.

No. 11 SINGLE-CYLINDER HORIZONTAL STEAM ENGINE. Fitted with balanced crankshaft, crosshead and centrifugal governor.

No. 12 STONE SAWING MACHINE. The model is equipped with adjustable work table and overhead trolley with self-sustaining chain hoist.

No. 13 MECCANOGRAPH. This wonderful model will draw hundreds of beautiful designs.

No. 14a GRANDFATHER CLOCK. A practical example of Meccano model-building. The model keeps accurate time.

No. 15 BALTIC TANK LOCOMOTIVE. The driving wheels are operated by an Electric Motor. An accurate reproduction of Walschaerts' Valve Gear is fitted.

No. 16a LOOM. This is perhaps the greatest Meccano success. The model weaves beautiful material.

No. 17 PLANING MACHINE. Fitted with quick-return motion.

No. 18 REVOLVING CRANE. This model is fitted with screw-operated luffing gear.

No. 19 STEAM SHOVEL. This model embodies travelling, rotating, racking and digging movements, and jib hoisting and lowering gear.

No. 19a STEAM EXCAVATOR, OR MECHANICAL DIGGER. A Meccano Steam Engine is incorporated in this model and provides the power for operating the four movements.

No. 20 MOBILE CRANE. This model has hoisting, luffing, travelling and slewing movements. It is fitted with an automatic brake on the hoisting shaft, an internal expanding brake on the front axle, and a limit switch to prevent over-winding of the jib in either direction.

No. 21 TRANSPORTER BRIDGE. The carriage automatically travels to and fro for as long as the motor is driven, pausing for a few seconds at each end of its travel.

No. 22 TRACTION ENGINE. A remarkably realistic model that will pull a boy of average weight. Fitted with two speeds.

No. 23 VERTICAL LOG SAW. While the saws are in motion, the logs are fed slowly to them.

No. 24 TRAVELLING GANTRY CRANE. The movements of this model comprise the traversing of the entire gantry, hoisting and lowering, and the traversing of the crane trolley.

No. 25 HYDRAULIC CRANE. The hydraulic ram is represented realistically by a powerful screw mechanism.

No. 26 TWIN ELLIPTIC HARMONOGRAPH. Some beautiful designs may be produced with this model.

No. 27 DRAGLINE. This imposing model of a giant excavator is fitted with travelling, luffing, slewing, and dragging movements.

No. 28 PONTOON CRANE. The movements of this model include the operation of the two hoisting blocks, slewing of the entire crane, and luffing.

No. 29 HAMMERHEAD CRANE. This is a very realistic and powerful model, comprising traversing, hoisting and slewing motions.

No. 30 BREAKDOWN CRANE. This model is equipped with travelling, slewing, luffing, and hoisting motions, and also is fitted with laminated springs, brakes, out-riggers, etc.

No. 31 WAREHOUSE WITH ELEVATORS. The two cages are driven automatically and work alternately, pausing at top and bottom positions.

No. 32 TWIN CYLINDER STEAM ENGINE AND BOILER. This is a realistic working model of a complete steam plant, equipped with valve gear, governor, balanced cranks, etc.

No. 33 SINGLE AND DOUBLE FLYBOATS. These two models represent popular pleasure-fair attractions.

No. 34 THREE-ENGINE BIPLANE. This is a realistic model of an "Argosy" machine, and is fitted with ailerons, elevators and rudders.

No. 35 LEVEL LUFFING GRABBING CRANE. A large and imposing model of novel design. The crane incorporates a level luffing gear, while the balanced jib is operated by crank action and is fitted with a "single suspension" grab.

No. 36 ELECTRIC DERRICK CRANE (Scotch Type). This imposing model is built to a scale of ⅜in. to 1 ft., the jib measuring 6 ft. in length. The movements include hoisting and lowering, luffing and slewing.

No. 37 6-in. HOWITZER, LIMBER AND TRACTOR. A splendid new working model of a complete mobile artillery unit. The Tractor incorporates "caterpillars" and the Howitzer will shoot accurately.

Prices of Meccano Super Model Leaflets :—

Leaflets Nos. 3, 5, 6, 7, 8, 9, 10, 11, 12, 14a, 17, 18, 19, 20, 21, 22, 23, 24, 25, 26, 28, 29, 36, 37—United Kingdom 2d., Australia 4d., New Zealand and South Africa 3d., Canada 5 cents.

Leaflets Nos. 1, 2, 13, 15, 16a, 19a, 27, 30, 31, 32, 33, 34, 35—United Kingdom 3d., Australia 6d., New Zealand and South Africa 4d., Canada 8 cents.

Leaflet No. 4—United Kingdom 6d., Australia 1/-, New Zealand and South Africa 8d., Canada 15 cents.

MECCANO LIMITED, Old Swan, LIVERPOOL, ENGLAND

(Overseas 3d Canada 5 C

Australia

Meccano Planing Machine

A Model Machine Tool

TOOLS have played a very important part in the history of civilisation. Before he learnt to use them, man was little better than the animals, but as soon as he realised that a bar of wood wielded by his powerful muscles was more effective both for peaceful and warlike operations than his bare hands, the slow process of civilisation had commenced. To-day his skill both in devising and using tools is such that he can fashion iron and steel to any shape that he desires : with their aid he can tunnel through the largest mountains, build canals, and produce machines with which to travel with great rapidity over the surface of the ground or beneath it, over or beneath the sea, or in the air.

Tools, like everything else, had small beginnings. The earliest tools were of the simplest character and were few in number, principal among them being the knife, the chisel, and the axe. These, with the primitive hammer, formed the stock-in-trade of the first mechanics.

Then came the introduction of the saw, which was considered of so great importance that its "inventor" was honoured with a place among the gods in the mythology of the Greeks ! Another very ancient tool was the file, which was used to sharpen weapons and implements. This is referred to in the Bible.

Such continued to be the chief tools in use down almost to our own period. The smith was at first the principal tool maker, but special branches of trade gradually were established, devoted to tool making.

Even at the time of James Watt nearly all the work on his engines had to be done by hand and we find him complaining to his partner of the failure of his engines through bad workmanship. Yet better work could not be had. First-rate workmen in machinery did not as yet exist; they were only in process of education, and the few tools used were of a very imperfect kind.

Nowadays the position is very different. The perfection of modern machine tools is such that the utmost possible precision is secured and the engineer can calculate on a

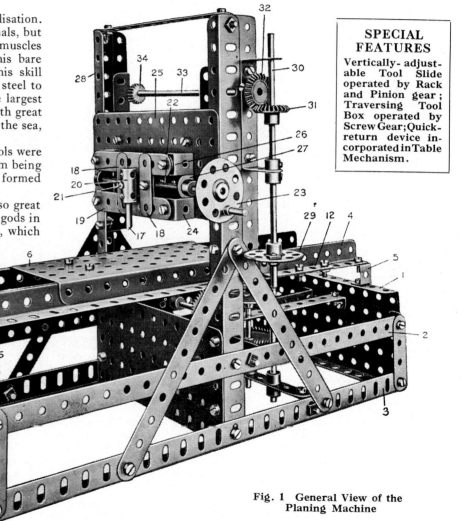

SPECIAL FEATURES

Vertically- adjustable Tool Slide operated by Rack and Pinion gear ; Traversing Tool Box operated by Screw Gear; Quick-return device incorporated in Table Mechanism.

Fig. 1 General View of the Planing Machine

928/5 Published by MECCANO LIMITED, BINNS ROAD, LIVERPOOL Printed in England degree of exactitude that does not admit of a deviation beyond the thousandth part of an inch. In some machines inaccuracies would mean disaster.

Bramah's Planing Machine

One of the most important machine tools is the Planing Machine. In a patent specification taken out in 1802 by Joseph Bramah, the famous engineer, a machine was described as a tool for producing smooth, straight and parallel surfaces on wood and various other materials. This record is the earliest in which a planing machine is mentioned, although several earlier inventions had led up to its final development. The cutting tools were fixed on frames driven by machinery, and revolved round an upright shaft. In another pattern the shaft was horizontal as in an ordinary wood-turning lathe, while in yet another design the tools were fixed on frames sliding in stationary grooves.

Another noted engineer, Joseph Clement, also devoted considerable study to the improvement of machine tools, such as they were in his time. He made a machine by means of which metal plates of large dimensions were planed with perfect truth—a great accomplishment!

It is probable that there were many others who contributed their experience and labours toward perfecting the planing machine and to whom credit is due. Indeed, a great deal of controversy has centred round the question as to who was the real inventor of this particular type of machine tool. In the case of Clement, however, it may be recorded that he had a machine specially designed for planing the bars of lathes and other work in use for some years previous to 1820. The success of this instrument encouraged him to produce a more elaborate machine, which he completed and set to work early in the year 1825.

As very few workmen were sufficiently skilled to operate such a machine Clement did not think it necessary to take out a patent for his invention, as he considered that no one but his own trained workmen would be able to operate a machine made to his plans, even if the idea was attempted.

Fox's and Murray's Planing Machines

James Fox was another engineer who interested himself in the planing machine. It is claimed that he made the first really practicable planing

machine in 1814. His machine was practically the same in principle as the planing machine now in general use. A self-acting ratchet motion for operating the slides of a compound slide rest was incorporated in the machine, and the table was self-reversing owing to an arrangement consisting of three bevel wheels, one of which was just an idler wheel running on a pivot. Of the remaining two bevels, one was fixed to the driving shaft while the other ran loose on the shaft. A clutch was arranged so that it could be moved into contact with either the fixed or the loose bevel wheels, and as these wheels revolved in opposite directions due to the idler wheel, the motion of the driven shaft thereby was reversed.

In 1814 Matthew Murray had a planing machine of his own make in use in his workshop. The machine was used to plane the back or circular part of the "D" slide valve, an improvement which Murray had by that time introduced in the steam engine. To make the valve work efficiently it was essential to obtain two perfectly plane surfaces on the valve. Like many other inventions of those days the machine was not patented, but was kept locked up in a small room. Only Murray himself had access to this room.

The history of the invention of the planing machine and of the various improvements that have been effected since the very early models is of considerable interest, but while a great deal more could be written of the trials and difficulties that each inventor had to overcome, our space will not permit of such matters being mentioned here.

A Modern Giant Planing Machine

To-day many types of planing machines are in use, each type differing widely in several important features, but the following description of a new

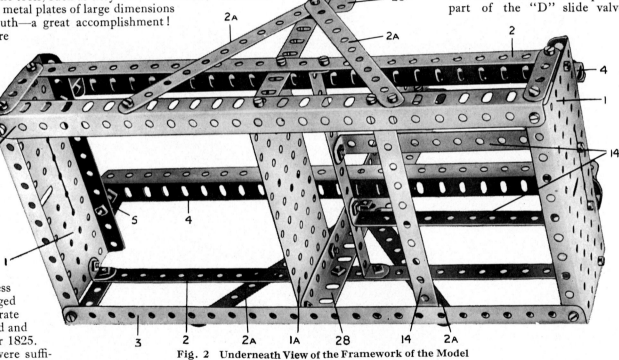

Fig. 2   Underneath View of the Framework of the Model

planing machine recently installed at an engineering works in the north of England may serve to give some idea of the leading dimensions and features of a large modern planer.

The moving work table or platen is 32 feet long and the overall height of the machine is 26 feet. A very elaborate and intricate gear box forms a special feature of the machine, which will operate at a cutting speed of 150 feet per minute and a return speed of 180 feet per minute. It is one of the fastest planing machines yet designed. Two tool holders are used on the machine and are carried on a cross rail, both tool boxes being operated by a square-threaded screw. The bed or work table is cast in one section and contains T-slots, as is the usual practice. The table is moved to and fro by means of a rack and pinion movement, the rack being of cast steel and running the whole length of the table.

A special type of electric motor is mounted directly overhead on the cross piece of the vertical members and transmits the drive by means of double leather belts to the main countershaft connected with the gear box.

How a Planing Machine Works

The following is a brief description of the manner in which the usual type of planing machine is operated.

Before starting the machine the work to be planed is secured to the long table or platen by means of special bolts sliding in the T-slots cut in the table. Then the cutting tools are fixed into the tool holders or "boxes" attached to the cross piece and the whole cross piece is lowered and adjusted so that the tools will take the right depth of cut from the metal. Power is generally supplied by an electric motor and the table moves to and fro, carrying the work towards and from the cutting tool. After each cutting stroke of the table the tool holder moves across the table the width of the cutting tool, and so takes a fresh cut each time the work moves toward it.

Having now learnt something about planing machines in general, we may turn to the construction of the Meccano model. The Meccano planing machine embodies the principal features of the machines in actual practice. No difficulty should be

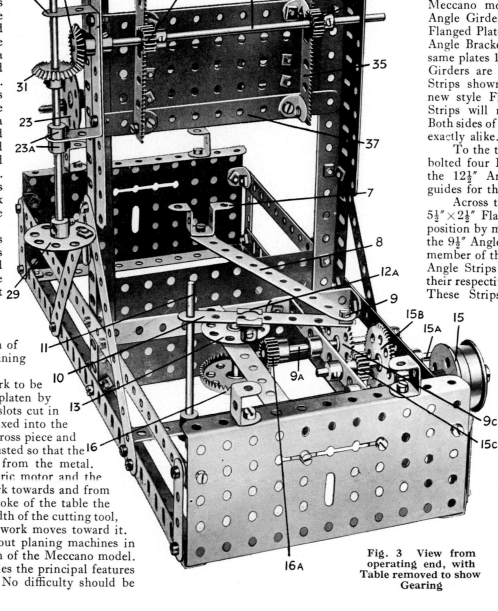

Fig. 3 View from operating end, with Table removed to show Gearing

experienced in building it, since each part is described in detail.

The Meccano Model : The Framework

To construct the framework of the Meccano model first bolt the two 12½″ Angle Girders 3 (Fig. 2) to the 5½″×2½″ Flanged Plates 1 and secure—by means of Angle Brackets—two 12½″ Strips 2 to the same plates 1. The ends of the two Angle Girders are spanned vertically by the 2″ Strips shown in the illustration. If the new style Flanged Plates are used these Strips will not be necessary, of course. Both sides of the framework are constructed exactly alike.

To the top Flanges of the Plates 1 are bolted four Double Brackets 5 that carry the 12½″ Angle Girders 4 forming the guides for the moving work table 6.

Across the centre of the framework a 5½″×2½″ Flat Plate is placed and held in position by means of bolts passing through the 9½″ Angle Girders forming the vertical member of the machine. The 5½″ Double Angle Strips 14 should now be secured to their respective Angle Girder as illustrated. These Strips 14 form the journals for the shafts of the driving gear, so care should be taken to ensure that each Strip is in perfect alignment.

The 9½″ Angle Girders 28 that support the tool rest are bolted on the inside of the Strips 2 and held rigid by means of the four 5½″ Strips 2a placed as shown. To the upper end of the Angle Girders 28 are bolted two Flat Girders 28a, and to one of these is secured a 2½″×1″ Double Angle Strip 28b in such a position as to form a journal for the shaft 30 (Fig. 1).

The vertical Angle Girders 28 are spanned across the top by means of a 5½″ Strip secured to the Girders with Angle Brackets. This completes the construction of the framework of the model, and the work table and operating mechanism may now be assembled.

Main Gear Train (Figs. 3 and 4)

As only one of the two "strokes" of the work table performs any actual work so far as planing is concerned, a special device is incorporated in the mechanism so as to cause the table to move slowly during the working "stroke" and quickly during the return stroke, thus speeding up production by a considerable amount. This difference of speed in the operation of the table is obtained automatically by a quick-return device. This is shown clearly in Fig. 4 but before commencing the construction of this part it is necessary to proceed with the gears and shafts of the main drive as illustrated in Fig. 3.

The main driving Pulley 15 (formed from two Flanged Wheels) is carried on a 3½" Rod journalled in one of the Strips 2 and in a Double Angle Strip 14 (Fig. 2). The Rod also carries a ½" Pinion (see Fig. 4) engaging a 57-teeth Gear Wheel 15b carried on the Rod 15a. The Rod 15a also carries the ½" Pinion 15c (Fig. 3) that engages with a 57-teeth Gear Wheel 9c on the Rod 9a. On the inner end of the latter is a ½" Pinion 16a driving a Contrate Wheel 16 secured on the Rod of the Bush Wheel 13.

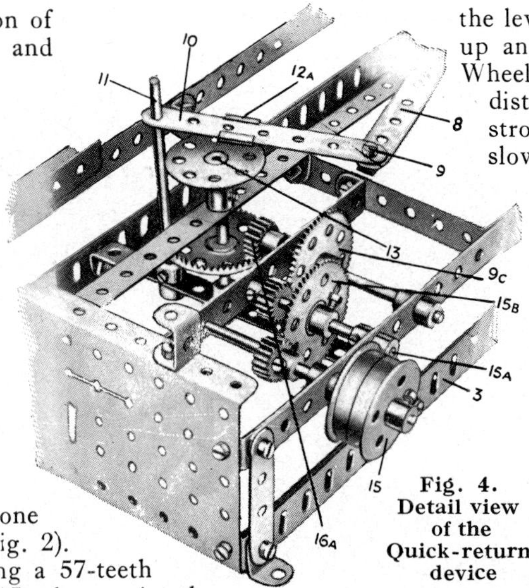

Quick-return Motion (Figs. 3 and 4)

The table 6 (Fig. 1) consists of a 5½" Flanged Plate arranged to slide to and fro on the upturned flanges of the Girders 4. The method of operation is as follows :—

The Plate 6 is bolted to a Double Bent Strip 7 (see Figs. 3 and 4) which is attached pivotally by means of a bolt and two nuts (see Standard Mechanism No. 262) to the 5½" Strip 8. (Note : Fig. 1 shows an old-style Flanged Plate used as the table, but if preferred, a new-style Plate will serve equally well). The end of the Strip 8, in turn, is attached pivotally by similar means at 9 to a 3½" Strip 10 pivoted on a Rod 11. The Rod 11 passes through one of the elongated holes in the Angle Girder 4 and to prevent play of the Rod a 2½" Strip 12 (Fig. 1) is bolted to the flange of the Girder 4 so that the Rod also passes through the end hole of this Strip.

The Strip 10 (Fig. 3) engages an Eye Piece 12a secured by its set-screw to the shank of a bolt passed through the Bush Wheel 13. The bolt should be given sufficient play to permit of its turning freely in the Bush Wheel. The latter rotates in a clockwise direction, rocking

Fig. 4.
Detail view
of the
Quick-return
device

the lever 10 and arm 8 to and fro, and the swivel-guide 12a slides up and down on the lever as it follows the movement of the Bush Wheel. Consequently, the guide 12a (Figs. 3 and 4) is at a greater distance from the pivot or fulcrum of the lever during the forward stroke than it is on the return, with the result that the point 9 moves slowly on the forward stroke and more rapidly on the return.

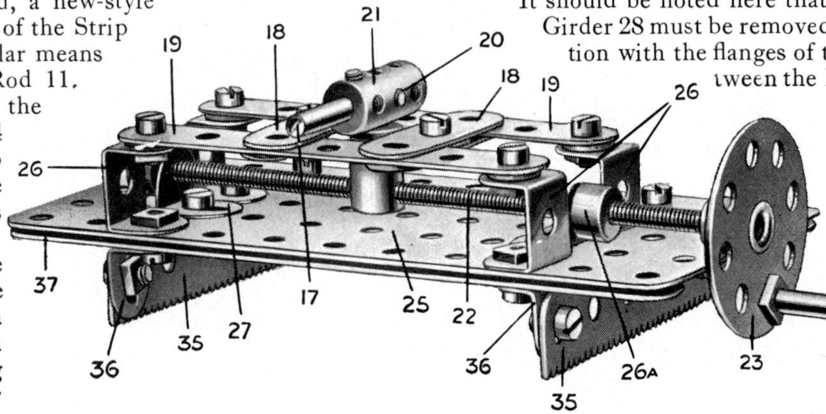

The Tool Carrier

The cutting tool 17 is carried in a Coupling 21 (Fig. 5) which is connected by a Threaded Pin to a Threaded Boss on a 5½" Threaded Rod 22. Before passing the Coupling 21 over the Threaded Pin a 1½" Strip should be placed on the Pin. In the illustration (Fig. 5) the ends of this Strip can just be seen between the 1½" Strips 18, which form guides for the tool holder. These Strips 18 are placed in pairs and their ends are arranged to slide on 3½" Strips 19, which are supported by Double Brackets 26, the latter being attached to the Flat Plate 25. Washers are placed between the Strips 19 and the Double Brackets in order to give the necessary clearance for the Threaded Boss on the Threaded Rod 22.

The rotation of the handwheel 23 causes the tool holder to advance along the Threaded Rod 22 in a direction depending on the direction of rotation. The Rod 22 is held in position by Collars with set-screws placed at each end against the Angle Brackets in which the Rod is journalled.

The vertical movement of the Plate 25 on the upright Angle Girder 28 is effected from the Bush Wheel 29 (Figs. 1 and 3) mounted on a Rod 30, a Bevel Wheel 31 on this Rod engaging a corresponding Bevel 32 on a Rod 33. The latter carries two Pinions 34, which engage the Rack Strips 35 secured in position by Angle Brackets. Two 5½" Strips 37 (Fig. 5), are bolted to the Flat Plate 25 with spacing Washers between so that a clearance is provided between their ends and the Plate 25. In the slots so formed the flanges of the Angle Girders 28 are free to slide (see Fig. 3).

It should be noted here that the 5½" Strip spanning the top of the Angle Girder 28 must be removed to allow the tool holder to be placed in position with the flanges of the Angle Girders 28 occupying the space between the Flat Plate 25 and the ends of the 5½" Strips 37.

Fig. 5.   The Tool Slide and Tool Box

Parts required :

	No.		No.		No.
2 of	1	5 of	16	1 of	48b
7 ,,	2	1 ,,	18a	5 ,,	48d
3 ,,	3	2 ,,	20	1 ,,	50
1 ,,	5	3 ,,	24	2 ,,	52
4 ,,	6	5 ,,	26	12 ,,	59
3 ,,	6a	2 ,,	27a	1 ,,	63
4 ,,	8	1 ,,	28	1 ,,	64
2 ,,	8a	2 ,,	30	2 ,,	70
8 ,,	11	74 ,,	37	1 ,,	80
12 ,,	12	3 ,,	37a	2 ,,	103
1 ,,	14	9 ,,	38	2 ,,	110
1 ,,	15	2 ,,	46	2 ,,	115

(Overseas 3d Canada 5 Cents)

Meccano Revolving Crane

SPECIAL FEATURES

Luffing is effected by means of a simple but powerful screw gear. Luffing and hoisting movements are controlled by separate levers and may be operated separately or simultaneously. A reversing motion is fitted to the luffing gear, and the whole structure is capable of revolving upon the wheels mounted in the base. Much interest will be added to the model if the electro magnet is used in the manner described in this leaflet.

Fig. 1. General view of the Meccano Revolving Crane

MANY of the cranes in practical use, such as the giant block-setters and floating cranes, are so large and impressive that there is perhaps a danger of over-looking altogether the smaller but equally useful members of the crane family that are to be found in almost any large engineering works or railway siding.

The prototype of the Meccano model described in this leaflet is used, amongst other purposes, for loading and unloading railway wagons, lorries, etc. It rotates about a pivot mounted on a fixed base. In the case of the larger types of revolving cranes, some mechanical means would be provided to effect the swivelling movement, and if desired the necessary mechanism may easily be added to the Meccano model. To do this the Flanged Wheels on which the model rests should be mounted on a circular fixed base. The swivelling gear may then be coupled by any suitable means to the fixed pivot. Alternatively, the model could be mounted on the new Meccano Ball Bearing (Part No. 168) and a shaft inserted vertically in the crane so that a Sprocket Wheel on its lower end may be connected by a Sprocket Chain to the circumference of the lower fixed Ball Race.

The Meccano Model

Commence to build the crane by constructing the base platform (Fig. 2) mounted

Published by MECCANO LIMITED, BINNS ROAD, LIVERPOOL.

Printed in England

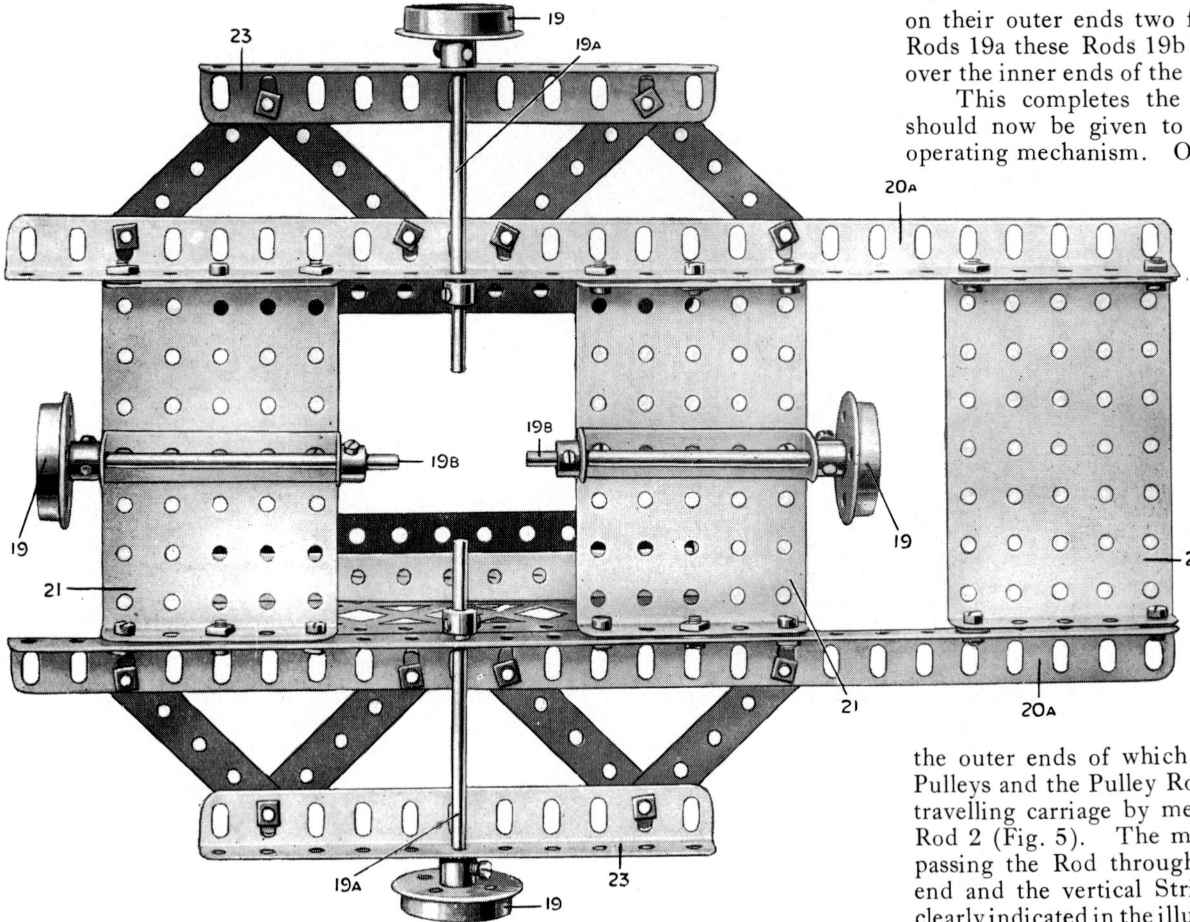

on their outer ends two further Flanged Wheels 19. As in the case of the Rods 19a these Rods 19b are secured in position by means of Collars slipped over the inner ends of the Rods and placed against the Double Angle Strips.

This completes the construction of the base platform and attention should now be given to the construction of the supporting frame for the operating mechanism. On referring to Figs. 4 and 5 the method of building this part should be fairly clear. The 5½″ Braced Girders shown in Fig. 1 are bolted to the 5½″ vertical Strips 2a (Fig. 5) and to vertical 3½″ Strips. Attached also to these Strips are two 5½″×2½″ Flanged Plates which form the sides of the gear box.

Two 5½″ Strips should next be bolted to the Flanged Plates (as shown in Fig. 1) so that they overhang the latter at the rear by five holes. These Strips carry a 3½″×2½″ Flanged Plate which supports the pivot 5 of the lever 7 (Fig. 5).

Construction of the Jib

The jib is formed by 12½″ Angle Girders, braced at the sides by the 5½″ and 3½″ Strips shown in Fig. 1. The upper and lower sides of the jib are braced by 3½″ Strips placed crosswise and the Girders are spanned at the top by 1½″ Strips.

Attached to the upper ends of the Angle Girders forming the underside of the jib are extension pieces consisting of 2″ Strips (see Fig. 1) the outer ends of which are attached to the 3″ Strips carrying the two jib Pulleys and the Pulley Rod. When completed the jib may be attached to the travelling carriage by means of a Rod 2 (Fig. 5). The manner of passing the Rod through the jib end and the vertical Strips 2a is clearly indicated in the illustration. Collars are slipped over the Rod and secured at either end, thus holding the jib securely yet loosely pivoted in position.

Luffing Gear (Figs. 4 and 5)

The movement of the jib 1 (Fig. 4) about the pivot formed by the Axle Rod 2 is obtained from the handle 3, which is secured to a short Rod carrying the 1″ Gear Wheel 4 that engages with another 1″ Gear Wheel 4 carried on the 4½″ Rod 5a. Also carried on the Rod 5a are two Bevel Wheels 5 and 6 (see Fig. 5), either of which may be brought into engagement

Fig. 2. Underneath view of base of model, showing method of mounting the wheel axles.

on Flanged Wheels 19. It is formed by bolting three 3½″×2½″ Flanged Plates 21 between the two 12½″ Angle Girders 28. Before the Plates are finally secured, however, two 5½″ Strips 29 (Figs. 4 and 5) and two 3½″ Strips should be bolted in a vertical position ready to hold the sides of the gear box. These Strips are shown more clearly in Fig. 1.

The "outrigger" arrangements carrying the Axle Rods 19a (Fig. 2) are made up from pairs of 2½″ Strips bolted to the Angle Girders 20a and to 5½″ Angle Girders 23. The Rods 19a, which are 4½″ long, are passed through the centre holes of the Girders 23 and through the Girders 20a. They are held in position by Collars and Set-screws secured to their inner ends against the inner sides of the Girders 20a. The outer ends of the Rods 19a carry the Flanged Wheels 19.

To the centre of the Flanged Plates 21 now bolt 2½″×½″ Double Angle Strips as shown in Fig. 2 and through these pass the Rods 19b, which carry

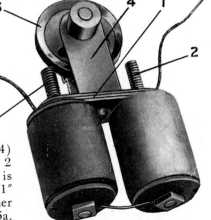

**Fig. 3.
The Meccano Electro Magnet.**

with the Bevel Wheel 9. The Rod 5a is arranged to slide longitudinally in its bearings and is controlled in this movement by the Strip 7. The latter is pivoted at 5 on a Threaded Pin, and on its inner end a Double Bracket is mounted pivotally by means of a bolt and two nuts (see Standard Mechanism No. 262). This Double Bracket engages Rod 5a and is spaced between the Bevels 5 and 6 by means of Washers.

The Bevel Wheel 9 is carried on the end of a 2" Rod 10 that is connected by the Coupling 11 to a 5" Screwed Rod 12. The Rod 10 is journalled in a 2½"×1" Double Angle Strip carrying a Double Bent Strip and placed as shown in Fig. 5, the whole arrangement being loosely pivoted on the Rod 5a (see Fig. 4).

The 5" Screwed Rod 12 engages the transverse threaded hole in a Coupling 13, which is carried pivotally on two 2" Rods 14 so as to give a clear way for the Screwed Rod 12. When the Screwed Rod 12 is set in motion, the Coupling 13 travels up or down—according to the direction of rotation —and carries the jib with it.

When the lever 7 is in the central position all three Bevels 5, 6 and 9 are disengaged. A slight movement of the lever to one side or the other, however, brings one of the Bevels 5 and 6 into mesh with the Bevel 9, thus actuating the luffing mechanism.

Hence it will be seen that the jib may be raised or lowered without altering the direction of rotation of the handle 3, and the load may be moved simultaneously, but in a different direction, to the jib.

Hoisting and Lowering Gear

The Rod of the handle 3 also carries a ½" Pinion 15 which is adapted to engage and drive a 57-teeth Gear Wheel 16, round the spindle of which is wound the cord 17 (Fig. 4) by means of which the load is raised or lowered. The spindle is caused to slide in its bearings, and so engage the Gear 16 with the Pinion 15, by means of the 3½" Strip 18 (Fig. 5) pivoted at 19 on a bolt lock-nutted to the Flanged Plate. The other end of the Strip 18 is bent up to engage between the boss of the Gear Wheel 16 and a Collar carried on the Rod of the latter.

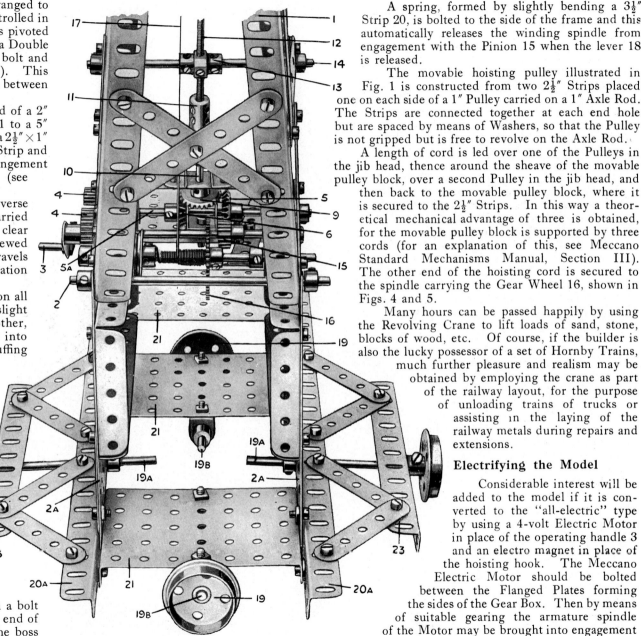

Fig. 4. Front view of Crane, showing hoisting mechanism, etc.

A spring, formed by slightly bending a 3½" Strip 20, is bolted to the side of the frame and this automatically releases the winding spindle from engagement with the Pinion 15 when the lever 18 is released.

The movable hoisting pulley illustrated in Fig. 1 is constructed from two 2½" Strips placed one on each side of a 1" Pulley carried on a 1" Axle Rod. The Strips are connected together at each end hole but are spaced by means of Washers, so that the Pulley is not gripped but is free to revolve on the Axle Rod.

A length of cord is led over one of the Pulleys in the jib head, thence around the sheave of the movable pulley block, over a second Pulley in the jib head, and then back to the movable pulley block, where it is secured to the 2½" Strips. In this way a theoretical mechanical advantage of three is obtained, for the movable pulley block is supported by three cords (for an explanation of this, see Meccano Standard Mechanisms Manual, Section III). The other end of the hoisting cord is secured to the spindle carrying the Gear Wheel 16, shown in Figs. 4 and 5.

Many hours can be passed happily by using the Revolving Crane to lift loads of sand, stone, blocks of wood, etc. Of course, if the builder is also the lucky possessor of a set of Hornby Trains, much further pleasure and realism may be obtained by employing the crane as part of the railway layout, for the purpose of unloading trains of trucks or assisting in the laying of the railway metals during repairs and extensions.

Electrifying the Model

Considerable interest will be added to the model if it is converted to the "all-electric" type by using a 4-volt Electric Motor in place of the operating handle 3 and an electro magnet in place of the hoisting hook. The Meccano Electric Motor should be bolted between the Flanged Plates forming the sides of the Gear Box. Then by means of suitable gearing the armature spindle of the Motor may be brought into engagement with the Gear Wheels 4 (Fig. 5). A 4-volt Meccano Accumulator placed on the rear

Plate 21 (Fig. 2) and held in position by Angle Girders bolted to the Plate will easily supply the necessary current for both Motor and magnet.

Lifting Loads by Magnetism

The electro magnet will serve splendidly in place of the ordinary hoisting hook for lifting such objects as scrap pieces of iron or tin, Meccano Strips, Rods, and Girders, etc. The necessary magnet (see Fig. 3) is quite easily made and with the aid of the following description no difficulty should be experienced by any Meccano boy who decides to construct one.

Commence by winding two Bobbins to full capacity with 26 S.W.G. wire, and attach the completed Bobbins to the yoke 1, which is composed of three 1½" Strips, by the Pole Pieces 2. A wire protruding from one of the magnet coils should be connected to one of the wires of the second coil, and in order to select the proper wires for connection, it should be imagined that the electric current, starting from the input end (represented by the wire attached to the Accumulator) of the first coil, flows round that coil in a clockwise direction. It then passes to the second coil and flows round it in an anti-clockwise direction. By connecting the two magnets in this way, one is given a north and the other a south polarity.

It is important that the two leads to the coils should be of sufficient length to permit the magnet being raised and lowered by the crane. The hoisting cord may be rove round the 1" Pulley 3, which turns upon a 1" Axle Rod journalled in a Cranked Bent Strip 4 bolted to the yoke 1.

The Bobbins when completed may be covered with brown paper; this improves their appearance and protects the insulation of the wire.

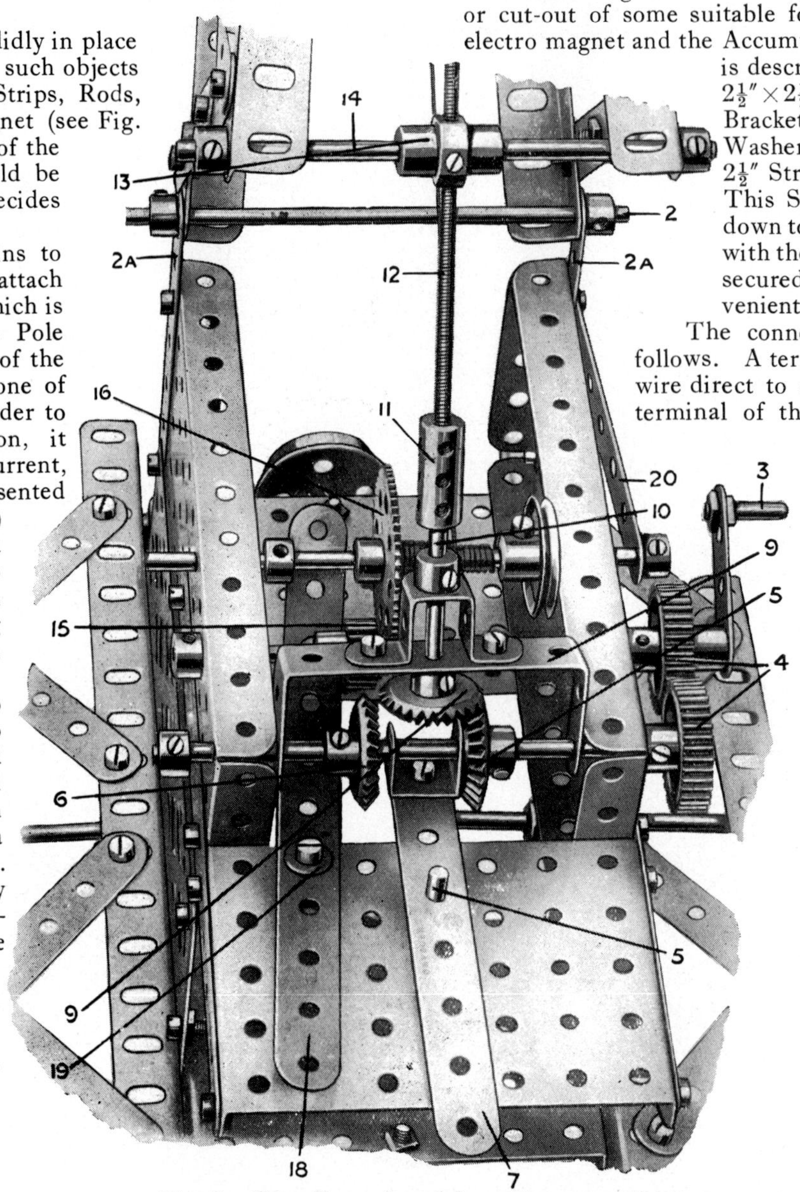

The Wiring Circuit

In order to drop the load whenever desired it is necessary to de-magnetise the electro magnet momentarily by cutting off the current supply. A switch or cut-out of some suitable form is therefore required in circuit with the electro magnet and the Accumulator. A knife switch suitable for the purpose is described in the Electrical Manual. It consists of a 2½" × 2½" Flat Plate to which are connected two Angle Brackets insulated from the Plate by Insulating Washers. The knife of the switch is formed by a 2½" Strip that is pivoted to one of the Angle Brackets. This Strip should be so arranged that on pressing it down toward the Flat Plate rubbing contact will be made with the other Angle Bracket. A Threaded Pin may be secured to the end of the 2½" Strip to form a convenient operating handle.

The connections for the electro magnet circuit are as follows. A terminal of the magnet should be connected by a wire direct to a terminal of the Accumulator, and the other terminal of the magnet should be joined by wire to one of the Angle Brackets of the switch. The remaining Angle Bracket of the switch is connected to the other terminal of the Accumulator. It is important to note that separate switches will be required for controlling the Motor and the magnet, but one Accumulator will supply all the necessary current.

As an "all-electric" crane the model will be found exceptionally interesting and well worth constructing. The electro magnet may be fitted to almost any Meccano Crane, of course, and much fun and interest can be gained by using it in place of the hoisting hook. The load is dropped whenever required by switching off the current.

Many powerful cranes fitted for electro magnetic hoisting are to be found in various iron and steel works throughout the country, where they prove very useful in conveying castings, etc. Their use saves the time that would be required fixing hoisting hooks.

Fig. 5. Gear Box, viewed from the rear, showing luffing mechanism with reversing gear, etc.

Parts required :

9	of No.	2	2	of No.	15
17	,,	3	2	,,	15a
2	,,	4	4	,,	16
10	,,	5	4	,,	17
2	,,	6	1	,,	18a
2	,,	6a	6	,,	20
6	,,	8	1	,,	22
2	,,	9	1	,,	22a
1	,,	11	1	,,	23
4	,,	12	1	,,	26

Parts required (continued)

1	of No.	27a	1	of No.	57
3	,,	30	14	,,	59
2	,,	31	1	,,	62
2	,,	35	1	,,	63
83	,,	37	1	,,	63a
18	,,	38	1	,,	80
1	,,	45	2	,,	100
1	,,	46	1	,,	111
2	,,	52	2	,,	115
4	,,	53			

Meccano Steam Shovel

A model of unlimited interest and application that performs all the operations of an actual steam shovel or mechanical navvy

Built with Meccano Outfit L

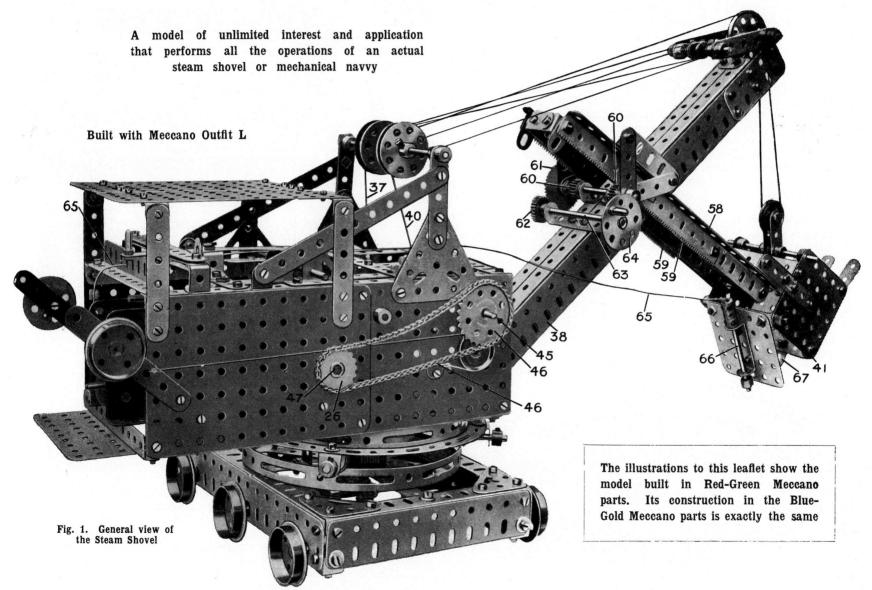

Fig. 1. General view of the Steam Shovel

The illustrations to this leaflet show the model built in Red-Green Meccano parts. Its construction in the Blue-Gold Meccano parts is exactly the same

MANY labour-saving devices are available to present-day engineers, and among these there is probably none more useful than the steam shovel, or mechanical navvy as it is sometimes called.

The truth of this statement will be realised when it is learned that a large steam navvy can move as much material in one day as could be excavated by 2,000 men with picks and shovels! Picture for a moment 2,000 men at work on a site. Imagine the commotion of such a crowd wielding 2,000 picks and shovels.

Then again, think of all the stoppages to "take a breath" or to move from one spot to another. What a dinner hour it would be—2,000 cans of tea to be made and 2,000 baskets of food to be opened!

This is surely a picture of wasted energy and much valuable time when one considers the mechanical equivalent, the Steam Shovel that weighs perhaps 100 tons.

Working from morning to night without a stop to rest or cogitate, it moves with unvarying precision, and requires only three men to look after it.

Fed on coal and water, and working at about four strokes to the minute, it is capable of digging out 6,000 yards of material in a working day, and in addition loading it on to waiting railway wagons.

No wonder, then, that engineers and contractors prefer the mechanical method to human labour.

A Typical Steam Shovel

The bucket is mounted at the end of a beam that in turn is connected with the jib by two long racks meshing with gear wheels driven by steam engines mounted on the shovel frame. This makes it possible to rack the bucket arm in or out as desired, thus varying the working radius. As in the case of a crane, a wire rope passes over a pulley at the top of the jib, and on to a winding drum, with the result that as soon as the gear is thrown in the drum winds in the rope and the bucket is pulled upward, describing an arc about the point at which the bucket arm is pivoted to the jib. These movements, together with the raising or lowering of the jib, enable the bucket to excavate a large area without having to alter the position of the entire machine.

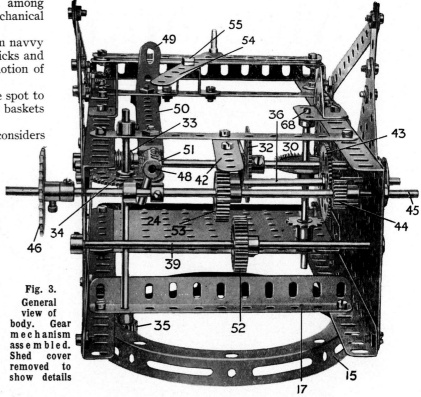

Fig. 3. General view of body. Gear mechanism assembled. Shed cover removed to show details

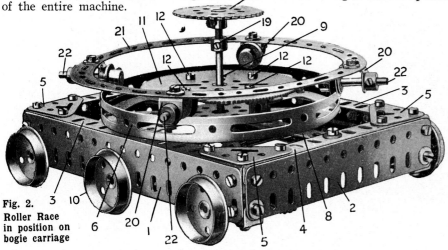

Fig. 2. Roller Race in position on bogie carriage

The leading edge of the bucket is fitted with a cutting lip, armed with a number of teeth. These are made of the hardest steel, and dig their way into the material to be removed. In most machines, the jib is attached direct to the main frame, in which the gears, engines and boiler are housed. The whole revolving superstructure is mounted on an undercarriage and this runs on rails, the travelling motion being taken from the main engines.

From the description given it will be seen that steam shovels are not unlike cranes with large scoops attached, and while they are interesting to inspect when at rest, it is only when they are at work on a cliff face that the reality of their power can be fully appreciated.

The bucket is thrust against the side of the cliff and then is slowly raised, its sharp teeth tearing and ripping open the solid material. When the bucket is full the operator pulls a lever and the whole superstructure swings round, until the bucket is over a waiting railway wagon. A further lever opens the bottom of the bucket and the removed material is deposited. Then the shovel swings back for a further load.

The largest shovels are able to lift 10 tons of material at one stroke and make four strokes per minute.

The whole movement occupies only a few minutes, but it is a fascinating display of great strength coupled with almost human intelligence.

The Meccano Steam Shovel has been designed after careful study of a typical Shovel in practical use, and every feature that figures in its prototype figures also in the Meccano model. Each part of the model is described in detail and will offer no difficulty in construction.

Construction of the Model

Commence construction with the base frame as shown in Fig. 2. The sides 1 are formed from $7\frac{1}{2}''$ Flat Girders and these are joined to $5\frac{1}{2}''$ Flat Girders 2 to form a box-like frame. The Angle Girders 3 and 4 are $7\frac{1}{2}''$ and $5\frac{1}{2}''$ respectively and are joined to the top edges of the Flat Girders 1 and 2 as shown. The top corners of the framework are braced with Corner Brackets 5 and the bottom corners with Angle Brackets.

A Hub Disc 6 is bolted to a $7\frac{1}{2}''$ Strip 8 which is secured across the Angle Girders and also bolted to the side Angle Girders 3.

A vertical $4\frac{1}{2}''$ Rod 9 is then passed through the centre hole of the Strip 8 and beneath is secured a Bevel Wheel. This Wheel engages another Bevel Wheel on the Axle which carries the central travelling wheels 10. This axle is connected by Sprockets and chain to the rear axle. The large $3\frac{1}{2}''$ Gear Wheel 11 is then secured to the Hub Disc by four $\frac{1}{2}''$ Reversed Angle Brackets, which are held by bolts 12. The remainder of the base frame and the Sprocket Wheel 18 should be added at a later stage and will be dealt with in due course.

If desired the new Meccano Ball Race may be used in place of the built-up roller race, and if it is decided to use the Ball Race unit several alterations will be necessary. The Pinion 35 (Fig. 3) together with its Rod will have to be removed and a Sprocket drive arranged. The slight alterations required will be apparent to all Meccano boys who prefer to use the Ball Race, and a detailed description should not be necessary.

The body consists of two $5\frac{1}{2}''\times3\frac{1}{2}''$ Flat Plates overlapped three holes to form each side. These are secured to $9\frac{1}{2}''$ Girders 13 (Fig. 4) along the upper and lower edges and these Girders are connected across by $5\frac{1}{2}''$ Girders 14. Beneath the body or superstructure of the model a Circular Girder 15 is secured by means of bolts 16, and held by the same bolts is a $5\frac{1}{2}''$ Angle Girder 17. Through this Angle Girder passes the $4\frac{1}{2}''$ Rod 9 carrying a

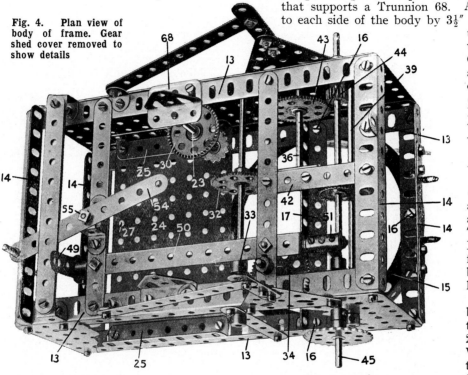

Fig. 4. Plan view of body of frame. Gear shed cover removed to show details

$2''$ Sprocket Wheel 18 (Fig. 2). A Collar 19 engages above the Angle Girders 17 (Figs. 3 and 4).

Next build up the Roller Race (Fig. 2), which is formed of four Double Brackets 20 bolted to a Circular Strip 21.

The $1\frac{1}{2}''$ Rods 22 carry $\frac{1}{2}''$ fast Pulleys and are journalled in the Brackets 20. The whole is then placed on the top edge of the Hub Disc and the body is passed over the Rod 9 in the centre hole of the Angle Girder 17. After the Collar 19 is secured in position, the Sprocket Wheel 18 is bolted to the Rod 9.

The top bearing for the $3\frac{1}{2}''$ Rod 23 (Fig. 4) is formed by a $1\frac{1}{2}''$ Flat Girder that supports a Trunnion 68. A $5\frac{1}{2}''\times3\frac{1}{2}''$ Flat Plate 24 is secured to each side of the body by $3\frac{1}{2}''$ Angle Girders 25 in the second hole up. This provides a bed to which the Electric Motor (Fig. 5) is secured. On the lower part of Rod 23 is secured a $\frac{3}{4}''$ Sprocket Wheel from which a chain drives the Sprocket Wheel 18 (Fig. 2) which in turn operates the Bevels beneath the base frame thus transmitting the drive to the travelling wheels.

Assembling the Mechanism

Now build up the Motor unit, (Fig. 5) but leave off the Rod 25 and Sprocket 26. (The Gear Wheels and Rod are clearly seen in Fig. 5.) The Motor is then secured to the Plate 24, the correct position being found when the fourth hole from the back of the Motor registers with hole 27 in the $5\frac{1}{2}''\times3\frac{1}{2}''$ plate (Fig. 4).

When the Electric Motor has been secured in position, owing to the Rod 28 being slidable the Pinion 29 may be engaged with the Contrate Wheel 30 or the Gear Wheel 31 with the Gear Wheel 32. The spindle of this latter Gear Wheel 32 carries a Worm 33 (Fig. 3), which engages a Gear Wheel 34. On the spindle of Gear Wheel 34 is a $\frac{1}{2}''$ Pinion, which engages and drives the $3\frac{1}{2}''$ Gear Wheel 11 (Fig. 2), thus rotating the shovel.

On the $3\frac{1}{2}''$ Rod 36 is wound the cord 37 by means of which the raising and lowering of the jib 38 is carried out, and on the $6''$ Rod 39 is wound the cord 40 which operates—i.e., raises and lowers—the shovel 41. The Rod 36 is journalled in a Trunnion bolted underneath the Strip 42 and carries a $1\frac{1}{2}''$ Gear Wheel 43 which is engaged by a Pinion 44 on an $8''$ Rod 45. This is driven by means of the $1\frac{1}{2}''$ Sprocket Wheel 46 from the $1''$ Sprocket Wheel 26 on the driving spindle 47 of the Electric Motor.

The Spindle 45 is slidable by the rotation of an $8''$ Rod 48 operated by the Crank 49, the Rod being journalled in the ends of a $5\frac{1}{2}''\times2\frac{1}{2}''$ Double

Fig. 5. Electric Motor Unit

Angle Strip 50, a Coupling 51 carrying a 1″ Rod which engages between two Collars on the Rod 45. In this way the Pinion 44 may be meshed with the Gear Wheel 43 in order to raise or lower the jib, or a 1″ Gear Wheel 52 on the Rod 39 may be engaged with a 1″ Gear Wheel 53 to raise or lower the shovel arm 58.

The Rod 25 (Fig. 5) is slidable by a 4½″ Strip 54 pivoted at 55 (Fig. 3), the end of which engages between two Cranks 56. These engage on each side of a 1½″ Gear Wheel 57 (Fig. 5), Washers being placed between the Cranks to take up the slack. When the gear trains have been assembled the only remaining portions to be constructed are the shovel proper and the movable arm on which it operates.

The Construction of the Shovel Arm

The shovel arm, which is shown in Fig. 1, carries the bucket or shovel proper and is a kind of sliding frame consisting of 9½″ Angle Girders 58 to which are bolted Racks 59. The inner surfaces of the 9½″ Angle Girders are fitted or lined as it were with 9½″ Strips. The latter are bolted at either end to the Girders but are spaced away by Washers, thereby allowing space between the Strips and the Girders 58 to accommodate the heads of the bolts securing the Rack Strips 59. The jib has an uninterrupted sliding surface throughout the length of the boom. The latter is held in position so that the Rack Strips engage the Pinions 60, by means of two 2½″ Angle Girders bolted to 2½″ Strips that pivot about the ends of the Rod carrying the Pinions.

A 50-teeth Gear Wheel 61 is driven by a ¾″ Pinion 62 on a 3½″ Rod 63 which is operated by the hand wheel 64.

The bottom of the shovel is released by a cord 65 connected to a sliding Rod 66, the end of which enters the aperture of a Flat Bracket 67.

The Shovel (Fig. 6)

If desired the Meccano Digger Bucket can be used on this model in place of the built-up shovel shown. The shovel illustrated is a Standard Meccano Mechanism and is bolted to the arm 58 (Fig. 1) which pivots from a point in the jib of the excavator.

The bottom Plate 2a of the bucket is hinged to the Rod 3a and is closed or opened as desired by means of a sliding Rod 66 operated by a cord 65.

During the cutting stroke, the bottom Plate 2a is held in a closed position by the end of the Rod 66 engaging the Bracket 67. The bucket or shovel is raised or lowered by a cord engaging a Pulley 8a pivotally carried on a Rod 9a. The radius of the cut is regulated by altering the length of the arm 58 which is controlled by the Rack and Pinion mechanism in the jib. The sides of the shovel are formed from 2½″ × 2½″ Flat Plates as is also the shovel bottom 2a.

The sliding Rod 66 is carried loosely in a Double Angle Strip as illustrated and carries on its upper end a Coupling. A glance at the various illustrations will make any further details quite clear.

Before setting the model in motion apply a little oil to all gears and shafts so that the mechanism will work smoothly.

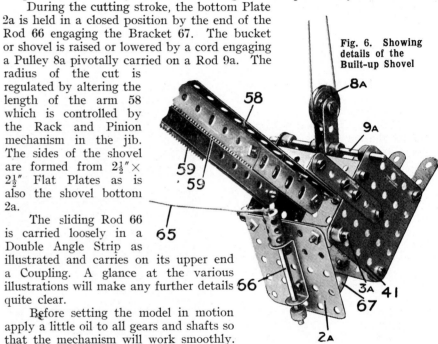

Fig. 6. Showing details of the Built-up Shovel

Parts Required

2 of No.	1a	7 of No.	9	1 of No.	15a	5 of No.	24	220 of No.	37	2 of No.	63	2 of No.	103b	1 of No.	143
1	1b	2	9b	7	16	1	25	24	38	2	70	2	103f	1	145
7	2	4	9d	4	16a	9	26	1	40	4	72	1	103h	1	147b
1	2a	4	9f	1	18a	1	27	1	45	2	76	2	103k		
4	3	7	10	5	18b	7	27a	1	48	2	77	4	110		
5	4	6	11	8	20	1	27b	3	48a	36″	94	4	111	**E6 Electric**	
5	5	11	12	1	21	1	28	1	48d	1	95	2	115	**Motor**	
7	6	4	12b	2	22	2	30	5	52a	1	95a	1	118		
4	8	2	13a	4	22a	2	31	1	53a	3	96	4	125		
6	8a	8	14	2	23	1	32	36	59	1	96a	3	126		
4	8b	2	15	4	23a	5	35	3	62	2	103	4	133		

Price 3d.
(Overseas 4d.)
(Canada 8c.)
Australia 6d.

Model No. S.31.

Steam Excavator
OR MECHANICAL DIGGER

A VERY important branch of modern engineering work might be described as "digging holes in the ground." In this category are such undertakings as canals, tunnels, reservoirs and the sinking of deep foundations of very large buildings. Years ago big excavation works involved the employment of vast numbers of men because little or no machinery was available and all the work had to be done by manual labour. This state of affairs continued to a considerable extent until comparatively recent times. To-day, however, although

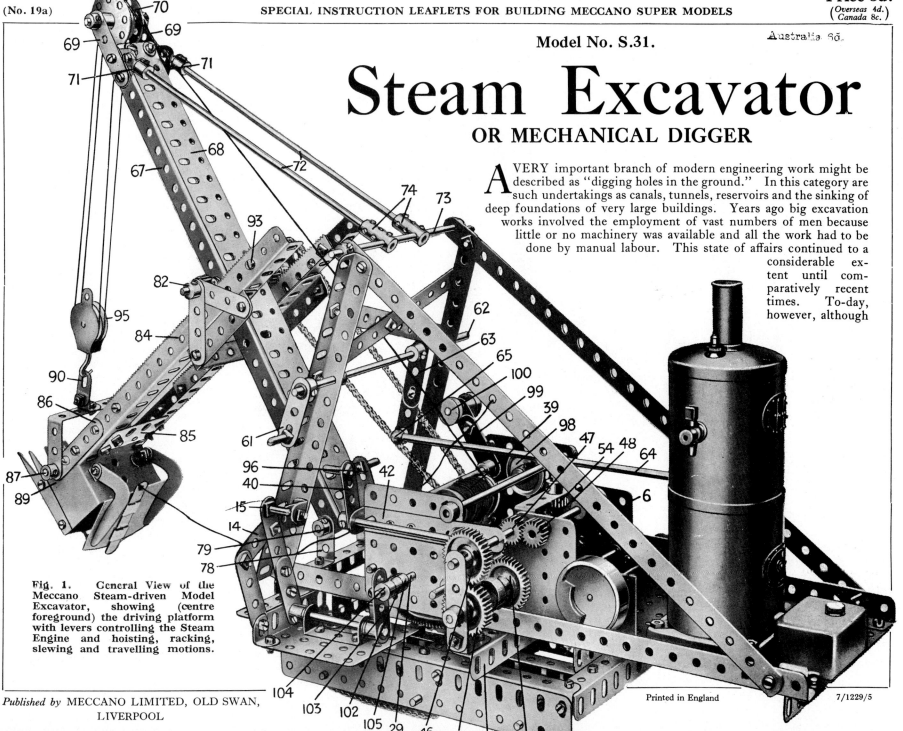

Fig. 1. General View of the Meccano Steam-driven Model Excavator, showing (centre foreground) the driving platform with levers controlling the Steam Engine and hoisting, racking, slewing and travelling motions.

Published by MECCANO LIMITED, OLD SWAN, LIVERPOOL

Printed in England

7/1229/5

large numbers of men have to be employed on any big undertaking, the bulk of the work is carried out by mechanical power. The spade wielded by hand is still necessary, but most of the digging is done by gigantic machines operated by steam or electric power, and each capable of doing the work of many hundreds of men.

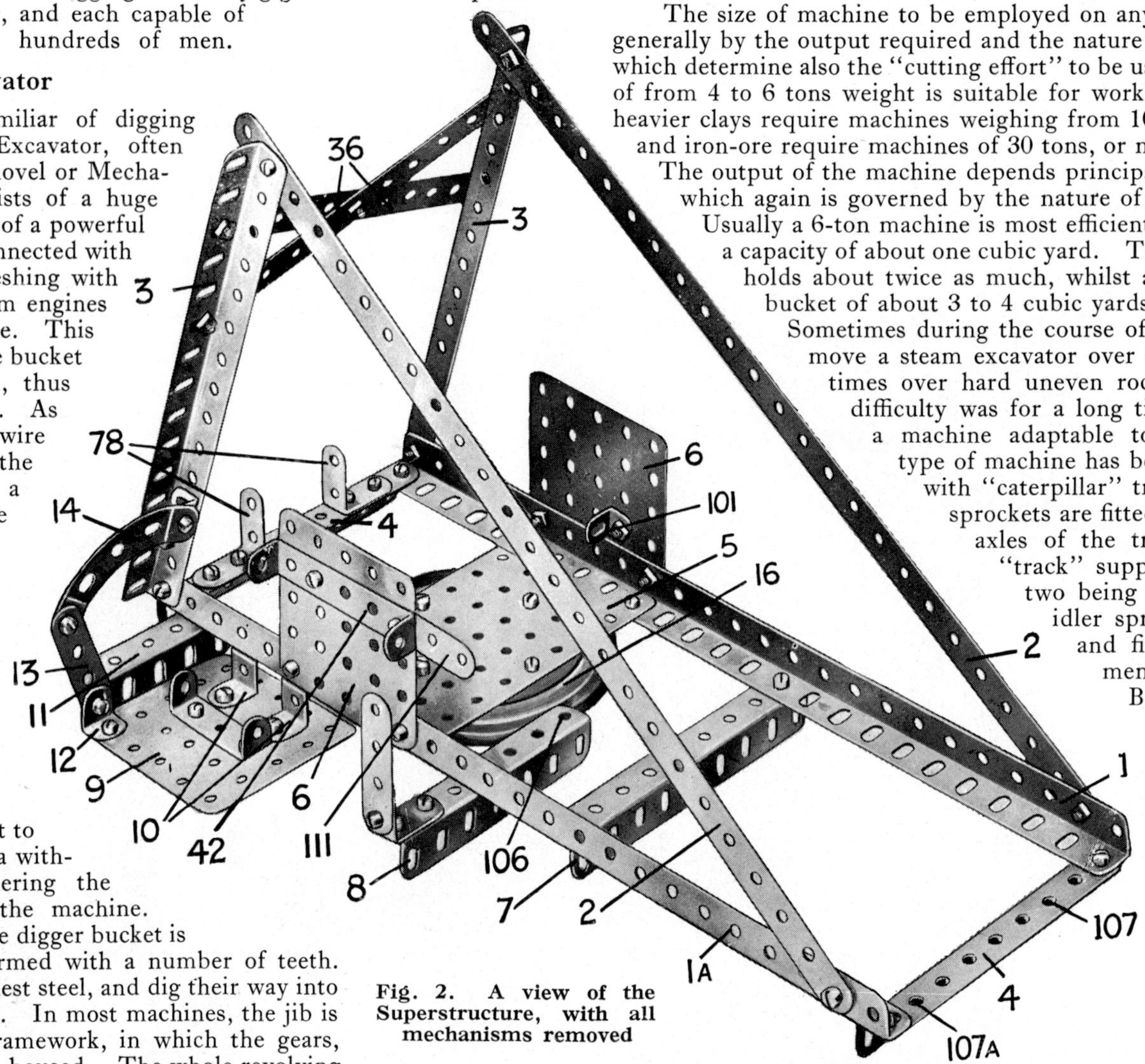

A Typical Steam Excavator

One of the most familiar of digging machines is the Steam Excavator, often referred to as the Steam Shovel or Mechanical Navvy. This consists of a huge shovel mounted on the end of a powerful steel arm that, in turn, is connected with a jib by two long racks meshing with gear wheels driven by steam engines mounted on the shovel frame. This makes it possible to rack the bucket arm in or out as desired, thus varying the working radius. As in the case of a crane, a wire rope passes over a pulley at the top of the jib, and on to a winding drum, with the result that so soon as the gear clutch is thrown in the drum winds in the rope and the bucket is pulled upward, describing an arc about the point at which the bucket arm is pivoted to the jib. These movements, together with the swivelling of the superstructure, enable the bucket to excavate a considerable area without the necessity of altering the position of the base of the machine.

The leading edge of the digger bucket is fitted with a cutting lip armed with a number of teeth. These are made of the hardest steel, and dig their way into the material to be removed. In most machines, the jib is attached to a swivelling framework, in which the gears, engines and boiler, etc., are housed. The whole revolving superstructure is mounted on an under carriage and this runs on rails, the travelling motion being taken from the main engines.

Improvements in Modern Designs

Steam navvies have been improved very considerably in recent years.

Fig. 2. A view of the Superstructure, with all mechanisms removed

The earliest types were able to swing through little more than half a circle, but the more modern machines are able to complete a full circle. These machines are now made in several sizes.

The size of machine to be employed on any particular work is governed generally by the output required and the nature of the material to be worked, which determine also the "cutting effort" to be used. For instance, a machine of from 4 to 6 tons weight is suitable for working earth or light clay. The heavier clays require machines weighing from 10 to 20 tons, whilst limestone and iron-ore require machines of 30 tons, or more.

The output of the machine depends principally on the size of the bucket, which again is governed by the nature of the material to be excavated. Usually a 6-ton machine is most efficient when fitted with a bucket of a capacity of about one cubic yard. The bucket of a 12-ton machine holds about twice as much, whilst a 20-ton machine will have a bucket of about 3 to 4 cubic yards capacity.

Sometimes during the course of excavation it is necessary to move a steam excavator over soft boggy land and at other times over hard uneven rocky ground and considerable difficulty was for a long time experienced in designing a machine adaptable to all occasions. Recently a type of machine has been designed that is equipped with "caterpillar" travelling gear. Four "track" sprockets are fitted and these are secured to the axles of the travelling wheels, two of the "track" supports being driven, the other two being idle. The axle carrying the idler sprockets is mounted in guides and fitted with screws for adjustment of the "track" tension. Between the sprockets on each side are the rollers for supporting the track, these being carried on a separate framing and so situated that any roller can be dismantled without having to jack up the machine. The sprockets are also easily detachable.

The "caterpillar" track itself consists of massive cast steel links to which are secured mild steel pads, these being heavy steel pressings which are practically unbreakable, and if bent through exceptionally severe usage can readily be straightened. Separate driving clutches are fitted to each track so that either of them may be operated independently of the other. When one track only is driven the machine can be turned in practically its own length or steered with ease in any direction.

Fig. 3. The Ball Bearing unit, with upper Race raised to show details

The "Berry" 8-ton Steam Excavator

Fig. 4 illustrates a "Berry" 8-ton Steam Crane Excavator, a machine that may be accepted as typical of steam shovels generally.   It will be seen from the illustration that the Meccano model is a close reproduction of this machine. It is of the type used by contractors for many kinds of excavating work, such as trenching for the foundations of large buildings, reservoirs, and narrow cuttings for railways.   It is used also at brickworks and quarries where a large output is required.

A very interesting feature of this machine is that after excavating is finished, the bucket and its gear can be removed from the jib and the machine used as a crane.   The following details will give some idea of its mechanical construction.   The length of the jib is 24 ft., and it is made from mild steel plates and angles, firmly tied and rivetted together.   The lifting, turning and travelling movements are controlled by the main engines while the depth of cut may be regulated by a pair of engines fixed on the jib and working through a rack and pinion.   Lifting is carried out by means of wire rope, and the hoisting barrel is grooved.   The machine is provided with two sets of travelling wheels having respective gauges of 4 ft. 8½ ins. and 7 ft. 8 ins.

In the majority of steam shovels designed especially for clayworking the bucket has a capacity of about one cubic yard and the engine is capable of

exerting a cutting effort of 6 tons upon the bucket teeth.   With a bucket of this type it is easily possible to excavate 250 to 300 cubic yards of clay in one working day !

It will thus be seen that a mechanical excavator has many advantages over manual labour, not the least of which is the fact that a machine will go on working in all kinds of weather, whereas labourers often are unable to work under bad weather conditions.

Considerations affecting Construction

One of the principal considerations affecting both the size and constructional details of excavating machines is the distance from the machine that it is required to discharge the excavated material.   For instance, many steam shovels discharge the excavated material at distances of up to 32 ft. from the machine centres, and by adding a longer jib it is possible to discharge the material at distances of up to 60 ft.   Such machines are used for quarrying mineral buried beneath a top covering of earth, and will excavate ordinary soil or clay at the rate of 25 to 50 cubic yards an hour.

The lengthening of the jib in this manner makes it necessary to decrease considerably the cutting effort on the teeth, as compared with that on the standard machine.   If this were not done the machine would be unstable. The bucket is therefore made smaller and handles only 1¼ cubic yards, or roughly about a quarter the quantity handled by the standard bucket.

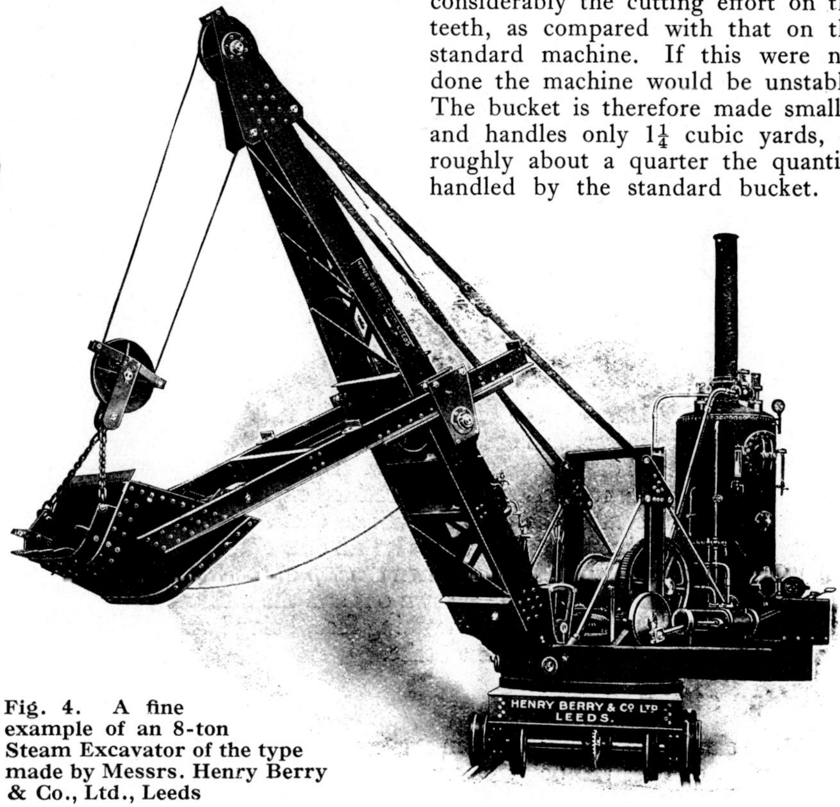

Fig. 4.   A fine example of an 8-ton Steam Excavator of the type made by Messrs. Henry Berry & Co., Ltd., Leeds

On the radius over which the machine effectively operates depends also the depth to which it is able to cut. Modified machines, such as are referred to above, will excavate soil, etc., to a depth of 15 to 20 ft. and deposit it at points up to 60 ft. distance. If it is desired to excavate to a greater depth than this, machines with even longer reaches must be constructed.

If the material to be excavated is heavier than soil or clay, very powerful machines must be used. Some large machines now in use are equipped with rock-loading buckets having capacities of 3½ cubic yards. Although naturally slower in operation than the lighter types, they are able to complete a cycle of operations in about a minute! They can eat their way through 300 cubic yards of material in an hour and discharge their loads at any given point over a radius of 100 ft.!

Controlling the Machinery

Having seen something of the construction of these giant shovels we may consider for a moment how a machine of the standard type is operated.

When commencing operations, the bucket hangs in a vertical position, with the teeth resting on the ground opposite the face of the material that is to be removed. The driver starts up the engines and throws in the hoisting clutch. This action drags the bucket forward and upward, to the face. At the same time it is thrust outwards by means of the racks along the bucket arm until it is cutting away the material to the required depth.

With one hand on the control-lever of the main engines, and the other on the control-lever of the racking engines, the driver is able to control the depth of cut so that an equal thickness is taken throughout the whole length of the stroke. He thus ensures that the bucket is completely filled when the top of the stroke is reached. At this stage, the hoisting clutch is thrown out and the racking motion draws in the bucket until it is clear of the working face, being held in the meantime on the free drum by means of the brake.

Working at High Speed

The slewing mechanism is then started up, and the bucket is swung over the wagon, or over the point where the material is to be dumped. When the correct position is reached, the driver pulls a cord by his side, and this

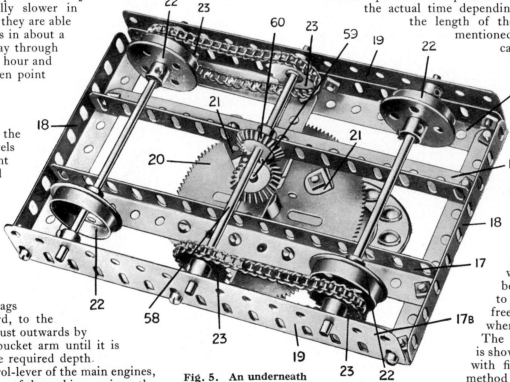

Fig. 5. An underneath view of the Chassis

action withdraws a bolt on the bucket door, allowing the contents of the bucket to be discharged.

The slewing motion is then reversed and the bucket is swung back into position to take the next cut from the working face. The bucket is allowed to return to the bottom of the stroke by releasing the winding drum, which is loose upon its shaft. When free of the clutch it is under the driver's control by means of a foot-brake.

All these operations take place almost as quickly as they can be described, the actual time depending on the size of the machine and the length of the jib. As an illustration may be mentioned a special test of a steam shovel capable of dealing with about 150 cubic yards of soil or clay per hour, or from 60 to 100 yards of iron-ore per hour. In the tests referred to, it regularly completed the cycle of operations in from 25 to 35 seconds!

Building the Meccano Model

This fascinating model performs all the motions of which the actual machine is capable. Provided that the following instructions are followed carefully no boy should experience difficulty with its construction. Care should be taken whilst building the model to see that all gears and rods work freely, so as to ensure successful working when it is completed.

The framework of the superstructure is shown in Fig. 2 and should be proceeded with first. The illustration indicates the method of construction very clearly. The side members 1 and 1a are 12½″ Angle Girders; 2 are two 12½″ Strips; 3, two 7½″ Angle Girders braced by two 5½″ crossed Strips; 4, two 4½″ Angle Girders; 5, a 4½″×2½″ Plate; 6, two 2½″×2½″ Plates; 7, a further 4½″ Angle Girder; 8, a 3½″ Angle Girder; 9 is a 2½″×2½″ Plate that is secured to the Angle Girder 1a by two Reversed Angle Brackets 10. To a 2½″ Angle Girder 11 is secured a 2″ Strip, to the end of which a 2½″ Curved Strip 14 is bolted. This latter forms the quadrant for the lever 15 (Fig. 1). The upper disc of a Ball Race 16 (Fig. 2) is secured to the Plate 5. The 3″ Strip 111 and 2½″×½″ Double Angle Strip 42 are both secured by the same bolts to the Plate 6.

After completing the superstructure framework, the base frame (Fig. 5) should be built. Four 7½″ Angle Girders 17 and 17a are secured to two

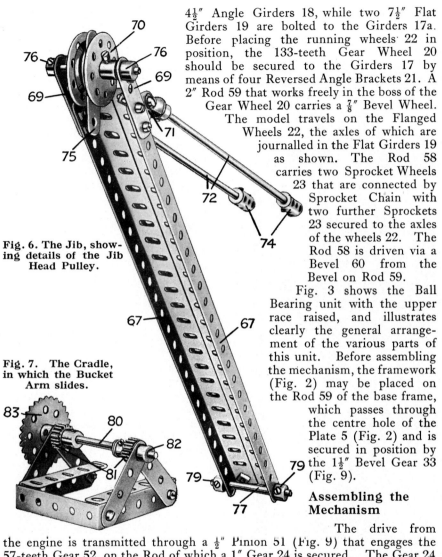

4½" Angle Girders 18, while two 7½" Flat Girders 19 are bolted to the Girders 17a. Before placing the running wheels 22 in position, the 133-teeth Gear Wheel 20 should be secured to the Girders 17 by means of four Reversed Angle Brackets 21. A 2" Rod 59 that works freely in the boss of the Gear Wheel 20 carries a ⅞" Bevel Wheel.

The model travels on the Flanged Wheels 22, the axles of which are journalled in the Flat Girders 19 as shown. The Rod 58 carries two Sprocket Wheels 23 that are connected by Sprocket Chain with two further Sprockets 23 secured to the axles of the wheels 22. The Rod 58 is driven via a Bevel 60 from the Bevel on Rod 59.

Fig. 3 shows the Ball Bearing unit with the upper race raised, and illustrates clearly the general arrangement of the various parts of this unit. Before assembling the mechanism, the framework (Fig. 2) may be placed on the Rod 59 of the base frame, which passes through the centre hole of the Plate 5 (Fig. 2) and is secured in position by the 1½" Bevel Gear 33 (Fig. 9).

Fig. 6. The Jib, showing details of the Jib Head Pulley.

Fig. 7. The Cradle, in which the Bucket Arm slides.

Assembling the Mechanism

The drive from the engine is transmitted through a ½" Pinion 51 (Fig. 9) that engages the 57-teeth Gear 52, on the Rod of which a 1" Gear 24 is secured. The Gear 24 engages a further 1" Gear 25 on the Rod 26, at one end of which is a ¾" diameter ¾" wide Pinion 27 that transmits the drive through the 50-teeth Gear 28 to the slidable gear change Rod on which the Pinion 31 and the Bevel 30 are secured.

From this Rod the drive may be transmitted, through one of three different gear trains to produce the following movements—traversing, racking of the digger arm, and the raising or lowering of the bucket. Any of these movements

may be brought into operation by means of the lever 15 (Fig. 1) that controls the sliding of the Rod.

The arrangement of the lever is shown fairly clearly in the illustration. The Collar 102, which is placed between Collars 104 and 105 secured to Rod 29, is connected pivotally by a Bolt inserted in its set-screw hole, to a Crank secured to the Rod of the lever 15. Hence, by moving the lever 15 the Rod 29 is caused to slide longitudinally in its bearings. The Collar 102 is of course free on the Rod 29, the bolt that is passed through the Crank 103 being screwed into the Collar sufficiently to allow locking it by a nut but without securing the Collar to the Rod. This type of gear change lever forms the subject of Standard Mechanism No. 78.

The traversing motion is effected by pushing the lever 15 hard over to the left (as seen in Fig. 9), thus bringing the Bevel 30 into engagement with the Bevel 33. This movement throws the Pinion 31 clear of the 50-teeth Gear 35. The Bevel 33 is mounted on a Rod 59 (Fig. 5), on the lower end of which is a 26-teeth Bevel Gear engaging a similar Bevel Gear 60 that imparts motion to the running wheels 22 through the Sprockets and Chains 23.

The digger arm is brought into operation by moving the lever 15 slightly over to the right, thus throwing the Pinion 31 into engagement with the 57-teeth Gear Wheel 34 and disengaging the Bevels 30 and 33. A ¾" Sprocket Wheel 36, secured on the Rod of Gear 34, transmits the drive by Sprocket Chain 38 to the Sprocket Wheel 83 on the side of the jib cradle (Fig. 7) and causes the digger arm to be drawn in or out according to the direction of rotation of the engine.

By moving the lever 15 slightly over to the left and disengaging Pinion 31 and Gear 34, the third movement, raising or lowering the bucket, is brought into operation. The driving Pinion 31 (Fig. 9) now engages the Gear 35 on the Rod 94 of the winding drum 39 and the latter being rotated, the bucket is either raised or lowered by means of the Cord, according to the direction in which the drum revolves.

The fourth operation, slewing of the jib, is effected from the lever 40 that controls a Dog Clutch 44a and 44b. The Strip

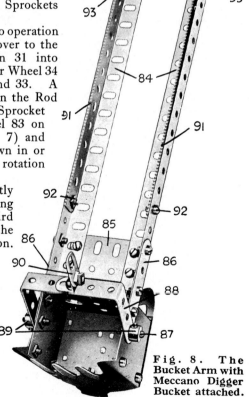

Fig. 8. The Bucket Arm with Meccano Digger Bucket attached.

forming the lever is secured to a 3″ Rod 41 that carries a Crank 43 in the arm of which a Threaded Pin is held. The Rod is journalled in a $2\frac{1}{2}″ \times \frac{1}{2}″$ Double Angle Strip 42.

The Threaded Pin of the Crank 43 engages the groove of a slidable Socket Coupling 44 (part No. 171) to one end of which is secured the male dog clutch member 44a. The female dog clutch section 44b is secured on the Rod of the Gear 52. At the other end of the Socket Coupling is a 1″ Gear Wheel 45, so that when the clutch is engaged the motion is taken from the Gear 45 to another 1″ Gear 46, on the Rod of which is a $\frac{1}{2}″$ Pinion 47. The Pinion 47 engages with a similar $\frac{1}{2}″$ Pinion 48 on the Rod 49, the latter being journalled in the side plates of the engine frame and held in position by a Collar 50. A Worm Wheel 53 on the Rod of Pinion 48 engages a $\frac{1}{2}″$ Pinion 54 on a Rod 55 that is journalled through the $2\frac{1}{2}″ \times \frac{1}{2}″$ Double Angle Strip 56 and the base of the engine frame.

On the lower end of rod 55 is a $\frac{1}{2}″$ Pinion 57 (see Fig. 3) which engages the $3\frac{1}{2}″$ Gear Wheel 20 of the ball bearing unit. From this it will be seen that, whilst the sliding Rod 26 controls the hoisting, racking, and travelling movements, the swivelling mechanism is operated only when the lever 40 throws the clutch into engagement. Hence the swivelling may be carried out simultaneously with any of the other movements.

Building the Jib

The construction of the jib is shown clearly in Fig. 6. It comprises essentially two $12\frac{1}{2}″$ Girders 67 connected together by a $12\frac{1}{2}″$ Flat Girder 68 (see also Fig. 1). To each side of the outer end, 2″ Strips 69 and 1″ Triangular Plates 71 are bolted. The

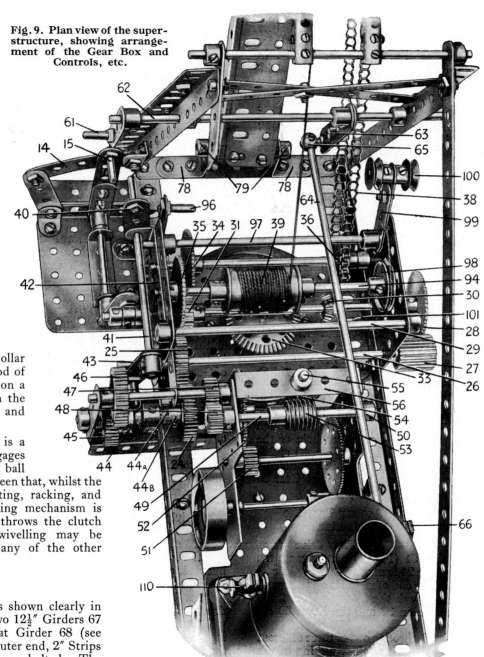

Fig. 9. Plan view of the super-structure, showing arrangement of the Gear Box and Controls, etc.

Strips form the bearings for the axle of the jib head Pulley 70, while the Triangular Plates serve for connections to the 8″ Rods 72, the actual connection to the jib being made by Small Fork Pieces (part No. 116a). The other ends of the Rods 72 carry Couplings 74 by means of which they are connected to the Rod 73 (Fig. 1) of the superstructure. It is to be noted that the Rods 72 are mounted loosely on the Rod 73. The jib head pulley 70 is formed from two Bush Wheels and two 1″ loose Pulleys, between which a 2″ Strip 75 (Fig. 6) is placed. The whole is held in position on a 2″ Rod that is maintained in the jib head by the Collars 76. The foot of the jib is connected pivotally to the body of the machine by the Rod 77 that is journalled through two $1″ \times 1″$ Angle Brackets 78 (Fig. 2) and held by the Collars 79 (Figs. 1 and 6).

The Shovel Arm (Fig. 8)

The shovel arm carries the bucket or shovel proper and comprises two $9\frac{1}{2}″$ Angle Girders 84, joined together by a 2″ Flat Girder 85 and attached to the Digger Bucket by $2\frac{1}{2}″$ Strips 86, one of which is placed on either side. The arms, Bucket, and a $2\frac{1}{2}″ \times 1\frac{1}{2}″$ Double Angle Strip 88 are assembled together on Threaded Pins 87 and held by Collars 89. The Flat Bracket 90 is attached to the Double Angle Strip 88 by an Angle Bracket, and both are lock-nutted together to form the connection to the hook of the hoisting cord.

Two $6\frac{1}{2}″$ Rack Strips 91 are secured to the inside faces of the Girders 84 by bolts 92. At a later stage the arm will be threaded through the cradle (Fig. 7), after which two further bolts are secured in the holes 93 to hold the Rack Strips firmly in position.

The shovel arm slides in the cradle shown in Fig. 7, the construction of which does not need description. The cradle is connected to the jib by the Rod 80 that is journalled through the centre holes of the jib and held in position by the Collar 82 and the 1½″ Sprocket Wheel 83. The two ½″ Pinions 81 carried by the Rod 80 engage the teeth of the Rack Strips. A length of Sprocket Chain 38 (Fig. 9) may now be passed round the Sprocket Wheel 83 of the cradle and the Sprocket Wheel 36, as indicated in Fig. 1.

One end of the hoisting cord (Figs. 1 and 9) is fixed to the winding drum 39 and passes over one of the Pulleys at the jib head, then through the block 95, and is tied finally to the Strip 75 (Fig. 6)

Brake Mechanism and Engine Control

The brake control lever 96 (Fig. 1) comprises a Crank carrying a Threaded Pin, the Crank being secured to the 5″ Rod 97 (Fig. 9) on which is a second Crank 99 to the arm of which a 2″ Strip is bolted to carry a weight consisting of two ½″ fast Pulleys 100 that are secured on a Rod passed through the end hole of the Strip.

A 1″ Pulley 98 is secured to the Rod 94 of the winding drum. The brake band comprises a piece of Cord that is connected to the Angle Bracket 101 (Fig. 2) and then carried over the Pulley 98 and tied to the Crank 99 (Fig. 9). The pressure of the Cord round the Pulley 98 should be slackened by moving the lever 96 when hoisting operations are commenced.

The working of the Meccano Steam Engine is controlled by the lever 61 (Fig. 1) that is formed from a Crank and Threaded Pin secured to a Rod 62.

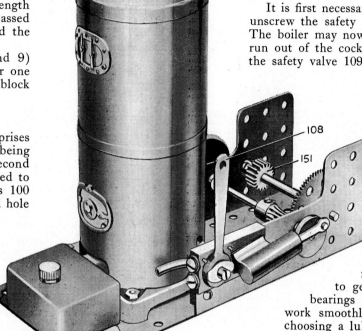

Fig. 10. The new Meccano Steam Engine Unit

This Rod carries also a second Crank 63, the arm of which is extended by a 2″ Strip overlapped as shown. A Handrail Support 65 that is pivotally held in the end hole of the 2″ Strip connects with an 8″ Rod 64, the other end of which is connected by a further Handrail Support 66 (Fig. 9) to the steam throttle lever 108 of the Steam Engine (Fig. 10).

Directions for Working the Steam Engine

It is first necessary to fill the boiler with water. To do this unscrew the safety valve 109 and open the cock 110 (Fig 9). The boiler may now be filled with water until it commences to run out of the cock. Now turn off the cock 110 and replace the safety valve 109. The lamp is to be filled with methylated spirit and placed in the guides provided in the engine bedplate. After lighting the wick allow a few minutes to elapse in order to raise ample steam to commence working. It might be mentioned here that the spirit container is placed outside the boiler in order to avoid any danger from the spirit becoming heated and boiling over. When the spirit in the lamp is exhausted the boiler should be re-supplied with water as before and the lamp refilled.

Before setting the engine to work make it a rule always to apply a little oil to gears and shafts, piston, guides, and all the bearings of the model, so that the mechanism will work smoothly. Particular care should be exercised in choosing a lubricant. If the wrong oil is used, it will decompose under the influence of heat and steam and will resolve itself into vegetable substances that will clog the steam parts and prevent steam reaching the cylinder.

Parts required to build the Meccano Steam Excavator :—

2 of No.	1	1 of No.	9b	1 of No.	16a	1 of No.	25	4 of No.	31	2 of No.	48a	1 of No.	95a	2 of No.	116a
2 ,,	2	3 ,,	9d	3 ,,	16b	1 ,,	25a	1 ,,	32	1 ,,	53a	4 ,,	96	6 ,,	125
1 ,,	2a	1 ,,	10	3 ,,	17	6 ,,	26	125 ,,	37	24 ,,	59	1 ,,	96a	2 ,,	136
1 ,,	4	3 ,,	12	1 ,,	18b	3 ,,	27	3 ,,	37a	8 ,,	62	1 ,,	103b	1 ,,	144
4 ,,	5	3 ,,	12a	4 ,,	20	1 ,,	27a	21 ,,	38	2 ,,	63	1 ,,	103g	1 ,,	152
9 ,,	6	3 ,,	13a	2 ,,	20b	1 ,,	27b	1 ,,	40	3 ,,	72	2 ,,	103k	1 ,,	163
4 ,,	8	3 ,,	14	1 ,,	22	2 ,,	30	1 ,,	46	2 ,,	77	2 ,,	110a	1 ,,	168a
2 ,,	8a	7 ,,	15	2 ,,	22a	1 ,,	30a	1 ,,	47	1 ,,	90	2 ,,	111a	1 ,,	168c
6 ,,	8b	1 ,,	15a	2 ,,	23a	1 ,,	30c	1 ,,	48	1 ,,	94	7 ,,	115	1 ,,	169
5 ,,	9a	3 ,,	16	2 ,,	24									1 ,,	171

MECCANO SUPER MODELS

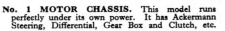

Our expert designers have produced for us 34 super models that reach the highest pinnacle ever attained in Meccano construction. Each model in this series is a masterpiece and there is not a boy who will not be eager to build them all.

These models are so important that we have engaged expert engineers to describe them and a special leaflet with beautiful half-tone illustrations has been written for each of them. A selection of the leaflets is illustrated on this page.

A brief description of each model in the series is given below and the number and price of the special Instruction Leaflet are indicated. Copies of the leaflets may be obtained from any Meccano dealer or direct from us, post free, at the prices shown at foot.

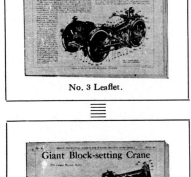

No. 6 Leaflet.

No. 3 Leaflet.

No. 4 Leaflet.

No. 8 Leaflet.

No. 19 Leaflet.

No. 1 Leaflet

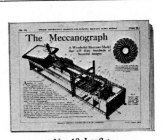

No. 13 Leaflet.

No. 16 Leaflet.

No. 1 MOTOR CHASSIS. This model runs perfectly under its own power. It has Ackermann Steering, Differential, Gear Box and Clutch, etc.

No. 2 SHIP COALER. All the movements of a real ship-coaler are reproduced in this model.

No. 3 MOTOR-CYCLE AND SIDECAR. The sidecar is of stream-line design and is mounted on springs. The motor-cycle is complete with lamps, horn, exhaust pipes, etc.

No. 4 GIANT BLOCK-SETTING CRANE. This realistic model is fitted with an accurate reproduction of Fidler's block-setting gear.

No. 5 TRAVELLING BUCKET DREDGER. In this model trucks and wagons can run underneath the chute through which falls the material raised by the dredger buckets.

No. 6 STIFF-LEG DERRICK. This model has many interesting movements, including hoisting, luffing and swivelling, which are controlled by suitable levers.

No. 7 PLATFORM SCALES. This model will weigh articles up to 4½ lbs. with remarkable accuracy.

No. 8 ROUNDABOUT. This model is most attractive when in motion. As the roundabout rotates the cars spin round and the horses rise and fall.

No. 9 BAGATELLE TABLE. This is an interesting model that will give hours of fun to the players.

No. 10 LOG SAW. In this model the saw is driven rapidly to and fro while the work table travels beneath it.

No. 11 SINGLE-CYLINDER HORIZONTAL STEAM ENGINE. Fitted with balanced crank-shaft, crosshead, and centrifugal governor.

No. 12 STONE SAWING MACHINE. The model is equipped with adjustable work table and overhead trolley with self-sustaining chain hoist.

No. 13 MECCANOGRAPH. This wonderful model will draw hundreds of beautiful designs.

No. 14 GRANDFATHER CLOCK. A practical example of Meccano model-building. The model keeps accurate time.

No. 15 BALTIC TANK LOCOMOTIVE. The driving wheels are operated by an Electric Motor. An accurate reproduction of Walschaerts' Valve Gear is fitted.

No. 16 LOOM. This is perhaps the greatest Meccano success. The model weaves beautiful material.

No. 17 PLANING MACHINE. Fitted with quick-return motion.

No. 18 REVOLVING CRANE. This model is fitted with screw-operated luffing gear.

No. 19 STEAM SHOVEL. This model embodies travelling and rotating mechanisms and jib hoisting and lowering gear.

No. 21 TRANSPORTER BRIDGE. The carriage automatically travels to and fro as long as the motor is driven, pausing for a few seconds at each end of its travel.

No. 22 TRACTION ENGINE. A remarkably realistic model that will pull a boy of average weight. Fitted with two speeds.

No. 23 VERTICAL LOG SAW. While the saws are in motion, the logs are fed slowly to them.

No. 24 TRAVELLING GANTRY CRANE. The movements of this model comprise the traversing of the entire gantry, hoisting and lowering, and the traversing of the crane trolley.

No. 25 HYDRAULIC CRANE. The hydraulic ram is represented realistically by a powerful screw mechanism.

No. 26 TWIN-ELLIPTIC HARMONOGRAPH. Many beautiful designs may be produced with this model.

No. 27 DRAGLINE. This imposing model of a giant excavator is fitted with travelling, luffing, slewing and dragging movements.

No. 28 PONTOON CRANE. The movements of this model include the operation of the two hoisting blocks, slewing of the entire crane, and luffing.

No. 29 HAMMERHEAD CRANE. This is a very realistic and powerful model, comprising traversing, hoisting and slewing motions.

No. 30 BREAKDOWN CRANE. This model is equipped with travelling, slewing, luffing, and hoisting motions, and also is fitted with laminated springs, brakes, out-riggers, etc.

No. 31 WAREHOUSE WITH ELEVATORS. The two cages are driven automatically and work alternately, pausing at top and bottom positions.

No. 32 TWO-CYLINDER STEAM ENGINE AND BOILER. This is a realistic working model of a complete steam plant, equipped with valve gear, governor, balanced cranks, etc.

No. 33 SINGLE AND DOUBLE FLYBOATS. These two models represent popular pleasure-fair attractions.

No. 34 THREE-ENGINE BIPLANE. This is a realistic model of an "Argosy" machine, and is fitted with ailerons elevators and rudders.

INSTRUCTION LEAFLET PRICES.

Leaflet Nos. 3 5 6 7 8 9 10 11 12 17 18 19 21 22 23 24 25 26 28 29—United Kingdom 2d., Overseas 3d., Canada 5 cents.

Leaflet Nos. 1 2 13 14 15 16 27 30 31 32 33 34—United Kingdom 3d., Overseas 4d., Canada 8 cents.

Leaflet No. 4—United Kingdom 6d., Overseas 8d. Canada 15 cents.

MECCANO LIMITED - Old Swan - LIVERPOOL

Model No. 7.15

Electric Mobile Crane

Special Features Include

Four distinct movements: luffing, hoisting, slewing, and travelling, all of which are controlled from the "operator's seat." Slewing is effected by rotation of the pivoted "castor" at rear of chassis. A safety limit switch is provided, preventing overwinding of jib. An automatic brake controls the hoist shaft, and brakes are fitted to luffing shaft and road axle.

Fig. 1. General view of the model. An interesting comparison is provided by the illustration (right) of an actual "R. and R." Petrol-electric Mobile Crane at work.

IN recent years numerous devices have been invented in an endeavour to solve the problem of high speed handling and transportation of materials and merchandise. One of the most interesting of these is undoubtedly the Petrol-electric Mobile Crane, which is manufactured to patented designs by the well-known firm of Ransomes and Rapier Ltd., of Ipswich, and forms the subject of the Meccano model described in this leaflet.

The crane comprises an entirely self-contained power unit and combines the stability and efficiency of a stationary crane with extreme mobility, and as its travel is not confined to a set of rails, or hindered by trailing cables from an external power supply, its range of utility is well nigh unbounded.

The power unit consists of a petrol engine which drives a generator that, in turn, supplies current to the luffing and hoist motors and to the two traction motors incorporated in the "castor" that is pivoted at the rear of the chassis—hence the term "petrol-electric." The crane is slewed by rotation of the pivoted castor, which is connected to an orthodox steering wheel placed in front of the operator's seat, while the luffing, hoisting, and travelling operations can each be brought into play by the movement of levers within easy reach of the operator. The task of controlling one of these cranes is consequently very similar to driving a motor car!

7/1229/5   *Published by* MECCANO LIMITED, OLD SWAN, LIVERPOOL   Printed in England

The Meccano model reproduces all the functions of the actual crane, with the aid of a single Meccano 6-volt Motor and an ingenious gear box. The model also includes a limit switch to prevent overwinding of the jib, an automatic brake on the hoist shaft, and foot brakes on the luffing and road shafts.

Construction of the Model : The Jib

As will be seen from Fig. 1, the Meccano model consists of two main units, i.e., the chassis incorporating the gear box, Motor and steering mechanism, and the crane jib.

For convenience, the constructor should assemble the jib first, and lay this on one side while the chassis is completed, after which the jib may be secured in position and final additions made to the model.

The main frame of the jib consists of two 18½″ Angle Girders held apart at the rear end by a 4½″ Girder and at the front by a 2½″ Angle Girder ; a 3½″ Strip is also bolted between the 18½″ Girders as shown in Fig. 1. The jib is braced by a framework secured to its under surface.

A 2½″ Flat Girder is secured to each of the 18½″ members and a pair of 5½″ Girders are attached to the Flat Girders and also to the end holes of the 18½″ Girders. A pair of 13½″ compound girders, each built up from one 5½″ and one 9½″ Girder, are also bolted to the Flat Girders, while their upper ends are secured to the front of the jib frame.

In order to counteract any tendency to bend or "buckle" under load, the compound 13½″ Girders are braced by 2½″, 3½″ and 5½″ Strips secured diagonally between them. Two diagonal 5½″ Strips are also bolted to the pair of 5½″ Girders at the rear of the frame. Angle Brackets are bolted to each of the 13½″ compound girders near the top of the jib to provide journals for a 2½″ Axle Rod carrying two 1″ loose Pulleys, these being kept in position on the Rod by means of Collars. A 5″ Axle Rod 61 (Fig. 3) is journalled in the frame of the jib at the rear end, and carries four 1″ loose Pulleys, 1, 2, 3, 4, and two Flat Brackets 5. Collars are placed between each of the Pulleys and also on either end of the Rod itself in order to prevent lateral movement. The jib is now complete and may be laid on one side while the construction of the chassis is proceeded with.

The Chassis : Fitting the Motor and Gearing

The chassis frame can be seen in Figs. 2 and 4. Its sides comprise U-section girders, each built up from two 9½″ Girders, and a 4½″ Angle Girder is bolted to these at the front and rear. A further 4½″ Girder is bolted between the two side members, six holes from the front end of the chassis, and a 3″ Girder is secured to the centre of this and also to the 4½″ Girder forming the front end of the frame. The rear of the frame is covered by a footplate consisting of a 4½″ × 2½″ Flat Plate while a 2½″ × 2½″ Plate is attached to the front right-hand side of the frame. Flat Plates are also attached in an upright position to the front and side girders, but these should not be bolted in place until a later step in the construction of the model.

Two 2½″ Angle Girders are secured to the 2½″ × 4½″ Flat Plate and to the rear 4½″ Flat Girder, and 2½″ × 2½″ Flat Plates are bolted to them. These Plates form journals for the shafts of the gear box and also provide support for one end of the Electric Motor. The Motor gearing should now be built up, and the Motor itself may afterwards be secured in position on the chassis, and the gear box and other fittings added.

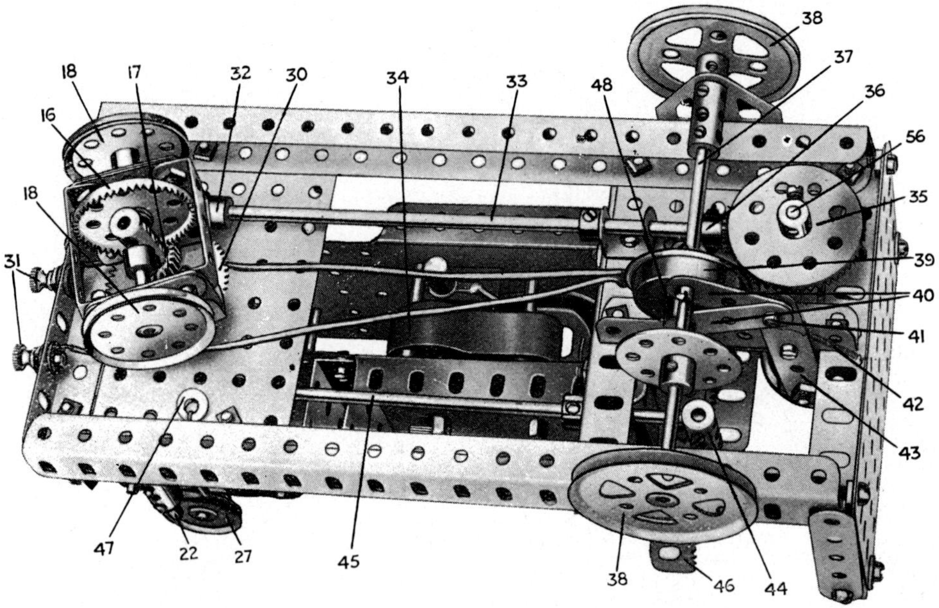

Fig. 2. Underneath view of chassis, showing "castor," steering transmission, and internal expanding brake on front road axle.

A Worm 26 (Fig. 4) mounted on the armature shaft of the Motor meshes with a ½″ Pinion 25 (Fig. 3) which is secured to one end of a 2″ Axle Rod journalled in a Channel Bearing bolted to the Motor side plate. In fixing the Bearing to the side plate of the Motor, a Washer should be placed on each of the securing bolts to space the Bearing the correct distance from the Motor.

A Bevel 24 is secured to the other end of the 2″ Axle Rod and meshes with a further Bevel that is mounted on a shaft journalled in the Motor side plates. This latter shaft also carries the ½″ diameter ½″ wide Pinion 51 (see Fig. 4).

The Motor is secured to the side plates of the gear box by means of a 3″ Axle Rod passed through the top holes of the 2½″ × 2½″ Flat Plates and through the perforations in the Motor side plates, Collars being employed to keep this Rod in place. Packing, in the form of three Washers, should also be slipped on to the Rod against the right-hand side plate of the Motor in order that perfect rigidity may be obtained. The front of the Motor rests on the lateral 4½″ Angle Girder, and is secured rigidly to this by means of ½″ × ½″ Angle Brackets.

The operator's seat (see Figs. 1 and 4) consists of a 3″ Flat Girder attached directly in front of the Motor switch to the lateral 4½″ Girder by means of 1″ × ½″ Reversed Angle Brackets. A 3½″ Rack Strip 46 (Fig. 4) is bolted to the seat and projects from the left-hand side, where it acts as a "catch plate" for the gear shift lever 57.

Assembly of the Gear Box

Before placing the gears and shafts in the gear box the support for the gear control shaft 45 (Fig. 2) and selector arm must be fitted. This consists of an Angle Bracket that is secured to a 2½″ × ½″ Double Angle Strip bolted between the side plates of the gear box in the position shown in Fig. 3, the round hole of the Angle Bracket providing one journal for the Rod 45. The latter is supported at the front end of the model in the lateral 4½″ Girder.

The Rod 45 carries a Crank, which forms the "selector arm" and is fitted with a bolt secured in its slotted hole, the web of the Crank being butted against the face of the Angle Bracket in which the Rod 45 is journalled. A Coupling 44 (Fig. 2) is secured to the front end of the Rod and carries a 2″ Axle Rod 57 fitted with a Collar forming the gear control lever, the Rod 57 being pressed tightly against the teeth of the Rack 46, thus preventing unwanted movement of the gears in the gear box.

The sliding primary shaft of the gear box consists of a 3½″ Axle Rod carrying a 57-teeth Gear Wheel which takes the drive from the Pinion 51 (Fig. 4) a ¾″ Pinion 49, and two Collars placed one on either side of the bolt secured in the Crank forming the selector arm. A Collar 20 (see Fig. 3) is also secured to the extreme end of this shaft.

A secondary shaft, which does duty as the hoist drum, is journalled in the 2½″ × 2½″ Plates two holes directly above the sliding primary shaft, and carries the 50-teeth Gear 7, a 1″ fast Pulley 27 and two Collars, one of which is fitted with a standard bolt in place of its set-screw to provide an "anchorage" to which one end of the hoist cord may be tied.

The luffing shaft 15 carries a 50-teeth Gear 14 (Figs. 3 and 4) and a 1″ fast Pulley 9, the two Collars securing this Rod in place each being equipped with a standard bolt to which the ends of the luffing cord are secured. A further 3½″ Rod, mounted two holes above the shaft 15, carries two 1″ fast Pulleys 8 and 28 and a Flat Bracket 6 mounted between two Collars in a central position on the Rod.

The operation of the gears in the gear box is as follows. The Gear 10 remains constantly in mesh with the Pinion 51. For travelling, the gear lever 57 is pulled hard over to the right against the end of the operator's seat. This causes the $\frac{3}{4}''$ Pinion 49 to engage with the $\frac{3}{4}''$ Contrate 29, and the drive from the Motor is then transmitted to one of the road wheels of the castor, in the manner to be described later.

To operate the jib, the lever 57 is pushed slightly to the left, thus disengaging the $\frac{3}{4}''$ Pinion 49 from the $\frac{3}{4}''$Contrate 29, and bringing it into mesh with the 50-teeth Gear 14 on the luffing shaft.

The last of the three movements—that of hoisting the load—is brought into action by moving the lever 57 still further to the left. Pinion 49 is then disengaged from the Gear Wheel 14 and engaged with the 50-teeth Gear 7 mounted on the hoisting shaft. The action of moving the sliding primary shaft into this position also causes the Collar 20 which is mounted upon it to press against the Rod 22, and thus releases the automatic band brake on the hoisting shaft. The construction of the brake mechanism is detailed later.

The Castor and Steering Gear

The underneath view of the Chassis, Fig. 2, shows the construction of the castor and the method of coupling the steering gear to it. The frame of the castor is composed of two $1\frac{1}{2}''$ Angle Girders to which are bolted $1\frac{1}{2}''$ Flat Girders. Two $1\frac{1}{2}'' \times \frac{1}{2}''$ Double Angle Strips are bolted between these, and the flanges of the Angle Girders are secured to the face of the 57-teeth Gear Wheel 30 by means of $\frac{3}{8}''$ Bolts, Collars being placed on the shanks of the bolts to space the Girders away from the Gear Wheel. The road axle consists of a $2\frac{1}{2}''$ Rod which carries two $1\frac{1}{2}''$ Pulley Wheels 18, the $1\frac{1}{2}''$ Contrate 16, a Coupling, and three Collars. Of the two road wheels one is fixed to the shaft, while the set-screw of the other is removed and the wheel is held in place on the end of the shaft by a Collar.

The complete castor pivots about a $2''$ Axle Rod that is passed through the $2\frac{1}{2}'' \times 4\frac{1}{2}''$ Flat Plate forming the floor of the gear box (Figs. 2 and 3) and is journalled in the centre hole of the $2\frac{1}{2}'' \times \frac{1}{2}''$ Double Angle Strip secured between the sides of the latter (Fig. 3) and in the end of the Coupling on the road axle. The $\frac{3}{4}''$ Contrate Wheel 29 previously referred to, is secured to the upper end of this Rod and a $\frac{1}{2}''$ Pinion is slipped on to its lower portion between the Gear 30 and the Coupling.

The castor is rotated by means of a Worm 32 (Fig. 2), secured on an $8''$ Rod 33. This Rod is journalled at its rear end in the $4\frac{1}{2}''$ Angle Girder forming the end of the chassis frame (a $1\frac{1}{2}''$ Strip being bolted to the Girder to provide a round hole as a bearing for the Rod) while a Double Bracket provides the front journal.

A $\frac{1}{2}''$ Bevel 36 is fastened on the front end of the Rod 33 and gears with a $1\frac{1}{2}''$ Bevel 35 mounted on the Rod 56, which represents the steering column. This Rod is journalled in the $2\frac{1}{2}'' \times 2\frac{1}{2}''$ Flat Plate secured to the front of the frame and also in a Double Bent Strip bolted to the Flat Plate. A $1\frac{1}{2}''$ Pulley Wheel 55 fastened to the top of the Rod 56 represents the steering wheel.

The Brakes and Control Gear

The brakes fitted to the model are realistic and effective. There is an automatic band

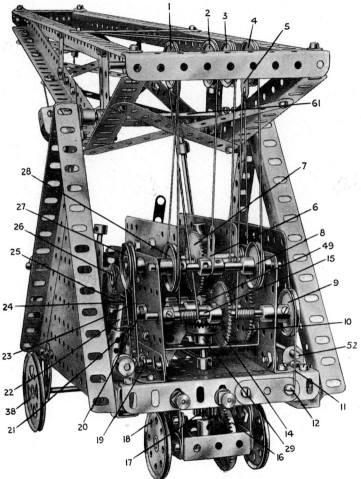

Fig. 3. Rear view of complete crane. This illustration will be helpful when assembling the Gear Box and luffing mechanism.

brake acting on the hoisting drum, a foot brake fitted to the luffing mechanism, and a further foot brake acting on a drum secured to the front road shaft, the last mentioned brake being of the internal-expanding pattern.

The automatic brake fitted to the hoisting shaft (see Fig. 3) consists of a $1''$ Pulley 27 acting as the brake drum around which a length of cord 23 is passed. One end of this cord is pushed through a hole in the chassis base plate and tied to a Washer 47 (Fig. 2) underneath the frame. The other end of the cord is fastened round the shank of a $\frac{3}{8}''$ Bolt 19 secured in the tapped hole of a Collar mounted on a $2''$ Rod. This Rod is journalled in a $1\frac{1}{2}'' \times \frac{1}{2}''$ Double Angle Bracket secured to the frame of the crane, and also carries a Coupling in which is secured a $1''$ Axle Rod 22.

A piece of Spring Cord 21 is twisted round the Rod 22, and its other end is attached to the gear box side plate by means of a bolt and nut. The Spring 21 and Cord 23 are adjusted so that the cord is normally taut around the groove of the Pulley 27 and the brake is therefore "on." On moving the sliding primary shaft in the gear box until the $\frac{3}{4}''$ Pinion 49 engages with the 50-teeth Gear on the hoist shaft, the Collar 20 strikes the Rod 22, thus causing the bolt 19 to move upward, thereby releasing the tension of the cord around the Pulley 27.

This brake ensures that the hoist shaft is "locked" at all times except when the lowering or raising of the load is being undertaken by means of the Motor, and in this way the possibility of an accident is avoided.

The foot brake acting on the luffing shaft 15 can be seen in Fig. 4, and comprises a $1''$ Pulley 9, which serves as the brake drum. Around this is passed a length of cord 11, one end of which is fastened underneath the head of the bolt 12, while the other end is tied to a short length of Spring Cord 50. The Spring Cord is secured to a bolt screwed into the tapped hole of a Collar mounted upon a $6\frac{1}{2}''$ Axle Rod 52. The forward end of this Rod 52 carries a Compression Spring 53 held in place by means of a Collar.

The "foot pedal" comprises a Crank 54 fitted with an Angle Bracket and mounted on a $1''$ Rod journalled in a Cranked Bent Strip which is attached to the under surface of the $3''$ Flat Girder forming the "operator's seat." The Crank is held to the $1''$ Rod by means of a $\frac{3}{8}''$ Bolt inserted in its set-screw hole, this bolt butting against the Collar attached to the end of the Rod 52. On depressing the "foot pedal," the Rod 52 is pushed backward against the force of the Spring 53, and the tension of the cord 11 around the Pulley 9 released. The luffing brake should only be released in this way when the luffing shaft 15 is in gear with the Motor.

The construction of the internal expanding foot brake fitted to the front axle can be seen in Fig. 2. The "brake drum" consists of a $1\frac{1}{8}''$ Flanged Wheel 39 mounted on the compound axle 37, which comprises a $4\frac{1}{2}''$ and a $1\frac{1}{2}''$ Rod joined together by a Coupling, and carries a $2''$ Pulley 35 at each end. Two $1\frac{1}{2}''$ Strips 40, each fitted with a Collar 48, form the brake shoes and are secured pivotally to the $2\frac{1}{2}''$ Strip 43 by a bolt 41 and two nuts, the lock-nut mechanism (S.M. 262) being employed. The Strip 43 is pivoted to a longitudinal $3''$ Girder fastened to the frame by a bolt and two nuts, and an Angle Bracket is secured to the upper end of this Strip to represent the "pedal."

A short length of Spring Cord 42 is attached between the bolt 41 and the frame of the model and serves to keep the brake in the "off" position. By depressing the brake pedal the Collars mounted on the Strips 40 are forced against the internal surface of the flange of the Wheel 39 and the necessary friction created. This brake, although simple, will be found remarkably efficient, only a slight movement of the foot pedal being necessary to "lock" the front axle.

On reference to Figs. 2 and 3 it will be seen that two 6 B.A. Terminals 31 are secured on 6 B.A. Bolts fastened to the 4½″ Girder forming the rear of the frame. These Terminals, which are of course insulated from the frame by Insulating Bushes and Washers, are connected to the terminals of the Electric Motor by lengths of rubber-covered flex. They thus provide a convenient "outlet" to which flexible cable from an external accumulator or transformer may be connected, so that the Motor may be set in motion.

General Assembly

The chassis now being complete, the crane jib may be secured in place. Two 7½″ Angle Girders are bolted to each side of the frame in the positions shown in Fig. 1, and are held together at their upper ends by means of 1″ Triangular Plates. A Crank is also bolted to the apex of each pair of Girders to provide bearings for the jib pivot Rod 61.

The 5½″ Axle 61 (Fig. 3) forms the pivot about which the jib rotates, and is passed through the top hole in each of the Triangular Plates, into the bosses of the Cranks, and also through the 2½″ Flat Girders forming part of the bracing members of the jib frame. Collars are slipped on to the Rod 61 in order to keep the jib frame central with respect to its journals.

The hoisting and luffing cords may now be attached, these being shown clearly in Fig. 3. One end of the hoist cord is attached to the Angle Brackets 6 and the cord then led over the loose Pulley 2 and round a similar Pulley on the hoist block. The cord is then returned over the Pulley 3, and finally is wound round the hoist shaft and its end tied to a bolt secured in a Collar mounted on this shaft.

The luffing gear is duplicated, each cord being first attached to a Flat Bracket 5 on the Rod journalled in the jib, is then passed round the Pulleys 8, 28, 1 and 4 and wound round the Rod 15. Both Cords are tied finally to the bolts secured in Collars on the shaft 15.

The automatic limit switch (see Fig. 1) should next be constructed. This consists of a 4″ Axle Rod 58 connected to one arm of the reversing switch of the Electric Motor by means of a Swivel Bearing 60. Two Collars and a Handrail Support 59 are placed on this Rod at its upper end, the Handrail Support being secured to the jib in the position shown in Fig. 1.

The Collars secured to the Rod 58 must be adjusted so that as soon as the jib approaches either a perpendicular or horizontal position, the Handrail Support presses against one or other of the Collars and the arm of the reversing switch of the Motor is pushed into the "off" position, thus "cutting out" the Motor.

A Threaded Pin secured in the boss of the Swivel Bearing 60 provides a means whereby the starting and stopping of the Motor may be controlled independently from the 3″ Flat Girder, which forms the operator's seat.

The illustrations of the crane included in this leaflet show the front and rear road wheels without tyres, but a considerable improvement, both in the appearance and operation of the model, will result if Meccano Dunlop Tyres are fitted. For the front pair of wheels Meccano 2″ Dunlop Tyres (part No. 142a) should be used, while 1½″ diameter Tyres (part No. 142c) may be fitted to the 1½″ Pulleys which form the "castor" wheels.

Final Adjustments

In connecting either an Accumulator or Transformer to the model a length of rubber-covered flex should be used. The wires should be scraped clean at one end and attached to the positive and negative terminals of the Accumulator, or the "output" terminals in the case of a Transformer. The other ends of the wires should also be cleaned of insulating material and secured to the Terminals 31 (Figs. 3 and 4) that are mounted on the rear of the chassis.

The Motor may now be set in motion and the gear lever 57 moved into different positions so that the various Gears are engaged. In all probability it will be necessary to make slight adjustments to the positions of the Gears and Pinions on the shafts in the gear-box before smooth working is obtained.

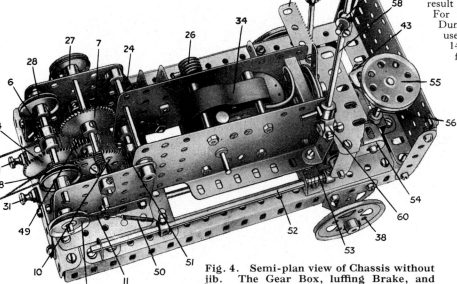

Fig. 4. Semi-plan view of Chassis without jib. The Gear Box, luffing Brake, and limit switch can be seen clearly in this illustration.

The adjustment of the automatic hoisting brake is quite a simple matter, successful operation depending on the length and tension of the Spring Cord 21 and the Cord 23. The luffing brake can be adjusted to give best results by moving the Collar mounted on the Rod 52 either backward or forward, thus increasing or diminishing the tension of the Spring 50.

The front road axle brake does not make use of a spring to keep it in the "on" position, this being effected by pressure on the foot pedal 43. The tension of the return spring 42 should therefore be adjusted so that it merely keeps the Collars 48 attached to the Strips 40, clear of the internal surface of the flange of the Flanged Wheel 39, when pressure on the pedal is released. All moving parts should be kept well oiled.

Parts required :

4 of No. 2	4 of No. 9d	2 of No. 16b	2 of No. 26	100 of No. 37	2″ of No. 58	2 of No. 111a	2 of No. 302
2 ,, 2a	1 ,, 9e	3 ,, 17	1 ,, 26a	24 ,, 38	45 ,, 59	3 ,, 111c	2 ,, 303
4 ,, 3	2 ,, 9f	4 ,, 18b	2 ,, 27	2 ,, 40	4 ,, 62	2 ,, 124	2 ,, 304
4 ,, 5	3 ,, 10	1 ,, 20	2 ,, 27a	1 ,, 44	4 ,, 63	4 ,, 126a	2 ,, 305
7 ,, 6a	8 ,, 12	2 ,, 20a	1 ,, 28	1 ,, 45	3 ,, 72	1 ,, 136	2 ,, 306
2 ,, 7a	1 ,, 13a	3 ,, 21	2 ,, 30	2 ,, 48	2 ,, 77	1 ,, 147a	12″ ,, 314
6 ,, 8a	1 ,, 14	4 ,, 22	1 ,, 30a	1 ,, 48a	1 ,, 103c	1 ,, 147b	Electric
4 ,, 8b	4 ,, 15a	6 ,, 22a	1 ,, 30c	2 ,, 52a	2 ,, 103f	1 ,, 148	Motor
4 ,, 9	5 ,, 16	1 ,, 24	2 ,, 32	2 ,, 53a	2 ,, 103h	1 ,, 160	
4 ,, 9a	4 ,, 16a	1 ,, 25	2 ,, 35	1 ,, 57	1 ,, 110	1 ,, 165	

Meccano Transporter Bridge

Suspension type: complete with Automatic Reversing Mechanism for controlling the movement of the Carriage

An L Outfit Model

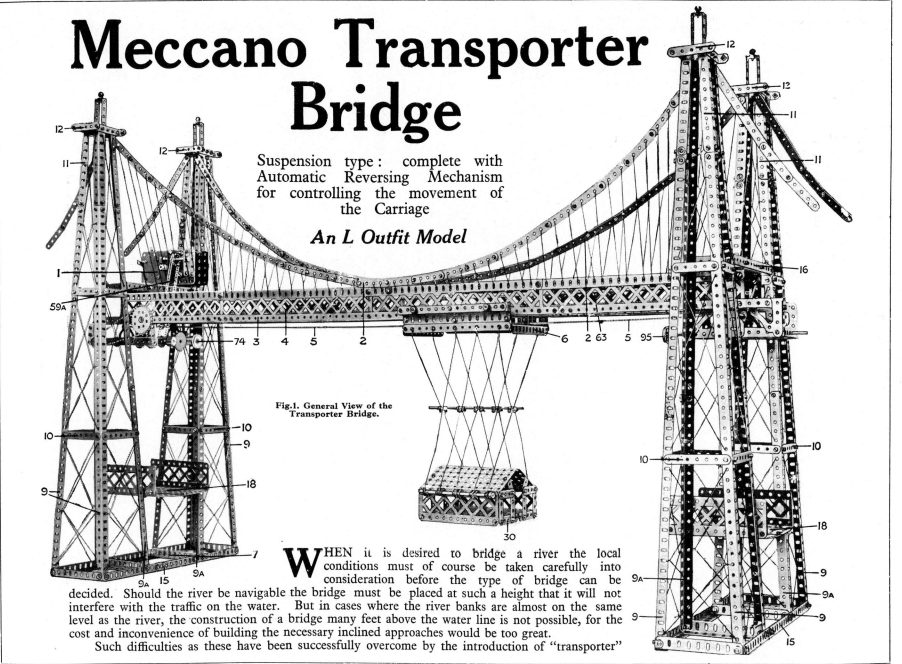

Fig.1. General View of the Transporter Bridge.

WHEN it is desired to bridge a river the local conditions must of course be taken carefully into consideration before the type of bridge can be decided. Should the river be navigable the bridge must be placed at such a height that it will not interfere with the traffic on the water. But in cases where the river banks are almost on the same level as the river, the construction of a bridge many feet above the water line is not possible, for the cost and inconvenience of building the necessary inclined approaches would be too great.

Such difficulties as these have been successfully overcome by the introduction of "transporter"

Published by MECCANO LIMITED, BINNS ROAD, LIVERPOOL 13, ENGLAND bridges. These consist essentially of a girder, suspended at such a height that it clears the tallest masts, and fitted with rails carrying a trolley from which a car is suspended by steel cables. The car is moved across the river by steam or electric power. The level of the car platform being the same as that of the approaches, traffic passes direct from the shore into the car, and vehicles and pedestrians are carried bodily across the river. A fine example of this type of bridge crosses the River Mersey between Runcorn and Widnes. It has been in successful and continuous operation for the last quarter of a century.

The Meccano model follows the general design of this bridge very closely and embodies most of its principal features. An automatic reversing device is incorporated by means of which the car is caused to travel from one end to the other of the bridge, pause for a few seconds, and then reverse, entirely without attention.

Construction of the Towers

The base of each tower is formed by bolting together two pairs of 9½″ Angle Girders 15 (Fig. 2) overlapped nine holes. These are connected crosswise by four 4½″ Angle Girders 7. The outer vertical members of each tower are constructed with 24½″ Angle Girders 9 butt-jointed to 5½″ Angle Girders 11. Each inner vertical member is built up from two 12½″ Angle Girders 9a bolted together and extended by 5½″ Angle Girders 11. The 3½″ Strips 10 and 2½″ Strips 14 connect the four girders of each tower, while the top is braced by 2½″ Strips 12 bolted to 2½″ Double Angle Strips 12a.

The pinnacles of the towers are formed by two 2½″×½″ Double Angle Strips 13 and two 1½″×½″ Double Angle Strips that, in turn, are bolted to the inside faces of the Double Angle Strips 12a. Handrail Supports secured to the top of the Double Angle Strips 13 complete the structure.

The landing stages 18 are each composed of a 5½″×2½″ and a 5½″×3½″ Flat Plate overlapped one hole and bolted together. Two 5½″ Angle Girders 19 bolted to these Plates carry two 5½″ Braced Girders 17. Each stage is attached to the vertical Angle Girders 9a of its respective towers by Angle Brackets. Two 7½″ Angle Girders 16 may next be secured to 2½″ Angle Girders bolted to the inner sides of the towers.

When each tower unit has been assembled completely, Meccano Cord may be laced through holes in the Girders as shown. This will give the towers a very realistic appearance, especially if care is taken to draw the cord quite tight.

Fig. 2. A pair of Towers, showing Motor in position

The Main Span

Each of the upper Girders of the main span or gantry (Fig. 1) is formed by bolting three 12½″ and one 9½″ Angle Girders end to end. Each of the lower Girders 3, on which the carriage 30 (Fig. 1) travels, consists of one 24½″, one 12½″, and one 9½″ Angle Girders bolted to Braced Girders 4. The wheels of the carriage travel on the out-turned flanges of the Angle Girders 3.

The two similar sides of the main span should now be joined together at each end of the bridge by bolting two 3½″ Angle Girders across the upper Girders. In addition to these 3½″ Angle Girders, a 3½″×2½″ Flanged Plate is fixed by the same bolts across each end, as shown at 98 in Fig. 4, and one is also secured across the centre of the main span, in order to hold the girders rigid.

To attach the main span to the towers proceed as follows. At the Motor end bolt the 3½″ Angle Girders to the transverse Angle Girders 16 (Fig. 2) of the towers. The non-Motor end is secured by bolting the Flanged Plate 98 (Fig. 4) to the Angle Girders 16 of its respective towers.

The suspension "cables" 2 (Fig. 1) are each constructed from twenty-four 2½″ Strips bolted end to end. Both chains are attached to the centre of the main span by Flat Brackets, and Meccano cord threaded as shown through the holes of the 2½″ Strips and the top Angle Girders of the main span represents the suspension bars of the actual bridge.

Although the model will be quite rigid without the use of "back-stays" or anchorages for the suspension cables, these would of course be absolutely essential in a real bridge, and as most Meccano boys will desire to make the model as correct as possible they should complete it by extending the ends of the cables down to the ground. If the model is mounted on a baseboard and the suspension cables are brought down and secured at each end to suitable anchorages, a very graceful and realistic model will be obtained.

The Operating Mechanism

The driving power is obtained from a Meccano Electric Motor, which may be of either the 6-volt or 20-volt type. The Girders 16, which have already been mentioned in connection with the main span, carry the Motor, indicated at 1. It is a good plan to secure the reversing lever in the correct position by a short length of cord. This precaution prevents the motor from being switched off either by accident or vibration.

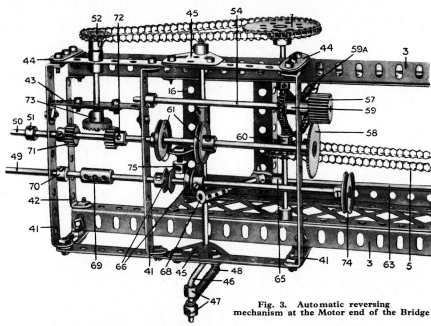

Fig. 3. Automatic reversing
mechanism at the Motor end of the Bridge

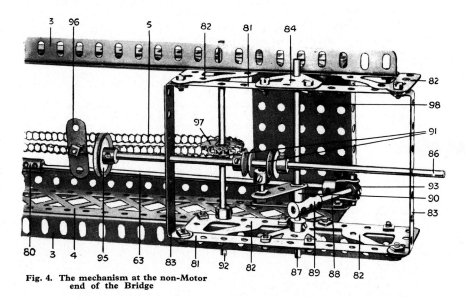

Fig. 4. The mechanism at the non-Motor
end of the Bridge

The armature spindle of the Electric Motor 1 carries a Worm 38 engaging the Pinion 37, which is mounted on a Rod that is journalled in 2″ Flat Girders 35 bolted to the Motor casing by means of 2″ Angle Girders. Additional support is given to the Rod by 2″ Strips bolted to the Flat Girders. The Rod of the Pinion 37 also carries a ¾″ Sprocket Wheel 36, which is connected by Sprocket Chain 59a (Fig. 3) with a ¾″ Sprocket Wheel 59 carried on a Rod 54 incorporated in the mechanism at the driving end of the main span. This mechanism is shown in detail in Fig. 3. The framework supporting it consists of 4½″×½″ Double Angle Strips 41 connected at their ends to 5½″ and 3½″ Strips overlapped three holes and bolted together. The framework is supported from the Angle Girders 3 of the main span by short Strips and 1″×½″ Angle Brackets bolted to the Girders.

The Rod 54 carries a ¾″ diam., ½″ width Pinion 57 that drives a 50-teeth Gear 58 carried on the end of the Rod 50, on the other end of which are two ½″ Pinions 71 and 72. The Rod 50 is slidable in its bearings, the sliding movement being controlled by a Crank fixed to the shaft of the 5½″ Crank Handle 46 and carrying a Threaded Pin to which is secured a Collar 75. The arm of the Crank engages between two 1″ Pulleys carried on the Rod 50 as shown, while the Collar 75 engages between two ½″ Pulleys 66 carried on a Rod 49 that is slidable in its bearings.

On the inner end of the Rod 49 is a 1″ Pulley 74. By pushing or pulling this Pulley the Rod 49 and the Crank are moved and the latter transmits movement to the Rod 50, thus bringing one or other of the Pinions 71 and 72 into engagement with the Contrate Wheel 73. It will be seen from Fig. 3 that by this means the direction of the rotation of the Contrate Wheel 73 may be reversed according to which of the Pinions 71 and 72 is in engagement.

A Spring 48 attached to the Crank Handle tends to bring the latter over sharply so soon as it has been moved past its "critical" position by the Crank

carrying the Collar 75. Hence one or other of the Pinions 71 and 72 is always held properly in mesh with the Contrate Wheel, and there is little possibility of its working out of engagement before the proper period has expired.

The Crank Handle 46 is journalled in Flat Trunnions 45 and carries a Coupling 68 in which is secured a 2″ Rod carrying a Swivel Bearing 65. This is connected with Rod 63, which runs the length of the main span and connects up with the mechanism at the other end of the bridge, as will be explained later. It will be necessary to couple three 11½″ and one 8″ Rod together in order to obtain the required length.

The final drive to the car is taken from the ¾″ Sprocket 52 (Fig. 3) carried on the Rod of the Contrate Wheel 73. This Rod is journalled in a Double Angle Strip 43 and the Strip of the frame as shown. The Sprocket Wheel 52 drives a 2″ Sprocket 53 on a Rod that is journalled in the Angle Girders 3. This Rod also carries a 1″ Sprocket 60 round which passes an 80″ endless length of Sprocket Chain 5 (see also Fig. 1) that carries a 1½″ Strip 96 (Fig. 4) and runs the whole length of the main span to the other tower, where it passes round a 1″ Sprocket 97 (Fig. 4) secured to a Rod 92 journalled in the Angle Girders 3. The purpose of the Strip 96 will be explained later, together with an explanation of the operation of the mechanism. This completes the reversing and traversing gear so far as the Motor end of the bridge is concerned.

Mechanism at the Non-Motor End

This is shown in Fig. 4. The framework that supports the Rods of the mechanism is constructed from 3½″×½″ Double Angle Strips 83, to which are bolted 5½″ Strips 81. The rectangular frame thus formed is attached to the Girders 3 of the main span by Architraves 82.

A Rod 87 journalled in Flat Trunnions 84 carries a Crank 90, in the end of which is a Threaded Pin carrying a Collar that engages between two ½″

Pulleys 91. These are fixed about $\frac{1}{2}''$ apart on the Rod 86, which also carries at its inner end a 1" Pulley 95. A Coupling 89 secured to the Rod 87 carries a 2" Rod 88, on the end of which is fastened the spider of a Swivel Bearing 93. It will now be seen that by pushing the Pulley 95 the Crank 90 will be actuated and in turn will operate the Rod 63 through the Coupling and Rod 88.

Details of the Travelling Carriage.

The travelling carriage, or "transporter," is shown in Fig. 5. It will be seen that it is composed of two parts—that which carries the travelling wheels 22 and the suspended portion forming the carriage proper.

The rectangular framework carrying the wheels 22 ($\frac{3}{4}''$ Flanged Wheels) is built up from two $5\frac{1}{2}''$ Angle Girders 6 bolted to $7\frac{1}{2}''$ Flat Girders 20 that carry Flat Brackets to which are bolted $7\frac{1}{2}''$ Strips 21. The travelling wheels 22 are secured to $1\frac{1}{2}''$ Rods journalled in the Flat Girders 20 and in the Strips 23. Two Double Bent Strips 24 are bolted to the Angle Girders 6; the purpose of these will be explained later.

The carriage proper is suspended from the trolley by means of Loom Heads 26 attached to the Rods 99 and 27, and spaced apart by Spring Clips. The carriage is composed of two $5\frac{1}{2}'' \times 2\frac{1}{2}''$ Flanged Plates 30 that form the base, and to which are secured $5\frac{1}{2}''$ Braced Girders 28. The Girders 28 carry Angle Brackets 31 in the holes of which are journalled the 5" Rods 27. The construction of the ends and roof of the carriage does not need detailed explanation as the illustration is sufficiently clear on these points.

After the carriage and trolley have been constructed the whole unit may be placed in position on the main span of the bridge. To do this it will be necessary to remove one side of the trolley in order to set the travelling wheels 22 to run on the flanges of the Girders 3 (Fig. 1). When the trolley is in position two Angle Brackets 25 (Fig. 5) are placed as shown so that they bear against the under surfaces of the Angle Girders 3 and thus prevent the trolley being lifted from the rails.

The Sprocket Chain 5 (Figs. 1, 3 and 4) is now passed round the Sprocket 97 (Fig. 4), thence through the Double Bent Strips 24 (Fig. 5) secured to the trolley, and round the Sprocket 60 (Fig. 3). The $1\frac{1}{2}''$ Strip 96 (Fig. 4) must be secured to the Chain 5 in a position between the Double Bent Strips, 24 so that as the Chain moves along, the Strip 96 bears against one or other of the Double Bent Strips, with the result that the carriage is moved along also. It is important to note that the Chain itself is not actually secured in any way to the trolley.

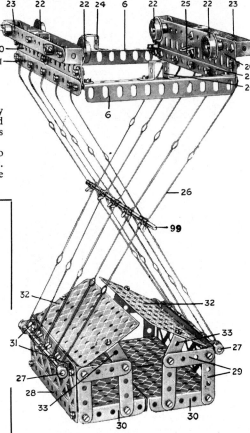

Fig. 5. The overhead Trolley, with suspended Carriage

Parts required to build the Transporter Bridge

4 of No.	1b	22 of No.	12	1 of No.	29	10 ft. of No.	49
8 ,,	2	1 ,,	12a	1 ,,	32	1 ,,	95
18 ,,	3	8 ,,	12b	26 ,,	35	2 ,,	96
112 ,,	5	3 ,,	13	507 ,,	37	3 ,,	96a
14 ,,	6	3 ,,	13a	162 ,,	38	6 ,,	99
6 ,,	6a	2 ,,	14	8 ,,	40	2 ,,	99a
10 ,,	7	4 ,,	15	1 ,,	43	6 ,,	100
26 ,,	8	2 ,,	15a	2 ,,	45	20 ,,	101
10 ,,	8a	3 ,,	16a	4 ,,	48	2 ,,	103g
4 ,,	8b	1 ,,	16b	17 ,,	48a	2 ,,	103k
22 ,,	9	2 ,,	17	3 ,,	48b	4 ,,	108
8 ,,	9a	4 ,,	18a	3 ,,	48c	2 ,,	115
4 ,,	9b	1 ,,	19	2 ,,	52	4 ,,	126a
4 ,,	9d	4 ,,	20b	2 ,,	52a	4 ,,	136
2 ,,	9e	4 ,,	22	4 ,,	53	2 ,,	165
6 ,,	10	4 ,,	23a	28 ,,	59	1 Electric	
6 ,,	11	1 ,,	25a	2 ,,	62	Motor	
		3 ,,	26	7 ,,	63		
		1 ,,	27	4 ,,	70		

Action of the Automatic Reversing Gear

When the carriage 30 (Fig. 1) moving to the left strikes the Pulley 74 (Figs. 1 and 3), of the reversing gear, the Crank 75 on the Crank Handle 46 is moved round until the Spring 48 on the Crank Handle pulls the latter hard over. In doing so, however, the end of the Crank presses against one of the Pulleys 61 on the Rod 50, thereby throwing the $\frac{1}{2}''$ Pinion 71 out of engagement with the Contrate 73 and bringing its fellow Pinion 72 into engagement with the Contrate, thus reversing the direction of rotation of the Sprocket Wheels 52 and 53 and hence the direction of motion of the carriage. When the carriage reaches the other end of the bridge it strikes the Pulley 95 (Figs. 1 and 4) thereby actuating the reversing mechanism through the medium of the Rod 63 (Figs. 1, 3 and 4). This time the Pinion 72 is thrown out of engagement with the Contrate and Pinion 71 is brought into gear, while the Rod 49 carrying the Pulley 74 is returned to its original position, ready to meet the carriage again when the latter once more reaches the left-hand end of the bridge.

It should be noted that when the direction of the Sprocket Chain is reversed, the $1\frac{1}{2}''$ Strip 96 (Fig. 4) must travel from one Double Bent Strip 24 (Fig. 5) to the other before setting the trolley in motion. Hence the carriage pauses realistically at each end of its travel before returning, thus giving the passengers plenty of time to embark or return to terra firma!

Fig. 6. The Transporter Bridge over the River Mersey at Runcorn, Cheshire. The Meccano model closely follows the general design of this famous bridge.

Meccano Traction Engine

Fig. 1. General View of the Traction Engine.

Special Features

The model is driven by a 6-volt Electric Motor supplied with current from a 6-volt 20 amp. hour Meccano Accumulator. The engine is capable of two speeds forward or reverse, and is fitted with worm and chain steering gear, external-contracting screw-operated brake, and imitation dynamo. The cylinder, crankshaft and reciprocating mechanism of an actual steam engine are produced realistically in the model.

The Meccano Traction Engine hauls its driver along quite easily!

THE Meccano Traction Engine is not only a most realistic model, but it is extremely powerful. The illustration at the foot of this page actually shows the model pulling more than ten times its own weight! Any Meccano boy of average weight should be able to build the model and then take himself for a ride with it !

The Traction Engine was originally designed to be driven by a 4-volt Motor supplied with current from a 4-volt 8 amp. hour Meccano Accumulator. and in Fig. 1 the Accumulator is shown in the bunker at the rear of the model. Since the Tractor was designed, however, the 4-volt Motor and 4-volt 8 amp. hour Accumulator have become obsolete, and have been replaced by a 6-volt Motor and a 6-volt 20 amp. hour Accumulator.

The use of the new Motor does not involve any alteration in the construction of the model itself, but the Accumulator cannot be placed in the bunker on account of its larger size. It therefore must be carried on a separate trailer hauled by the Tractor, or else placed on the ground and connected to the model by a suitable length of twin flex. The trailer may be constructed on the

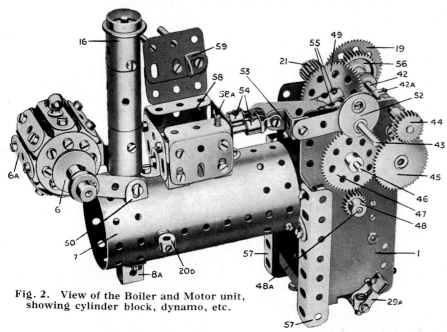

Fig. 2. View of the Boiler and Motor unit, showing cylinder block, dynamo, etc.

is important to note, must be free to move up and down on the Rod. The brake cord is attached to a bolt on the frame, thence passed round the brake drum 30 and secured to the Threaded Boss carried on the Screwed Rod 5a. On turning the handle 5 the cord is tightened on the brake drum or slackened.

Boiler and Motor Unit

The construction of this portion, which embodies the main gear train controlling the travelling movements of the model, is shown in detail in Fig. 2. Two $3\frac{1}{2}''$ Angle Girders 57 bolted to the flanges of the Electric Motor form the supports by which the completed unit is secured later to the rear portion of the model.

A Boiler 7 with front end plate is bolted to the Girders 57 and carries on its upper surface the cylinder block 58, which is built up from six $1\frac{1}{2}''$ Flat Girders, eight $\frac{1}{2}'' \times \frac{1}{2}''$ Angle Brackets, two $1\frac{1}{2}''$ Angle Girders and two $1\frac{1}{2}'' \times \frac{1}{2}''$ Double Angle Strips. The sides of the block are connected to the back and front cylinder covers by Angle Brackets, whilst the top (consisting of two $1\frac{1}{2}''$ Flat Girders) is attached to the sides by means of the $1\frac{1}{2}''$ Angle Girders. The entire block is secured to the boiler top by means of two $1\frac{1}{2}''$ Double Angle Strips bolted to the bottom edges of the side Flat Girders, and also by two Angle Brackets.

The top of the cylinder block carries on the inside an Angle Bracket 59, in the hole of which one of the $2''$ Rods 54 is journalled. This Rod represents the piston rod and carries an End Bearing to which one end of a $2''$ Strip is attached pivotally by means of a nut and bolt. The other end of the $2''$ Strip is pivoted on the pin of the crankshaft 43.

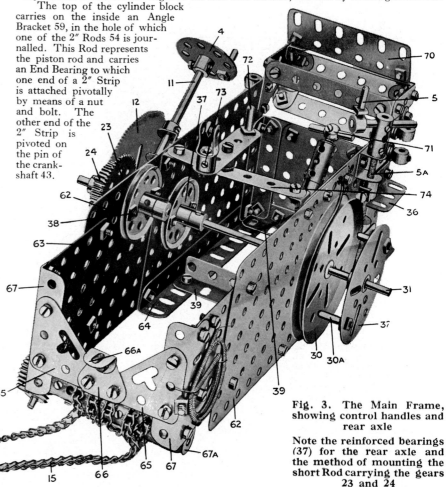

Fig. 3. The Main Frame, showing control handles and rear axle

Note the reinforced bearings (37) for the rear axle and the method of mounting the short Rod carrying the gears 23 and 24

lines of the one illustrated on the front page. The base of this consists of longitudinal $24\frac{1}{2}''$ Angle Girders spaced apart by $12\frac{1}{2}''$ Angle Girders. A raised rear portion is constructed of further $12\frac{1}{2}''$ Angle Girders, and this may be used as a seat for the driver. The trailer is mounted on four Wheels (Part No. 19a).

Main Frame, Coal Bunker, etc.

The framework of the rear portion (Fig. 3) is constructed from two $5\frac{1}{2}'' \times 3\frac{1}{2}''$ Flat Plates 62 overlapped four holes and bolted together to form each side of the main frame. The rear end is composed of two $2\frac{1}{2}'' \times 2\frac{1}{2}''$ Flat Plates overlapped four holes and bolted to Angle Girders secured to the Flat Plates 62. Two $5\frac{1}{2}''$ Angle Girders 64 are bolted to the lower edges of the Plates 62 and are spanned by two $3''$ Angle Girders 39. Two $5\frac{1}{2}'' \times 2\frac{1}{2}''$ Flat Plates are secured to the Angle Girders 64 of the main frames.

Two $2\frac{1}{2}'' \times 2\frac{1}{2}''$ Flat Plates 63 bolted to the front ends of the Plates 62 (Fig. 3) carry two $2\frac{1}{2}''$ Angle Girders to which are bolted Corner Brackets 65 connected in the centre by the $1''$ Triangular Plate 66 that carries an Angle Bracket 66a.

A $6\frac{1}{2}''$ Rod 31 is journalled in the side Plates 62 and in $1\frac{1}{2}''$ Pulley Wheels 37, which are secured to the inside faces of the Plates to reinforce the bearings of the Rod. This Rod forms the axle for the rear road wheels, and is held in position by Collars placed against the bushes of the Pulley Wheels 37. The brake drum 30 is a $3''$ Pulley Wheel secured to the Rod 31, which also carries (on the opposite end) a $3\frac{1}{2}''$ Gear Wheel 12 placed so as to engage a $1''$ Gear Wheel 24. The latter is carried on a $2''$ Rod journalled in one side Plate only of the frame and in another $1\frac{1}{2}''$ Pulley 38 bolted to the Plate. This $2''$ Rod is held in position by a Collar secured against the bush of the $1\frac{1}{2}''$ Pulley. It carries in addition to the Gear 24, a 57-teeth Gear Wheel 23 that engages the $\frac{1}{2}''$ Pinion 22 (Fig. 1) of the Motor unit. The Gear 23 (Fig. 3) is spaced from the frame Plate 62 by its boss and several Washers, so as to give clearance for the steering column 11.

External-contracting Screw-operated Brake

A Threaded Pin 5 (Fig. 3) is secured in a Collar on a $1\frac{1}{2}''$ Rod and the latter is passed through the end of a Coupling in which is carried a $3\frac{1}{2}''$ Screwed Rod 5a journalled in two Double Brackets bolted to the frame Plates as shown. The Screwed Rod carries a Threaded Boss which, it

The latter is built up as follows : Two Couplings 55 are secured at right angles to two 2″ Rods 43 (the Couplings should be fixed very securely on their respective Rods by employing two Grub Screws in each Coupling) and a ¾″ Bolt is passed through their end holes to form the crank pin. The crankshaft is journalled in the Motor side plates in the centre of the top row of holes.

The valve rod is formed by the other 2″ Rod 54 journalled in the end cylinder cover and also in an Angle Bracket secured by means of a bolt 58a to one of the 1½″ Angle Girders of the cylinder block 58. This Rod carries an End Bearing that is attached rigidly by nut and bolt to a ½″ Reversed Angle Bracket, which, in turn, is connected pivotally by a bolt and two nuts (see Standard Mechanism No. 262) to a Single-throw Eccentric 52 carried on the end of the crankshaft.

A "safety valve" composed of two Couplings carrying 1½″ Rods (see Fig. 1) may now be mounted on the cylinder block as shown.

The chimney 16 (Fig. 2) is composed of three Sleeve Pieces placed end to end with the centre Sleeve Piece overlapping each of the other two by ⅜″. A 3½″ Rod passed lengthwise through the centre of the three Sleeve Pieces carries at one end a ¾″ Flanged Wheel that forms the top of the chimney. The top and bottom Sleeve Pieces are held in place by means of bolts passed through them and inserted in the holes of new-style Collars carried on the 3½″ Rod.

The dynamo is mounted on two 2″ Strips secured to two Angle Brackets 50. It consists of two Bush Wheels each carrying seven Angle Brackets to which are secured 1½″ Strips. A 2½″ Axle Rod passed through the two Bush Wheels carries two ¾″ Flanged Wheels 6, one wheel being placed on either side of the dynamo. A ½″ loose Pulley also is placed on one end of the Rod and is spaced from the ¾″ Flanged Wheel by a Collar, while a further Collar secured to the Rod on the outer side of the ½″ Pulley holds the latter in position ready to receive the belt from the Flywheel. The dynamo lifting hook is formed by a Handrail Support fitted to one of the 1½″ Strips forming its frame.

When this stage of the construction has been reached, the Motor unit (Fig. 2) may be secured to the rear portion (Fig. 3) by bolts passed through the Angle Girders 57 of the Motor unit and the end holes of the frame plates 62 (Fig. 3) as shown at "D" in Fig. 1. The lower surface of the Boiler is bolted to the Angle Bracket 66a (Fig. 3). The two units are thus held securely in position.

The Main Gear Train

The main gear train is shown complete in Fig 5 but its principal components are illustrated more clearly in Fig. 2. The armature spindle of the Motor (48a in the latter illustration) carries a ½″ Pinion 48 that engages with a 57-teeth Gear Wheel 47, on the Rod of which is also carried a ½″ Pinion. The latter engages a 57-teeth Gear 49 on the crankshaft 43.

The crankshaft also carries a ½″ Double-width Pinion 21 that meshes with a 57-teeth Gear Wheel 19 secured to a 3½″ Rod 42, on which is also secured a 1″ Gear Wheel 56. On the other end of the Rod 42 is a ¾″ Pinion 44. The Rod is slidable in its bearings and is controlled by the lever 72 (Fig. 5). The latter is connected pivotally to a Small Fork Piece (see Figs. 3 and 5) which engages a Collar 42a (Fig. 5) carried on the Rod 42.

A 1″ Gear Wheel 56a (Fig. 5) is secured to a 4½″ Rod journalled in the Motor side plates, and a ½″ Pinion 22 and a 50-teeth Gear Wheel 45 are carried at either end of the same Rod. It will be seen from Fig. 5 that by moving the lever 72 either of two gear trains may be brought into operation, viz. :—the 1″ Gear Wheel 56 may be brought into engagement with the 1″ Gear 56a, or the ¾″ Pinion 44 into engagement with the 50-teeth Gear 45 (in both cases the Gear 19 remains in mesh with the Double-width Pinion 21). Hence the Motor drive may be transmitted through two different gear ratios, resulting in a "fast" and "slow" speed of the engine.

It will be noted that the Rod 42 and the Rod carrying Gears 45 and 56a are mounted in reinforced bearings composed of 1½″ Strips bolted to the Motor side plates.

When it is desired to run the engine without the tractor moving (such as when driving the dynamo) the lever 72 should be placed in the central position. In this position both the Gear Wheel 56 and the Pinion 44 are disengaged from their respective gears and no power is transmitted to the driving wheels. The reverse movement for either speed is obtained of course simply by reversing the Motor.

Steering Mechanism

The front road wheels 3 (Fig. 6), which consist of 3″ Wheels, are carried on 1½″ Axle Rods 27 journalled in the holes of a 3½″ × ½″ Double Angle Strip. The latter is secured to the inside of a channel girder formed by two 3½″ Angle Girders 26 bolted together as indicated. The inner ends of the Rods are journalled in

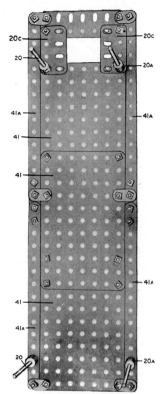

Fig. 4. The Canopy, underneath view

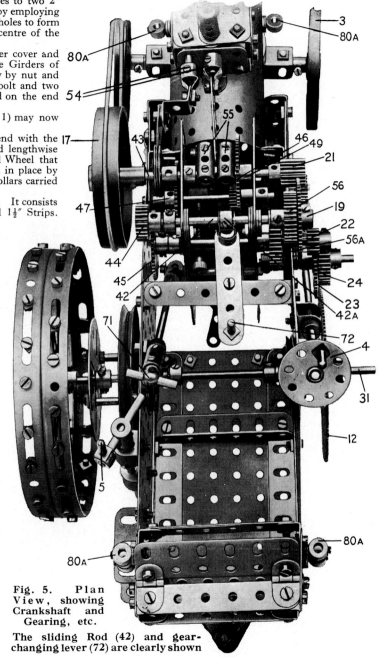

Fig. 5. Plan View, showing Crankshaft and Gearing, etc.

The sliding Rod (42) and gear-changing lever (72) are clearly shown

Angle Brackets bolted to the Girders and are held in position by Collars secured to the Rods against the faces of the Angle Brackets.

The Wheel Flange 8 is secured to the Girders 26 by bolts passed through a 2″ Sprocket Wheel, and a 1½″ Rod secured in the latter acts as a pivot for the front axle unit. The Rod is journalled in a Double Bent Strip 8a (Fig. 2) bolted to the underside of the Boiler and in the second hole of the Boiler, and is held loosely in position by means of a Collar placed on the Rod inside the Boiler.

The steering mechanism is controlled from a steering wheel 4 (Figs. 1 and 3) secured to an 8″ Rod 11 that is journalled in Double Brackets bolted to the side frame plate of the rear portion. The steering Rod 11 carries at its lower end a Worm 10 engaging a ¾″ Pinion 9 on a 3½″ Rod 28 (Fig. 6), which is journalled in 1½″ Strips bolted to the side plates of the framework.

The Rod 28 carries several Couplings and Collars 28a, the heads of the grub screws of these serving to grip a 16″ length of Sprocket Chain that is wound round the Coupling five or six turns and thence passed round the 2″ Sprocket Wheel attached to the front axle. The ends of the chain are of course joined together. By reason of this arrangement the front wheels may be directed either to right or left according to the direction in which the steering wheel is turned.

Building the Driving Wheels

The actual construction of the driving wheels should offer little difficulty. Two Hub Discs bolted together and secured to a Bush Wheel (which acts as a hub) form both the right and the left-hand wheel but slightly differing methods are adopted to secure them to the axles. For the right-hand wheel the method is as follows :—

Two ¾″ Bolts are secured by nuts to the Hub Discs (Fig. 1). When the wheel is placed on the Axle Rod 31 (Fig. 5), it will be found that the shanks of the bolts will engage in the holes or slots of the 3½″ Gear Wheel 12. The idea of this arrangement is to provide a more secure hold for the road

wheel than would be possible simply by tightening the set-screws of the Bush Wheels secured to the Hub Discs.

In the case of the left-hand driving wheel it is necessary to space it from the frame plate of the rear portion in order to allow sufficient clearance for the Flywheel 17 (Fig. 5), and for this purpose a Face Plate 32 (Fig. 3) carrying two Threaded Pins is passed over the Rod 31 and its set-screw tightened so that it is secured with the Threaded Pins engaging slots or holes in the brake drum 30. The driving wheel may now be placed in position, the ¾″ Bolts of the wheel engaging holes in the Face Plate.

The Motor Control

The control handle for the 6-volt Electric Motor is shown at 71 (Fig. 5). By pulling or pushing this handle the Motor may be started, stopped, or reversed. The handle, which consists of a 1″ Rod inserted in a Handrail Support, is secured by a Coupling to a 4½″ Rod on the lower end of which is a Swivel Bearing 29a (Fig. 6) attached pivotally by a bolt 29 to one of the Motor switch arms.

A support and guide for the 4½″ Rod is formed by a Collar pivotally attached by a bolt to the side plate of the frame, the bolt being locked in position against the Collar by a nut (see Fig. 5). It is important to note that the bolt does not nip the 4½″ Rod ; the latter must be quite free so that the Motor switch may be moved by pushing or pulling the handle 71.

The canopy (Fig. 4) may now be constructed. It is built up from three 5½″ × 3½″ Flat Plates 41 joined together with the centre Plate overlapping the rear end Plate by three holes and the front end Plate by four holes. The sides of the canopy are extended by 7½″ Strips 41a joined to the Plates 41 by Flat Brackets, and the portion that surrounds the chimney is formed by 2″ Flat Girders 20c secured to the front Plate 41 and to a 3½″ Flat Girder, the latter being joined to the 7½″ Flat Strips 41a by Flat Brackets.

The 3½″ Rods 20 forming the supports for the canopy are secured in Couplings 20a, which in turn are secured by bolts to the Plates 41. The lower ends of the Rods are secured in Collars 80a carried on the Boiler and bunker frame Plates (see Fig. 5).

To complete the model steps 36 (Fig. 6) consisting of 1½″ Angle Girders should be bolted to the Plates of the main frame. Two Double Brackets to which are bolted two 1″ Triangular Plates form the coupling 33 by means of which the trailer draw-bar may be attached.

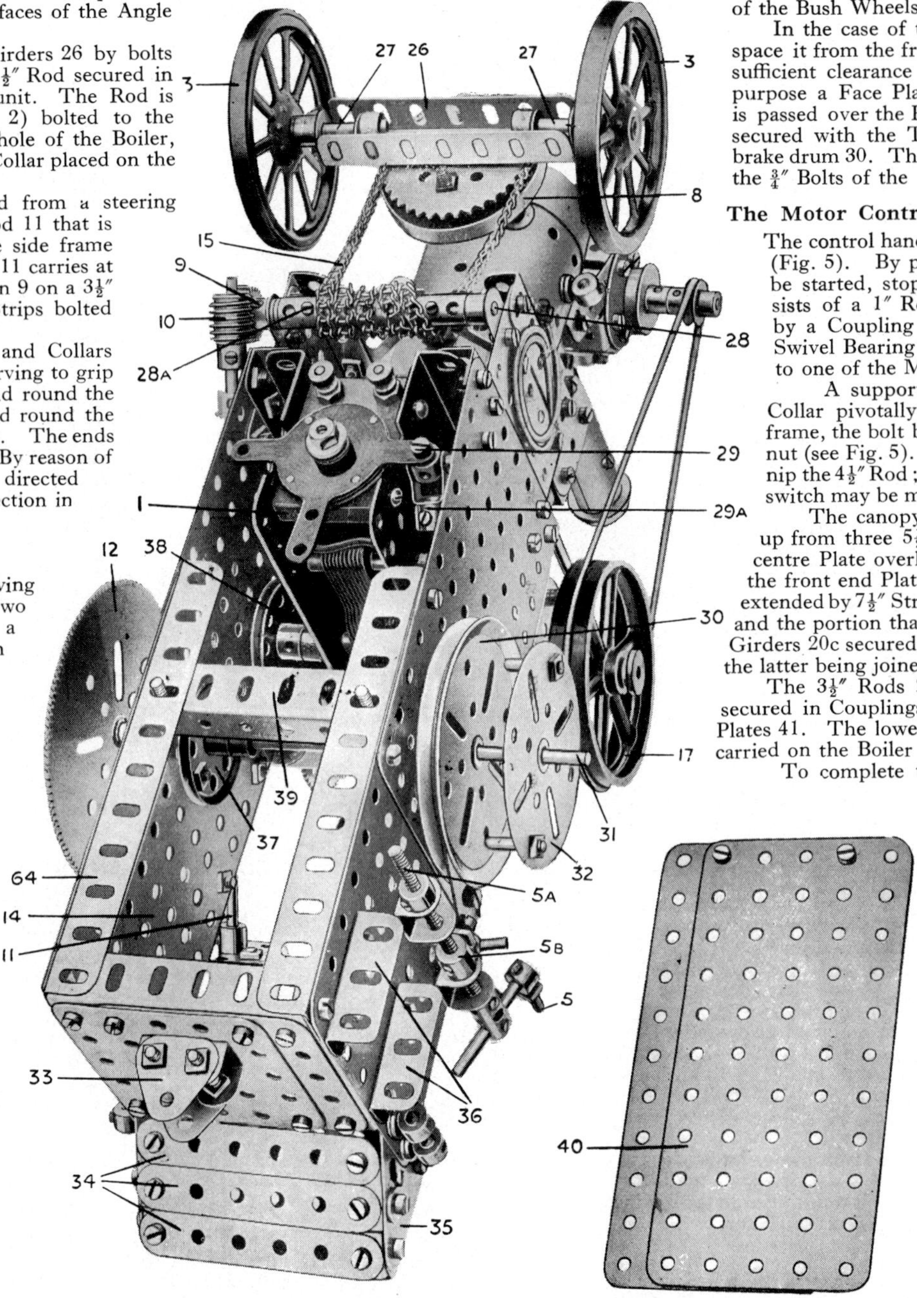

Fig. 6. Underneath view, showing Steering Gear and Electric Motor, etc. The Brake on the rear axle is also clearly brought out in this view

Parts required

4	of No.	1b	3 of No.	18a
6	,,	4	1 ,,	18b
1	,,	5	2 ,,	19a
6	,,	6	1 ,,	19b
13	,,	6a	3 ,,	20b
2	,,	9	3 ,,	21
4	,,	9b	5 ,,	24
2	,,	9c	2 ,,	25
4	,,	9d	3 ,,	26
4	,,	9f	1 ,,	26a
6	,,	10	1 ,,	27
6	,,	11	4 ,,	27a
33	,,	12	1 ,,	27b
1	,,	13a	3 ,,	31
1	,,	14	1 ,,	32
1	,,	15	263 ,,	37
9	,,	16	31 ,,	38
1	,,	16a	1 ,,	45
6	,,	17	4 ,,	48

Parts required—(contd.)

1	of No.	48b	6 ,,	111
7	,,	52a	10 ,,	111c
17″	,,	58	2 ,,	114
28	,,	59	5 ,,	115
11	,,	63	1 ,,	116a
1	,,	64	4 ,,	118
2	,,	70	1 ,,	125
4	,,	72	1 ,,	132
3	,,	77	4 ,,	133
1	,,	80a	2 ,,	136
18″	,,	94	1 ,,	137
1	,,	95	1 ,,	162
1	,,	103d	3 ,,	163
1	,,	103e	1 ,,	164
2	,,	103g	1 ,,	165
6	,,	103h	2 ,,	166
1	,,	109	1 ,,	170

1 6-volt Electric Motor
1 6-volt 20-amp. Accumulator

Vertical Log Saw

SPECIAL FEATURES

Timber fed lengthwise into one end of the machine is automatically carried along on rollers and brought into contact with the saw blades. In actual practice the reciprocating motion of the blades enables them to cut their way easily through the timber, which emerges from the other end of the machine in the form of planks.

Fig. 1. The Meccano Model Vertical Log Saw : view from front (or supply) end.

FROM the earliest times man has found it necessary to use tools of various kinds to enable him to make the many and varied articles which he uses in his daily life.

One of the most useful of all the tools which man has devised is the saw. From prehistoric days, implements with serrated edges have been employed to rend or divide various kinds of substances, especially metals and stone. Present-day saws are made of the highest grade steel, the teeth being very sharp and "set" with a high degree of exactitude, but in the very early days saws made of bronze were used, while others were made with flints embedded in a wooden blade and held in place by a form of glue known as bitumen. Even sharks' teeth and the serrated edges of sea shells have been employed to form the saws of savage tribes.

Saws Made of Jewels

Some remarkable forms of saw were used by the ancients. In the early Egyptian civilisation saws were in great demand for the cutting of stone with which to build pyramids and temples, etc., and for this purpose these ingenious people used implements made of bronze set with precious jewels for teeth !

The chief use of the tool as we know it to-day is, of course, to saw wood, and the enormous logging operations carried on in the vast forest regions of Canada and Australia, etc., have given a great impetus to the improvement of the saw both in design and the methods of manufacture.

The oldest form of saw is the straight type, which is reciprocating in action and has a flat blade with a straight edge. There are now various other types of saws, such as the circular or disc pattern, and the band saw, the latter being a continuous ribbon or band of metal running over two pulleys and having teeth cut along one edge.

Years ago timber was cut with a saw worked by two people, one standing over the log and drawing the saw upward while the other stood in a pit below and took the downward stroke. This arrangement was known as the "pit-saw."

The "gate-saw" was a later development and came into existence with the application of power to timber-working machinery. The gate-saw was superseded by the "muley," or mill saw, which differed only in the manner in which the blade was fixed. Eventually, as the need for more rapid sawing increased, the "gang-saw" was devised. In this a number of blades, varying from two to forty, were strained in a "gate" or frame, with spacing between each blade, as the thickness of the timber demanded, the whole log thus being cut into many boards at one operation.

In the modern log saw the blades are fixed on frames attached to a reciprocating beam, which, in the vertical pattern, moves in an up and down direction. The log is fixed to the table of the machine and carried slowly against the edges of the saws while the latter are in motion. Since the blades are adjustable the timber can be sawn into planks of any thickness.

Brunel's Improvements in Design

Among famous inventors and engineers who devoted time and labour to the improvement of sawing machines may be mentioned the name of Sir Isambard Brunel, who, in 1805, took out a patent for a machine designed "for sawing timber in an easy and expeditious manner."

His invention embodied certain improvements on the method then in use for holding the log on the travelling carriage and he also devised a means by which the machine could saw both ways, that is, each stroke of the table—both forward and reverse—was made a cutting stroke. This improvement meant a considerable saving in the cost of sawing, as work could be accomplished in half the time required when cutting in one direction only.

Logging Operations in North America

Nowadays the great demand for timber has necessitated the erection of large and powerful saw-mills in many parts of the world, especially in the forest regions of North America. America's forests furnish a large proportion of the vast amount of timber which is used so extensively throughout the many branches of industry. Every year some millions of trees are cut down to be used eventually for a variety of purposes. Trees selected for "felling" are chosen with great care, and whenever possible those located near a river are selected, as they may be conveniently rolled into the stream and floated away to the saw-mills, which are generally situated at the junction of two or more rivers and thus serve several districts. Once they reach the mill modern machinery takes hold of the situation and soon reduces the logs to the size and shape required.

The earlier saw-mills were operated by wind power and the use of water power soon followed. The mill consisted of a wooden pitman attached to the waterwheel shaft, while the log to be sawn was carried on rollers suspended from a framework above the wheel

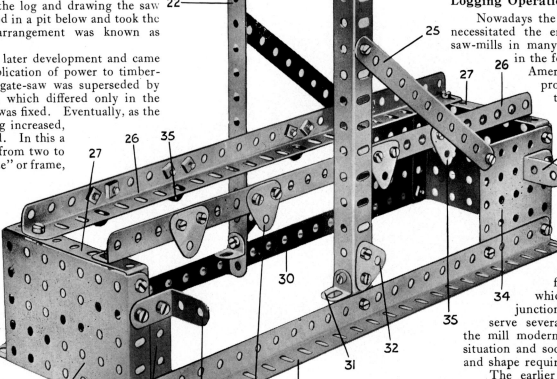

Fig. 2. View showing construction of the Framework, looking from rear or discharge end.

and gradually fed by means of hand levers towards the reciprocating saw blade.

About 1634 several saw-mills were erected on the Atlantic coast of North America. The saws employed here were rather ponderous affairs, the blade being attached by a long pitman from the waterwheel shaft to a massive "gate" running in wooden slides, while a rack and pinion device operated the saw table on which the log was placed. Later, however, the demand for timber so increased that it was essential to find means for more rapid production, and the machines were improved continuously until, finally, the saw-mill as we know it to-day was evolved.

Details of a typical Logging Mill

A logging mill usually stands on the banks of a river or pond and huge poles driven into the bed of the river serve to hold long pieces of timber to which chains are attached, the whole forming a boom into which the logs are floated and kept until required.

A special conveyor known as a "jack ladder" projects from the mill and down under the water, so that the logs may be floated on to it, and by means of a series of spikes which dig into the logs the latter may be hauled up the incline of the conveyor to the mill floor. Here each log is rolled upon "runners" and carried to the sawing machine, where, by a touch of a lever, which causes an arm to rise in the "runners," the log is thrown on to the saw table. Another lever is then pulled, thereby operating an iron "dog," or grip, which digs into the log and holds it tightly in position ready to be cut.

As the lumber is sawn it drops from the machine on to rollers which carry it to an edging machine and afterwards to a trimmer—an ingenious arrangement of

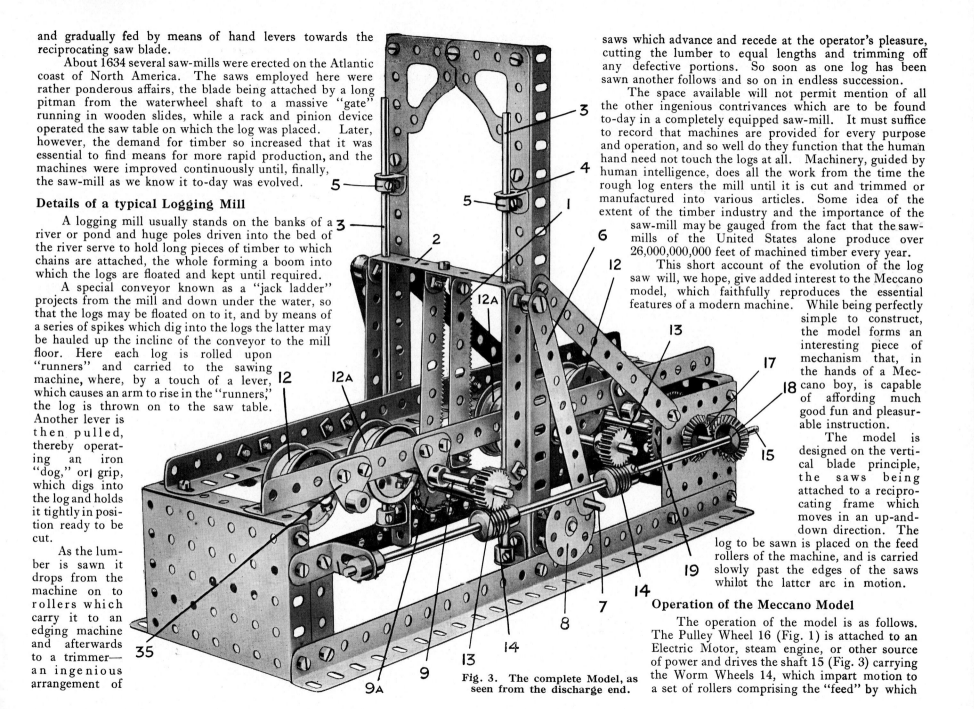

Fig. 3. The complete Model, as seen from the discharge end.

saws which advance and recede at the operator's pleasure, cutting the lumber to equal lengths and trimming off any defective portions. So soon as one log has been sawn another follows and so on in endless succession.

The space available will not permit mention of all the other ingenious contrivances which are to be found to-day in a completely equipped saw-mill. It must suffice to record that machines are provided for every purpose and operation, and so well do they function that the human hand need not touch the logs at all. Machinery, guided by human intelligence, does all the work from the time the rough log enters the mill until it is cut and trimmed or manufactured into various articles. Some idea of the extent of the timber industry and the importance of the saw-mill may be gauged from the fact that the saw-mills of the United States alone produce over 26,000,000,000 feet of machined timber every year.

This short account of the evolution of the log saw will, we hope, give added interest to the Meccano model, which faithfully reproduces the essential features of a modern machine. While being perfectly simple to construct, the model forms an interesting piece of mechanism that, in the hands of a Meccano boy, is capable of affording much good fun and pleasurable instruction.

The model is designed on the vertical blade principle, the saws being attached to a reciprocating frame which moves in an up-and-down direction. The log to be sawn is placed on the feed rollers of the machine, and is carried slowly past the edges of the saws whilst the latter are in motion.

Operation of the Meccano Model

The operation of the model is as follows. The Pulley Wheel 16 (Fig. 1) is attached to an Electric Motor, steam engine, or other source of power and drives the shaft 15 (Fig. 3) carrying the Worm Wheels 14, which impart motion to a set of rollers comprising the "feed" by which the logs are brought to the saws. The saw frame itself is operated by means of connecting rods and cranks, which cause the frame to oscillate in a vertical plane, with the cutting edges toward the log. The latter is fed slowly on to the saw teeth by the revolving rollers and is thus cut into planks, the width of which depends on the distance between the saw blades. If preferred the shaft carrying the Pulley Wheel 16 (Fig. 1) may be fitted with a handle built up from standard Meccano parts (see Meccano Standard Mechanisms Manual, details Nos. 255 to 259) thus dispensing with the Motor or engine.

In order to simplify the construction, each detail of the Meccano model Vertical Log Saw is described separately, so that with the aid of the various illustrations no difficulty should be experienced in building a successful model.

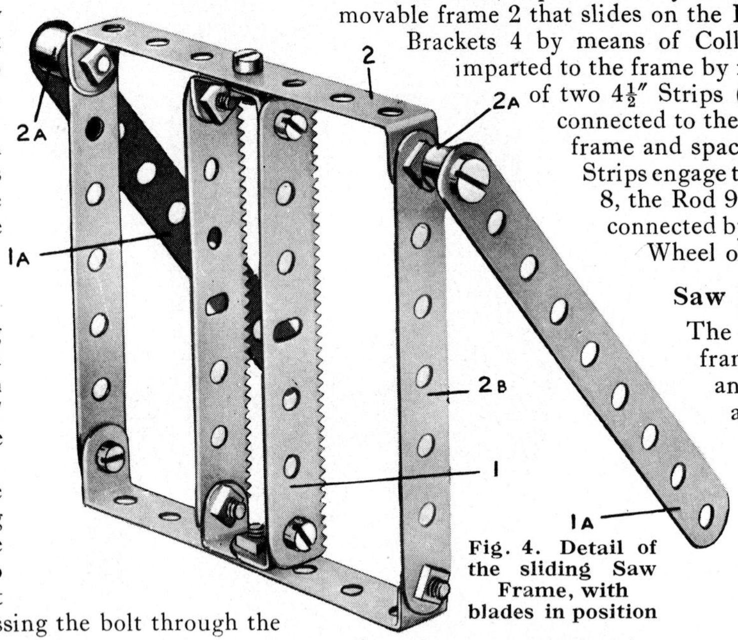

Constructing the Framework

Proceed to build up the framework by bolting two 12½″ Angle Girders 30 to two 3½″×2½″ Flanged Plates 28, as shown in Fig. 2. To the top of each end Flanged Plate 3½″×½″ Double Angle Strips 27 are secured to form a support for the two 12½″ Angle Girders 26, which may now be secured in position.

The two vertical 9½″ Angle Girders 22 are bolted to the Angle Girders 30, the bolts passing through the thirteenth holes in the latter. The Angle Girders 22 are spanned at the top by two Architraves 23 joined together as shown. Now bolt two Angle Brackets 24 to the Angle Girders 22, passing the bolt through the sixth hole from the top end of the Girders.

At the operating end of the base frame two 2½″×2½″ Flat Plates 34 are bolted to the Angle Girders 30 and to the sides of the Flanged Plates 28. At the front end of the framework a 2″ Strip 29a is secured as shown and to this is attached a 1″×1″ Angle Bracket, while a further 1″×1″ Angle Bracket 33 is secured to one of the Flat Plates 34. It is important to note here that the outer end holes in the Angle Brackets 33 and 29 must be exactly opposite each other as these two Brackets carry the shaft 15 (Fig. 3).

To the outer sides of each Angle Girder 26 (Fig. 2) are bolted four 1″ Triangular Plates 35, and two Angle Brackets 31 are fastened to the lower ends of the Girders 22. These Brackets, together with the Angle Brackets 24, form the supports for the guide Rods 3 (Fig. 3) carrying the saw frame. Any further details of the framework will be quite clear from the illustrations.

Roller Feed Mechanism

The log is caused to move past the saws by the pairs of reversed Flanged Wheels 12 and 12a (see Fig. 3). The centre pairs of these wheels are positively driven from the two ¾″ Pinions 13, which are engaged by the Worms 14 carried on the Rod 15. The Rod 15 is held in its bearings 29 and 33 (Fig. 2) by means of two Collars placed one on each side of the Angle Bracket 29.

The movements of the Flanged Pulleys 12 and 12a and of the saws 1 are

Fig. 4. Detail of the sliding Saw Frame, with blades in position

effected simultaneously from the driving Pulley Wheel 16 (Fig. 1), the Rod of which carries a ½″ Pinion that engages a 57-teeth Wheel 19 (Fig. 3). A Bevel Wheel 17 is carried on the outer end of the Rod of the gear 19 and engages a corresponding Bevel 18 carried on the Rod 15.

The saws, represented by the Rack Strips 1, are carried in a vertically movable frame 2 that slides on the Rods 3, the latter being held in the Angle Brackets 4 by means of Collars 5, and a reciprocating movement is imparted to the frame by means of the link Strips 6. These consist of two 4½″ Strips (one on each side of the machine) and are connected to the frame 2 by Pivot Bolts lock-nutted to the frame and spaced with Collars. The lower holes of the Strips engage the Threaded Pins 7 carried in Bush Wheels 8, the Rod 9 of which carries a ¾″ Sprocket 9a and is connected by a Sprocket Chain 10 (Fig. 1) to a Sprocket Wheel on the spindle of the Gear Wheel 19.

Saw Blade Unit

The saw blades are secured in a rectangular framework built up from two 3½″ Strips and two 3½″×½″ Double Angle Strips, as shown in Fig. 4. Two 3½″ Rack Strips represent the saw blades and are bolted by Angle Brackets to the inside of the frame. The remaining portions of the saw blade unit have already been mentioned in the section dealing with the saw motion. The model when completed should be carefully inspected for alignment and all moving parts lubricated so as to ensure perfect freedom of movement.

The machine may be set in motion by means of a Meccano Electric Motor of either the high or low voltage type. If the latter type Motor is used a Meccano 4-volt 8 or 20 ampere-hour Accumulator will be found quite satisfactory, but if a high voltage Motor is available the necessary energy may be taken from the house electric lighting circuit. Before attempting to plug the Motor into the house circuit, however, the reader is advised to consult the special leaflet dealing with this matter and describing the apparatus required. This leaflet may be obtained from all Meccano dealers, or information will be forwarded, on request, by Meccano Ltd., Liverpool.

PARTS REQUIRED

2 of No.	2	1 of No.	15	1 of No.	27a	2 of No.	72
2 ,,	2a	4 ,,	15a	2 ,,	30	10 ,,	77
3 ,,	3	2 ,,	16	2 ,,	32	12″ ,,	94
1 ,,	6	8 ,,	20	59 ,,	37	2 ,,	96
4 ,,	8	1 ,,	20a	6 ,,	37a	2 ,,	108
2 ,,	8a	2 ,,	24	2 ,,	48b	2 ,,	110
8 ,,	12	2 ,,	25	2 ,,	53	2 ,,	115
2 ,,	12a	1 ,,	26	17 ,,	59	2 ,,	147b
1 ,,	13						

Meccano
Travelling Gantry Crane

(Overseas 3d. Canada 5 Cents.)

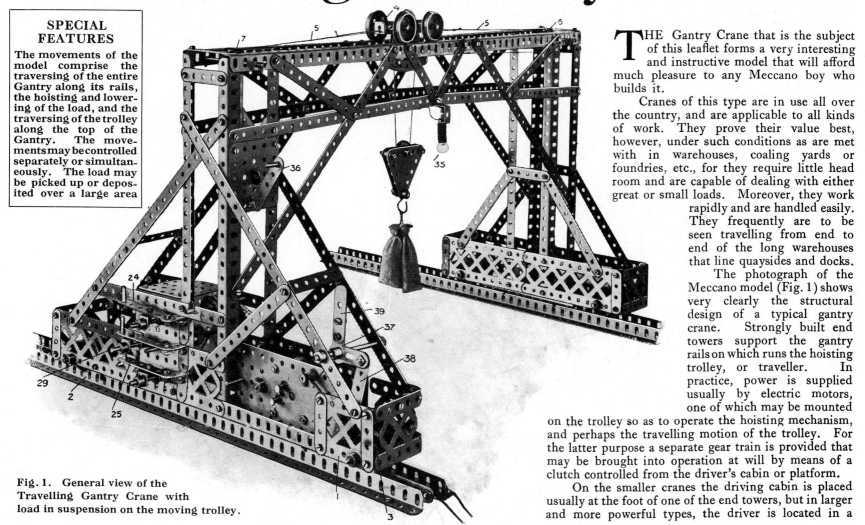

SPECIAL FEATURES

The movements of the model comprise the traversing of the entire Gantry along its rails, the hoisting and lowering of the load, and the traversing of the trolley along the top of the Gantry. The movements may be controlled separately or simultaneously. The load may be picked up or deposited over a large area

Fig. 1. General view of the Travelling Gantry Crane with load in suspension on the moving trolley.

THE Gantry Crane that is the subject of this leaflet forms a very interesting and instructive model that will afford much pleasure to any Meccano boy who builds it.

Cranes of this type are in use all over the country, and are applicable to all kinds of work. They prove their value best, however, under such conditions as are met with in warehouses, coaling yards or foundries, etc., for they require little head room and are capable of dealing with either great or small loads. Moreover, they work rapidly and are handled easily. They frequently are to be seen travelling from end to end of the long warehouses that line quaysides and docks.

The photograph of the Meccano model (Fig. 1) shows very clearly the structural design of a typical gantry crane. Strongly built end towers support the gantry rails on which runs the hoisting trolley, or traveller. In practice, power is supplied usually by electric motors, one of which may be mounted on the trolley so as to operate the hoisting mechanism, and perhaps the travelling motion of the trolley. For the latter purpose a separate gear train is provided that may be brought into operation at will by means of a clutch controlled from the driver's cabin or platform.

On the smaller cranes the driving cabin is placed usually at the foot of one of the end towers, but in larger and more powerful types, the driver is located in a box-like arrangement situated on or beneath the gantry trolley. This position enables him to see all that is taking place on the site over which the crane is working, an advantage that is very important when handling a heavy load.

The Electrical System

Sometimes the electric current is fed to the motors by a shoe that runs on a special rail placed alongside the ordinary metals on which the gantry runs, and is returned through the travelling wheels to the ordinary rails. In other cases only two rails are provided and the current is picked up by the wheels running on one rail, passes through the motors and completes the circuit via the wheels running on the other rail. It is, of course, necessary to insulate each set of road wheels from the framework of the crane in order to prevent short circuiting of the current.

As is the case with almost every other machine, there are several types of Gantry Cranes that, although the same in principle, differ in constructional details. If the crane is to be employed in a long high building such as a warehouse or foundry, it is preferable to dispense with the end towers and ground rails as these would occupy valuable floor space. To do this the gantry is mounted on rails attached to and arranged parallel with the walls of the building and placed high up near the roof. This arrangement brings the whole of the floor space within the range of the hoisting hook, and loads can be picked up or deposited anywhere in the building.

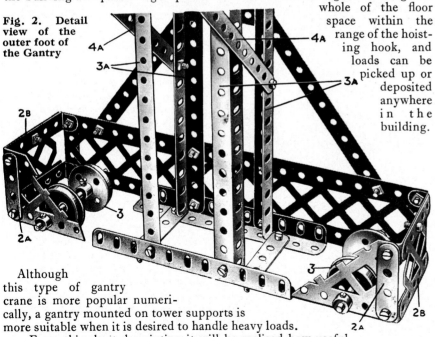

Fig. 2. Detail view of the outer foot of the Gantry

Although this type of gantry crane is more popular numerically, a gantry mounted on tower supports is more suitable when it is desired to handle heavy loads.

From this short description it will be realised how useful this class of crane is. It may safely be stated that, given suitable conditions of working, there is no other class of crane that can handle with the same rapidity and ease either great or small loads.

The above remarks regarding gantry cranes in general will add interest, it is hoped, to the Meccano model, the construction of which is described in detail below. With the aid of the various illustrations any Meccano boy should be able to build the model successfully.

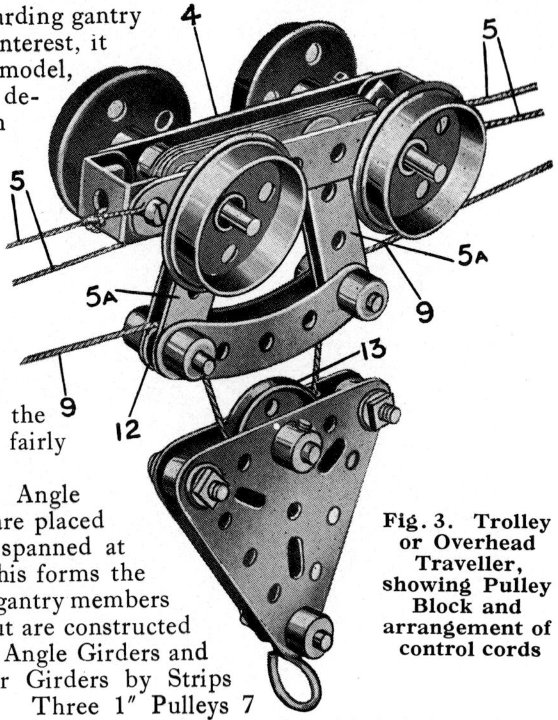

The Meccano Model

The construction of the model should be commenced by building the gantry or upper part of the framework. This will be fairly clear from Fig. 1.

Two pairs of $12\frac{1}{2}''$ Angle Girders joined end to end are placed parallel to each other and spanned at each end by $2\frac{1}{2}''$ Strips. This forms the top of the gantry; the lower gantry members are built in the same way but are constructed from $12\frac{1}{2}''$ Strips in place of Angle Girders and are connected to the upper Girders by Strips placed as shown in Fig. 1. Three $1''$ Pulleys 7 are carried loosely on a $3\frac{1}{2}''$ Rod journalled in the third holes of the upper Girders.

Fig. 3. Trolley or Overhead Traveller, showing Pulley Block and arrangement of control cords

Construction of the End Towers

It should be noted that in the base of the tower that carries the Electric Motor (Fig. 1) the centre portion is composed of $12\frac{1}{2}''$ Angle Girders at the lower edge, extended at one end by $2\frac{1}{2}''$ Braced Girders 1 overhanging four holes and on the other end by $5\frac{1}{2}''$ Braced Girders 2 overhanging five holes.

The shorter tower base is shown in Fig. 2 and it will be noticed that this differs from the tower base that carries the Electric Motor. $2\frac{1}{2}''$ Braced Girders 2b (Fig. 2) form the ends of the tower bases, while additional support is given by means of the $2\frac{1}{2}''$ Strips 2a placed as shown. Four $12\frac{1}{2}''$ Angle Girders 3a are secured in position vertically and form the main structure of the towers. The outer pair of vertical Angle Girders on each tower are spanned near the top by $2\frac{1}{2}''$ Strips. The travelling wheels 3 (Figs. 1 and 2) are carried on $3\frac{1}{2}''$ Rods journalled in holes in the Braced Girders forming the sides of the tower bases.

Two $2\frac{1}{2}'' \times 3\frac{1}{2}''$ Flanged Plates 30a (Fig. 5) should be bolted to the Braced Girders 2 of the tower base. These Plates are only to be fitted to the long base; they are not required on the shorter base. They may be secured further by means of $7\frac{1}{2}''$ Strips bolted to the Flanged Plates 30a and also to the upright Girders 3a and to the Girders of the base. The top edges of the Flanged

Plates 30a may be spanned by a 2½"×2½" Flat Plate, but this should not be attached until the gears have been assembled. Any other constructional details of the towers and bases may easily be obtained from the various illustrations.

Constructional Details of the Trolley

The overhead trolley is built up as follows. Two 3½" Strips 4 (Fig. 3) are joined by Double Brackets to form a box-like structure. The Axle Rods carrying on their ends the travelling wheels are journalled in these Strips. They also carry several 2½" Strips the weight of which serves to ensure the proper adhesion of the trolley wheels on the gantry rails. Four 2" Strips 5a are bolted to these 2½" Strips, and their lower ends are spaced apart by 2½" Curved Strips. The lower ends of the Strips 5a carry ½" Pulleys on 1" Rods. The construction of the pulley block will be evident from the illustration.

Assembling the Mechanism

The Motor spindle 19 (Fig. 5) drives by the Chain 20 a 2" Sprocket Wheel 21 on a Rod 22, on which is a ½" Pinion 23 (Fig. 4).

The Rods 10 and 8 are slidably controlled by the clutch operating handles 24 and 25, which are bolted and lock-nutted to Double Brackets 26, engaging between Collars 27 nipped on the Rods. On the outer end of the Rod 10 is a 57-teeth Wheel 28 and a similar wheel is secured on the outer end of the Rod 8. By operating the clutch handles 24, 25 either or both of the Gear Wheels 28 or 28a may be brought into engagement with the ½" Pinion 23 and thus cause the load to be raised or lowered, or the trolley to be traversed.

The third clutch handle 29 similarly controls the sliding movement of a Rod 30, on which is secured a 57-teeth Gear Wheel 31 and a ½" Pinion 32. On the Rod 22 is secured another ½" Pinion 33, while on the Rod 14 is a further 57-teeth Gear Wheel 34.

By moving the handle 29 the Gear Wheel 31 and the Pinion 32 may be brought into engagement respectively with the Pinion 33 and the Gear Wheel 34, thus providing a reducing gear train from the driven Rod 22 to the Rod 14. The latter effects the travelling of the whole gantry upon the wheels 3 and carries a 1" Sprocket Wheel connected by a Chain 16 with a further 1" Sprocket Wheel 17 carried on the Rod 18 of a pair of travelling wheels 3.

The reversal of the Motor is controlled by the lever 39. It is only necessary to reverse the Motor, of course, to change the direction of movement of any one of the various operations of the crane.

Fig. 4. Operating Mechanism and control levers.

Trolley Control Mechanism

The traversing of the trolley on the gantry rails is effected by a cord 5, which passes from the far end of the trolley, round a Pulley 6 (Fig. 1) and is then returned and passed over one of the 1" Pulleys 7 down to the Rod 8, round which it is given three turns. The cord then passes up and around another of the Pulleys 7, and finally is connected to the near end of the trolley. In consequence of this arrangement rotation of the Rod 8 will wind up one end of the traversing cord and pay out the other end, so causing the trolley to travel to and fro along the gantry rails.

Load Hoisting Arrangement

A separate cord 9 controls the hoisting and lowering operations of the load. It is wound round the upper Rod 10 (Fig. 4) and thence round the guide pulley 11, round the third of the Pulleys 7 (Fig. 1) and over the ½" Pulley 12 (Fig. 3). Thence it passes beneath the 1" Pulley 13 on the load block, then round another ½" Pulley, and is made fast on the far end of the gantry frame.

If Rod 10 (Fig. 4) is not rotated the trolley travels to and fro without the load being either raised or lowered. So soon as the Rod 10 is rotated, however, the load is raised or lowered according to the direction of rotation of the Rod.

While every effort has been made to make the constructional details as clear as possible, considerable help can be obtained by studying the various illustrations carefully, thus gaining a correct idea as to the function each part has to perform. When completed, the model should be carefully adjusted and each shaft and gear wheel brought into perfect alignment, as much depends on the ease and freedom with which the model works. Apply a little oil to all rotating rods and journals and also to the gear wheels. If these matters are attended to, much trouble and annoyance which might otherwise result by the model working stiffly, will be avoided and the little extra attention given to details like these is always amply repaid.

The Electric Circuit

The rails on which the model runs are formed by Girders placed in pairs parallel to each other and secured preferably to a board or other suitable base. Fig. 1 clearly shows this arrangement.

Between the rails on which the longer tower base travels is placed a centre rail consisting of 12½" Strips bolted end to end and secured by Angle Brackets to the base board. These Strips form the conductor rail from which the electric current is taken to the Motor by means of a 1½″ Strip bolted to the end Girders of the base. The Strip is given a spring tension by bending it a little. It may then be arranged to make a good rubbing contact with the top of the centre rail.

The 1½″ collector Strip must be insulated from the base of the model by means of Insulating Bushes and Washers placed between the bolt head and the Strip and between the Strip and the Girder, while further Insulating Washers should be placed between the securing nut and the Girder.

A length of insulated wire may now be joined to the 1½″ Strip by means of a bolt and nut and the other end of the wire taken to one of the terminals on the Motor. The remaining terminal of the Motor is connected to the framework of the crane at any suitable point. The current supply is connected by one wire to the centre rail and by another to one of the outer rails.

Illuminating the Model

A 4-volt Accumulator will be required if the low voltage Meccano Motor is used, but if the Motor is of the high voltage type the necessary energy may be taken from the house lighting current provided a suitable resistance is placed in series. In this connection a word of warning is necessary as we cannot too strongly emphasise the precaution necessary in taking current from the house supply, and we advise the reader to consult the special Meccano leaflet dealing with this matter, or, better still, to call in the aid of a competent electrician. If high voltage current is used it should not be led through the rails as described above, but taken direct to the model through a length of flex.

A small electric bulb may be mounted on the crane and controlled by

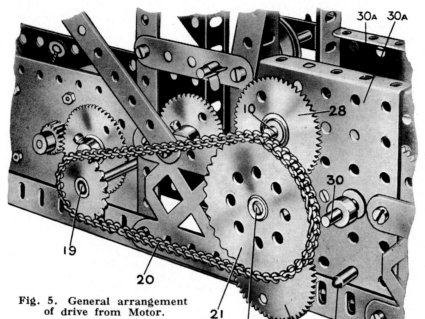

Fig. 5. General arrangement of drive from Motor.

a simple switch as illustrated on Fig. 1, but this is, of course, a matter for individual choice. The control switch for the lamp is shown at 36, Fig. 1.

The base of the switch is composed of a 2½″ × 2½″ Flat Plate and the arm is formed by two 2½″ Strips pivoted on a bolt passed through an Angle Bracket secured to the Flat Plate.

When closed, the switch arm makes contact with an Angle Bracket secured to the Flat Plate, the vertical edge of the Bracket passing between the two Strips forming the arm. The Angle Bracket on which the arm pivots must be insulated from the Flat Plate by means of Insulating Bushes and Washers.

The Lamp Holder, a standard Meccano part (No. 310), is secured to a Double Bent Strip attached to a Girder of the gantry as shown in Fig. 1. The electrical connections are as follows : a wire from one of the accumulator terminals is taken direct to the Angle Bracket on which the switch arm pivots, while the other Angle Bracket of the switch is connected to the outer casing of the Lamp Holder. The contact screw in the Lamp Holder is connected directly to the other terminal of the Accumulator.

If it is desired to run the Lamp and Motor from the same source of supply, they may be coupled in series. The necessary connections are as follows. The Lamp Holder should be in electrical contact with the frame of the model. As in the circuit already described, the collector shoe is connected to one terminal of the Motor, but the other Motor terminal is connected by an insulated wire to the Angle Bracket on which the switch arm pivots. The other Angle Bracket, which makes contact with the arm, is connected to the contact screw in the Lamp Holder. With this arrangement the switch controls the Motor and Lamp simultaneously.

List of Parts Required to Build the Travelling Gantry Crane

12 of No.	1	6 of No.	7	11 of No.	16	3 of No.	26	9 of No.	48a	1 of No.	95	5 of No.	303
12 ,,	2	10 ,,	8	1 ,,	16a	3 ,,	27	2 ,,	53	3 ,,	96	4 ,,	304
6 ,,	3	2 ,,	9	2 ,,	17	3 ,,	27a	1 ,,	57	8 ,,	98	8 ,,	305
3 ,,	4	6 ,,	11	4 ,,	18a	11 ,,	35	30 ,,	59	6 ,,	100	1 ,,	310
17 ,,	5	4 ,,	12a	12 ,,	20	149 ,,	37	1 ,,	72	2 ,,	111	1 ,,	311
14 ,,	6	2 ,,	15	8 ,,	22a	10 ,,	37a	2 ,,	76	1 ,,	128	1 Electric	
1 ,,	6a	2 ,,	15a	2 ,,	23	38 ,,	38	2 ,,	90	5 ,,	302	Motor	
				2 ,,	25	3 ,,	44	26″ ,,	94				

Meccano Hydraulic Crane

Fig. 1. General view of the Meccano Hydraulic Crane.

SPECIAL FEATURES

Separate control handles for each of the operations, viz., hoisting and lowering of the load, swivelling and travelling. The hydraulic ram is represented realistically by a very powerful screw mechanism that enables loads of great weight to be hoisted easily and smoothly.

THE numerous portable cranes that are to be found scattered here and there in a large works or dockyard form very interesting objects for reproduction in miniature by means of the Meccano system. They cannot compare, of course, with the great derricking cranes so far as lifting capacity is concerned, but they are nevertheless extremely important features of modern engineering works owing to the ease with which they travel from one site to another.

Sometimes at a large works it becomes necessary to carry a load from one department to another, as for instance, a casting from the foundry to the machine shops, and for this purpose there is nothing handier or more suited than a small capacity travelling crane. This may be one of several types, the commonest being the revolving, short jib, steam- or electrically-driven crane. Portable steam cranes have a lifting capacity varying between fairly wide limits, the smallest lifting five tons while the larger ones will lift comfortably anything up to 50 tons. The power is derived usually from a boiler and engine mounted on a revolving superstructure, the boiler generally being of the vertical fire tube type.

Electrically-driven cranes either carry their own batteries from which to obtain the supply of current, or receive the supply from an exterior source, by means of either a flexible cable attached to the frame and trailing along behind, or from rails on which the crane travels. In the latter case the electric circuit is completed through the road wheels, which are in direct electrical communication with the motors contained in the superstructure of the crane, and a conductor rail or overhead wire.

As a rule separate motors are provided for controlling each of the movements of which the crane is capable, the power of these motors ranging from 5 h.p. to 50 h.p. or more.

828/5   Published by MECCANO LIMITED, BINNS ROAD, LIVERPOOL.   Printed in England

Although the steam and electric types are the more popular, there are two other types of portable crane that are equally interesting and efficient. These are pneumatically- and hydraulically-operated cranes.

Portable Pneumatic Cranes

The pneumatic or air-driven crane is seldom used, owing to the special air compressors that are necessary to provide the required power. In some large engineering shops, however, compressed air is employed for a number of purposes, such as working riveting hammers, drilling machines, etc., and in these cases it is no uncommon sight to see one or two compressed-air driven cranes as well.

The necessary power is developed by a small air engine designed especially for high speed. The compressed air enters the cylinders through ports arranged very similarly to those in an ordinary steam engine, the only difference lying in the amount of lap or lead of the valve. As compressed air has no expansion factor such as steam possesses, the air enters the cylinders throughout the whole of the stroke, the pressure thus remaining constant.

These air-driven engines revolve at a great speed and develop considerable power when their size is compared with a steam engine. The pressure of the air supply is usually something like 60 lbs. per square inch.

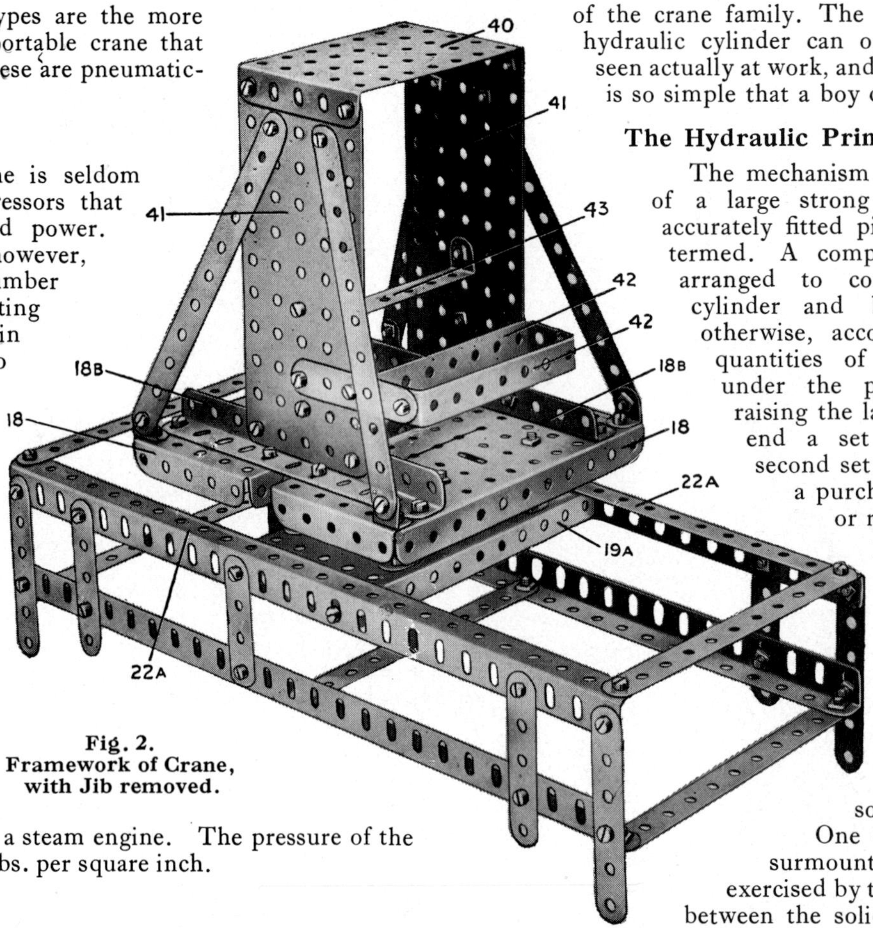

Advantages of Hydraulic Power

The possibility of using water as a source of power had not received much attention until in 1795 Joseph Bramah, the famous engineer, devoted his attention to the matter. He invented a press that was operated by the aid of water, and as soon as the success of this machine became known other engineers directed their activities in the same direction, and it was not long before water power was used to work all kinds of machines. To-day hydraulic machinery may be found in almost every shipyard and engineering works. It is employed to work—amongst other tools—shearing machines that can cut at one stroke steel plates 2″ thick.

Hydraulic machinery is used whenever enormous loads have to be moved. As long ago as 1848 the gigantic tubes of the Britannia Bridge were hoisted into their bed by hydraulic machines. During the construction of this bridge the weight raised by a single machine was over 1,100 tons! While the hydraulic crane may be placed among the smaller cranes so far as structural size is concerned, its capacity for lifting entitles it to a place amongst the giants

Fig. 2.
Framework of Crane,
with Jib removed.

of the crane family. The prodigious force that is exercised by a hydraulic cylinder can only be appreciated when the machine is seen actually at work, and yet the control of such tremendous power is so simple that a boy could easily manage such a machine.

The Hydraulic Principle

The mechanism of a hydraulic crane consists primarily of a large strong cylinder, inside which works a very accurately fitted piston or plunger, as it is more correctly termed. A comparatively small bore forcing pump is arranged to communicate with the bottom of the cylinder and by operating the pump—by hand or otherwise, according to the size of the crane—small quantities of water may be forced in succession under the piston in the cylinder, thus gradually raising the latter. The piston rod carries at its upper end a set of pulleys which are connected to a second set by means of chain or rope so as to form a purchase block. The free end of the chain or rope is attached to the load hook. As the piston slowly rises, it forces the two sets of pulleys further apart, with the result that the load hook is raised. The object of the purchase block is merely to convert the small movement of the piston rod to a great movement of the load.

It may be mentioned here that only after many difficulties had been overcome did the use of water as a source of power become a practical reality. One of the principal obstacles that had to be surmounted arose from the tremendous pressure exercised by the pump, which forced the water through between the solid piston and the side of the cylinder in which it worked, in such quantities as to render the machine useless for practical purposes.

Bramah himself was completely baffled by this difficulty. It will be observed that the problem was to secure a joint sufficiently free to let the piston slide up through it, and at the same time, so watertight as to withstand the internal force of the pump.

In this dilemma an engineer named Henry Maudsley came to the rescue. The solution came in a flash of genius and the result was Maudsley's self-tightening collar, the action of which a few words description will render easily intelligible. A collar of sound leather, the convex side upwards and the concave downwards, was fitted into the recess turned out in the neck of the cylinder. Immediately on the high pressure water being turned on it forced its way into the leather concavity, "flapped out" the bent edges of the collar; and in so doing, caused the leather to apply itself to the surface of the rising ram so closely and tightly as to seal up the joint, the closer exactly in proportion to the pressure of the water in the cylinder. On the other hand, so soon as the pressure was let off and the ram desired to return, the collar collapsed and the ram slid gently down, perfectly free and yet perfectly water-tight. Such is briefly the principle on which present-day hydraulic machines work.

In the Meccano model hydraulic crane it has not been possible to use water, for obvious reasons, but in order to illustrate as closely as possible the principles on which hydraulic cranes work, a vertically-rising and falling rod is provided. This is driven by Meccano screw mechanism, and its movement corresponds exactly to the movement of the ram or hydraulic piston rod of the actual crane.

Construction of the Model

The general view (Fig. 1) shows very clearly the arrangement of the principal parts of the crane. The load is raised or lowered at will by means of the handle 1 while the whole superstructure may be swivelled on the base by rotating the handle shown in position at the side of the model. The crane travels on the four wheels 22, which are driven by Sprocket Wheels and Chain through a Contrate Wheel and Pinion operated by the handle 23.

The construction of the model should be commenced by building up the base frame that carries the road wheels. Details of this are shown clearly in Figs. 1 and 2. The main part of the frame is composed of four $12\frac{1}{2}''$ Angle Girders 22a connected at their ends by means of $5\frac{1}{2}''$ Strips and at their sides by $3''$ Strips 20a as indicated. A $5\frac{1}{2}'' \times 2\frac{1}{2}''$ Flanged Plate 19a occupies the centre of the top of the frame and is bolted to the upper pair of Angle Girders 22a. Two $2\frac{1}{2}''$ Double Angle Strips 18a (Fig. 6) should be secured to the Plate 19a. They are held in position by means of Angle Brackets.

The $2\frac{1}{2}''$ Strips 22b (Fig. 1) carry the Axle Rods for the travelling wheels 22 ($3''$ Pulley Wheels), the Rods passing through the lower end holes of the Strips. The front wheel axle carries a $2''$ Sprocket Wheel connected by means of a Sprocket Chain to a $1''$ Sprocket Wheel carried on a $6\frac{1}{2}''$ Rod that is journalled in the $3''$ Strips 20a bolted to the Angle Girders 22a.

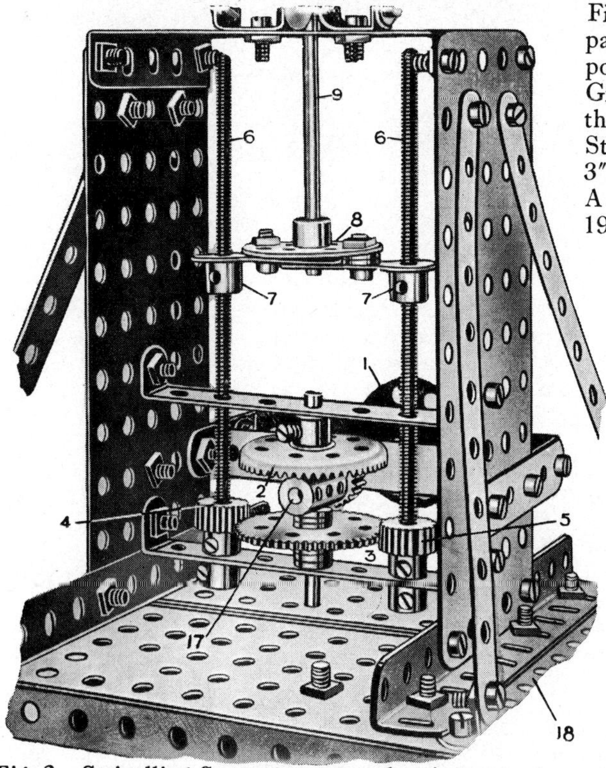

A $1\frac{1}{2}''$ Contrate Wheel mounted on the $6\frac{1}{2}''$ Rod engages a $1\frac{1}{2}''$ Pinion on the lower end of the shaft carrying the handle 23 so that when the handle is rotated, movement is transmitted via the Pinion and Contrate Wheel through the Sprocket Chain to the front wheel axle, thus causing the crane to travel either forward or backward according to the direction of rotation of handle 23.

The $6\frac{1}{2}''$ Rod carrying the $1\frac{1}{2}''$ Contrate Wheel is held in position by Collars with set-screws placed on the Rod against the inner sides of the $3''$ Strips.

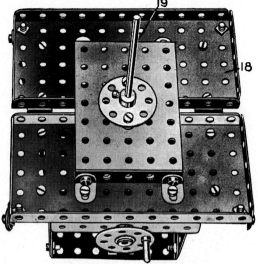

Fig. 4. Underneath view of Superstructure.

Assembling the Superstructure

The framework for the mechanism is carried on a platform 18 (Fig. 2) that pivots about a vertical Rod 19 (Fig. 4) on which is a 57-teeth Gear Wheel. The latter is driven by a Worm carried on the shaft of the handle shown at the side of the base frame (Fig. 1). The Worm and Gear Wheel cannot be seen as they are hidden by the Flanged Plate (19a in Fig. 2).

The constructional details of the crane platform are shown in Fig. 4, which is an underneath view of this part of the model. The platform 18 is built up from two $5\frac{1}{2}'' \times 2\frac{1}{2}''$ Flanged Plates connected by means of the $5\frac{1}{2}''$ Angle Girders 18b (Fig. 2) the latter being bolted to the upper side of the platform. A Rod 19 (Fig. 4) is fixed in the boss of a Bush Wheel secured to the $3\frac{1}{2}'' \times 2\frac{1}{2}''$ Flanged Plate that, in turn, is bolted to the underside of the platform 18.

The framework that houses the operating mechanism is shown more clearly in Figs. 2 and 3. Two $5\frac{1}{2}'' \times 2\frac{1}{2}''$ Flat Plates are bolted to the Angle Girders 18b and are spanned at the top by the $3\frac{1}{2}'' \times 2\frac{1}{2}''$ Flanged Plate 40. Four $5\frac{1}{2}''$ Strips brace the frame securely to the platform, the lower ends of the Strips being secured to the Plates 18 by Angle Brackets. Two $3\frac{1}{2}'' \times \frac{1}{2}''$ Double Angle Strips 43 are secured in the interior of the frame and form journal bearings for the Threaded Rods 6 of the mechanism.

Operating Mechanism

The screw gear and operating mechanism may now be assembled. The load hook is raised or lowered on operation of the hand wheel 1, the arrangement of the gears being as follows.

Fig. 3. Swivelling Superstructure, showing arrangement of Mechanism.

Fig. 5.
Arrangement of Hoisting Gear and Cords.

The Rod of the wheel 1 is journalled in Double Angle Strips 42 (Fig. 2), and carries a $\frac{1}{2}''$ Pinion that gears with a $1\frac{1}{2}''$ Contrate Wheel 2 (Fig. 3), on the Rod of which is a 57-teeth Gear Wheel 3. The latter engages the two $\frac{1}{2}''$ Pinions 4 and 5 secured on the vertical Threaded Rods 6, so that these Rods are rotated in the same direction on rotation of the handle 1. The Threaded Rods 6 pass through the Double Angle Strip 43 and engage the bosses of Threaded Cranks 7 (Fig. 3) secured to a Bush Wheel 8 in the boss of which is fixed a 6" Rod 9. The latter passes through the Plate 40 (Fig. 2) and is secured at the top in a Coupling 9a (Fig. 5) to which are connected on a 1" transverse Rod two Cranks that support another 1" Rod forming a bearing for two 1" Pulleys 10 and 11.

The inner end of the Rod of the Bush Wheel 1 is journalled in a Coupling 17 (Fig. 3) and is held in position by the wheel 1 on one side of the outer Double Angle Strip 42 and by a Collar and set-screw on the other side. The vertical Rod carrying the Contrate Wheel 2 is free to turn in the centre transverse hole of this Coupling, the latter being held in position by means of two or three Washers.

Two $\frac{1}{2}''$ Pulleys 12 and 13 are mounted loosely on a 2" Rod at the base of the jib on one side and a single $\frac{1}{2}''$ Pulley 14 on another 2" Rod at the other side.

Constructing the Jib

Although the construction of the jib is a very simple matter, a little descriptive detail will no doubt be helpful.

The main elements of the jib are formed by four $12\frac{1}{2}''$ Strips spaced by Double Brackets as shown in Figs. 1 and 5. The lower ends of the $12\frac{1}{2}''$ Strips are joined by means of 3" Strips, while the upper ends incline towards each other and are bolted together as illustrated. A $1\frac{1}{2}''$ Rod passing through the upper end holes of the lower Strips and held in position by Spring Clips, carries a $1\frac{1}{2}''$ Pulley Wheel 16 over which passes the hoisting cord 15.

Four Flanged Wheels are carried on a Rod journalled in the end holes of $5\frac{1}{2}''$ Strips attached to the base of the jib at the rear. These Wheels act as balance weights and help to distribute the strains more evenly about the pivoting centre of the crane.

When completed the jib may be secured to the Plate 40 of the gear frame (Fig. 2) by bolts passed through the lower spacing Double Brackets.

Arrangement of the Hoisting Cord

This model has been designed specially to demonstrate how a very small movement of the operating mechanism can be multiplied greatly by a special arrangement of the hoisting cord. In a real hydraulic crane, the movement or stroke of the piston is quite small—usually only a matter of a few feet—and in order to raise a load through say 15 or 20 feet, it becomes necessary to magnify the movement of the piston by an arrangement on similar lines to that embodied in the model. As already stated, the small vertical movement imparted by the Threaded Rods to the Rod 9 may be likened to that of the hydraulic ram in the actual crane.

The hoisting cord 15 (Fig. 5) passes over the Pulley 16 at the top of the jib, thence round the Pulley 12, over the Pulley 10, round the lower Pulley 14, back round the other Pulley 11 at the top of Rod 9, and then round the small Pulley 13. Finally it is made fast to the Coupling 9a.

Fig. 6.
Base Framework, showing platform for Superstructure.

By turning the handle 1 (Fig. 3) the Contrate Wheel 2 is rotated, thus driving the Pinions 4 and 5 and rotating the Threaded Rods 6. The movement of the latter causes the Threaded Cranks—and therefore the Rod 9 carrying the Pulley Wheels 10 and 11—to be raised or lowered. As the Pulleys 10 and 11 are forced upward, the cord 15 travels round all the Pulleys, and due to the number of loops of the cord, the small vertical movement of the upper Pulleys 10 and 11 results in a much larger movement of the load hook.

The model having been completed it may be set in operation when it will be found that considerable loads can be lifted by the expenditure of very little effort. It is advisable to place a little oil on the screws and shafts to ensure smooth and easy working.

List of Parts Required to Build the Hydraulic Crane

4 of No.	1	3 of No.	14	2 of No.	27a	1 of No.	57
11 ,,	2	3 ,,	16	2 ,,	28	14 ,,	59
2 ,,	3	4 ,,	17	1 ,,	32	4 ,,	62
4 ,,	4	2 ,,	18a	2 ,,	35	2 ,,	62a
8 ,,	5	4 ,,	19b	104 ,,	37	3 ,,	63
2 ,,	6	4 ,,	20	18 ,,	38	2 ,,	70
4 ,,	8	1 ,,	21	1 ,,	45	2 ,,	80
2 ,,	9	2 ,,	22a	2 ,,	48a	30" ,,	94
5 ,,	11	3 ,,	23	4 ,,	48b	1 ,,	95
12 ,,	12	4 ,,	24	3 ,,	52	3 ,,	115
2 ,,	13a	4 ,,	26	2 ,,	53		

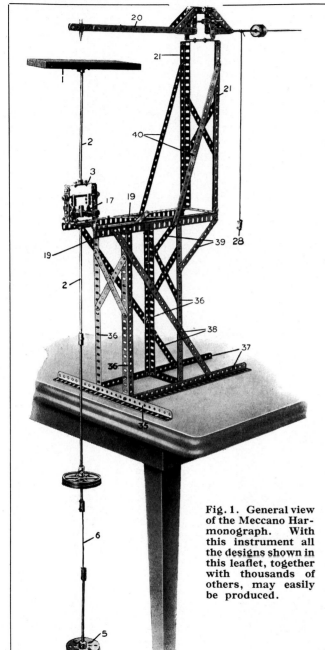

Fig. 1. General view of the Meccano Harmonograph. With this instrument all the designs shown in this leaflet, together with thousands of others, may easily be produced.

Meccano Twin-Elliptic Harmonograph

Model No. 7.31:

THE Meccano Harmonograph fulfils two functions. It forms a fascinating toy with which many pleasant hours may be passed by producing an innumerable variety of beautiful designs, and it is also a scientific instrument by means of which it is possible to record harmonic motions in a permanent visual form. Harmonic motion is a general term applied to a reciprocating motion like that of a piston or pendulum. The records obtained by means of an instrument of this kind are invaluable to the scientific investigator as a means of studying the laws of vibration, for the movements of a pendulum are vibrations just as much as are the rapid movements of the particles of a heated body.

There is something very thrilling in operating the Meccano model and speculating as to what form the design will take. The Meccano boy—and his friends and parents as well—will find abundant pleasure in watching the Harmonograph at work, producing thousands of fascinating and lovely patterns in endless succession.

In its earliest form the Harmonograph consisted of a heavy weight hung on the end of a cord and so arranged that when set in motion the weight was free to move in any direction according to the manner in which it was set swinging. A pointer attached to the weight traced in sand or other suitable material the path through which the weight travelled.

It was found that by varying the mass of the weight and altering the length of the cord by which it hung considerable difference could be produced in the design drawn by the pointers. It was also discovered that if instead of only one pendulum, two or more were employed and so arranged that their combined movements operated the same pencil or pointer the resultant designs became much more complex and beautiful. Based on the information gained from these early experiments it has been possible

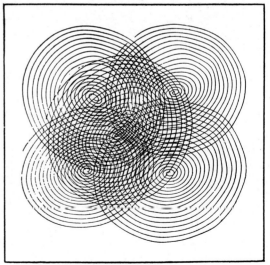

A specimen Harmonograph design, obtained by superimposing five similar patterns.

to construct harmonographs which will produce at will practically any type of design.

It may be thought that it is necessary to possess artistic skill in order to make beautiful designs such as are illustrated in this leaflet, but really it is so simple that even a child can obtain equally successful results. All that is necessary is to pin a sheet of white paper to the table of the harmonograph, fill the pen with ink—which by the way may be either black or coloured—and then set the pendulum rod and weights swinging.

How a Harmonograph Works

To produce the finest designs it is necessary to know something of how the instrument operates. Referring to Fig. 1, which is a general view of the Meccano Harmonograph, it will be seen that the table 1 is supported from a frame that is pivoted on knife edge bearings. Attached to the lower side of the frame is a primary weighted pendulum. A second pendulum is attached to the primary pendulum by means of a piece of cord, the whole thus forming a single compound pendulum.

The pen is held in a pivoted arm, the latter being provided with an arrangement of weights whereby the pressure of the pen on the table may be adjusted.

Owing to the knife-edge pivots the table is able to move in all directions quite freely. To set the instrument in operation the pendulum is given a steady swinging movement in any direction. When the secondary pendulum is given a different movement to that of the primary, the movement of the table will be very complex, and it is this "double or compound pendulum" effect that enables such an endless variety of designs to be produced. When one gets used to the instrument it will become quite easy to set the compound pendulum swinging in the correct manner to produce practically any pre-decided design.

Making the Special Glass Pen

A special pen has been designed for use with the model and is made quite easily as follows. Secure a piece of $\frac{1}{8}''$ or $\frac{1}{4}''$ diameter glass tubing about 6″ long. Hold this in a Bunsen or other flame until quite soft (see Fig. 4) then draw the ends of the tube slowly apart until only a very fine portion remains in the

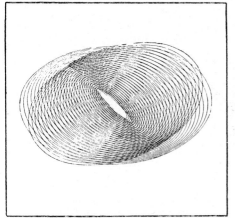

Notice the beautiful watered-silk effect obtained in this simple Harmonograph design.

Page 2

centre as shown in the illustration. Withdraw the glass from the flame and allow it to cool gradually (it is necessary to place the heated glass on a slightly warmed surface when cooling, otherwise the sudden contraction of the outer shell of the tube will produce fractures in the glass). When quite cold break the glass in two pieces at the centre of the tapered portion and hold the point of one piece in the flame again until the end is rounded off. It will probably be found that after doing this the hole in the point is sealed, in which case the point should be rubbed on an oilstone until it is possible to just blow through the tube when using a fair amount of pressure.

Load the pen with ink by means of the rubber bulb of a fountain pen filler placed over the upper end of the glass tube ; by this method, particles of dirt larger than the hole in the point cannot enter the pen to clog it.

Construction of the Framework

The base of the framework is built with two $12\frac{1}{2}''$ Angle Girders 37 and one $12\frac{1}{2}''$ Angle Girder 35 (Fig. 1), bolted together at right angles as shown. To these are bolted at vertical right angles four $12\frac{1}{2}''$ Angle Girders 36, which are braced by four $5\frac{1}{2}''$ Strips placed crosswise and secured to the Girders 36. To the tops of the four vertical Girders are secured two further $12\frac{1}{2}''$ Angle Girders 19 and to the rear ends of these are bolted two more $12\frac{1}{2}''$ Angle Girders secured in a vertical position and spanned across their upper ends by a $3\frac{1}{2}'' \times \frac{1}{2}''$ Double Angle Strip (see Fig. 3).

The $12\frac{1}{2}''$ Strips forming the stays 40 (Fig. 1) may now be attached between the Angle Girders 21 and 19. The position of the other stays used for strengthening the framework can be readily ascertained by reference to the illustration.

The paper on which the design is to be drawn is placed on the

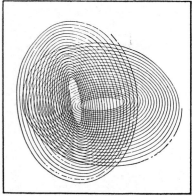

Another composite design, which also gives a watered-silk effect.

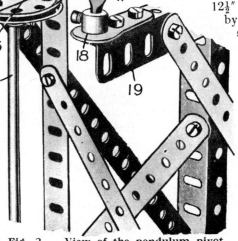

Fig. 2. View of the pendulum pivot frame, showing details of the knife edge bearings, etc.

Designing Table 1 (part No. 107) carried on the upper 8″ Rod 2, to the lower end of which is secured a Bush Wheel 3, which, in turn, is bolted to a frame 4 (Fig. 2). This frame is composed of two 2½″ × 1″ Double Angle Strips and two 2½″ Strips bolted together to form a square as shown. Outside the 2½″ Strips forming the vertical sides of the square are bolted two Cranks 8 that provide support for a 3½″ Rod 9 passed through and secured in the Crank bosses.

The lower portion of the pendulum 2 (Fig. 1) consists of two 8″ Rods and an 11½″ Rod, and in order to obtain a "compound" movement of the table 1, the lower 8″ Rod is coupled flexibly to the remainder of the pendulum by a piece of string 6. This arrangement forms in reality two pendulums compounded into one. The weight 5 may be made up with several 3″ Pulley Wheels or other parts.

The Knife-edge Bearings

On the Rod 9 (Fig. 2) are mounted Couplings 10, in the longitudinal holes of which are secured two Centre Forks. These form knife-edge bearings and engage between the teeth of two ½″ Pinions 12 fixed on a 2″ Rod 13, which is secured in the end holes of a centre Coupling 14 that also carries in its centre transverse hole a 3½″ Rod 15, mounted at right-angles to the Rod 13. On the outer ends of the Rod 15 are carried two further ½″ Pinions 16 which rest upon Centre Forks 17 forming further knife-edge bearings and secured in the bosses of Cranks 18 bolted to the ends of the Angle Girders 19 (see also Fig. 1). As a result of this arrangement the frame 4 is balanced and free to swing in any direction about the knife-edge bearings 17 and 11.

The ink pen is held between the ends of the two 12½″ Strips 20 (Fig. 1) that form an arm which is supported pivotally as shown in Fig. 3. At the

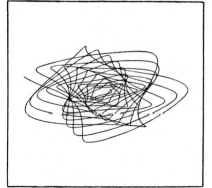

An intricate little design produced under the combined influence of the two pendulums.

top of the vertical frame 21 (Fig. 1) is a 2½″ × 1½″ Double Angle Strip to which two Cranks 22 (Fig. 3) are secured. A Rod 23 mounted in the bosses of these Cranks carries two ½″ Pinions 24. The Strips 20 are coupled to the yoke formed by 3″ and 2″ Strips and 2½″ × ½″ Double Angle Strips as shown, in the rear of which is fixed a Rod 26 carrying a "balance weight" 27 composed of four 1″ fast

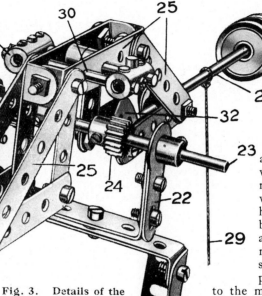

Fig. 3. Details of the pencil arm pivot, yoke and balance arm.

Pulleys. A further weight 28 (Fig. 1) consisting of a Coupling is suspended from the Rod 26 by the cord 29.

The Rod 26 is secured by passing it through Double Brackets that are held between the 3″ and 2″ Strips 25 forming the sides of the yoke. Collars placed on the Rod against the faces of the Brackets serve to hold it in position.

In the upper 2½″ × ½″ Double Angle Strips forming the yoke 25 are inserted two Rods 30 carrying Couplings 31 and in the centre holes of these Couplings are secured Centre Forks 32 forming knife-edge

Fig. 4. Showing method of drawing the glass pen point.

bearings, which engage the ½″ Pinions 24. The entire arm is free to swing about this point.

The pressure of the pencil on the paper is adjusted by means of the balance weight 27, which can be moved along the Rod until the pen rests just lightly on the table 1, when the extra weight 28 is lifted. When the weight 28 is hanging free (as in Fig. 1) the pen point should be lifted clear of the table. To operate the apparatus, the weight 5 is given a swinging movement. This oscillates the table 1 and the stationary pencil describes a diagram on the paper, which may be varied indefinitely according to the minutest alteration in the direction in which the weight is made to swing.

The paper should be of good quality and afford an even surface. Rough paper should be avoided as also paper with a highly finished surface such as "art" paper, as it is too absorbent. Excellent results are obtained on Bristol Board.

List of Parts required.

8 of No.	1		2 of No.	12		3 of No.	22		1 of No.	48b
10	,,	2	2	,,	13	2	,,	22a	4	,,	59
3	,,	3	2	,,	13a	2	,,	24	6	,,	62
4	,,	4	1	,,	14	6	,,	26	9	,,	63
6	,,	5	3	,,	16	86	,,	37	6	,,	65
4	,,	6	2	,,	16a	2	,,	37a	1	,,	107
11	,,	7	1	,,	17	2	,,	38	2	,,	111
5	,,	11	1	,,	21	3	,,	46		

Specimen Designs drawn by the
Meccano Harmonograph

THE designs on this page are selected at random from the many thousands of varied and beautiful patterns which may be produced on the Meccano Harmonograph. They are so delightfully simple to make that any boy can start to produce them immediately he has completed the construction of the model.

Each corner design is a composite one ; that is to say, it consists of two or three simple designs placed one upon the other. Each one makes use of the "spiral" pattern, to produce which it is necessary to remove the secondary pendulum 5 (Fig. 1) so that the table is influenced by only one pendulum. The star-shaped pattern superimposed on the spiral in the top right-hand corner was produced with the weight 5 re-attached to the upper portion or primary pendulum, with the result that the table was influenced by the vibrations of two separate pendulums. The remaining examples are all "compound" designs, and were produced with the aid of both pendulums and weights.

It is interesting to note the beautiful watered-silk appearance of the design in the lower right-hand corner. It was formed by superimposing two single pendulum designs, the paper having been moved very slightly after finishing the first and before drawing the second design.

The same effect is obtained in the examples on page 2.

Meccano Giant Dragline

A wonderful Electrically-operated Model of a
300-ton Excavating Machine, incorporating
five distinct movements.

Special Features

The model is driven by a 4-volt Electric Motor and comprises the following five movements, all of which may be thrown in or out of gear on operation of a lever or hand wheel: Digging, hoisting and lowering, luffing, slewing, and travelling. The Gear Box is of a particularly simple and ingenious design.

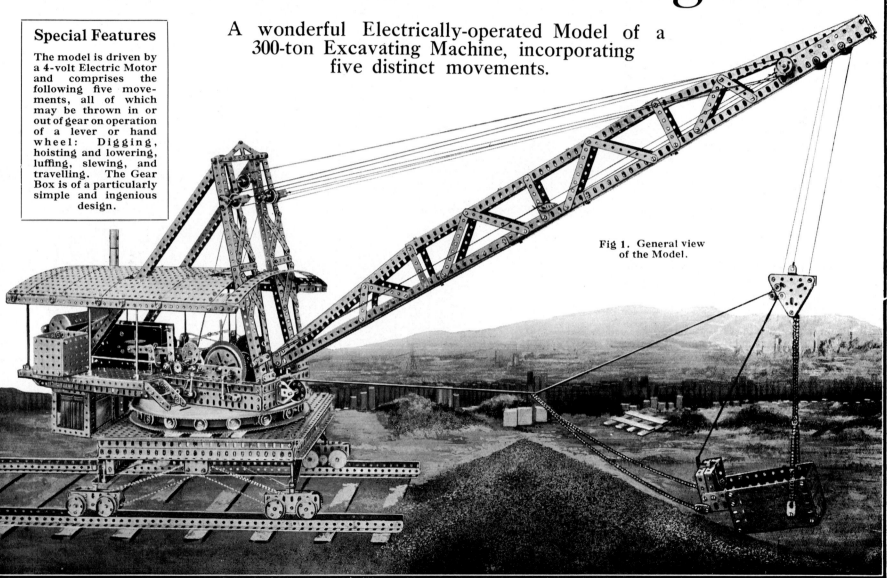

Fig 1. General view of the Model.

THE dragline is a wonderful machine employed largely on excavation work, such as the making of canals and railway cuttings, etc. In construction it is somewhat similar to the steam shovel (or mechanical navvy, as it is sometimes termed), but differs considerably in its method of operation.

The name "dragline" is derived from the fact that the digging bucket is dragged towards the machine on a flexible rope, instead of being mounted on an arm pivoted to a jib, as in the case of an ordinary steam shovel. While steam shovels excavate above the level of the ground on which they stand and advance into the excavation as the work proceeds, a dragline excavates below the level on which it stands and travels backwards when it has excavated all the material within reach. Owing to its construction and method of operation it is possible to place a dragline some distance away from the scene of the excavation, and because of this feature a dragline is of exceptional value where the ground is too soft to allow a steam shovel with its short jib to stand.

As an example of the great practical value of this type of excavating machine, it will be of interest to mention that during the construction of the Panama Canal, draglines, used in conjunction with steam shovels, did the work of thousands of labourers at a fraction of the cost. Apart altogether from the fact that their upkeep was nothing like the amount that would have been required for wages if men had been employed, they helped considerably in solving the difficult problem of housing and feeding. The Panama Canal was cut through a practically uninhabited zone, and it was therefore necessary to erect large numbers of shelters and temporary houses for the workmen. Even when every conceivable form of labour-saving device was used, it was still necessary to employ over sixty thousand men. These men, with their wives and families, had to be housed and fed in what was practically a desert area. This in itself was a very big task, but if it had not been for the employment of wonderful mechanical devices such as steam navvies and draglines, the number of labourers required would have been so enormous that it would have been practically impossible to find accommodation for them, which only goes to show how great a part mechanical devices really played in the construction of this famous canal.

The Prototype of the Meccano Model

The Meccano model has been designed to resemble as closely as possible the largest dragline in the world. Its huge prototype was built by Ruston and Hornsby, Ltd. (Lincoln), for service in connection with irrigation schemes in India, and the following details of this machine will no doubt add interest to the construction of the model.

When fully equipped and in working order the machine weighs 300 tons. In less than one minute it will dig seven or eight cubic yards of material—a

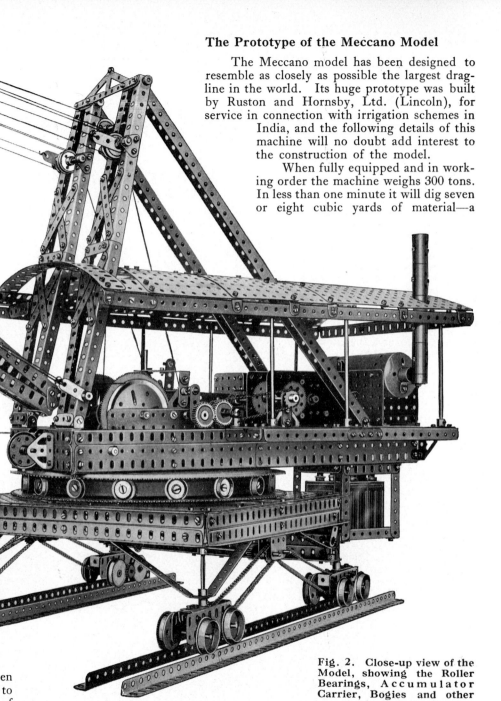

Fig. 2. Close-up view of the Model, showing the Roller Bearings, Accumulator Carrier, Bogies and other mechanical details.

single bucket load—and deposit it 200 feet away from the point whence it was excavated. This means that it would nearly fill an 8-ton coal wagon in one cut ! The jib is 120 feet in length and the drag-rope from the bucket $1\frac{3}{4}''$ in diameter. The main engines develop 400 h.p. and, in addition to these, separate engines of 200 h.p. are fitted for slewing the jib and superstructure. The machine may also be used as a crane, in which capacity it will lift a load of 22 tons at a radius of 125 feet.

The cycle of operations—i.e., digging, slewing, discharging, slewing back, and dropping the bucket in readiness for another cut—is completed in the short period of 45 to 55 seconds, according to the material being excavated.

Building the Model : The Base

The construction of the model dragline should be commenced by building the base (Fig. 3). Each of the sides are exactly similar ; they are composed of four $12\frac{1}{2}''$ Angle Girders 1 bolted to a $12\frac{1}{2}''$ Flat Girder so as to form an H-section girder of great strength, and they are connected together at the corners by $1''\times1''$ Angle Brackets.

Four $12\frac{1}{2}''$ Angle Girders 2 are secured to the top of the frame thus formed and a Geared Roller Race 3 is bolted thereto by means of $\frac{3}{8}''$ Bolts, three Washers being placed on the shanks of the bolts between the Angle Girders and the Race, for spacing purposes. A $5\frac{1}{2}''\times3\frac{1}{2}''$ Flat Plate is attached at each corner in order to fill in the spaces left by the Race at the corners of the base.

The bogies at the front end of the machine (which is the far end in the illustration under consideration) are mounted on $3\frac{1}{2}''$ Rods 4 passed through the holes in the Angle Girders 1 at each corner and retained in position by Collars ; the Rods are supported further by means of $5\frac{1}{2}''$ Strips bent as shown and bolted to the $12\frac{1}{2}''$ Girders.

Secured halfway along the Angle Girders 1 are two Channel Bearings placed one on either side ; in each of these Channel Bearings is journalled two $1\frac{1}{2}''$ Rods carrying two $\frac{3}{4}''$ Sprockets 5 and two $\frac{1}{2}''$ Pinions 6. An $11\frac{1}{2}''$ Rod 7, also journalled in the Channel Bearings, is further supported near its centre by

2″ Strips that are bolted to Trunnions secured to a $2\frac{1}{2}''\times2\frac{1}{2}''$ Flat Plate that is bolted across the centre pair of Girders 2 by $\frac{3}{8}''$ Bolts. The Trunnions are packed up with Washers so that the end holes of the 2″ Strips shall be in alignment with those in the Channel Bearings and allow the Rod 7 to turn freely. The latter Rod carries at either end a $\frac{1}{2}''$ Pinion that meshes with both the Pinions 6 on the Rods carrying the $\frac{3}{4}''$ Sprockets 5. A $\frac{7}{8}''$ Bevel, secured to the Rod 7, meshes with a second Bevel on the vertical Rod 8 that passes up into the gear box and forms the pivot about which the superstructure turns.

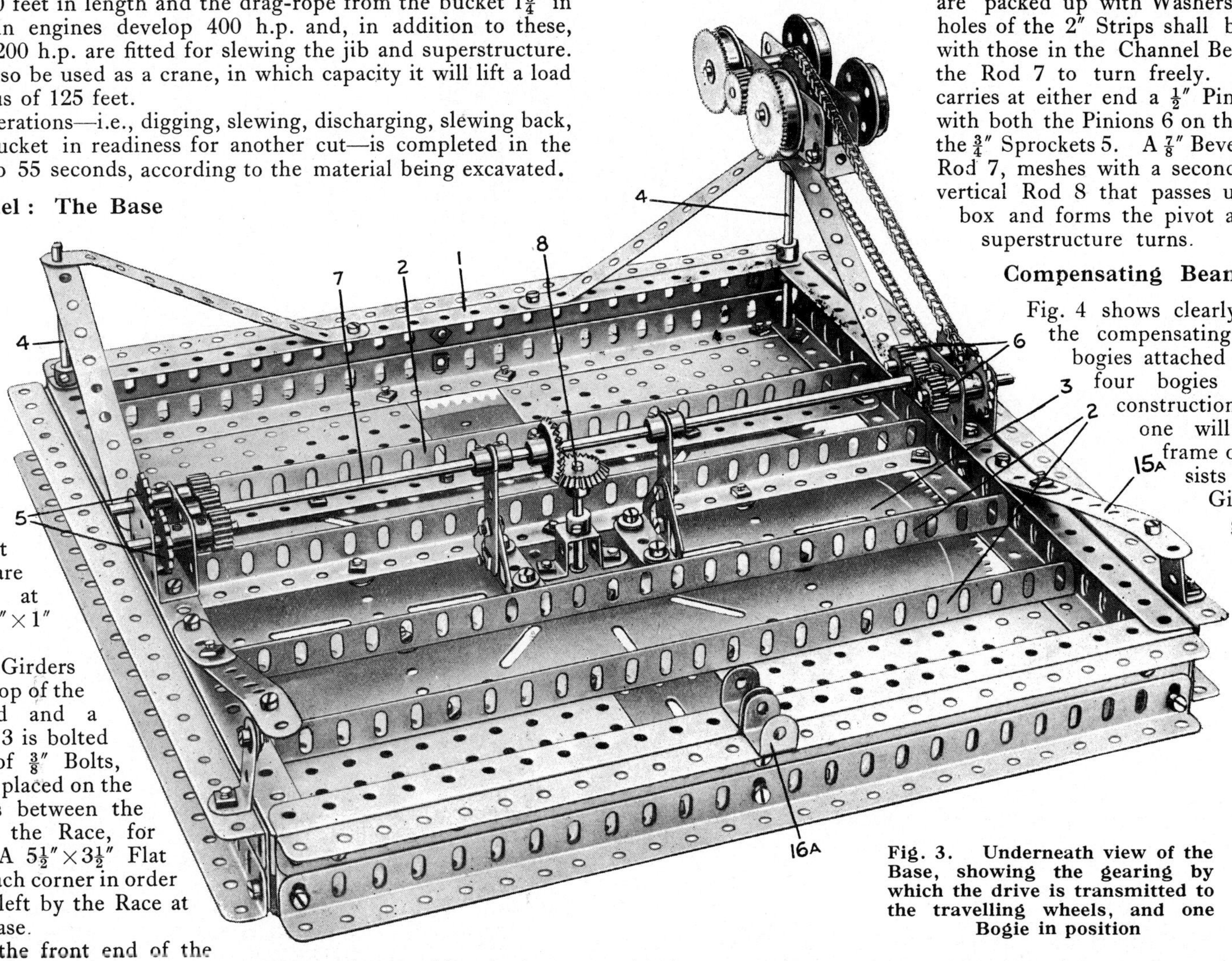

Compensating Beam and Bogies

Fig. 4 shows clearly the details of the compensating beam and the bogies attached thereto. As all four bogies are similar in construction a description of one will suffice. The frame of the bogie consists of two $3\frac{1}{2}''$ Flat Girders held together by three Double Brackets, to two of which the Crank 9 is bolted. The drive for each bogie is taken off the $\frac{3}{4}''$ Sprocket 5 (Fig. 3) by means of Sprocket Chain to the 1″ Sprocket 10 mounted on a short Rod that is journalled in the bogie

Fig. 3. Underneath view of the Base, showing the gearing by which the drive is transmitted to the travelling wheels, and one Bogie in position

side frames and which carries a $\frac{3}{4}''$ Pinion. The latter meshes with the 50-teeth Gear Wheels 11 secured on the wheel axles. By this means it will be seen that the drive is transmitted to all the sixteen wheels, a fact which ensures the maximum adhesion and reduces wheel slip to a minimum.

The compensating beam consists of two $12\frac{1}{2}''$ Angle Girders 12 between the flanges of which is bolted a $12\frac{1}{2}''$ Flat Girder. To the lower edge of the Flat Girder four $5\frac{1}{2}''$ Angle Girders are bolted flanges outward, the space between their centre ends being filled in by a $1\frac{1}{2}''$ Angle Girder on each side of the Flat Girder. As will be seen the Angle Girders are arranged on the slant, in order to give the maximum depth in the centre of the beam and a taper towards each end, this shape in practice giving a girder of great strength and rigidity. Extra strength is given to the lower flanges of the compensating beam by the addition of a 12½″ Flat Girder bolted along the bottoms of the 5½″ and 1½″ Angle Girders. A Threaded Crank 13, bolted to the underneath of the flange of the Girder 12 at each end, carries in its bore a 1″ Threaded Rod having a Bush Wheel 14 secured to its upper end. The functions of these and of the compensating beam are described in the "General Notes" that will be found at the end of the leaflet.

Construction of the Jib

Each bottom longitudinal member of the jib (Fig. 5) is built up from two 18½″ and one 9½″ Angle Girder, each of the former overlapping the latter by four holes. Each top longitudinal member is composed of one 18½″ and two 12½″ Angle Girders. The top and bottom members of the jib are connected by 3″ Strips at the centre portion of their length, whilst they taper down at each end to 1″ Triangular Plates 17, which form the jib foot, and to 5½″ Flat Girders 18 at the top end which form the bearings for the head pulley spindles. The 1″ loose Pulleys 19 are carried on a 3½″ Rod, whilst the 1″ loose Pulleys 20 and 21 are mounted on 2½″ Rods.

As will be seen the jib is adequately braced by Strips. The cords 22 are attached to points halfway up the jib and near the jib head, their lower ends being secured to 1½″ Strips that will eventually be placed on the jib pivot pin 17a. The purpose of these cords is to prevent the swaying of the jib from side to side and thus take abnormal stresses off the jib pivot. In practice the cords are composed of very strong wire rope.

The A-Frames and Roof

The A-frames or vertical members shown in Fig. 9 each consist of four 7½″ Angle Girders spaced apart in the centre by a 2″ Strip and at each end

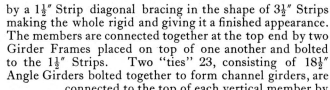

Fig. 4. The Compensating Beam, with Bogies attached.

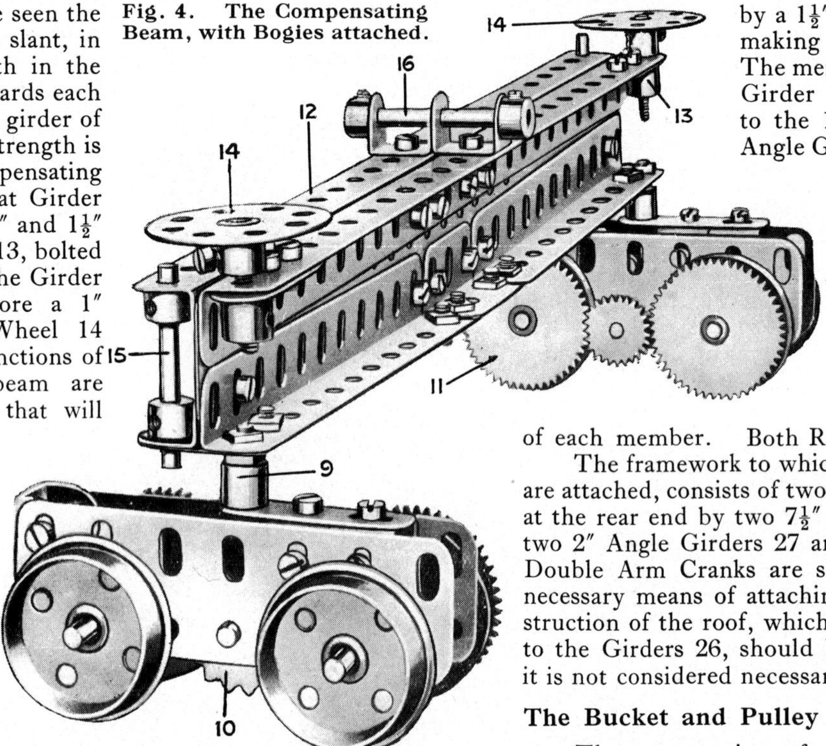

by a 1½″ Strip diagonal bracing in the shape of 3½″ Strips making the whole rigid and giving it a finished appearance. The members are connected together at the top end by two Girder Frames placed on top of one another and bolted to the 1½″ Strips. Two "ties" 23, consisting of 18½″ Angle Girders bolted together to form channel girders, are connected to the top of each vertical member by means of 2″ Rods that are passed through the top end holes of the vertical members and through the girders 23, and retained in position by Collars.

The 1″ loose Pulleys 24 are mounted on 2½″ Rods that are carried by 1″ Triangular Plates attached to the side flanges of the 7½″ Angle Girders. A further 1″ Pulley 25 is carried by a 3″ Rod inserted in the third hole from the top of each member. Both Rod and Pulley are retained in position by Collars.

The framework to which the 5½″ × 3½″ Flat Plates forming the roof proper are attached, consists of two 18½″ Angle Girders 26 (Fig. 8) connected together at the rear end by two 7½″ Angle Girders, which are overlapped nine holes; two 2″ Angle Girders 27 are attached to the front ends of these Girders 26. Double Arm Cranks are secured in the positions indicated to provide the necessary means of attaching the Rods 28 that support the roof. The construction of the roof, which is secured to a number of Flat Brackets attached to the Girders 26, should be quite clear from the illustration and therefore it is not considered necessary to give a detailed description.

The Bucket and Pulley Block

The construction of the bucket (Fig. 10) is extremely simple. The sides and the bottom are composed of 4½″ × 2½″ Flat Plates joined together by 4½″ Angle Girders, while the back end is filled in by a 2½″ × 2½″ Flat Plate that is attached to 2½″ Angle Girders bolted to the edges of the 4½″ Plates. The front edge of the bottom Plate (which is the cutting edge in practice and digs into the material to be excavated), is provided with "tines" or teeth consisting of 2″ Strips. The Sprocket Chain "bridle" 29 is connected to the front portion of the bucket by Flat Brackets, which are attached thereto by locknutted bolts, the same method applying to the other Sprocket Chain connecting the pulley block and bucket. It will be noted that a cross-piece or yoke, consisting of a 2½″ × ½″ Double Angle Strip, spaces the two lengths of the latter chain apart, and prevents them fouling the sides of the bucket. The Double Angle Strip is attached to the Sprocket Chain by ⅜″ Bolts, which are forced between the links of the Chain and retained in place by nuts.

The pulley block comprises two 2½″ Triangular Plates that are connected together by a Double Bracket at each corner. A 1½″ Pulley forming the

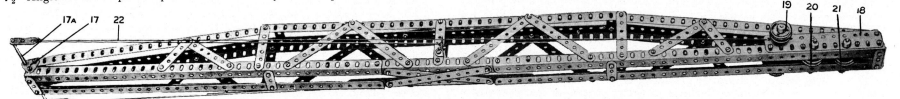

Fig. 5. Construction of the Jib, showing the jib head pulleys, pivot pin, etc.

"sheave" is carried on the Rod 30, and is spaced from the sides of the block by Washers. Two 1″ Triangular Plates carry a short Rod on which is mounted a ½″ loose Pulley. The bolts securing the 1″ Triangular Plates to the block, have a Washer placed under each of their heads in order to prevent the shanks of the bolts fouling the sheave. A length of cord is secured to the front portion of the bucket as indicated in the illustration, and led over the ½″ loose Pulley; it will eventually be attached to the Hook 31 on the end of the digging rope. This cord regulates the tilt of the bucket.

Construction of the Swivelling Superstructure

Fig. 7 shows the complete unit with Gears, Motor, etc., in place, whilst Fig. 6 gives a very good idea of the construction of the framework with all gears removed. We will consider first the latter illustration.

Each side member of the frame consists of two parallel 18½″ Angle Girders 32 and 33 (Figs. 6 and 7) and two 9½″ Flat Girders bolted end to end. The arrangement of these parts will be clear on reference to Fig. 2. The front end of the members are joined together by two 5½″ Angle Girders and a 5½″ Flat Girder arranged in a similar manner to those of the side members and connected to the latter by means of 1½″ Angle Girders. Two 1½″ × ½″ Double Angle Strips 34 are bolted to the top 5½″ Angle Girder and two Trunnions 35 are secured to the 5½″ Flat Girder as shown in the illustrations. A Washer is placed on the shank of each retaining bolt between the flange of the Trunnion and the Flat Girder, in order that the rim of the Pulley 35a shall clear the latter.

Two 5½″ Angle Girders bolted to the rear end of the frame carry the 5½″ × 2½″ Flat Plates between which the boiler is mounted. The Motor "bearers" 36, consisting of further 5½″ Angle Girders, are bolted across the Girders 33 in the positions shown. The 5½″ × 2½″ Flat Plates 37 are attached to 5½″ Angle Girders that are bolted—flanges outward—to the Angle Girders 33, 5½″ and 2½″ Angle Girders being attached to their outer edges to strengthen them. Double Arm Cranks 28a are bolted to the Plates 37; they will receive the ends of the Rods 28 supporting the roof. The coal bunker 38 is built up from 2½″ × 2½″ Flat Plates and 2½″ Angle Girders, and secured in position on the Plates 37 by nuts and bolts.

The sides of the gear box proper consist of two 5½″ × 2½″ Flat Plates 39 that are secured to the Angle Girders 33 by 5½″ Angle Girders bolted to the underside of the former Girders. As will be seen from the illustration, the

entire structure is mounted on the upper, or movable, Geared Roller Race 3a, to which are bolted in the position shown, two Trunnions that carry the 2½″ Strips 40. The 4½″ Double Angle Strip 41 is bolted between 1½″ Strips secured to the Plates 39 by Flat Trunnions 42. This completes the swivelling structure and it only remains now to insert the gearing.

Details of the Gear Box

Fig. 7 is a plan view with all the Gears, Motor, brakes, etc., in position. Provided that the directions are followed intelligently and carefully, little difficulty should be experienced with this portion of the model.

The Motor is bolted down to its bearers 36, its front end being attached to the Angle Brackets 36a (Fig. 6). A 2″ Rod, journalled in the side plate of the Motor, carries a 57-teeth Gear Wheel in mesh with a ½″ Pinion on the armature spindle, and also a ½″ Pinion that engages with another 57-teeth Gear on the 4½″ Rod 43a. This Rod also carries a Sprocket 43 and a Worm 64, and is journalled in the Motor side plates and in an additional bearing 37a (Fig. 6) consisting of a 1½″ Strip bolted to a Trunnion that is secured to the Angle Girder 33.

Now let us consider the hoisting and digging winches. The hoisting winch consists of a 3½″ Gear 44 secured on a 2½″ Rod that is journalled in one of the Plates 39 and in the centre bearing 40. One Bush Wheel, one Collar, and three Washers secured in place on the 2½″ Rod, represent the "barrel" of the winch, on which the hoisting rope is wound. A 3″ Pulley 45 secured to the 3½″ Gear by means of ⅜″ Bolts, comprises the brake drum round which the brake band is passed. One end of the latter is fixed to a portion of the framework and the other end is attached to a Coupling that is secured at right angles to a short Rod journalled in both the side plate 39 of the gear box and in the 9½″ Flat Girder comprising the side member. The outer end of the Rod carries a Crank (see Fig. 1) in the end holes of which a 1½″ Rod 46 is mounted pivotally by means of a Collar. A set-screw is passed through the end hole of the Crank and screwed home in the tapped hole of the Collar. The brake is kept in the "off" position by means of a short length of Spring Cord fastened by nuts and bolts to the Crank and to the 7½″ Flat Girder above it; the Crank

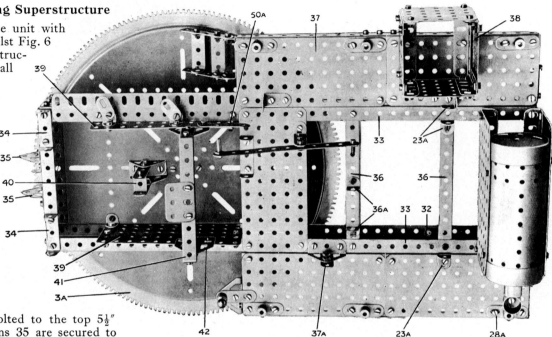

Fig. 6. Plan view of the swivelling Superstructure, with Roof and all gears removed.

is spaced away from the side by two Washers on the Rod. When it is desired to hold the brake on for any length of time, the Rod 46 or "brake pedal" is pushed down, thus applying the brake, and the pivoted Flat Bracket is swung over the end of the brake pedal to hold it down.

The details of the digging winch are exactly similar to that just described, with the exception that the brake-actuating cranks are secured on a 6½″ Rod 47 that passes completely across the gear box and is journalled in the side frames. A 5″ Rod 48, journalled in the third hole from the top and the fourth from the back edge of the Flat Plates 39, carries a Worm and a 50-teeth Gear 48a in the positions shown.

The luffing winch consists of a 5″ Rod 49 to which is secured a 50-teeth Gear Wheel 49a, and a Ratchet Wheel. The Pawl 50, which engages with the teeth of the Ratchet, is mounted on a Pivot Bolt attached to the Strip 50a (Fig. 6). The Pawl carries a Threaded Pin in its tapped hole, by which disengagement with the Ratchet Wheel may be effected when luffing out the jib.

Slewing and Travelling Motions

A Socket Coupling 58 (part No. 171) carries at its upper end the male portion of a Dog Clutch and at its lower extremity a ½″ Double Width Pinion that is in constant engagement with the Worm on the Rod 48. The Socket Coupling is placed on the Rod 8 and should be perfectly free to revolve on it and only turn the Rod when pushed up into engagement with the female portion of the Dog Clutch that is secured rigidly to the Rod. It should be clearly understood that the Rod 8 is shown in position in the gear box in order to make the working of the latter quite clear; actually the Rod forms part of the travelling base (Fig. 3) and is not in place in the gear box until the entire superstructure is mounted on the lower Roller Race.

The lever 59 controls the travelling movement, and consists of a 3″ Strip that is attached by means of a Crank to a short Rod journalled in a 1½″

Double Angle Strip, which is bolted to the floor plates. Attached to the Rod by means of a Coupling is a 2½″ Rod carrying at its extremity a Threaded Pin which is secured to the Rod by a Collar; the tip of the Threaded Pin engages with the groove turned in the Sleeve Coupling. The vertical movement for engagement or disengagement with the Dog Clutch must not be excessive, otherwise the Double Width Pinion will come out of mesh with the Worm.

The special Pinion (Part No. 167c) engaging with the teeth of the lower fixed Race 3, is secured to a 4½″ vertical Rod 60 journalled in the 5½″ Angle Girder 36 and also in a second 5½″ Girder and Double Arm Crank that is bolted to the lower 18½″ Angle Girders 32 (Fig. 6). One portion of a Dog Clutch and a 57-teeth Gear Wheel are connected together by means of a Socket Coupling 61, the complete unit being shown in Fig. 7 removed from its Rod for the sake of clearness. Actually, of course, it is placed on the Rod 60 and operated by the lever 62, the ¾″ Bolt in the end of which engages with the groove of the Socket Coupling.

A 1″ Gear 56 is secured to a short Rod carrying also a 1″ Sprocket Wheel that is connected by Sprocket Chain to the ¾″ Sprocket 43 on the shaft 43a driven by the Motor. A Coupling is secured to the inner end of the short Rod in such a manner that the other end of the Coupling may be fitted on to the projecting end of the Rod 49 and be free to turn thereon. This arrangement forms a convenient support for the inner end of the short Rod, and its outer end is journalled in a bearing consisting of a Handrail Support, which is secured in the boss of a Threaded Crank that is bolted to a Trunnion and to a 5½″×2½″ Plate that forms part of the flooring. This bearing may be seen in Figs. 2 and 6. Both bearings are worthy of note as they provide a neat and efficient support for a Rod in a difficult situation.

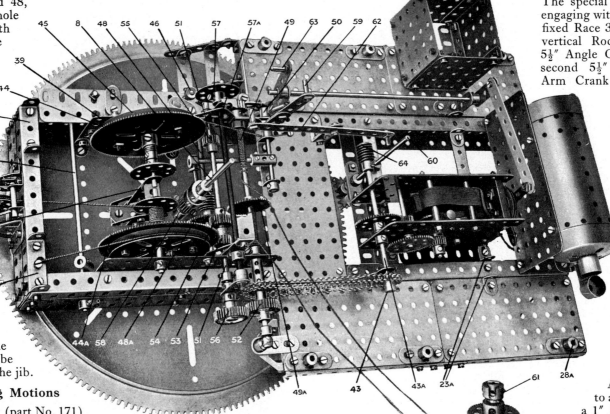

Fig. 7. Plan view of the Superstructure, showing Gear Box, Motor, etc.

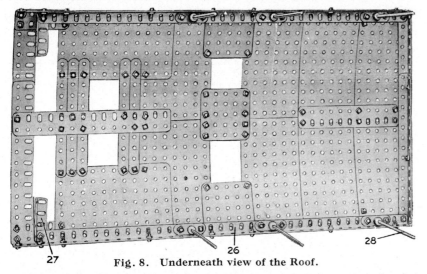

Fig. 8. Underneath view of the Roof.

The correct location of the various Pinions on the 6½″ Rod 51 is of the utmost importance to ensure the proper working of the model. Hence the following instructions should be followed most carefully.

Adjusting the Gear Box

The Rod should first be placed at the extremity of its travel to the left (looking toward the front of the model) and the 1″ Gears 52 and 56 so arranged as to be just in mesh with each other. (A Collar on the other end of the Rod will be secured in place when all the other movements have been adjusted to prevent any further movement of the Rod to the left). In this position of the Rod the ½″ Pinion 53 is in mesh with the 3½″ Gear Wheel 44a of the digging winch, as will be seen from Fig. 7.

A slight movement of the Rod to the right (caused by turning the gear selector wheel 57) should result in the Pinion 55 being brought into engagement with the gear 44 of the hoisting winch, and the Pinion 53 out of engagement with the Gear 44a. By continuing the movement of the Rod to the right, the Gear 44 will eventually become disengaged, at which point the 50-teeth Gear 48a on the Rod 48 should be in mesh with the ¾″ Pinion 54. (The Worm on the latter Rod meshes with the ½″ Double Width Pinion held in the Socket Coupling 58 on the Rod 8, as explained previously). At the extreme limit of the travel of the Rod to the right the ¾″ Pinion 54 comes into mesh with the Gear Wheel 49a on the luffing winch barrel 49, round which the luffing ropes are wound.

It will most probably be found that the Gears 48a, 49a both remain in mesh with the ¾″ Pinion 54 in this extreme position of the Rod 51. This does not matter, however, so long as the Gear 48a comes into engagement with the ¾″ Pinion before the Gear 49a. It is necessary of course that the gears 52 and 56 are n mesh throughout the complete travel of the Rod 51.

I l e sideways movement of the Rod 51 when changing gear is effected in the to lowing manner : A Threaded Crank runs on the end of the 5″ Threaded Rod 57a, which is journalled in the Trunnions 42 and restrained from sideways motion. The Rod 51 passes through the end hole of the Crank, which is retained in position on the Rod by Collars on both sides as shown. When the hand-wheel 57 secured to the Threaded Rod is rotated, the Threaded Crank advances or recedes along the Rod and so moves the Rod 51. The great advantage of this method of gear selection is that it is impossible for the gears to become disengaged through vibration, etc., as is the case with some other forms of gear changing devices.

The Motor switch is operated from the central controlling position of the model by means of the Crank 63. This is secured to an 8″ Rod journalled in 1″ × 1″ Angle Brackets and carrying at its other end a second Crank that is connected pivotally to the Motor switch arm by a 4½″ Strip.

Final Assembly of the Model

The compensating beam 12 is placed in position by passing the Pin 16 through the Double Brackets 16a, which are bolted to the Girder 1 (see Figs. 3 and 4), and the Rods 15 through the end holes of the Strips 15a so that the Rods slide freely in them. The Strips 15a brace the beam and prevent it from twisting; they each consist of one 4½″ Strip and a 2″ Slotted Strip. The Sprockets 5 may now be connected to the Sprockets 10 by suitable lengths of Sprocket Chain. The base is completed with the addition of the Ring Frame (part No. 167b) carrying the sixteen ¾″ Flanged Wheels on which rolls the upper Race 3a bolted to the underside of the swivelling superstructure.

The swivelling superstructure is now lowered on to the Ring Frame, the Rod 8 passing through the Bush Wheel bolted to the upper Race. At this juncture the Socket Coupling 58 is slipped on to the Rod 8, the end of which is then passed through the Flat Girder attached to the Double Angle Strip 41. (The latter Strip has been broken away in Fig. 7 to show the gearing more clearly). The upper Race should now bed quite firmly down on the ¾″ Flanged Wheels forming the rollers and be free to turn on them, the merest touch sufficing to rotate the entire superstructure.

The A-frames (Fig. 9) are secured to the 1½″ Double Angle Strips 34 (Fig. 7) and the rear ties attached to the Angle Brackets 23a. The 1″ Triangular Plates 17 (Fig. 5) at the jib foot are pivoted on the 6½″ Rod 17a that is passed through holes in the Girders of the A-frames and held in place by Collars on the Rod ; the 1½″ Strips attached to the ends of the ropes 22 forming the stays for the jib are placed also on the end of this Rod.

One end of the luffing rope is attached to a 1½″ Strip on the Rod carrying the 1″ Pulleys 24, and is taken round one of the Pulleys 19 at the jib head and back over one of the Pulleys 24. Thence it passes round the last Pulley 19 and then over the remaining Pulley 24 to the luffing winch barrel 49, on which it is

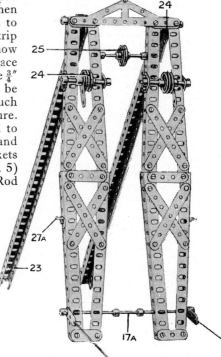

Fig. 9. The A-frames ready for attaching to the Superstructure.

secured by a Collar. The other set of luffing ropes on the other side of the jib is treated in a manner similar to that just described.

The hoisting rope is secured to the ½" Reversed Angle Bracket on the pulley block (see Fig. 10), led over the Pulley 21 at the jib head and then is rove through the sheave of the block; thence it passes over the other Pulley 20 at the jib head and down to the hoisting winch barrel over the Pulley 25. The digging rope is secured to the digging winch barrel and is led over the 1½" Pulley 35a, the Hook 31 on its end being attached to the Sprocket Chain bridle 29 of the bucket.

Lastly the roof is placed in position. In order to accomplish this, it is necessary to remove temporarily the ties 23 of the A-frames and the Flat Girders forming the front portion of the roof. The 2" Angle Girders 27 (Fig. 8) of the roof are bolted to the Angle Brackets 27a on the sides of the A-frames (Fig. 9), and the Rods 28 are secured in the bosses of the Double Arm Cranks 28a. The front portion of the roof and the ties may now be replaced in their former positions as indicated in the general view.

The Accumulator carrier is composed of 3½" Angle Girders. To the Angle Girders forming the top, 3½" Flat Girders are secured so that their edges project outwards. It will be found that these Flat Girders will slide on the flanges of the Girders 32, so that the Accumulator may be withdrawn easily for recharging, etc. Electrical connection between the Motor and Accumulator is effected by means of two short lengths of insulated wire. Rubber covered wire will be quite satisfactory.

The chimney consists of five Sleeve Pieces and one Chimney Adaptor attached to a 6½" Rod by bolts passed through them and inserted in the set-screw holes of new-style Collars. A circular hole may be cut in the roof for the chimney to pass through, although this need not be done; the Rod only can be passed through the roof and the Sleeve Pieces arranged above and below the Plate.

General Notes on the Working of the Model

A glance at Fig. 7 will show how all the controls for the various movements of the model have been brought to a central position, making their manipulation very easy besides following actual practice, and below we describe how the model should be set to work. It will make matters much more interesting if a heap of gravel, etc., is deposited in front of the machine into which the bucket may dig as if engaged on actual excavations!

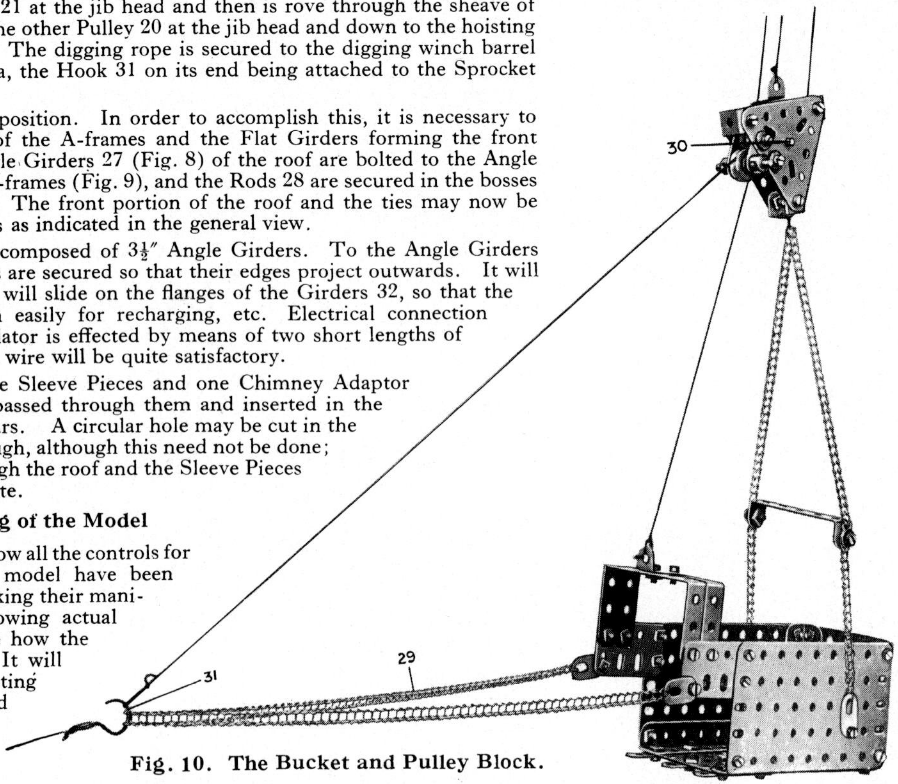

Fig. 10. The Bucket and Pulley Block.

Both the hoisting and digging winches should first be disengaged by turning the gear selector wheel 57, and the brakes of both winches manipulated so that the bucket lowers and comes to rest in a horizontal position at the far edge of the heap of gravel. The digging winch is now engaged, leaving the hoisting winch disengaged, and the Motor started by moving the Motor control handle 63. The bucket will now be dragged towards the machine, digging its way into the sand as it moves forward. By allowing the hoisting winch to run out freely a maximum cut is obtained, but by lightly applying the brake of the hoisting winch, a shallower cut results. When the end of the cut has been reached, the hoist is engaged and the digging winch disengaged. The latter is allowed to run out under the control of the brake whilst hoisting is in progress in order to keep the bucket in a horizontal position. This precaution is necessary to prevent the contents of the bucket being spilt.

It may now be necessary to slew the model so that the contents of the bucket may be deposited in a truck or elsewhere. In order to accomplish this, the gear selector wheel 57 is turned until none of the Gears 44, 44a, or 49a are in engagement with their respective Pinions on the Rod 51; this is "neutral." The slewing control lever is then pulled upward, thereby lowering the Socket Coupling 61 and bringing the Gear attached thereto into mesh with the Worm 64 on the shaft 43 driven by the Motor. At the same time the portions of the Dog Clutch attached to the Sleeve Coupling and the Rod 60 come into engagement and turn the Rod, thus rotating the superstructure about the central pivot.

For travelling, the control lever 59 is moved toward the rear of the model. This slides the Sleeve Coupling 58 upward so that the portion of the Dog Clutch secured in its upper end engages with the other portion of the Dog on the Rod 8. The latter is thus rotated and drives the travelling wheels through the gearing shown in Fig. 3. (The Rod 51 should be left in its neutral position for the travelling or slewing movements).

As the purpose of the compensating beam to which the rear bogies are attached may not be very clear to some of our readers, we append a brief explanation.

If an object carrying a great weight and supported at each corner, such as the base of the dragline, travels over an uneven surface, abnormal stresses will be induced in it, for it may be that, occasionally, only three corners are supported, the remaining corner receiving little or no support. An illustration of this is provided when one leg of a four-legged table is packed up; it will be observed how the table is strained and twisted when a heavy weight is placed on it. Now when a three-legged table is treated in the same way, it remains perfectly steady and no undue stresses are exhibited under these conditions. For these reasons cameras and other apparatus are mounted on tripods—really three-legged tables.

It is this principle of "three point suspension" that is employed in the Ruston Dragline and that has been so well brought out in the model. It will be seen that the base is supported by the two front bogies and at a single point—the pivot 16 of the compensating beam—at the rear. The Bush Wheels 14 with their 1" Threaded Rods form jacks, and when these are screwed down out of contact with the underside of the base, the bogies are free to rise and fall over uneven ground, thereby transmitting no undue stress to the frame and fulfilling the conditions of the three point suspension system. When the machine is in operation the jacks are tightened up, so as to distribute the load evenly when working "cross track." All four bogies are free to turn about their pivots, of course, to enable the machine to travel round curves when necessary. If the bogies were fixed the machine would be liable to derailment.

In the prototype the race supporting the swivelling superstructure is 30 feet in diameter in order to render the machine as stable as possible. In the model the Geared Roller Race gives a steadiness, in comparison, almost as great as that of the original machine, thereby affording a striking example of the efficiency of the new part.

Parts required to build the Dragline.

14 of No. 2	2 of No. 8a	6 of No. 12a	10 of No. 18a	1 of No. 26a	1 of No. 45	9 of No. 62	5 of No. 96	2 of No. 113	2 of No. 160
11 ,, 2a	8 ,, 8b	5 ,, 12b	3 ,, 18b	10 ,, 27	2 ,, 47	4 ,, 62a	5 ,, 96a	6 ,, 115	1 ,, 162
15 ,, 3	21 ,, 9	1 ,, 13	2 ,, 19b	3 ,, 27a	6 ,, 48	13 ,, 62b	1 ,, 103	1 ,, 125	5 ,, 163
5 ,, 4	2 ,, 9a	2 ,, 13a	16 ,, 20	2 ,, 27b	1 ,, 48a	4 ,, 63	5 ,, 103a	8 ,, 126	2 ,, 164
8 ,, 5	10 ,, 9b	4 ,, 14	2 ,, 21	2 ,, 30	1 ,, 48c	9 ,, 70	6 ,, 103b	2 ,, 126a	1 ,, 167
10 ,, 6	13 ,, 9d	8 ,, 15	2 ,, 22	2 ,, 31	14 ,, 52a	9 ,, 72	10 ,, 103d	2 ,, 133	2 ,, 170
20 ,, 6a	2 ,, 9e	2 ,, 15a	9 ,, 22a	2 ,, 32	3 ,, 53a	2 ,, 76	2 ,, 103f	1 ,, 136	
4 ,, 7	6 ,, 9f	3 ,, 16	1 ,, 23	555 ,, 37	2 ,, 55a	8 ,, 77	2 ,, 103g	2 ,, 144	1 4-volt Electric Motor
16 ,, 7a	18 ,, 10	5 ,, 16a	5 ,, 24	8 ,, 37a	1 ,, 57	1 ,, 79a	1 ,, 103h	1 ,, 147a	
2 ,, 7b	20 ,, 11	1 ,, 16b	5 ,, 25	14 ,, 38	3 " 58	2 ,, 82	3 ,, 103k	3 ,, 147b	1 Accumulator 8 amp.-hr.
26 ,, 8	22 ,, 12	14 ,, 17	10 ,, 26	6 ,, 40	82 ,, 59	57" ,, 94	22 ,, 111c	1 ,, 148	

MECCANO PONTOON CRANE

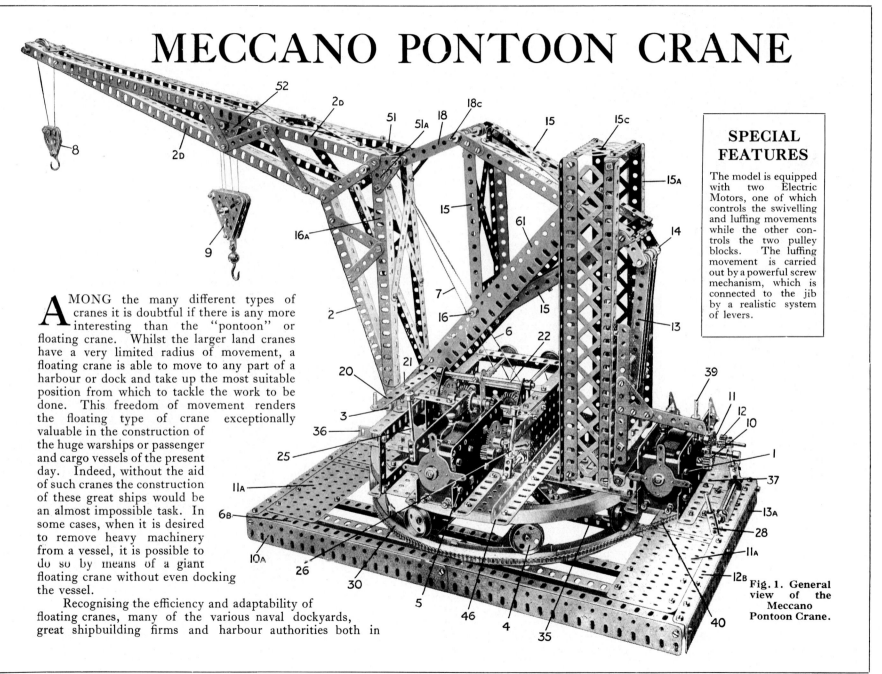

SPECIAL FEATURES

The model is equipped with two Electric Motors, one of which controls the swivelling and luffing movements while the other controls the two pulley blocks. The luffing movement is carried out by a powerful screw mechanism, which is connected to the jib by a realistic system of levers.

A MONG the many different types of cranes it is doubtful if there is any more interesting than the "pontoon" or floating crane. Whilst the larger land cranes have a very limited radius of movement, a floating crane is able to move to any part of a harbour or dock and take up the most suitable position from which to tackle the work to be done. This freedom of movement renders the floating type of crane exceptionally valuable in the construction of the huge warships or passenger and cargo vessels of the present day. Indeed, without the aid of such cranes the construction of these great ships would be an almost impossible task. In some cases, when it is desired to remove heavy machinery from a vessel, it is possible to do so by means of a giant floating crane without even docking the vessel.

Recognising the efficiency and adaptability of floating cranes, many of the various naval dockyards, great shipbuilding firms and harbour authorities both in

Fig. 1. General view of the Meccano Pontoon Crane.

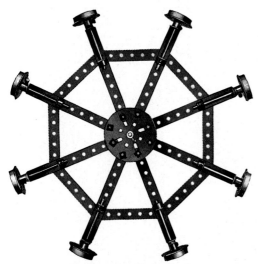

Fig. 2. The Wheel Race removed from the Roller Bearing

this country and abroad, have placed orders for giant cranes of this class during the last few years, with the result that to-day there are numerous exceptionally fine floating cranes at work in various parts of the world.

Giant Crane Lifts 350 Tons

A monster floating crane that has been designed and built for a Japanese shipyard is capable of lifting 350 tons. The task of transferring this huge crane from the site where it was built to the shipyard in Japan necessitated special arrangements. It was erected sectionally in England by the builders, after which it was towed by tugs to Japan, where the various sections were assembled. The following details of this crane will give some idea of its great size and power, while the more important features described may be taken as typical of all the larger pontoon cranes.

Carrying a load of 350 tons it is capable of revolving through a complete circle with the load at 100 feet radius, and it can lift this load vertically to a height of 140 feet! For lifting loads of 200 tons or more, two main blocks are provided, each of which has a capacity of 175 tons, the operating machinery being so arranged that the blocks may be used either coupled together or independently, as desired. At the end of the jib a further purchase is provided, the capacity of this being 50 tons. The distance between the main purchase and the auxiliary purchase is 40 feet. This latter or secondary block has a vertical lift capacity of 200 feet.

Carried on a trolley that travels along the underside of the jib is another auxiliary purchase of 50 tons capacity, and this is capable of moving the load through a distance of about 75 feet, measured horizontally. This last purchase is an extremely useful feature in that it enables the crane to deal with comparatively small loads at high speed and without any necessity for using the derricking motion of the jib. When the jib is at its minimum radius, the overall height to the top of the crane is 240 feet. The maximum working radius of the jib is 121 feet, and the minimum 50 feet.

The crane is carried on a pontoon 270 feet in length and 92 feet in width. The draught is about 10 feet when the crane is unloaded, so it will be seen that it is possible to use the crane in comparatively shallow water. This feature is of considerable importance when it is necessary to carry out operations at low tide. No ballast whatever is necessary, owing to the vast size of the pontoon. Behind the crane a large portion of the deck area is reserved for the carrying of a deck load.

The Propelling Machinery

Placed amidships, the propelling machinery consists of twin-screw compound engines which are supplied with steam from two single-ended boilers working at a pressure of 150 lbs. per square inch. The hull is built entirely of steel and is divided transversely by bulk heads, forming water-tight compartments.

As such a crane as this is sometimes required to make long journeys by sea it is necessary to carry various articles of deck equipment, and these include a steam windlass, steam capstans, steam and hand steering gear, davits, lifeboats, and all the accessories necessary for a sea-going vessel. This floating crane (which might almost be termed a ship) is navigated from a steel bridge extending the whole width of the deck and situated immediately in front of the crane base.

A floating crane of this type is well suited for reproduction in Meccano. The model described in this leaflet will be found to embody all the principal features of its huge prototype, and while it is not of course practical to actually construct in Meccano a pontoon that could be floated on water, nevertheless the model forms an accurate replica of the actual crane.

Besides forming a pleasing toy of unlimited application, the model affords also valuable instruction in the principles of mechanics and the various ways and means which have to be employed in order to build a structure of sufficient strength to withstand tremendous stresses and strains.

Building the Meccano Model

The base or "pontoon" consists of two 18½″ Angle Girders 6b (Fig 1.), to the ends of which are bolted two 12½″ Angle Girders 12b.

To the longer sides of the frame thus formed, two 9½″ Flat Girders 10a are secured and overlapped one hole, while 12½″ Flat Girders 13a are bolted to the shorter sides.

The base frame is strengthened by five additional 18½″ Angle Girders placed between the outer Girders 6b that, besides

Fig. 3. The base of the Jib and portion of the assembled Roller Bearing

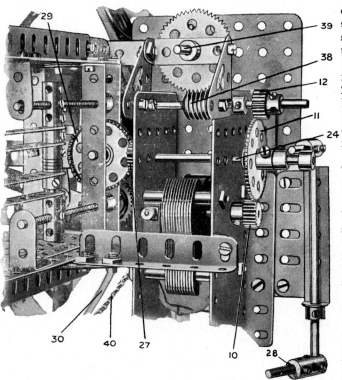

Fig. 4. Plan view, showing Electric Motor and Gearing controlling Swivelling and Luffing Motions.

offering extra strength, also serve to support the deck plates 11a that are formed by $5\frac{1}{2}'' \times 2\frac{1}{2}''$ Flat Plates bolted to the $18\frac{1}{2}''$ Angle Girders, as shown in Fig. 1.

The Roller Bearings

The roller bearings 30 are shown in Fig. 1. The lower race, formed of Channel Segments, is secured to the base or pontoon and an upper race is bolted to two $12\frac{1}{2}''$ Angle Girders 36 attached to the body of the model. The spider frame (Fig. 2) carries a series of Flanged Wheels which run on the edges of the upper and lower races. Each race consists of sixteen Channel Segments.

Both the spider frame and the upper race swivel freely round a vertical Rod which is journalled in a hole of the centre $18\frac{1}{2}''$ Angle Girder 35 (Fig. 1) in the base of the crane. This Rod is held in position by means of Collars placed on the Rod against each side of the Girder 35. The spider frame (Fig. 2) is built up of eight $4\frac{1}{2}''$ Strips attached to a centre Face Plate. To the $4\frac{1}{2}''$ Strips $1\frac{1}{2}'' \times \frac{1}{2}''$ Double Angle Strips are bolted, the holes in the turned-up ends acting as journals for the wheel axles, which are secured by Collars in their respective bearings.

It may be mentioned that the new Meccano Geared Roller Bearings may be used in place of the built up bearings if desired, in which case it would be necessary to make a slight alteration in the position of the Electric Motor, so as to allow the special Pinion to engage properly with the lower fixed Race. One or two minor alterations in the general layout would also be entailed, but they are of such simple character that no difficulty would be experienced.

Crane Rotating Mechanism

Two $12\frac{1}{2}''$ Angle Girders 36 (Fig. 3) bolted to the upper wheel race carry a $5\frac{1}{2}'' \times 3\frac{1}{2}''$ Flat Plate 37 (Fig. 1) that is secured in the last holes at one end of the Girders 36. This Plate 37 carries the Electric Motor 1, which drives the Rod 24 (Fig. 4) by means of the $\frac{1}{2}''$ Pinion 10 and the 57-teeth Gear Wheel 11. The Rod 24 carries a further Pinion 27 and slides in its bearings, being so arranged that on operation of the lever 28 it engages a Contrate Wheel 29 or the Pinion 12, while the Gear Wheel 11 remains constantly in mesh with the Motor Pinion 10.

The method of constructing the lever 28 can be seen from Fig. 4. A Worm 38 on the Rod of the Pinion 12 engages with a 57-teeth Gear Wheel on a vertical Rod 39, on the lower end of which is mounted a 1" Sprocket Wheel (this wheel cannot be seen in the photograph) engaging the Sprocket Chain 40 which passes round the lower fixed wheel race 30.

Thus by throwing the Gear 11 into mesh with the Pinion 12 the Sprocket Wheel on the Rod 39 is rotated, and since the Sprocket Chain 40 tends to grip the base 30, the Sprocket Wheel travels round the Chain 40, so rotating the superstructure bodily about its pivot on the roller bearings.

The Jib and Luffing Mechanism

The vertical member of the jib consists of two $9\frac{1}{2}''$ Angle Girders 2 (Fig. 1) and two $9\frac{1}{2}''$ Angle Girders 16a bolted together at their lower ends and braced at the sides by $2\frac{1}{2}''$ and 3" Strips and at the rear by $5\frac{1}{2}''$ Strips placed crosswise.

The vertical member of the jib is attached to the Flat Girders 61 by the 5" Axle Rod 3, about which the entire jib pivots. The Rod is carried in two Architraves bolted to the Angle Girders 36. The horizontal arm of the jib is built up from $18\frac{1}{2}''$ Angle Girders 2d braced by Strips of various lengths as shown.

The positions of the Rods carrying the purchase Pulleys 51 and 52 will be made quite clear by a glance at Fig. 1, which also indicates the method of attaching the jib members to the $3\frac{1}{2}''$ Strips forming the links 18.

Four $12\frac{1}{2}''$ Angle Girders 15a form the box-like column between the sides of which works the triangular frame 15. The lower ends of the Angle Girders 15a are bolted to the Angle Girders 36. The mechanism controlling the movements of the jib is arranged as follows :—

The $1\frac{1}{2}''$ Contrate Wheel 29

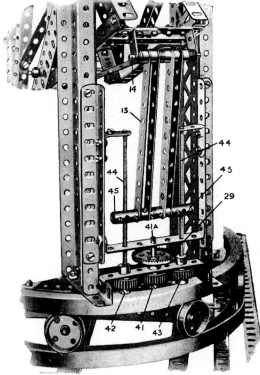

Fig. 5. View of the screw Luffing Gear, showing links, etc.

(Fig. 4) which may be engaged by the Pinion 27, is mounted on a short Rod journalled in $3\frac{1}{2}''$ $\times \frac{1}{2}''$ Double Angle Strips bolted to $5\frac{1}{2}''$ Angle Girders which, in turn, are bolted to the Girders 15a, as shown in Figs. 1 and 5. This Rod carries also a $1''$ Gear Wheel 41 (Fig. 5). The latter meshes with two other $1''$ Gears (42 and 43) mounted on the Threaded Rods 44, which carry two Couplings 45 connected by a $3''$ Rod.

Four $5\frac{1}{2}''$ Strips 13 are connected pivotally to the Rod of the Couplings 45 and to the Rod 14 carried on the triangular framework 15 (see also general view of model). The Strips 13 are spaced by Collars carried on the pivot Rod 14 and on the Rod of the Couplings 45. The Rod 14 is journalled in two $1'' \times 1''$ Angle Brackets secured to the underside of the lower member of the triangular frame.

The three members of the triangular frame are each built up with $7\frac{1}{2}''$ Angle Girders 15 (Fig. 1) and braced by $5\frac{1}{2}''$ Strips placed crosswise, and they are joined to each other by bolts passing through the end holes of each of the side Angle Girders 15. It will be noted from Fig. 1 that $1\frac{1}{2}''$ extension Strips are joined on to the Girders 15 of the upper member for the purpose of carrying the pivot Rod 18c, which connects the frame to the $3''$ Strips 18. The latter, in turn, are attached pivotally to the jib. The lower end of the triangular frame is pivoted at 16 on a Rod located in one of the holes in the Flat Girders 61.

It will now be seen that on moving the lever 28 (Fig. 4) so that the Pinion 27 is brought into gear with the Contrate Wheel 29, the Threaded Rods 44 (Fig. 5) are rotated and the Threaded Couplings 45 move up or down according to the direction of rotation of the Motor, so causing the jib to be elevated or lowered.

Fig. 6. The hoisting Motor, showing control and brake Levers.

Arrangement of the Hoisting Mechanism

The other Electric Motor 5 is mounted in a framework 46 (Figs. 1 and 6) formed by $9\frac{1}{2}''$ Angle Girders bolted to Flanged Plates 47 (Fig. 6) which, in turn, are bolted to the transverse $12\frac{1}{2}''$ Angle Girders 36 (Fig. 1). This Motor drives through $\frac{7}{8}''$ Bevels 19, 23, and 24 (Fig. 6) either one or other of the Rods 48 and 49.

The change-over is effected by means of the lever 20 (Fig. 6) pivoted at 21, which slides a $6\frac{1}{2}''$ Rod 22. The latter, in turn, slides the shaft carrying the two Bevel Wheels 19, to which it is connected by a Crank 50. Hence if the lever 20 throws one of the Bevels 19 into gear with the Bevel 23 on the Rod 48, the pulley block 9 (Fig. 1) is raised or lowered by means of the cord 7 (Figs. 1 and 6), which passes over one of the $1''$ Pulleys set between the two Bush Wheels 51 (Fig. 1) and over another Pulley similarly situated at 52. From there it is led to one of the Pulleys in the block 9, thence round the second Pulley at 52 and then over the second Pulley in the Block 9, finally being secured to one of the Bush Wheels at 52.

In a similar manner the pulley block 8 may be operated from the Rod 49 (Fig. 6), the cord 6 from which is led over the second Pulley at 51 (Fig. 1) to the Pulley in the end of the jib 2; from there it passes over a $\frac{1}{2}''$ Pulley in the block 8 and is secured to the jib.

The shafts 48 and 49 (Fig. 6) carry at their extreme ends two $1''$ Pulleys, the grooves of which are gripped by cords that are tied to Cranks secured to two $8''$ Rods arranged on either side of the Motor 5. These $8''$ Rods carry Couplings and shorter Rods 25 and 26 which act as brake levers in controlling the loads on the pulley blocks 8 and 9.

List of Parts required to build the Pontoon Crane

12 of No.	2	8 of No.	8a	2 of No.	13a	2 of No.	22	1 of No.	32	2 of No.	48d	6 of No.	63	4 of No.	103a
11 ,,	2a	6 ,,	8b	2 ,,	15	7 ,,	22a	135 ,,	37	2 ,,	52	4 ,,	70	4 ,,	103b
12 ,,	3	2 ,,	9	5 ,,	15a	1 ,,	23	58 ,,	38	2 ,,	52a	3 ,,	76	1 ,,	103f
15 ,,	4	10 ,,	9a	6 ,,	16	5 ,,	24	1 ,,	40	1 ,,	53	2 ,,	80	3 ,,	111
4 ,,	5	1 ,,	9b	13 ,,	16a	4 ,,	26	1 ,,	45	1 ,,	57	1 ,,	94	16 ,,	119
1 ,,	6	1 ,,	9d	1 ,,	17	5 ,,	27a	1 ,,	48	1 ,,	57b	1 ,,	96	2 ,,	126
3 ,,	6a	4 ,,	12a	3 ,,	18a	4 ,,	30	1 ,,	48a	62 ,,	59	1 ,,	97	2 ,,	126a
11 ,,	7a	16 ,,	12b	8 ,,	20	3 ,,	31	4 ,,	48b	3 ,,	62	2 ,,	99	5 ,,	133
8 ,,	8														

2 Meccano Electric Motors

MECCANO PONTOON CRANE

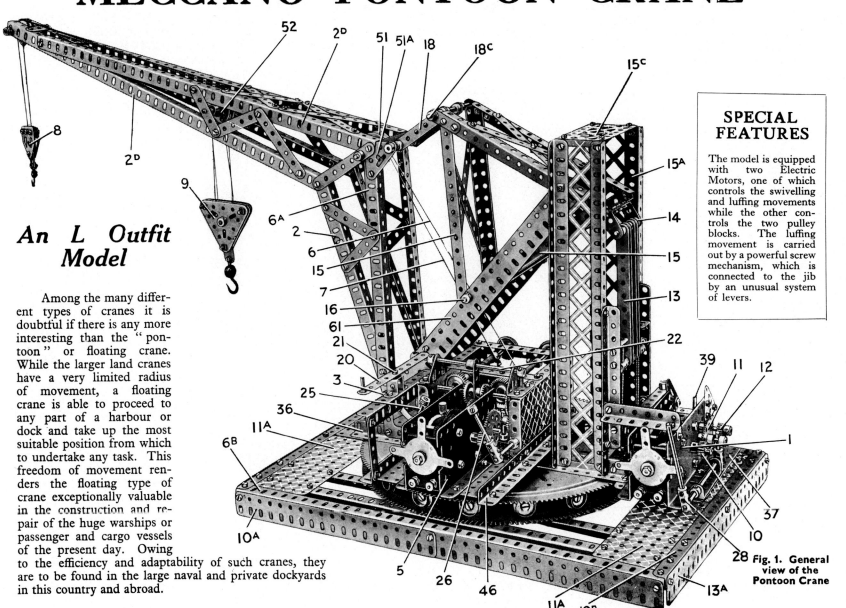

An L Outfit Model

Among the many different types of cranes it is doubtful if there is any more interesting than the "pontoon" or floating crane. While the larger land cranes have a very limited radius of movement, a floating crane is able to proceed to any part of a harbour or dock and take up the most suitable position from which to undertake any task. This freedom of movement renders the floating type of crane exceptionally valuable in the construction and repair of the huge warships or passenger and cargo vessels of the present day. Owing to the efficiency and adaptability of such cranes, they are to be found in the large naval and private dockyards in this country and abroad.

SPECIAL FEATURES

The model is equipped with two Electric Motors, one of which controls the swivelling and luffing movements while the other controls the two pulley blocks. The luffing movement is carried out by a powerful screw mechanism, which is connected to the jib by an unusual system of levers.

Fig. 1. General view of the Pontoon Crane

GIANT CRANE LIFTS 350 TONS

A monster floating crane that is in constant use in a Japanese shipyard is capable of lifting 350 tons. The task of transferring this huge crane from the site where it was built in England, to the shipyard in Japan, necessitated special arrangements. It was erected sectionally in England by the builders, after which it was towed by tugs to Japan, where it was assembled. The following details of this crane will give some idea of its great size and power.

Carrying a load of 350 tons, it is capable of revolving through a complete circle of 100 ft. radius, and it can lift this load to a height of 140 ft. For lifting loads of 200 tons or more, two main blocks are provided, each of which has a capacity of 175 tons, the operating machinery being so arranged that the blocks can be used either coupled together or independently, as desired. At the end of the jib a further purchase is provided and the capacity of this is 50 tons. The distance between the main purchase and the auxiliary purchase is 40 ft., and this gives the auxiliary a vertical lift of 200 ft.

A trolley that travels along the underside of the jib carries another auxiliary purchase of 50 tons capacity that is capable of moving the load through a distance of about 75 ft., measured horizontally. This last purchase is an extremely useful feature, for it is able to deal with comparatively small loads at high speed without any necessity for using the derricking movement of the jib. When the jib is at its minimum radius, the overall height to the top of the crane is 240 ft. The maximum working radius of the jib is 121 ft., and the minimum 50 ft.

The crane is carried on a pontoon 270 ft. long and 92 ft. wide, and the draught, which is about 10 ft. when no load is carried, makes possible its use in comparatively shallow water. This feature is of considerable importance when it is necessary to carry out operations at low tide. No ballast whatever is necessary, owing to the vast size of the pontoon. Behind the crane a large portion of the deck area is reserved for the carrying of a deck load.

The propelling machinery is placed amidships, and consists of twin-screw compound engines supplied with steam from two single-ended boilers working at a pressure of 150 lb. per sq. in.

A crane of this type is sometimes required to make long journeys by sea, and it is therefore necessary to carry various articles of deck equipment. These include a steam windlass, steam capstans, steam and hand steering gear, davits, lifeboats, and all the accessories necessary for a sea-going vessel. Navigation is carried out in exactly the same manner as with a ship, from a steel bridge extending the whole width of the deck immediately in front of the crane base.

The model described in this leaflet embodies all the principal features of its huge prototype, a crane stationed at Malta ; and while of course it is not practicable to construct in Meccano a pontoon that will float on water, the model forms an accurate replica of the actual crane.

BUILDING THE MECCANO MODEL

The base or pontoon consists of two $18\frac{1}{2}''$ Angle Girders 6b (Fig. 1), to the ends of which are bolted two $12\frac{1}{2}''$ Angle Girders 12b. To the longer sides of the frames thus formed, two $9\frac{1}{2}''$ Flat Girders 10a, overlapped one hole, are secured, and $12\frac{1}{2}''$ Flat Girders 13a are bolted to the shorter sides.

The base frame is strengthened by four additional $18\frac{1}{2}''$ Angle Girders placed between the outer Girders 6b, and these serve to support the deck plates 11a that are represented by $5\frac{1}{2}'' \times 2\frac{1}{2}''$ Flat Plates bolted to the $18\frac{1}{2}''$ Angle Girders, as shown in Fig. 1. The two inside Angle Girders carry the lower portion of a Geared Roller Bearing, and this is held in position by means of two nuts and bolts.

Two $12\frac{1}{2}''$ Angle Girders 36, Fig. 2, bolted to the upper portion of the Roller Bearing, carry a $5\frac{1}{2}'' \times 3\frac{1}{2}''$ Flat Plate 37, Figs. 1 and 3, that is secured in the last holes at the outer ends of the Girders. This Plate carries an Electric Motor 1 that drives the Rod 24 by means of a $\frac{1}{2}''$ Pinion 10 and a 57-teeth Gear Wheel 11. The Rod carries a Pinion 27, and slides in its bearings. It is so

Fig. 2. In this Illustration the method of fitting the two hoisting shafts is plainly shown

arranged that when the lever 28 is moved the Pinion 27 engages a Contrate Wheel 29, or a Pinion 12 with the Gear Wheel 11, this last remaining in mesh with the Pinion 10. The method of constructing the lever 28 can be seen from Fig. 3.

A Worm 38 engages with a 57-teeth Gear Wheel on a vertical Rod 39, on the lower end of which is mounted a 1" Sprocket Wheel 62, Fig. 5. A length of Sprocket Chain connects the Sprocket 62 with the Sprocket 63, and this last part is secured on a vertical Rod journalled in the Flat Plate 37 and also in the 4½" Angle Girder 64. The bottom end of the Rod carries the special Pinion supplied with the Geared Roller Bearing and this meshes with the lower race of the Bearing. Thus, when the Gear 11 is in engagement with the Pinion 12, the entire superstructure of the crane is rotated.

THE JIB AND LUFFING MECHANISM

The vertical member of the jib, Fig. 1, consists of two 9½" Angle Girders 2 and two 9½" Angle Girders 6a bolted together in pairs at their lower ends and braced at the sides by 2½" and 3" Strips. This vertical member pivots about a 5" Rod, indicated at 3, that forms also the support for two 9½" Flat Girders 61. The Rod is carried in two Architraves bolted to the Angle Girders 36. The horizontal arm of the jib is built up from four 18½" Angle Girders 2d braced by Strips of various lengths in the manner shown.

The positions of the Rods carrying the purchase Pulleys 51 and 52 are shown in Fig. 1, and from this illustration is seen the method whereby the three Strips 18 are attached. Two large Corner Brackets are bolted to the jib, and the outer holes of these carry a Rod on which are mounted the Strips 18. Collars are used to prevent unwanted side-play in the Strips and Rod.

Four 12½" Angle Girders 15a form the box-like column that carries the upper ends of the Flat Girders 61. The lower ends of the Angle Girders 15a are bolted to the Angle Girders 36, and each pair is held rigidly in a vertical position by means of a 12½" Braced Girder and connected at the top by a 3½" Braced Girder 15c.

Fig. 3. One of the two Electric Motors used for driving the slewing and luffing mechanisms

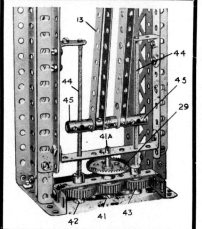

Fig. 4. The screw luffing movement

The mechanism controlling the movements of the jib is arranged as follows. A 1½" Contrate Wheel 29, Fig. 3, which can be engaged by the Pinion 27, is mounted on a short Rod journalled in 3½"×½" Double Angle Strips bolted to 5½" Angle Girders that are fitted in turn to the Girders 15a, as shown in Figs. 1 and 4. This Rod carries also a 1" Gear Wheel 41 that meshes with two other 1" Gears 42 and 43, mounted on the Threaded Rods 44. These Threaded Rods carry two Couplings 45 connected by a 2" Rod on which four 5½" Strips 13 are mounted pivotally. The upper ends of the Strips 13 are carried by the Rod 14 mounted in the triangular framework 15, and the Strips are spaced by Collars on the Rod 14, and also on the Rod mounted in the Couplings 45. The Rod 14 is journalled in two 1"×1" Angle Brackets secured to the underside of the lower members of the triangular frame. This frame is composed of three 7½" Angle Girders 15, Fig. 1, braced by 5½" Strips placed crosswise. These Strips are held in position by Bolts passing through their end holes, and also through the elongated holes of the Girders 15.

It will be seen from Fig. 1 that 1½" Strips are joined onto the upper Girders 15 for the purpose of carrying the pivot Rod 18c, which connects the frame to the 3" Strips 18. The latter, in turn, are attached pivotally to the jib, as already described. The lower end of the triangular frame is pivoted at 16 on a Rod located in suitable holes in the Flat Girders 61. On moving the lever 28, Fig. 3, so that the Pinion 27 is brought into gear with the Contrate Wheel 29, the Threaded Rods 44, Fig. 4, are rotated, and the Threaded Couplings 45 move up or down according to the direction of rotation of the Motor. In this manner the jib is raised or lowered.

THE HOISTING MECHANISM

Two 9½" Angle Girders 46 are secured at right-angles to the Girders 36 and are held in position by means of four ½"×½" Angle Brackets. To these 9½" Angle Girders are bolted the sides of the gear-box, which are formed from 5½"×2½" Flanged Plates 47. A 4½" Angle Girder and a 4½" Strip are bolted across the upper flanges of the Plates 47, as shown in Fig. 5, and the 4½" Strip forms a support for a 2½" Angle Girder. This last Girder and the 4½″ Angle Girder both support two 5″ Rods 48 and 49 that represent hoisting barrels for the pulley blocks 8 and 9.

The ends of the Girders 46 Fig. 2 have a 5½″×3½″ Flat Plate bolted between them, and this carries the second Electric Motor 5. A ½″ Pinion on the armature shaft of the Motor meshes with a 57-teeth Gear, locked on a short Rod together with a second ½″ Pinion. This drives a 57-teeth Gear carried on a 3½″ Rod, and on the outer end of this last part is mounted a ½″ Pinion. A 57-teeth Gear, in sliding engagement with this Pinion, is locked securely on a 5″ Rod that is able to move laterally in its bearings. On the Rod are mounted two ¾″ Contrate Wheels 19 and a Crank 50, the Rod passing through the slotted hole of this Crank. In the boss of the Crank a 5″ Rod 22 is accommodated, and this slides in the upper holes of two Trunnions bolted to the Flanged Plates 47.

One end of the Rod carries a single Collar, but the other end is fitted with two Collars, placed apart as shown in the illustration. The space so formed accommodates one end of a 4½″ Strip 20, mounted pivotally on the lock-nutted bolt 21 that is fitted onto a Double Bent Strip. This last mentioned part is joined to a 4½″ Angle Girder that is bolted to one of the Flanged Plates 47, and supported at its outer end by a 2½″ Strip. The Strip 20 carries also a Threaded Pin forming the control handle.

Fig 5. The fitting of the hoisting drum brakes is clearly shown in this view

When the control handle is moved to the left, one of the ¾″ Contrate Wheels 19 engages with the 1″ Gear 24, locked on the inner end of the Rod 49; and when the handle is moved to the right the remaining Contrate meshes with the 1″ Gear 23 on the Rod 48. When one of the Contrates is in engagement with the 1″ Gear 23, the pulley block 9, Fig. 1, is raised or lowered by means of the cord 7, which passes over one of the two 1″ Pulleys set between the two Bush Wheels 51, Fig. 1. This Cord passes also over one of the two 1″ loose Pulleys situated at 52. From there it is led to one of the Pulleys in the block 9, then round a Pulley at 52 and over the second Pulley in the block 9, and finally is secured to one of the Bush Wheels at 52.

In a similar manner the pulley block 8 may be operated from the Rod 49, the cord 6 being led over the second Pulley at 51, Fig. 1, to the Pulley at the end of the jib. From there it passes round a ½″ Pulley in the block 8 and is tied to a Flat Bracket carried on the Rod of the outer Pulley. The shafts 48 and 49, Fig. 5, carry at their extreme ends two 1″ Pulleys, round the grooves of which are passed cords that are tied to Couplings mounted on the ends of two 8″ Rods. These 8″ Rods have shorter Rods 25 and 26 fitted to them, which act as brake levers for controlling the loads on the pulley blocks 8 and 9.

Parts Required

10 of No. 2	6 of No. 8b	2 of No. 15	2 of No. 22	2 of No. 29	1 of No. 48a	4 of No. 70	2 of No. 108
4 ,, ,, 2a	3 ,, ,, 9	4 ,, ,, 15a-	7 ,, ,, 22a	5 ,, ,, 31	2 ,, ,, 48b	3 ,, ,, 76	3 ,, ,, 111
7 ,, ,, 3	2 ,, ,, 9a	1 ,, ,, 15b	1 ,, ,, 23	1 ,, ,, 32	2 ,, ,, 52	2 ,, ,, 80	3 ,, ,, 111a
7 ,, ,, 4	1 ,, ,, 9c	4 ,, ,, 16	5 ,, ,, 24	203 ,, ,, 37	2 ,, ,, 52a	12 ,, ,, 94	5 ,, ,, 111c
6 ,, ,, 5	1 ,, ,, 9d	6 ,, ,, 16a	1 ,, ,, 25	17 ,, ,, 37a	1 ,, ,, 53	2 ,, ,, 96a	1 ,, ,, 115
3 ,, ,, 6a	3 ,, ,, 10	3 ,, ,, 16b	3 ,, ,, 26	50 ,, ,, 38	1 ,, ,, 57b	1 ,, ,, 97	2 ,, ,, 126
11 ,, ,, 7	12 ,, ,, 12	4 ,, ,, 17	1 ,, ,, 27	2 ,, ,, 40	67 ,, ,, 59	2 ,, ,, 99	2 ,, ,, 126a
8 ,, ,, 8	3 ,, ,, 12a	1 ,, ,, 18a	4 ,, ,, 27a	1 ,, ,, 45	1 ,, ,, 62	4 ,, ,, 103a	4 ,, ,, 133
6 ,, ,, 8a	2 ,, ,, 13a	2 ,, ,, 18b	1 ,, ,, 28	1 ,, ,, 48	8 ,, ,, 63	4 ,, ,, 103b	1 ,, ,, 167

2 Electric Motors (1 Motor not included in Outfit)

(Overseas 3d. Canada 5 Cents.)

Meccano Hammerhead Crane

A powerful model of one of the massive cranes used in shipyards and harbours

Fig. 1. General view of the Model Hammerhead Crane.

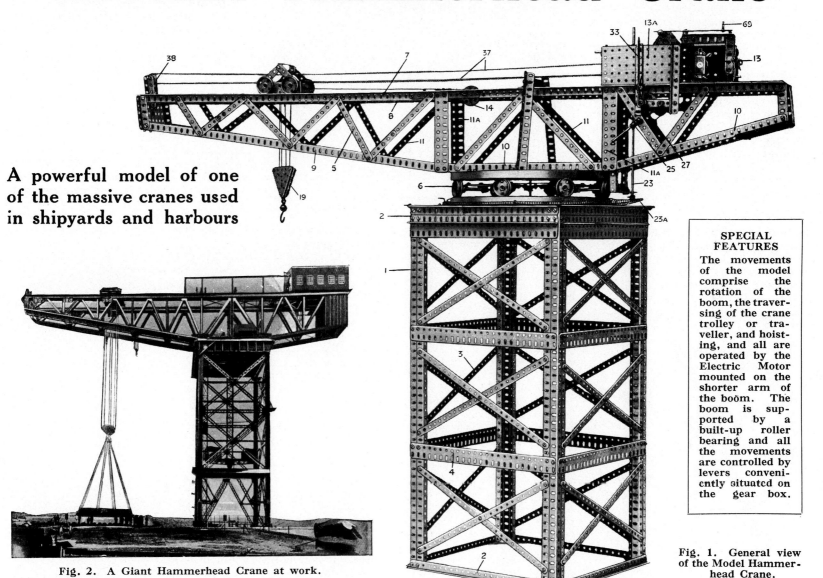

Fig. 2. A Giant Hammerhead Crane at work.

SPECIAL FEATURES

The movements of the model comprise the rotation of the boom, the traversing of the crane trolley or traveller, and hoisting, and all are operated by the Electric Motor mounted on the shorter arm of the boom. The boom is supported by a built-up roller bearing and all the movements are controlled by levers conveniently situated on the gear box.

Published by MECCANO LIMITED, BINNS ROAD, LIVERPOOL

Printed in England

THIS model is an elaborate and very interesting example of the latest Meccano construction. The particular type of crane from which it has been designed is known as the "hammerhead"—a title easily explained from a glance at the general shape of the structure—and the realistic appearance of the model is well shown by comparison with the illustration on the preceding page of an actual hammerhead crane.

Hammerhead cranes are used in ship-building yards and other places where it is required to move heavy loads over a large radius ; they have been specially adapted, also, to the construction of harbours, breakwaters, etc., and in this work they have proved their value in swinging into position the huge blocks of concrete, weighing tens of tons, which form so stout a defence against the might of the sea.

Building the Meccano Model

In building the model the main tower or pedestal should be constructed first. As in the actual crane this part is of very massive construction, for it must be capable of withstanding exceptional stresses and strains. Each vertical corner member 1 (Fig. 1) is composed of three $24\frac{1}{2}''$ Angle Girders, connected at the top and bottom by $12\frac{1}{2}''$ Angle Girders 2. The framework is held perfectly rigid by means of a series of ties and struts consisting of $12\frac{1}{2}''$ Strips 3 and Flat Girders 4.

The upper platform that carries the rotating boom is composed of a number of Flat Plates bolted to the $12\frac{1}{2}''$ Angle Girders that are secured transversely in the tower. This platform is shown in Fig. 5 and it will be noted that a space is left at its centre to accommodate the Axle Rod 34c (Fig. 3) of the wheel race. When the construction of the tower has been completed, attention may be given to the roller bearings on which swivels the rotating arm or boom of the crane.

Fig. 3. The Roller Bearings, completely assembled. Note how the main Boom is secured.

Fig. 4. The Spider Frame

the base by means of $1'' \times \frac{1}{2}''$ Angle Brackets 58. Care should be taken to see that the Segments meet correctly to enable the wheels to run smoothly.

Eight Flanged Wheels (Fig. 4) are mounted on $2\frac{1}{2}''$ Rods that are journalled in $1\frac{1}{2}'' \times \frac{1}{2}''$ Double Angle Strips. The latter are bolted to a frame, or "spider," composed of eight $4\frac{1}{2}''$ Strips placed radially round a Face Plate and bolted thereto. The frame thus formed is braced securely by means of eight $3\frac{1}{2}''$ Strips placed as shown.

The revolving upper race (31, Fig. 3) is secured to the base of the boom and rests upon the wheels 6, and a shaft 34c journalled in the bearing 61 (Fig. 5) forms a common

Arrangement of the Roller Bearings

Where a heavy mass is to be rotated about an axis, it is necessary to devise some method of relieving the tremendous strain that would be imposed upon that axis. The usual procedure is to distribute the weight of the mass over wheels or rollers arranged at a distance from and rotating round the central pivot. This arrangement is employed in the Hammerhead Crane to take the weight of the boom, and so allow it to rotate freely on its axis.

The construction of the main pivot and roller bearing, or wheel race, is shown in Figs. 3, 4 and 5. Fig. 3 shows the bearings completely assembled. Fig. 5 is a plan view of the lower wheel race, and Fig. 4 illustrates the spider or wheel frame. The lower or stationary race 30 (Fig. 3) is constructed from eight Channel Segments and forms a track upon which the spider frame revolves. From Fig. 5 it will be noted that the Channel Segments are bolted to

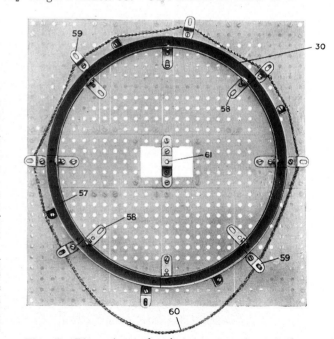

Fig. 5. Plan view, showing construction of the upper Platform and the lower fixed Roller Race.

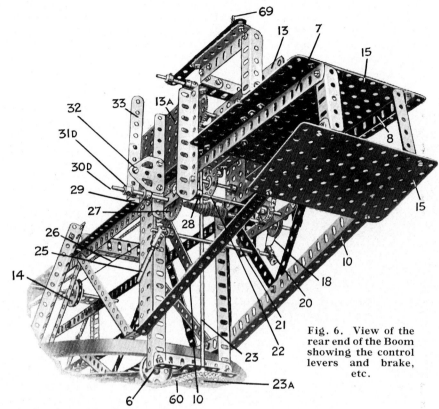

Fig. 6. View of the rear end of the Boom showing the control levers and brake, etc.

Constructing the Boom and Traveller

Each side 7 and 8 (Fig. 1) of the main boom is composed of two 24½″ Angle Girders bolted together. The lower portions of the boom consist of 24½″ Girders 9 and 12½″ Girders 10 braced by a series of ties and struts 5 and 11. A Pulley Wheel 14 is carried on a 4½″ Rod journalled in the Girders 7 and 8 and forms a guide Pulley for the hoisting cord.

The constructional details of the traveller are shown clearly in Fig. 7. The axle frame 62 is constructed from two 3½″ Flat Girders connected by two 2½″×1″ and one 2½″×½″ Double Angle Strips 68. The traversing movement is imparted by means of a Sprocket Chain 37, the ends of which are connected to the Double Angle Strips 68.

As will be seen from Fig. 1, the Chain 37 passes over a 1″ Sprocket Wheel 38 carried on a Rod that is journalled in two 2½″ Angle Girders secured to the 4½″×2½″ Flat Plate which spans the front end of the boom. At the rear end of the boom the Chain passes round a Sprocket Wheel 49 (Fig. 8) which is driven by the Electric Motor 13. It will thus be seen that when the Motor is set in operation, and providing that the gear control lever is placed correctly, the Sprocket Chain tends to either draw or pull the traveller along.

A feature of the traveller is the two-sheaved pulley 64 (Fig. 7) with specially deep grooves. This is built up by placing two 1″ loose Pulleys 63 between two Bush Wheels.

Operation of Control Mechanism

The three movements of the model—hoisting, traversing of the crane trolley, and slewing —are driven and controlled from the Electric Motor and gear box secured upon the upper side of the boom. The Motor (13, Fig. 6) is bolted to the 5½″×3½″ Flat Plates 15 carried on the main Girders 7 and 8 of the boom, while the sides of the gear box 13a are bolted directly to the inside flanges of the Girders.

The hoisting gear is operated as follows : the Motor, by means of a ½″ Pinion 15a (Fig. 8) on its armature spindle, drives a 57-teeth Gear Wheel secured to an axle carrying a 1″

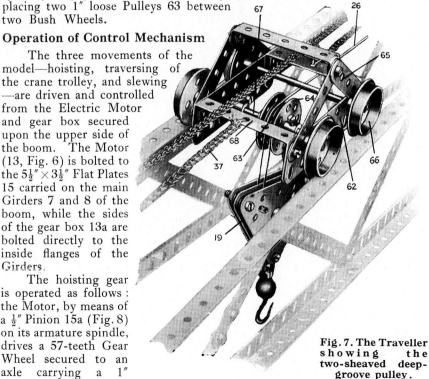

Fig. 7. The Traveller showing the two-sheaved deep-groove pulley.

axis for the spider frame and revolving race, both of which rotate at different speeds. The bearing 61 consists of a Double Bent Strip bolted to a 2½″ Strip that, in turn, is secured to the upper platform of the vertical tower. The shaft 34c should be secured in the Face Plate forming the hub of the upper race, but the spider frame should be allowed to swivel freely upon it.

A vertical driving Rod 23 (Fig. 6) situated on the rotating structure carries a 1½″ Sprocket Wheel 23a placed within and engaging the Sprocket Chain loop 60 (Fig. 5). The latter is arranged round the series of Reversed Angle Brackets 59. On rotation of the Sprocket Wheel 23a the chain grips the Brackets 59 and becomes immovable, whereupon the Sprocket commences to travel round the chain, carrying the pivoted superstructure with it.

For the interest of those readers who possess the new Meccano Geared Roller Bearings (Part No. 167), it may be mentioned here that this part can be used in place of the arrangement described. If it is decided to use the new part several slight alterations in the general layout will be required. The necessary adjustments are very simple and do not need a detailed description, for they will become at once apparent when the Roller Bearings are incorporated in the model.

Sprocket Wheel 16a. The 57-teeth Gear cannot be seen in the photograph as it is hidden by the casing of the Motor. The Sprocket Wheel 16a is connected by a short length of Sprocket Chain to a similar wheel mounted on a Rod 22 (Fig. 6) and a ½″ Pinion 28 secured to the latter Rod drives a 57-teeth Gear Wheel 27 on the winding shaft 30d.

The hoisting cord 26 passes from the winding shaft 30d over a guide Pulley 14 and over a sheave 63 in the traveller (Fig. 7) ; from thence it is led round one of the sheaves of the two-sheaved pulley block 19, back round the other sheave 63, then over the second sheave in the pulley block 19, and is finally secured in a hole in the Bush Wheels 64. The Bush Wheels are secured to the Rod 67 and do not revolve with the sheaves 63.

The Gear Wheel 27 (Fig. 6) may be moved in or out of engagement with the Pinion 28 on operation of a lever 33. The latter is pivoted to a Flat Trunnion at 32 and engages the Rod 30d by means of a Double Bracket 29 mounted between Collars 31d. The movement of the load is controlled by a friction brake consisting of a length of cord 18 tied to the end of a Coupling 20 and engaging a 1″ Pulley secured to the winding shaft. The grip of the cord 18 about the Pulley is relaxed on lifting the lever 25, which consists of a short Rod attached to the shaft 21 carrying the Coupling 20. The arrangement of the brake is shown clearly in Fig. 6.

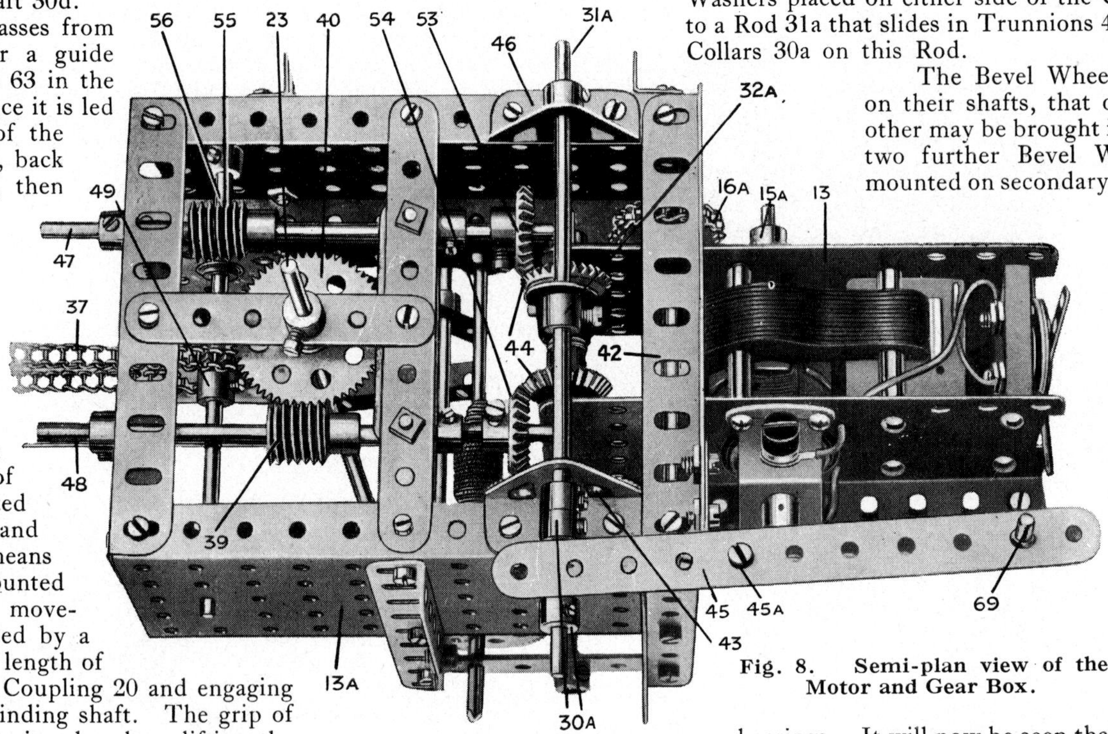

Rotating and Traversing Movements

The 57-teeth Gear Wheel which, as already mentioned, is mounted immediately behind the Sprocket Wheel 16a and is driven by the Motor Pinion 15a (Fig. 8), engages with a further ½″ Pinion secured to a short Rod journalled in the end row of holes in the side casing of the Motor. The latter Rod carries at its other extremity a further ½″ Pinion meshing with a 57-teeth Gear Wheel 43

secured to the Rod of the two Bevel Wheels 44. This Rod may be moved to and fro in its bearings on operation of the lever 45, which is pivoted at 45a. The end hole of a Crank 32a is threaded on the Rod between the bosses of the Bevel Wheels 44 and is retained in its position by means of two or three Washers placed on either side of the Crank, and the latter is secured to a Rod 31a that slides in Trunnions 46. The lever 45 rests between Collars 30a on this Rod.

The Bevel Wheels 44 (Fig. 8) are so arranged on their shafts, that on moving the lever 45 one or other may be brought into engagement with one of the two further Bevel Wheels 53 and 54, which are mounted on secondary shafts 47 and 48. The shaft 47 carries a Worm 55 driving a 57-teeth Gear Wheel on the Rod 56, and the 1″ Sprocket Wheel 49 on this Rod engages the Sprocket Chain 37, which, as already explained, operates the traveller.

The boom of the crane is rotated about the roller bearings by means of the second shaft 48. This carries a Worm 39 engaging with the 57-teeth Gear Wheel 40 on the vertical shaft 23 ; the latter carries at its lower end the Sprocket Wheel 23a (Fig. 6) which rotates in the Sprocket Chain that grips the circumference of the lower fixed guide of the roller bearings. It will now be seen that a slight movement of the lever 69 enables the Motor to operate either the traveller or the rotating boom.

Several Standard Mechanisms are used in the Hammerhead Crane. They are as follows :—S.M. 32 (Two-sheave Pulley Block), S.M. 39 (Guide Pulley), S.M. 69 (Drive-changing Gear), S.M. 101 (Roller Bearings), S.M. 155 (Overhead Trolley), and S.M. 169 (Traversing Gear), etc.

Fig. 8. Semi-plan view of the Motor and Gear Box.

Parts required to build the Hammerhead Crane

24 of No.	1	20 of No.	8	4 of No.	12	3 of No.	16b	4 of No.	30	1 of No.	48a	4 of No.	70	2 of No.	103d
4	,, 1b	4	,, 8b	2	,, 12a	1	,, 17	2	,, 32	2	,, 52	3	,, 76	1	,, 103h
13	,, 2	5	,, 9	16	,, 12b	1	,, 18a	447	,, 37	8	,, 52a	80″	,, 94	2	,, 109
10	,, 2a	15	,, 9a	1	,, 13	12	,, 20	5	,, 37a	2	,, 53a	1	,, 95a	3	,, 111
14	,, 3	2	,, 9b	1	,, 13a	1	,, 22	44	,, 38	1	,, 57b	3	,, 96a	16	,, 119
7	,, 4	7	,, 9d	2	,, 14	5	,, 22a	1	,, 40	32	,, 59	4	,, 103	8	,, 125
8	,, 5	2	,, 9f	5	,, 15	4	,, 24	1	,, 45	1	,, 62	12	,, 103b	2	,, 126
5	,, 6a	1	,, 10	3	,, 16	4	,, 26	2	,, 46	3	,, 63	1	,, 103c	1	,, 126a
18	,, 7	1	,, 11	8	,, 16a	5	,, 27a	8	,, 48						

1 Electric Motor.

Meccano Hammerhead Crane

An L Outfit Model

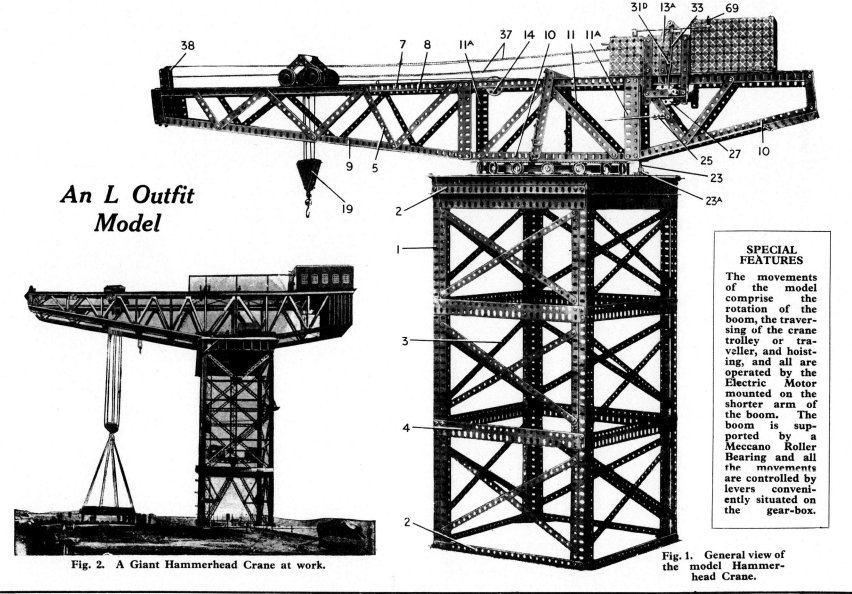

SPECIAL FEATURES

The movements of the model comprise the rotation of the boom, the traversing of the crane trolley or traveller, and hoisting, and all are operated by the Electric Motor mounted on the shorter arm of the boom. The boom is supported by a Meccano Roller Bearing and all the movements are controlled by levers conveniently situated on the gear-box.

Fig. 2. A Giant Hammerhead Crane at work.

Fig. 1. General view of the model Hammerhead Crane.

Published by MECCANO LIMITED, BINNS ROAD, LIVERPOOL 13, ENGLAND

Printed in England

Fig. 3. The top of the main tower showing the Roller Bearing.

Hammerhead Cranes are specially adapted for handling abnormal loads, and many are capable of lifting over 200 tons. They are unable to change their position while working, however, and for this reason they are usually found in shipbuilding yards and near fitting-out basins. In Fig. 2 is shown one of the largest hammerhead cranes in the world, capable of lifting a load of over 250 tons, installed in a large American dockyard.

The bottom of each of the four legs is set in a mass of concrete weighing many tons and the boom is free to rotate on a huge roller race. All the movements are operated electrically, and are under the control of one man stationed at the front of the engine house, built on to the boom. The main hoist consists of two separate pulley blocks suspended from a traveller. There is also an auxiliary hoist capable of lifting loads of a few tons and this enables light work to be carried out without the necessity for bringing the main hoist into operation.

The Meccano model Hammerhead Crane closely resembles that shown in Fig. 2. The construction is commenced by building up the main tower shown in Figs. 1 and 3. Each of the corner vertical girders is formed from

three 24½-in. Angle Girders, and these are secured at their upper and lower ends by the 12½-in. Angle Girders 2. Four additional 12½-in. Angle Girders are fixed in place at the top to form supports for the upper platform. Bracing is now added, and this consists of the 12½-in. Flat Girders 4 and 12½-in. Strips 3. The points of attachment of these parts are shown in Fig. 1. The four 12½-in. Angle Girders fitted to the top of the tower support a number of Flat Plates forming the upper platform. The arrangement of the Plates is shown in Fig. 3, and they are strengthened by two 12½-in. Angle Girders on their undersides. The lower Geared Roller Race of the Roller Bearing is secured, through the Flat Plates, to these last-mentioned Angle Girders, and the central Bush Wheel of the Roller Race forms a support for the short Rod 34c. A 7½-in. Strip, bolted to the centre section of the Roller Bearing pivots about this Rod.

BUILDING THE BOOM.

The main girders of the boom **7** and **8** are each built up from two 24½-in. Angle Girders overlapping two holes. At the point where the Girders are connected, two 5½-in. Flat Girders 11a are fitted, and these carry at their lower ends the Girders 9 and 10. A second pair of 5½-in. Flat Girders 11a, situated near the rear of the boom, carry the free ends of the Girders 10 and also the lower ends of the 12½-in. Angle Girders 10a. The upper ends of these latter parts are attached by 2½-in. Angle Girders to the main members 7 and 8 and three connecting 5½-in. x 3½-in. Flat Plates, two of which are indicated at **15**, are also incorporated as shown in Fig. 5. The fronts of the Girders 9 are bolted to the flanges of a 3½-in. x 2½-in. Flanged Plate that in turn is fixed to the Girders 7 and 8. This Flanged Plate supports two 2½-in. Angle Girders, the upper holes of which form bearings for a 1½-in. Rod on which is locked a 1-in. Sprocket Wheel 38. The boom is completed by the addition of bracing Strips 5 and 11,

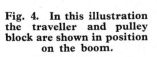

Fig. 4. In this illustration the traveller and pulley block are shown in position on the boom.

the sizes of which will be seen from Fig. 1. At this point of the construction the traveller, shown in Fig 4, is built. Two 3½-in. Flat Girders 62 are joined by means of two 2½-in. x 1-in. Double Angle Strips 68, and the bolts carrying these Double Angle Strips also secure in position the 2½-in. Strips 65. The upper ends of the Strips are connected together as shown, by a 2½-in. x ½-in. Double Angle Strip. Two Double Arm Cranks are bolted to the Flat Girders 62, and they carry a 2½-in. Rod 67 on which are mounted two 1-in. loose Pulleys 63 and two Bush Wheels 64. The Bush Wheels are gripped on the Rod and the Pulleys are free to turn between them.

The Pulley Block 19 is constructed from three 2½-in. Triangular Plates joined by three ¾-in. Bolts. Between the Plates on the shanks of each Bolt four washers are accommodated and the bolt at the lowest point of the pulley block also carries a Flat Bracket to which is attached a Large Loaded Hook. The centre holes of the Triangular Plates carry a 1½-in. Rod, held in position by two Collars, and on this two 1-in. loose Pulleys are free to turn.

The hoisting cord 26 passes over one of the loose Pulleys 63 and round one of the Pulleys of the pulley block 19. From this point it passes over the second Pulley at 63, round the remaining Pulley of the pulley block, and is finally secured to a Flat Bracket carried on the Rod 67 between the Pulleys 63. The Flanged Wheels 66, on which the traveller moves backward and forward, are gripped on the ends of 3½-in. Rods journalled in the upper holes of the Flat Girders 66.

THE GEAR-BOX.

The next section of the model to receive attention is the gear-box, and this is shown in Figs. 1, 5 and 6. The side of the gear-box consist of two 5½-in. x 2½-in. Flanged Plates 13a, joined together by two 4½-in. Strips, one of which is indicated at 42, Fig. 6. This Strip supports a 2½-in. Angle Girder, and the remaining 4½-in. Strip carries two 2-in. Angle Girders as shown. A 3-in. Strip, arranged longitudinally, connects both 4½-in. Strips,

and it will be used later to form a bearing for the Rod 23. The upper flanges of the gear-box side plates also carry two Trunnions 46, Fig. 6.

The Electric Motor 13 is secured on the 5½-in. x 3½-in. Flat Plate adjacent to the Plate 15, and it carries on one end of its armature shaft a ½-in. Pinion 15a. This meshes with a 57-teeth Gear fixed on a Rod that carries a ¾-in. Pinion on its opposite end and a 1-in. Sprocket Wheel 16a. The ¾-in. Pinion drives a 50-teeth Gear that is gripped on the same Rod as a 1-in. Gear. A second 1-in. Gear, engaging with the first is secured on a 4½-in. Rod and spaced from the Motor side plate by four Washers. A ½-in. Pinion on the 4½-in. Rod transmits the drive to a 57-teeth Gear carried on the sliding Rod of the ¾-in. Contrate Wheels 44. Between the two Contrates a Crank and 10 washers are inserted, and these are arranged in the manner shown in the illustration.

The left-hand side of the Rod, looking at the gear-box from the rear, carries three Collars 30a, Fig. 4. Of these, one is free to turn, and the other two prevent it from sliding along the Rod. The centre Collar is pivotally attached to a 5½-in. Strip 45 mounted at one end of a Pivot Bolt secured by its nuts to one of the 5½-in. x 2½-in. Flanged Plates of the gear-box. The opposite end of the Strip is fitted with the Threaded Pin 69.

When the lever 45 is moved to the left or the right, the Contrates 44 engage alternately with the ½-in. Pinions 53 and 54. The Pinion 53 is mounted on a 5-in. Rod 47 that carries also a Worm 55. The Worm meshes with a ½-in. Pinion gripped on the Rod 56, and this Rod has mounted on it a Sprocket Wheel 49. A length of Sprocket Chain 37 passes round this last-mentioned Wheel, and also round the 1-in. Sprocket 38, Fig. 1. The two ends of the Sprocket Chain are secured by short lengths of Cord to the traveller, as shown in Fig. 4. It will now be seen that, when the Pinion 53 is driven by the Motor through the Contrate 44, the traveller can be made to move along the boom in either direction by operating the Motor reverse lever.

The Pinion 54, which is driven when required by the Contrate 44, is carried

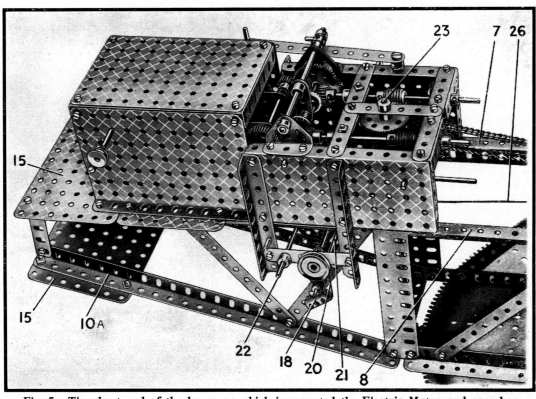

Fig. 5. The short end of the boom on which is mounted the Electric Motor and gear-box.

at one end of the Rod 48 on which is mounted a Worm 39, in constant engagement with a 57-teeth Gear Wheel 40 fixed on a vertical shaft 23. This shaft consists of a 6-in. and 3-in. Rod connected by a Coupling, and it is journalled at its upper end in a 3-in. Strip as already described. At its lower end the shaft is journalled in the centre hole of a 3½-in. x ½-in. Double Angle Strip, and it carries at its extremity a special Pinion 23a that is supplied for use with the Roller Bearing. This Pinion meshes with the lower section of the Roller Bearing carrying the boom, and when it is driven from the Motor, the entire boom and gear-box rotate.

The foregoing is a description of the gear trains controlling the racking of the traveller and slewing of the boom. The only remaining movement to be incorporated in the model is that controlling the hoisting and lowering of the pulley block and hook 19.

This movement is driven by the Motor through the Sprocket Wheel 16a. A length of Sprocket Chain connects this with a second Sprocket Wheel mounted, together with a ½-in. Pinion, on the Rod 22, Fig. 5. The Pinion meshes with a 57-teeth Gear Wheel 27 shown in Fig. 1 and 6, that forms the winding drum, and this is capable of sliding in its bearings. By sliding the Rod, the 57-teeth Gear 27 can be brought into engagement with its ½-in. Pinion. The end of the Rod is fitted with three Collars, the centre one of which is pivotally secured to the 5½-in. Strip 33, in the same way that

the Strip 45 is attached to the Collars 30a. The Strip 33 is free to turn on a ½-in. Bolt 31d, locked by two nuts to a Trunnion as shown. The upper end of the Strip is fitted with a Thraeded Pin, Fig. 6.

The end of the winding spindle Fig. 5, is fitted with a 1-in. fast Pulley round which passes a short length of cord 20. This cord is attached to a Coupling 18 that is gripped by its grub-screws on one end of a 6-in. Rod. On opposite end of this Rod is mounted a second Coupling 25, Fig. 1, in the longitudinal bore of which a 3-in. Rod is accommodated. This Rod forms the brake lever, and it exerts a constant pressure on the winding drum. When it is desired to lower the Hook without using the Motor, this Rod is lifted, thus slacking the Cord 20, Fig. 5.

The bearings for the winding shaft and also the Rod 22 are formed by bolting two 2½-in. Strips to four 4½-in. Angle Girders. Two of these Angle Girders are fitted to each 5½-in. x 2½-in. Flanged Plate of the gear-box as shown.

A cover for the Motor is next built, and this completes the model. Three 5½-in. x 3½-in. Flat Plates are joined together by two 5½-in. Angle Girders, two additional Girders being used to secure the assembly to the Plates 15. The back of the Motor cover consists of a 3½-in. x 2½-in. Flanged Plate. An End Bearing is pivotally attached to the reversing lever of the Motor, and in the boss of this is gripped a short Rod. This passes through one of the holes in the casing as shown in Fig. 6, and carries a Collar on its outer extremity.

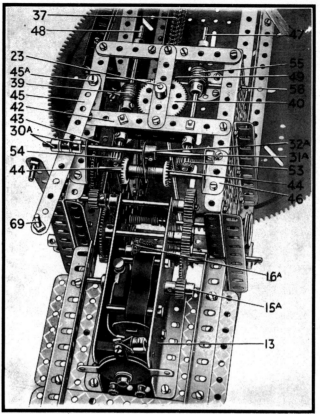

Fig. 6. A plan view of the gear-box.

Parts required to build the Hammerhead Crane

24 of No. 1	2 of No. 6a	3 of No. 9e	4 of No. 16	6 of No. 22a	2 of No. 31	2 of No. 48a	29 of No. 59	4 of No. 103	1 of No. 147b
4 „ „ 1b	18 „ „ 7	1 „ „ 10	2 „ „ 16a	6 „ „ 24	2 „ „ 32	1 „ „ 48b	1 „ „ 62	12 „ „ 103b	2 „ „ 166
17 „ „ 2	20 „ „ 8	3 „ „ 12	1 „ „ 16b	3 „ „ 25	375 „ „ 37	2 „ „ 52	4 „ „ 63	2 „ „ 103d	1 „ „ 167
3 „ „ 2a	7 „ „ 9	1 „ „ 13a	1 „ „ 18a	6 „ „ 26	3 „ „ 37a	12 „ „ 52a	4 „ „ 70	3 „ „ 111	1 „ „ 176
2 „ „ 3	4 „ „ 9a	2 „ „ 14	2 „ „ 18b	1 „ „ 27	52 „ „ 38	1 „ „ 53	3 „ „ 76	1 „ „ 111a	1 Electric
9 „ „ 4	1 „ „ 9b	7 „ „ 15	4 „ „ 20	4 „ „ 27a	2 „ „ 40	1 „ „ 53a	3 ft. 6 in. 94	2 „ „ 115	Motor.
4 „ „ 5	9 „ „ 9d	2 „ „ 15b	1 „ „ 22	2 „ „ 29	2 „ „ 46	1 „ „ 57b	4 of No. 96a	3 „ „ 126	

Railway Breakdown Crane

An L Outfit Model

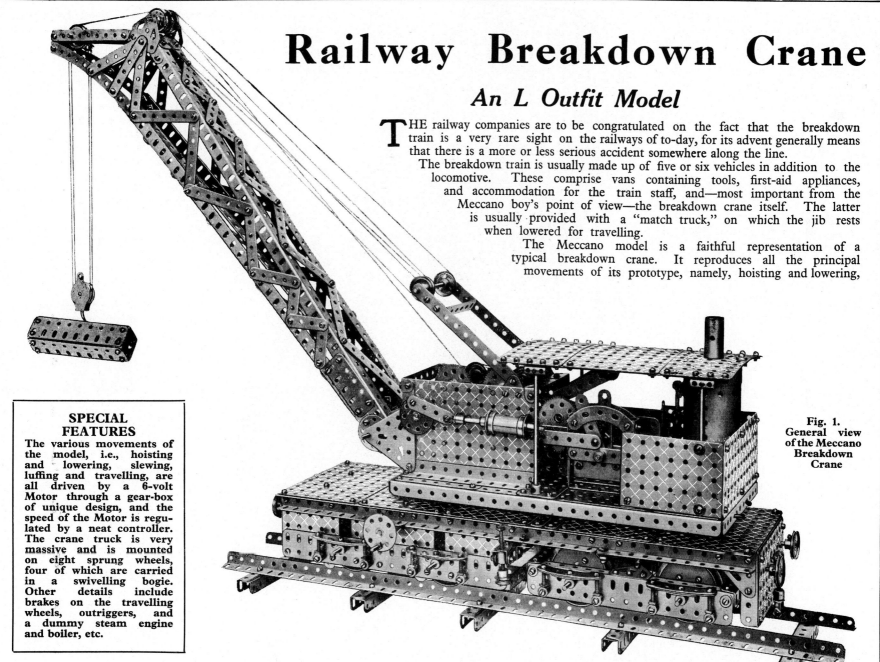

THE railway companies are to be congratulated on the fact that the breakdown train is a very rare sight on the railways of to-day, for its advent generally means that there is a more or less serious accident somewhere along the line.

The breakdown train is usually made up of five or six vehicles in addition to the locomotive. These comprise vans containing tools, first-aid appliances, and accommodation for the train staff, and—most important from the Meccano boy's point of view—the breakdown crane itself. The latter is usually provided with a "match truck," on which the jib rests when lowered for travelling.

The Meccano model is a faithful representation of a typical breakdown crane. It reproduces all the principal movements of its prototype, namely, hoisting and lowering,

Fig. 1.
General view of the Meccano Breakdown Crane

SPECIAL FEATURES

The various movements of the model, i.e., hoisting and lowering, slewing, luffing and travelling, are all driven by a 6-volt Motor through a gear-box of unique design, and the speed of the Motor is regulated by a neat controller. The crane truck is very massive and is mounted on eight sprung wheels, four of which are carried in a swivelling bogie. Other details include brakes on the travelling wheels, outriggers, and a dummy steam engine and boiler, etc.

luffing, slewing and travelling, and is fitted with brakes, outriggers and springs on all four axles. It is driven by a Meccano 6-volt Electric Motor, the speed of which may be regulated by a built-up Meccano controller. Since the prototype is steam-operated, a dummy boiler and engine are incorporated in the model. The crane truck is about 20" in overall length and is designed to run on 3" gauge rails, which may of course be built up from Meccano Angle Girders, etc.

Construction of the Crane Truck

The construction of the model should be commenced by building the crane truck. As will be seen from Fig. 1 and the various sectional views (Figs. 2, 3 and 5), the truck is very solidly built and is complete down to the smallest detail.

The main side girders 1 (Fig. 3) are channel in section, each being built up from one 18½", one 7½" and two 5½" Angle Girders. (The 7½" and 5½" Girders are used in order that the model may be built with an L Outfit; it would be preferable, of course, to use two 18½" Girders for each side member). The girders so formed are connected together at each end and at various other points by 4½" Angle Girders 2. The buffer beams are formed by 4½"×2½" Flat Plates which are attached to the 4½" Angle Girders at each end of the girders 1.

Two 2½"×2½" Flat Plates 5 and a 3½"×2½" Flanged Plate 6 are bolted to each girder 1, a gap being left between each Plate. The end Plates adjoining the buffer beam are connected to the latter by means of 2½" Angle Girders, while the buffer beam at the other end of the truck is reinforced by 2½" Angle Girders and Corner Backets, the latter forming a rigid connection between the 2½" Girders and the side members 1. A 9½" Flat Girder 7 is bolted along the lower edges of the Plates on each side of the truck, and since there is a gap of one hole between the Plates the slotted holes of the Flat Girder are unobstructed at this point. The purpose of this will be explained later.

The two 4½" Angle Girders 3 form a rigid means of attaching to the truck the 3½" Gear Wheel 4 (Fig. 5) which forms the lower portion of the ball race on which the model slews. It is attached to the truck by means of four ½" Bolts, Collars being used for spacing purposes. A reinforced bearing 3a (Figs. 2 and 3), composed of a 1½" Strip bolted to two 1½" Angle Girders, is then attached to the Girders 3. Care should be taken to ensure that a Rod,

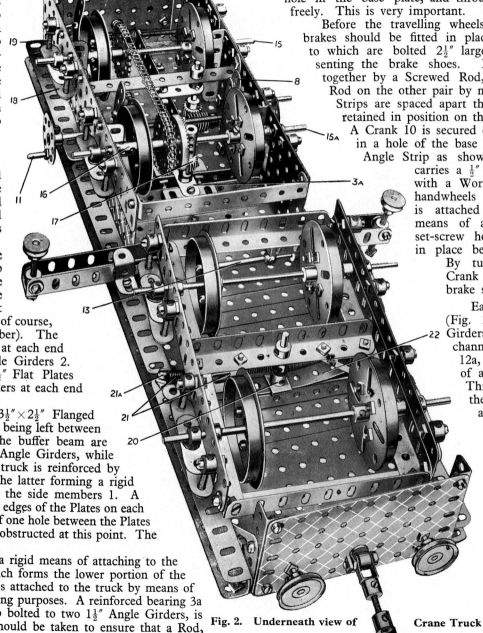

Fig. 2.   Underneath view of   Crane Truck

when passed through the boss of the Gear Wheel 4, through the hole in the base plate, and through the 1½" Strip, turns perfectly freely. This is very important.

Before the travelling wheels are mounted in position, the brakes should be fitted in place. They consist of 2½" Strips to which are bolted 2½" large radius Curved Strips 8 representing the brake shoes. Each pair of brakes is connected together by a Screwed Rod, which is linked to the Screwed Rod on the other pair by means of two 4½" Strips 9. The Strips are spaced apart the distance of five Washers and retained in position on the Rods by lock nuts.

A Crank 10 is secured on a short Rod that is journalled in a hole of the base plate and also in a 4½" Double Angle Strip as shown in Figs. 2 and 3. The Rod carries a ½" Pinion that is arranged to mesh with a Worm on a 6½" Rod on which the handwheels 11 are secured. The Crank is attached pivotally to the links 9 by means of a bolt that is inserted in the set-screw hole of a Collar, which is held in place between the links by a ½" Bolt. By turning the handwheels 11, the Crank swings slowly and presses the brake shoes on to the wheels.

Each of the "outriggers" 12 (Fig. 3) consists of two 3½" Angle Girders placed together to form channel section girders. The "jack" 12a, at the end of each, is composed of a 2" Screwed Rod working in a Threaded Boss that is attached to the Girders by bolts; the bolts are packed with Washers to prevent their shanks binding on the Rod. The outriggers slide on the underside of the main girders and are supported at their inner ends by Handrail Supports sliding on the Rod 13. They are also guided by Reversed Angle Brackets 14 which press them against the edges of the Plates 5. The object of the outriggers in actual practice is to afford additional support to the crane when lifting heavy loads and to relieve the axle springs.

The wheels and wheel springs 18 (Fig. 2) should now receive attention. Each of the springs 18 consists of two $2\frac{1}{2}''$ Strips and one $1\frac{1}{2}''$ Strip. A bolt with a Washer on its shank is passed through the centre hole of all three Strips and inserted in a Collar. The "spring hangers" 19 are $\frac{3}{4}''$ Bolts inserted in Collars that are attached pivotally to the frame by $\frac{1}{2}''$ lock-nutted Bolts. Fig. 4 shows the springs very clearly. The wheels themselves consist of Face Plates bolted to Wheel Flanges; eight in all are required.

The driving axle 15a (Fig. 2) has secured to it a $1\frac{1}{2}''$ Contrate that meshes with a $\frac{1}{2}''$ Pinion 17 on the Rod that forms the central pivot about which the crane turns and which also transmits the drive from the gear-box. The end of this Rod is journalled in the bore of a Coupling mounted loosely on the Rod 15a. Couplings 16 are employed in the place of Collars to prevent end play in the Rods 15 and 15a; if Collars were employed here their grub-screws would foul the flanges of the Plates 6.

The two axles 15, 15a are connected together by means of a length of Sprocket Chain passing over 2″ Sprocket Wheels secured to the axles. This arrangement ensures that the drive is distributed over all four wheels, thus obviating the possibility of wheel slip.

It will be noticed that the ends of the axles 15 and 15a are passed through the slotted holes of the Flat Girders 7 and are journalled in the Collars secured to the springs. The slots thus form guides which, while permitting the free vertical movement of the axles under the action of the springs, prevent any adverse side strain being applied to the springs.

The four buffers are 1″ fast Pulleys mounted on Threaded Pins that are secured to the buffer beams. The couplings by which additional trucks may be attached to the crane for towing purposes each consist of two Small

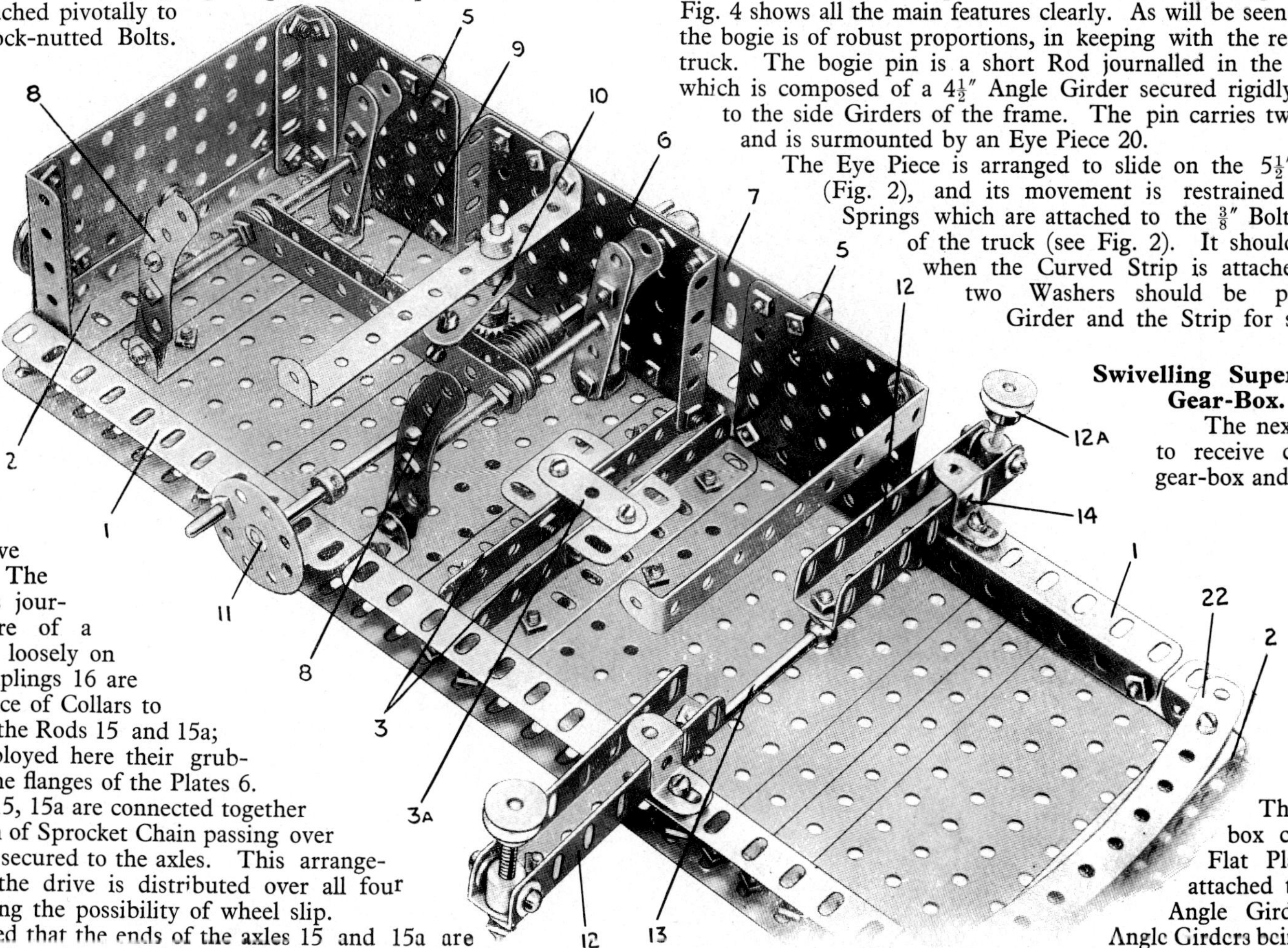

Fig. 3. Underneath view of Crane Truck, with one side and wheel mechanism removed to show the brake rigging and outriggers

Fork Pieces joined by a 1″ Screwed Rod. One coupling is provided at each end of the crane truck.

It only remains now to construct the bogie in order to complete the crane truck. Little explanation is needed regarding its construction, for Fig. 4 shows all the main features clearly. As will be seen from the illustration the bogie is of robust proportions, in keeping with the remainder of the crane truck. The bogie pin is a short Rod journalled in the bogie pin stretcher, which is composed of a $4\frac{1}{2}''$ Angle Girder secured rigidly by Flat Trunnions to the side Girders of the frame. The pin carries two tension springs 21 and is surmounted by an Eye Piece 20.

The Eye Piece is arranged to slide on the $5\frac{1}{2}''$ Curved Strip 22 (Fig. 2), and its movement is restrained by means of the Springs which are attached to the $\frac{3}{8}''$ Bolts 21a on each side of the truck (see Fig. 2). It should be mentioned that when the Curved Strip is attached to the Girder 2 two Washers should be placed between the Girder and the Strip for spacing purposes.

Swivelling Superstructure and Gear-Box.

The next item of the model to receive consideration is the gear-box and the base to which it is attached. The latter consists essentially of three $5\frac{1}{2}'' \times 3\frac{1}{2}''$ and one $5\frac{1}{2}'' \times 2\frac{1}{2}''$ Flat Plates bolted to two $12\frac{1}{2}''$ Angle Girders 23 (Figs. 6 and 7) the ends of which are spanned by $5\frac{1}{2}''$ Angle Girders.

The sides of the gear-box consist of $5\frac{1}{2}'' \times 3\frac{1}{2}''$ Flat Plates 24 that are attached to the base by $5\frac{1}{2}''$ Angle Girders 25 (Fig. 7), $3\frac{1}{2}''$ Angle Girders being added to the front edges of the Plates for stiffening purposes. Two $2\frac{1}{2}''$ Triangular Plates 27 (Fig. 6) secured to these Girders will eventually form the bearings for the jib pivot pin.

The reinforced bearings for the vertical Rods carrying the $1\frac{1}{2}''$ Bevel 41 and $\frac{1}{2}''$ Pinion 43 (Fig. 7) should next be secured in place. The Flanged Ball Race forming the upper portion of the Meccano Ball Bearing, on which the model turns, is fixed centrally under the latter bearing, being held in place by four $\frac{1}{2}''$ Bolts and spaced away from the underside of the superstructure by four Collars placed on the bolts.

The gear-box layout is remarkably simple, due to the employment of neat planetary, central selector transmission. The chief advantage of this gear-box is that none of the Axle Rods or Gears is required to slide transversely. Consequently the Gears may be engaged instantly on movement of a lever, and they do not require the accurate placing on the Rods that is usually necessary with the ordinary type of gear-box.

The Rod 30 (Figs. 6 and 7) is driven by the Motor through the medium of Sprocket Chain and forms the main shaft from which the four movements of the crane are derived. It carries two Double Arm Cranks 34 and 35 which are free on the Rod and carry respectively $\frac{1}{2}''$ Pinions 32 and 33. Each Pinion is mounted loosely on a $\frac{3}{4}''$ Bolt secured by double nuts to the end hole of its respective Crank; and both Pinions are in constant mesh with the Pinion 31, which is secured on the Rod 30.

The 57 teeth Gears 38 and 39 are secured to the luffing and hoisting winch barrels respectively, and by manipulating the lever 49 the Crank 34 is rocked backward or forward on its shaft and the Pinion 32 is brought into engagement with either of the Gears 38 or 39.

With regard to the travelling motion of the model, this is derived from the Rod on which a 57 teeth Gear 42 is secured. The Rod carries also a $\frac{1}{2}''$ Contrate that is in constant mesh with a $\frac{1}{2}''$ Pinion 43 secured on the top of the vertical Rod that forms the central pivot of the model and which has the Pinion 17 (Fig. 2) secured to its lower extremity. This vertical Rod, after passing through the Double Bent Strip and Plate in the base of the superstructure, is journalled freely in the Flanged Ball Race that is bolted directly underneath the Plate. The Rod also is free to turn in the boss of the Gear 4.

The slewing movement is obtained as follows: A 57 teeth Gear 40 is secured to a Rod carrying also a $\frac{1}{2}''$ Bevel in mesh with a Bevel 41. This Bevel is fixed to a short Rod carrying at its bottom end a $\frac{1}{2}''$ Pinion that will mesh with the Gear 4 (Fig. 5), which forms part of the Ball Bearing (see Standard Mechanisms No. 138). Both the Rods carrying the Pinion 17 and the Bevel 41 are journalled in the reinforced bearings mentioned previously, and the four Rods on which the Gears 38, 39, 40 and 42 are secured are journalled in the side Plates of the gear-box and are restrained from lateral movement by Collars.

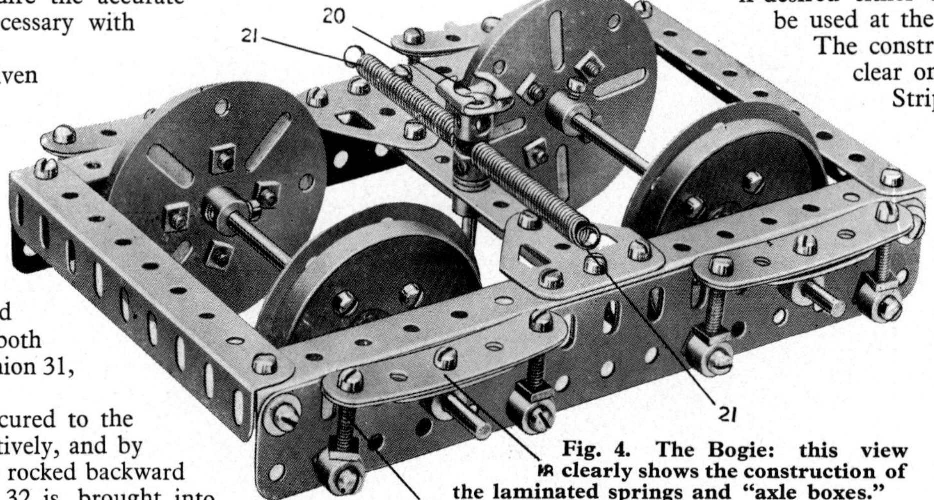

By moving the lever 50 either the travelling or slewing movements of the model may be brought into action and if desired either the luffing or hoisting motions may be used at the same time.

The construction of the lever frame will be clear on reference to Fig. 7. The $2\frac{1}{2}''$ Strips 49 and 50, forming the levers proper, are pivoted in their bottom holes on a Rod that is carried in two $2\frac{1}{2}''$ Strips forming part of the frame. The $5\frac{1}{2}''$ Strips 47 and 48 form the connecting links between the levers and their respective Double Arm Cranks, the connections being made by locknutted bolts. In order to lock the lever 49 in either hoisting, luffing or neutral positions, and the lever 50 in either travelling, slewing or neutral, set-screws from Swivel Bearings 49a are bolted in the second hole of each lever so that their pointed ends engage with holes in the quadrants after each movement of the levers. The latter should, of course, be spaced on their pivot rod so that the bolts are pressed firmly against the quadrants.

The Motor gearing is arranged as follows: A $\frac{1}{2}''$ Pinion on the armature spindle meshes with a 57 teeth Gear on a short Rod journalled in the side plates of the Motor, and this Rod also carries a second $\frac{1}{2}''$ Pinion that engages with a 57 teeth Gear on another Rod that is situated above the first. This Rod has a 1" Sprocket 51 secured to it. The Motor may now be bolted down in the position indicated in Fig. 6, and the Sprocket 37 on the main shaft 30 connected with that on the Motor by a length of Sprocket Chain.

The 1" fast Pulleys 45 and 46 on the hoisting and luffing winch barrels comprise the brake drums. A length of cord is wrapped round each Pulley, one end being fastened to a suitable part of the framework and the other to the appropriate brake lever 54 or 55 (Fig. 6). These levers consist of 3" Strips attached pivotally to a Single Bent Strip that is bolted to a $3\frac{1}{2}''$ Double Angle Strip spanning the sides of the gear-

Fig. 4. The Bogie: this view clearly shows the construction of the laminated springs and "axle boxes."

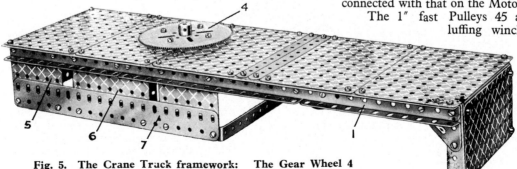

Fig. 5. The Crane Truck framework: The Gear Wheel 4 forms the lower or fixed portion of the Ball Bearing unit

box. The extremities of the brake levers are weighted with $\frac{1}{2}''$ fast Pulleys in order to maintain the cord in a slight state of tension round the brake drums, and thus prevent the load or the jib descending when the barrels are thrown out of gear.

Having assembled the mechanism, two Strips 28 may be attached pivotally to 1″ Triangular Plates that are bolted to the gear-box side Plates. The ends of the Strips are spaced apart by a $3''\times1\frac{1}{2}''$ Double Angle Strip and a $3\frac{1}{2}''$ Rod journalled in the extreme end holes carries the Pulleys 29.

The cylinder 36 (Fig. 6) gives additional realism to the model. It consists of a Sleeve Piece with two $\frac{3}{4}''$ Flanged Wheels forming the cylinder covers through which the piston rod passes. An End Bearing on the end of the latter is attached pivotally to the connecting rod, the other end of which is pivoted by a lock-nutted bolt to the crank disc. The crank disc consists of a Bush Wheel, and is secured on the Rod 44 (Figs. 6 and 7), which is driven from the main-shaft 30 through the medium of a length of Sprocket Chain passing over $\frac{3}{4}''$ Sprocket Wheels. The appearance of the cylinder, etc., will be gathered from the general view of the model.

The boiler is at-tached to a $5\frac{1}{2}''\times2\frac{1}{2}''$ Flat Plate that forms part of the coal bunker, the sides of which are formed from $3\frac{1}{2}''\times2\frac{1}{2}''$ Flanged Plates. Rods 26 - are secured to the Flanged Plates by means of Collars, the purpose of the Rods being to form supports for the roof. Two further Rods 26 are needed for this purpose and they are inserted in Double Arm Cranks that are secured to the base in the positions indicated in Fig. 6.

The boiler fittings include a pressure gauge, represented by a $\frac{1}{2}''$ loose Pulley, and a water gauge 52 composed of a $1\frac{1}{2}''$ Rod secured in two Handrail Supports and attached to the front of the boiler.

The Controller and Electrical Connections

The resistance controller 53 (Fig. 6), the function of which is to alter

the speed of the Motor, is extremely compact and is built entirely from standard Meccano parts. Fig. 6 shows the controller in place whilst Fig. 8 gives an idea of the underneath view of the device with the resistance elements in place. Fig. 9 is a detailed view of the switch arm and spring contact.

The resistance elements consist of a short length of Spring Cord that is attached at equal distances to the shanks of 6 B.A. Bolts 1 (Fig. 8), one of which carried a terminal 8. The 6 B.A. Bolts are care-fully insulated from the Bush Wheel 2 by means of Insu-lating Bushes and Washers, and the Spring Cord is drawn out so that no two adjacent turns touch each other. The 6 B.A. Bolt 3 is insulated in the usual man-ner but remains unconnected; it thus forms the "off" position of the controller in which no current is sup-plied to the Motor.

The switch arm (Fig. 9) consists of a Double Arm Crank 4 carry-ing a Spring Buffer 5, the head of which presses on the heads of the 6 B.A. Bolts forming the "contact studs"; thus smooth and efficient contact with the studs is assured. The Crank pivots on the top end of the supporting Rod 6 and is retained in position by the Collar 7. A Threaded Pin on the other extremity of the switch arm forms a convenient handle. In order to prevent the switch arm riding off the contact studs at either extremity of its travel, a stop consisting of the socket portion of a Spring Buffer is secured to the Bush Wheel 2.

One of the Motor terminals is "earthed" to the frame of the model by connecting it to the bolt 56 (Fig. 6) by a short length of wire. The other

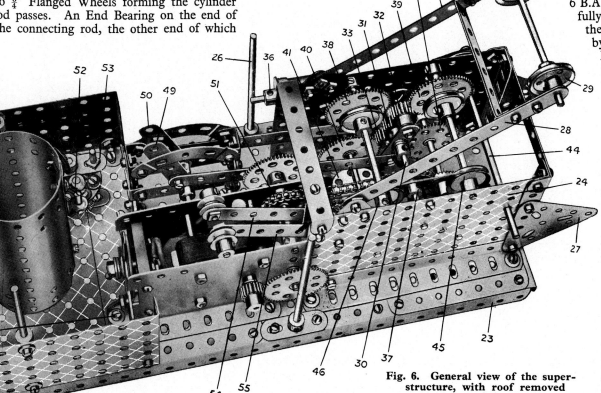

Fig. 6. General view of the super-structure, with roof removed

terminal of the Motor is connected to the 6-volt accumulator or Transformer by a length of wire, which passes out of the rear of the model. The other lead from the Transformer is connected to the terminal 8 of the controller.

When the spring contact 5 (Fig. 9) of the switch arm is pressing on the "off" stud 3, no current is supplied to the Motor, of course. But when the switch arm is moved on to the next stud, the Motor commences to revolve at a slow rate of speed, due to the fact that the current has to flow through the entire resistance and that its value is therefore small. (Actually it is the voltage that is "dropped" or expanded in the resistance. This causes the current to drop too, for voltage is the "driving force" or pressure forcing current through the resistance of a circuit).

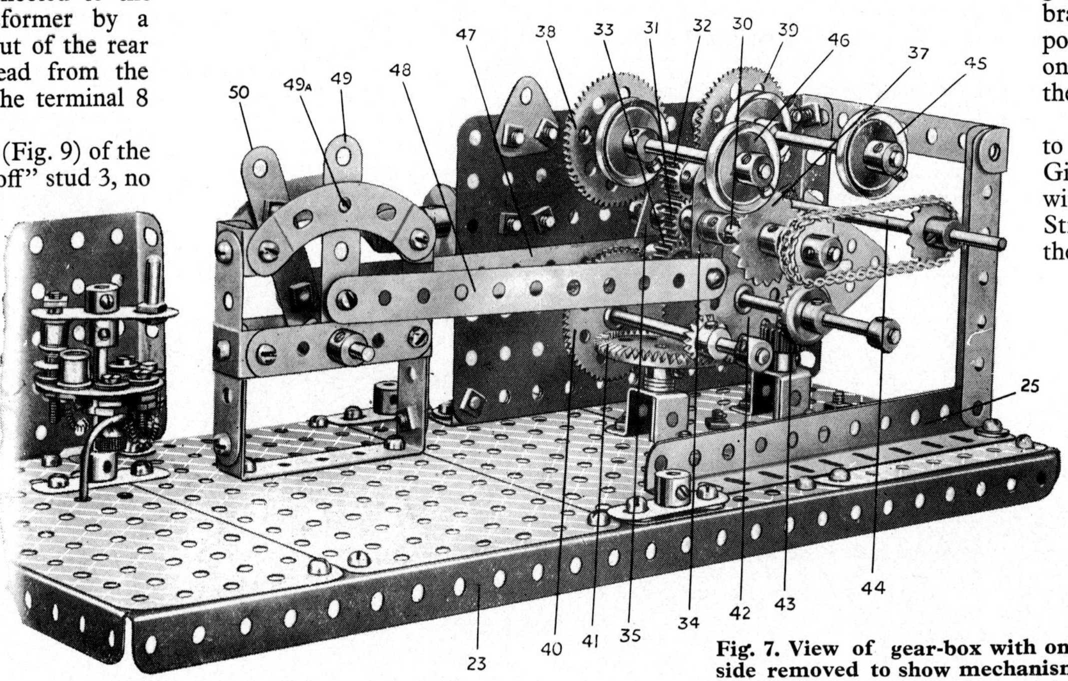

On moving on to the next stud, one stage of the resistance is cut out and the speed of the Motor increases. Step by step, as more resistance is taken out, the speed of the Motor mounts up until the switch arm is on the last stud carrying the terminal 8, when all the resistance is cut out and a straight-through path is afforded for the current from the Transformer to the Motor. The Motor now runs at its greatest speed and develops its maximum power.

Construction of the Jib and Roof

The underside of the roof is shown in Fig. 11. It consists essentially of one $5\frac{1}{2}'' \times 3\frac{1}{2}''$ and two $5\frac{1}{2}'' \times 2\frac{1}{2}''$ Flat Plates, to the edges of which Strips are added for the purpose of stiffening. Four Couplings are secured by means of bolts to each corner of the roof to receive the top ends of the supporting Rods (Fig. 6). A Boiler End is secured to the underside of the roof by a single bolt, which also retains a Chimney Adaptor in place on the reverse side of the roof and a Sleeve Piece to represent a chimney is fitted over the Chimney Adaptor.

The construction of the jib should be fairly clear from Fig. 10. The four main longitudinal girders are $18\frac{1}{2}''$ in length and are braced effectively by suitably disposed bracing Strips. The bracing on both sides is similar, and that on the top corresponds with the bottom.

A $5\frac{1}{2}''$ Curved Strip 60 is secured to each of the two lower $18\frac{1}{2}''$ Angle Girders, and a $4\frac{1}{2}''$ Strip 57, together with a $2\frac{1}{2}''$ large radius Curved Strip, is attached to each top girder, the $2\frac{1}{2}''$ Curved Strip forming the connection between the Girder and the Strip 57. The front ends of the Strips are joined by Double and Flat Brackets.

The Pulleys 59 are mounted on a $2''$ Rod that is journalled in Flat Trunnions bolted to the jib; they are spaced by Collars and two are loose on the Rod, the remaining one being a fast Pulley secured on the Rod against the Trunnion. The Pulleys 58 are similarly arranged, one being a loose Pulley and the other a fast Pulley secured to the Rod. A Flat Bracket is placed on the Rod between the two Pulleys to form a means of attachment for the standing end of the hoisting cord.

Assembling the Principal Model Sections

Having now completed the various units it only remains to assemble them into a complete model. The swivelling superstructure is lowered into place over the central pivot (i.e., the Rod transmitting the drive to the travelling wheels) care being taken that the Ball Casing containing the balls is first placed in position on the $3\frac{1}{2}''$ Gear 4 (Fig. 5), and that it registers correctly with the Flanged Ball Race which is bolted to the underside of the superstructure. It should also be seen that the $\frac{1}{2}''$ Pinion on the lower end of the Rod carrying the Bevel 41 is meshing properly with the teeth of the Gear 4. The Pinion 17 (Fig. 2) may now be secured to its Rod, and this will retain the superstructure in place.

The jib pivot pin, a $4\frac{1}{2}''$ Rod, is passed through the $2\frac{1}{2}''$ Triangular Plates 27 (Fig. 6) and through the bosses of the Bush Wheels 61 (Fig. 10) that are secured to the foot of the jib.

One end of the luffing cord is attached to the head of the jib and passed over one of the

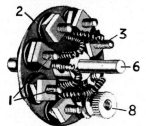

Fig. 8. Underneath view of controller unit, showing resistances

Fig. 7. View of gear-box with one side removed to show mechanism

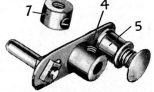

Fig. 9. Detail view of controller switch arm

Pulleys 29 (Fig. 6). It is then taken over a Pulley 59 at the jib head and back over the remaining Pulley 29. Thence it is led over the other Pulley 59 at the jib head and down to the luffing winch barrel, on which it is secured.

The hoisting cord is secured to a Flat Bracket on the Rod carrying the Pulleys 58 and passed round one of the sheaves of the two-sheave Pulley Block. Next it passes over one of the Pulleys 58, round the remaining sheave of the Block, over the other Pulley 58, over the centre Pulley 59, and so down to the hoisting barrel.

Finally the roof may be placed in position by fitting the Boiler End on to the Boiler and securing the ends of the Rods 26 in the centre transverse bores of the Couplings that are secured to the underside of the roof.

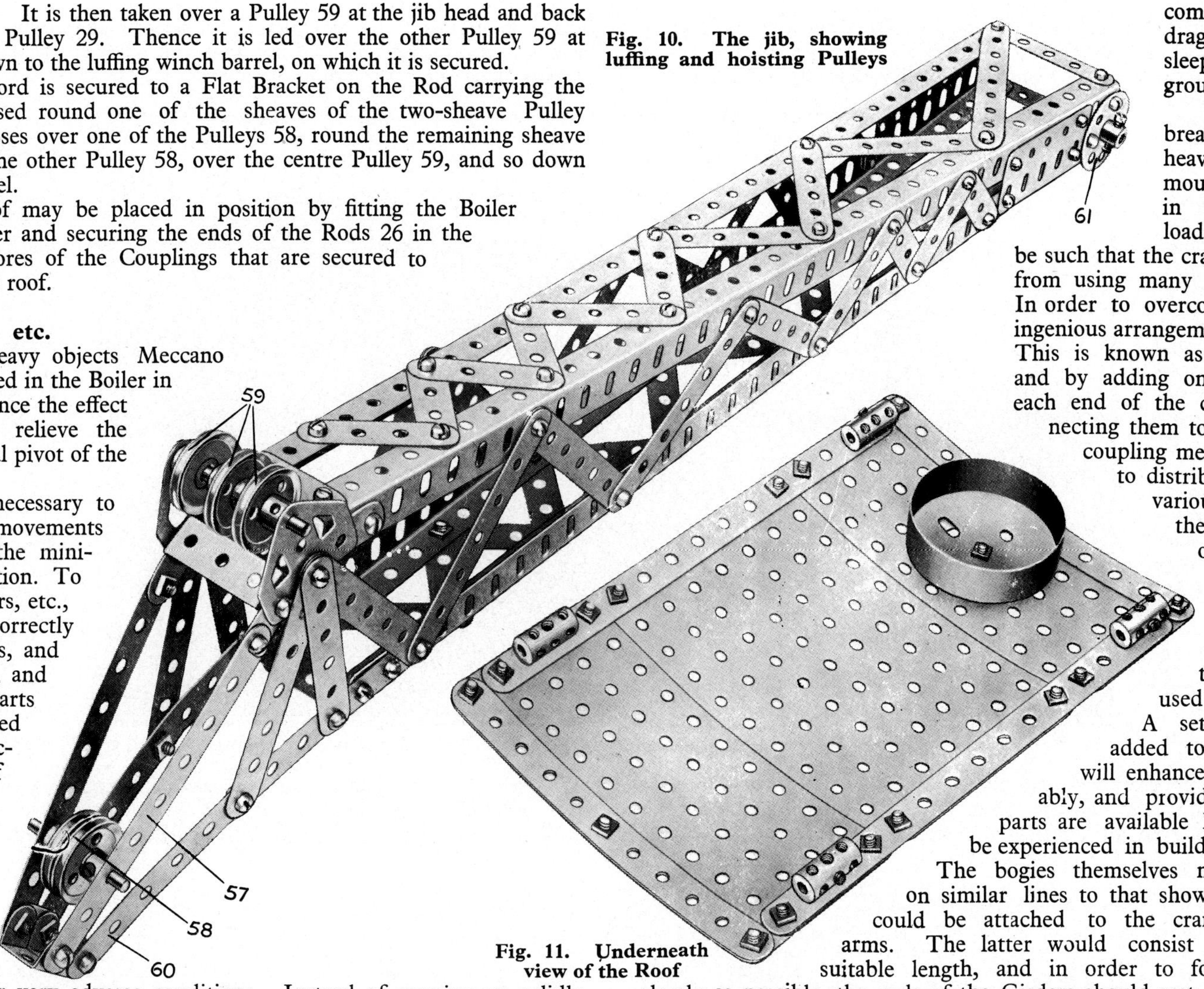

Operating Hints, etc.

When lifting heavy objects Meccano parts should be placed in the Boiler in order to counterbalance the effect of the load and so relieve the strain on the central pivot of the model.

It is scarcely necessary to add that all the movements should work with the minimum amount of friction. To ensure this the Collars, etc., must be spaced correctly on the various Rods, and the bearings, Gears, and all other moving parts should be lubricated with the special Meccano Oil, which is of the proper viscosity for machinery of this type.

In the prototype strong construction is necessary, for it is sometimes called upon to work under very adverse conditions. Instead of running on solidly laid lines, as is the case with dock or other industrial cranes, it often is required to stand on rails that may have been damaged by a collision or other accident and at the best are only laid in 5 inches of ballast. The crane truck must be of considerable length therefore, and mounted on several pairs of wheels, and in addition outriggers must be provided in order to bear some of the considerable strains and stresses that are set up when the crane is in operation.

It is common practice to clamp the crane to the rails, although cases have been known in which the crane, in attempting to lift too heavy a load, has

Fig. 10. The jib, showing luffing and hoisting Pulleys

Fig. 11. Underneath view of the Roof

commenced to tip up, dragging the rails and sleepers bodily out of the ground!

Some of the largest breakdown cranes are so heavy that if they were mounted on a crane truck in the usual way the loads on the axles would be such that the crane would be debarred from using many sections of a railway. In order to overcome this difficulty an ingenious arrangement has been designed. This is known as the "Stokes' bogie," and by adding one of these bogies to each end of the crane truck and connecting them to the latter by a novel coupling mechanism, it is possible to distribute the load over the various axles so as to enable the heaviest cranes to pass over any line in the country with absolute safety. The bogies are, of course, easily detachable and are only used as and when required.

A set of Stokes' Bogies added to the Meccano model will enhance its interest considerably, and provided that the necessary parts are available little difficulty should be experienced in building them.

The bogies themselves might be constructed on similar lines to that shown in Fig. 4 and they could be attached to the crane truck by pivoted arms. The latter would consist of Angle Girders of suitable length, and in order to follow the original as closely as possible, the ends of the Girders should rest on screw jacks on top of the bogies, so that by adjusting the jacks any desired proportion of the crane's weight might be transferred to the bogies.

Yet another interesting accessory may be added to the model in the shape of a match truck. Little need be said on the construction of such an addition for a careful study of Fig. 12, which shows a steam breakdown crane with its jib placed over on a match truck, should enable the reader to make one without encountering any great difficulty.

It has already been mentioned that the object of the match truck in practice is to provide a rest or support for the jib when the latter is lowered for travelling purposes. The jib must, of course, be dropped right down in order to pass under the bridges and tunnels, etc., of a railway, and the match truck enables the crane to travel safely and negotiate bends whilst in this position. When the jib is lowered on to the match truck the crane is spoken of as being in running order or "running trim," and it will pass under the standing railway loading gauge of 13 feet. During hoisting operations, however, the highest point of the jib may be more than 25 feet above the level of the rails.

The match truck is also made use of as a rule to carry the tools and other paraphernalia that are likely to be required in connection with the crane.

The clearing away of the heaps of debris and the restoration of the permanent way, which often suffers severely in a smash,

ready for removal. Consequently a very large variety of tools is required and it will readily be realised that the match truck is very useful as a means of carrying the various appliances.

The wreckage after an accident of any magnitude presents a wild scene. Everywhere lie fragments of the coaches, which may be torn to matchwood or telescoped one into another. The locomotive, completely off the road perhaps, may be lying upon its side with wheels wrenched off, frames twisted in amazing fashion, and other parts torn and distorted—a tangled mass enveloped in escaping steam.

To restore a fallen engine to the line requires a very powerful hoist and, considering the great size and weight of modern locomotives and rolling stock, it is not surprising that many of the latest breakdown cranes are capable of lifting easily loads of from 35 to 80 tons.

Fig. 12. The prototype of the Meccano model. A large steam Breakdown Crane with Match Truck

involves a variety of operations. In these, of course, the all-important crane is well to the fore, but its use often has to be preceded by much patient hacking and sawing to enable the shattered vehicles to be separated

In certain circumstances two breakdown cranes working in conjunction are necessary. Although hauled where required by attaching a locomotive, they are usually also equipped with self-propelling machinery.

Parts required to build the Meccano Railway Breakdown Crane:

2 of No. 1b	8 of No. 9a	2 of No. 18a	1 of No. 32	4 of No. 53	3 of No. 89	9 of No. 115	1 of No. 166	All the preceding parts are included in the Outfit, L with the exception of the following:—
8 „ 2	6 „ 9b	2 „ 20b	342 „ 37	2 „ 53a	6 „ 90	4 „ 116a	1 „ 168a	
6 „ 2a	4 „ 9d	10 „ 22	62 „ 37a	63 „ 59	2 „ 90a	1 „ 120a	1 „ 168b	
12 „ 3	2 „ 9f	5 „ 22a	82 „ 38	1 „ 62	2ft „ 94	2 „ 125	7 „ 182	1 of No. 152
10 „ 4	8 „ 10	3 „ 23	2 „ 43	6 „ 62b	2 „ 95a	4 „ 126a	7 „ 182a	
32 „ 5	6 „ 11	2 „ 23a	2 „ 45	9 „ 63	2 „ 96	2 „ 133	1 „ 1563	
15 „ 6	10 „ 12	5 „ 24	1 „ 47	2 „ 64	2 „ 96a	4 „ 136	7 „ 1575	
11 „ 6a	1 „ 12b	9 „ 26	1 „ 47a	4 „ 70	2 „ 103a	8 „ 137	14 „ 1583	
2 „ 7	5 „ 14	6 „ 27a	1 „ 48	4 „ 72	2 „ 103f	2 „ 147b	1 Electric Motor	
6 „ 7a	1 „ 15	1 „ 27b	1 „ 48a	2 „ 76	2 „ 103k	1 „ 152		
2 „ 8	5 „ 15a	1 „ 28	3 „ 48b	2 „ 77	8 „ 109	1 „ 162		
2 „ 8a	7 „ 16	1 „ 29	2 „ 48c	2 „ 80a	18 „ 111	1 „ 162a		
4 „ 8b	3 „ 16a	1 „ 30a	1 „ 50a	2 „ 81	24 „ 111a	2 „ 163		
8 „ 9	3 „ 17	1 „ 30c	11 „ 52a	2 „ 82	6 „ 111c	1 „ 164		

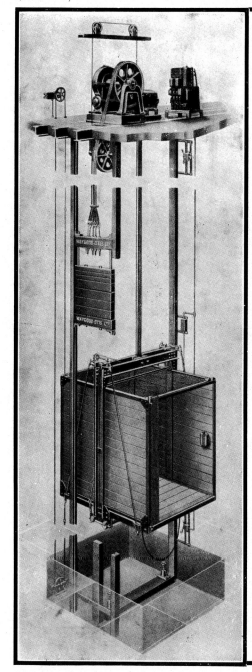

Goods Warehouse
with
Electric Elevators

An L Outfit Model

SPECIAL FEATURES.

The Warehouse is equipped with two Electric Elevators that are operated simultaneously. The mechanism is entirely automatic in action, the lift cages working alternatively and rising, pausing and descending without supervision. The Motor can be controlled from any floor of the Warehouse. Each cage is fitted with an ingenious safety catch which prevents the cage from falling should the lifting rope fail.

WITH the rapid development of our large cities and the corresponding rise in the value of building sites, economy in ground area has resulted in the erection of increasingly high buildings having a great number of floors. In such buildings the installation of passenger or goods lifts is necessary in order to render the upper floors easily accessible. These modern lifts are usually operated by electric motors, although there are some engineers who prefer to drive their lifts by hydraulic power or other means.

The hydraulically-operated lift is not met with so frequently, but in places where water under high pressure is readily obtainable it still holds its own against the electric type, especially if heavy loads have to be handled, because it is comparatively cheap in initial cost and upkeep. It is particularly suited for use where a lift is required to rise and fall through a short distance only.

In such cases it is usual to install the direct-ram machine, a device that consists essentially of a long cylinder containing a piston or ram, the whole being sunk into the ground beneath the lift well. The ram is attached directly to the underside of the lift cage, and the cylinder is fitted with valves so that water may be admitted at great pressure into the cylinder beneath the piston. The incoming water forces the ram and cage upward. To lower the lift it is only necessary to open the exhaust water valve on the cylinder and, the pressure being released gradually, the ram and cage descend by their own weight. The chief disadvantage of this system is, of course, the great length of cylinder and ram which would be required for a high building, and this is one of the reasons why the type is now but seldom employed. Other dis-

> The illustration on this page shows a modern Electrically-operated Goods Elevator made by Waygood-Otis, Ltd. It provides an interesting comparison with the Meccano Model.

Published by MECCANO LIMITED, BINNS ROAD, LIVERPOOL 13, ENGLAND

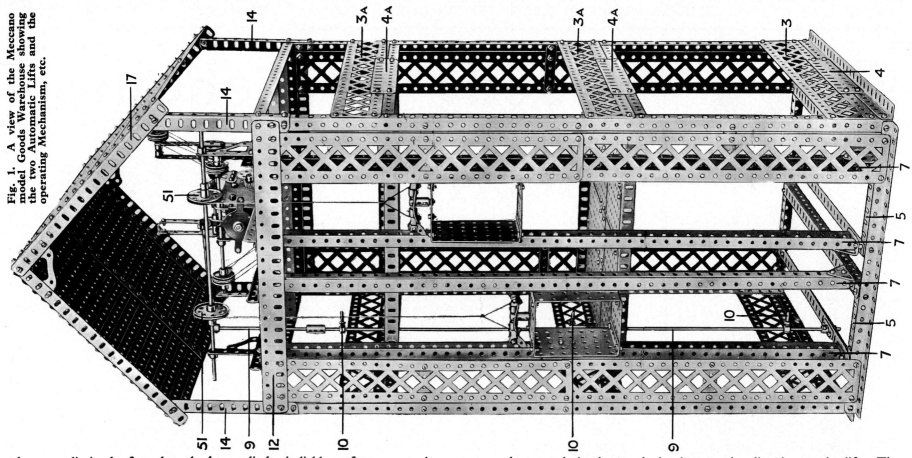

Fig. 1. A view of the Meccano model Goods Warehouse showing the two Automatic Lifts and the operating Mechanism, etc.

advantages lie in the fact that the long cylinder is liable to fracture or the pipes may burst under the great pressure.

In a few cases the hydraulic power is transmitted to the lift cage through a chain or rope passing over an overhead pulley, and the hydraulic cylinder is laid horizontally. This method, of course, facilitates erection and periodical inspection of the apparatus, but at the same time the frictional resistance of the movement is increased.

In hotels, hospitals and large mansions, lifts are sometimes installed that can be operated entirely by hand power. This type is extremely simple in operation, as it is only necessary to enter the cage and pull lightly on a rope, which passes through the cage. The rope is attached at one end to the roof of the cage and thence is passed over a series of pulleys placed at the top of the well and finally round a hauling wheel three or four feet in diameter. The free end of the rope is brought down through the interior of the cage itself.

This arrangement, which is really an adaptation of the pulley block, enables loads to be raised quite easily by pulling on the control rope. The weight of the cage itself is usually counterbalanced by means of a heavy weight

arranged to travel simultaneously in the opposite direction to the lift. The cage moves between guides, and automatic brakes are fitted so that in the event of the rope breaking, the brakes act instantly and prevent the cage from falling.

Modern High-speed Lifts

Lifts hauling goods traffic usually travel at the comparatively slow speed of 120 feet per minute, but it is the practice to provide variable speed gears in order that, if required, the lift may be operated at a higher speed. In restaurants, large shops and offices, etc., where there are several lifts, they are usually arranged in batteries, some of the lifts running "express" or non-stop to certain of the higher floors and others running "local," or stopping at all floors. The express lifts will obviously be high speed machines; they usually travel at speeds up to 300 or 400 feet per minute. A speed of 150 to 180 feet per minute is usually chosen for the "local" lifts in order to avoid violent acceleration and deceleration.

In designing any type of lift there are naturally many factors to be considered, one of the most important being the necessity for absolute safety. Also, when stopping at each floor, it is very desirable to be able to bring **the** lift from full speed to rest without jar or shock, and much attention has been given to this point during recent years.

Another important consideration is reliability, and it is principally on account of their proved reliability that electrically-operated lifts have gradually superseded other types and are now employed for all kinds of work and in all classes of buildings, including offices, hotels and hospitals.

A typical electric lift consists of several distinct parts, the most important of which are the lifting motor, the "cage" and its fitments, electric controls and, of course, the well and guides. In addition to the above, a modern passenger lift is fitted with automatic gate locks and various other refinements.

Hauling-Gear Safety Devices

In most modern lifts the cars are suspended by multiple-strand steel ropes, as past experience has proved that chains are unsatisfactory for the purpose. One of the great disadvantages of chain suspension is that a chain is liable to fail suddenly without giving any previous warning.

To prevent the cage from falling in the event of failure of the hauling ropes, a safety gear is fitted. It is usually arranged either above or immediately beneath the cage. Different makers, of course, fit different types of safety gear, and there are very many of these ingenious mechanisms in everyday use.

One of the foremost British firms has designed a type of gear which consists essentially of four cams, mounted on steel shafts and suitably supported under the floor of the cage. The apparatus is operated by a separate "safety" rope that is directly attached to the camshafts, and so designed that in the event of failure of the suspension ropes (which are attached to the body of the cage) the four cams will be drawn in and will grip simultaneously on the steel guides between which the cage travels. This type of gear is fitted to the lift shown on the cover page of this leaflet. It is manufactured by Waygood-Otis, Ltd., of London, one of the pioneer firms in the lift building industry.

This safety apparatus, while being quite efficient and reliable, has a

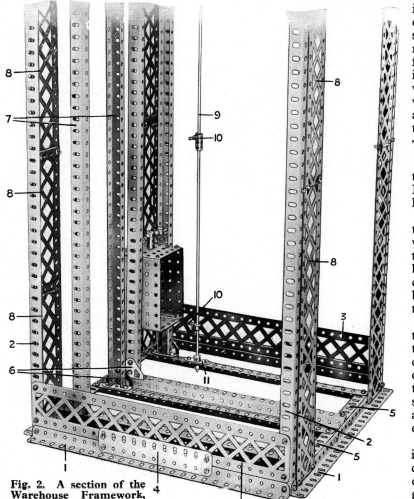

Fig. 2. A section of the Warehouse Framework, showing details of the Base and Lift Wells.

disadvantage in that it acts rather suddenly and brings the cage to a standstill with a jerk. In view of this it is hardly suitable for use with high-speed "express" passenger lifts and for such lifts a special type of gear has been devised by the same makers. It is brought into operation by a speed governor immediately the lift cage attains an excessive speed due to any failure in the brake machinery or of the wire lifting ropes. This form of safety device is arranged to come into operation gradually and stop the car without sudden shock or jerk—a feature which, as will be easily recognised, is absolutely essential in the case of a lift travelling at high speed.

The Lifting Machinery

The following are a few particulars of the mechanism supplied by Waygood-Otis, Ltd., with their electric goods and passenger lifts.

The winding motor is directly coupled to a worm and wheel reduction gear. The worm, which is placed immediately below the wheel and arranged so that it will always be running in a bath of oil, is made of solid cut steel, while the wheel is of phosphor-bronze. They are enclosed in a special type of gear-box.

To reduce wear and tear on the gear teeth, ball thrust-bearings are fitted to take the thrust of the worm shaft. The main driven shaft is fitted with a hoisting drum of large diameter that has four grooves turned in its surface to take four stranded steel wire lifting ropes which are connected at one end to the "cage" and at the other end to a heavy counterbalance.

A powerful automatic magnetic brake is fitted and is arranged to engage with a drum that forms the outer portion of the coupling between the motor and the worm gearing. In the event of the electric current failing the brake instantly comes into operation and brings the cage to a standstill. In large lifts, two such brakes are fitted so as to ensure absolute safety.

How the Controls are Arranged

The older types of lift or those intended for goods handling are often controlled by a hand rope led through the "cage" in a suitable position and connected to the switch or valve gear. In the case of the more elaborate lifts,

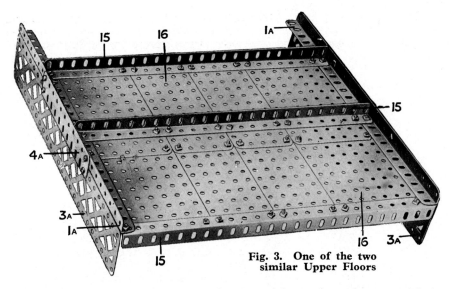

Fig. 3. One of the two similar Upper Floors

either from the inside or outside unless the cage is present at the floor level, and the cage cannot be moved away from a floor unless all the doors are closed. In the older lifts the cage sometimes "over-ran" the limits of its travel, with consequent danger of damage not only to the cage itself but also to the winding gear. Nowadays, however, emergency electric switches operated by the ascending or descending lift are fitted at certain definite points in the cage pit and these render over-running impossible by switching off the electric supply to the motor.

The Meccano Model

The Meccano model represents a type of lift to be found in large goods warehouses and industrial buildings of all kinds. The model is entirely automatic in action and the two cages will continue to ascend and descend alternately just as long as the electric supply is maintained. As in a real warehouse lift, a special type of safety device is fitted to each cage.

The lifting mechanism is operated by a 6-volt Meccano Electric Motor mounted at the top of the warehouse. It can be stopped or started from any of the floors in the warehouse. The lifting mechanism employed is particularly novel. The model is quite simple to build and when completed will afford hours of enjoyment, especially if the cages are made to carry various small articles such as Meccano Loaded Sacks, etc. Each part of the model is dealt with in detail and the various parts should be built in the order described.

Construction should be commenced by building the framework. Referring to Figs. 1 and 2 it will be seen that this comprises four vertical 24½″ Angle Girders 2 that are bolted at their lower ends to four 12½″ Angle Girders 1. The method of securing the latter to the vertical girders will be quite clear from the illustrations. To the Angle Girders 1 are attached 12½″ Braced Girders 8 that are further supported by means of 2½″ Strips bolted across the Braced Girders and secured to the Angle Girders 2. The sides of the base are enclosed by means of two 12½″ Braced Girders 3 bolted in the positions shown and secured by means of a 5½″ Flat Girder 4, the latter being bolted to the Braced Girders and to the side Angle Girders 1 in the base.

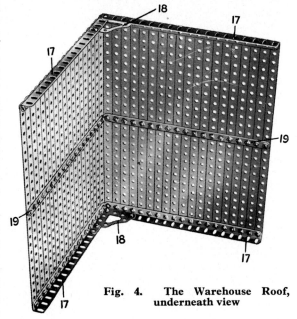

Fig. 4. The Warehouse Roof, underneath view

however, where it is usual to employ a special attendant, the control is by means of a switch placed in the cage and fitted with a "self-centring" handle, the idea being that should the attendant release the handle inadvertently it will automatically take the "off" position.

In some cases, however, it is not possible to employ a special attendant to operate the lift, and this fact has necessitated the invention of an automatic system, so that anyone can operate the lift as required. The automatic control system is used largely in lifts installed in warships and ocean liners, etc., as well as in office and hotel passenger lifts.

The system as fitted by Smith, Major and Stevens Ltd., of Northampton, consists of a series of electric "push" buttons provided at each floor of the building. By pressing one of the buttons for an instant, the cage is brought to the particular floor at which the button is situated, where it stops automatically and unlocks the entrance door which, by the way, cannot be opened until the cage arrives. The intending passenger can now enter the cage, but to avoid accidents the electric circuit is so arranged that he cannot move the cage away until he has closed the lift and entrance doors.

The passenger finds in the cage several buttons which are marked with numbers to correspond to the various floors in the building. The required button is selected and pressed for a moment, and the cage starts away upward or downward as the case may be. Immediately the cage moves away it relocks the entrance door it is leaving, and continues to travel until it reaches the selected floor, when it again stops automatically and unlocks both doors, when the passenger is at liberty to leave. The "cage" is then at the disposal of the next comer.

It is usual to fix an additional button in the cage to enable the lift to be stopped at will in case the wrong button has been pressed. This type of control renders lift working extremely safe as a door cannot possibly be opened

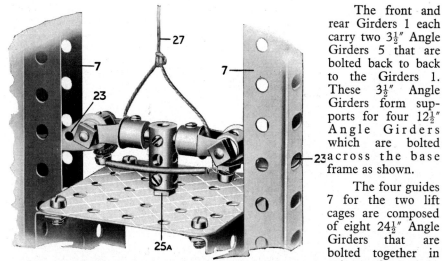

Fig. 5. One of the Cages in position between its guides. The hoisting cord is slack, hence the Pawls of the Safety Device engage holes in the Guides.

The front and rear Girders 1 each carry two 3½″ Angle Girders 5 that are bolted back to back to the Girders 1. These 3½″ Angle Girders form supports for four 12½″ Angle Girders which are bolted across the base frame as shown.

The four guides 7 for the two lift cages are composed of eight 24½″ Angle Girders that are bolted together in pairs to form channel section girders, and they are secured in position with the channels facing each other. To secure them, Trunnions 6 are bolted to the lower ends of the guides and to the transverse 12½″ Angle Girders in the base. It will be noted that the flanges of the Trunnions are turned inwards, that is, underneath the ends of the Angle Girders 7.

Details of the Upper Floors

The warehouse contains two floors above the base and each of these is constructed as shown in Fig. 3, which is an underneath view of one of them.

Two 12½″ Angle Girders 1a are bolted to three further 12½″ Angle Girders 15, one of the latter being bolted across the ends of the Girders 1a, while the other two are bolted in the eleventh and nineteenth holes from those ends respectively.

As in the base, the sides of the first and second floors are enclosed with 12½″ Braced Girders 3a that are bolted to the Girders 1a by means of 5½″ Flat Girders 4a. The floor proper 16 comprises four 5½″×3½″ and four 5½″×2½″ Flat Plates that overlap and are bolted to the Angle Girders 15. The floors are secured in position by bolts passed through the Girders 2 (Figs. 1 and 2) of the main framework and also through the Angle Girders 1a (Fig. 3).

When the floors are in position the projecting ends of the Angle Girders 1a (Fig. 3) must of course be at the front of the model. This arrangement will leave a recess between the front edge of the floor and the frame of the warehouse, so as to allow room for the cage guides and for movement of the cages.

The next step is to bolt the 5½″ Angle Girders 14 (Fig. 1) to the upper ends of the four vertical Angle Girders 2. After this, four 12½″ Angle Girders 49 (Fig. 7) are bolted to the 5½″ Girders 14 (see also Fig. 1).

Four 12½″ Angle Girders 47 and 48 (Fig. 7) are now bolted to the Angle Girders 49 and two 5½″ Angle Girders 47a are fitted in the positions shown. These Girders serve to support the lifting mechanism, as will be described later.

The construction of the warehouse proper is now complete with the exception of the roof. This is shown in Fig. 4 and consists of a number of 12½″ Strips placed side by side and bolted at their ends to 9½″ Angle Girders 17. Two equal sides each comprising nineteen Strips are constructed, and these are bolted together at an angle of 90 degrees by means of two Architraves 18. Two 9½″ Strips 19, bolted across the Strips forming each side of the roof, help to brace the whole firmly together. The roof should not be secured in position until the lifting mechanism has been assembled.

Construction of Cages and Safety Devices

One of the two similar cages is shown in Fig. 6. It consists of two 3½″×2½″ Flanged Plates 20 to the flanges of which are bolted 2½″×2½″ Flat Plates 22. Single Bent Strips 21 are bolted to the sides of each cage in such positions that when the cages are placed between the guides 7 (Fig. 1) the Single Bent Strips 21 will slide in the channels of the guides and so form guide blocks for the cages.

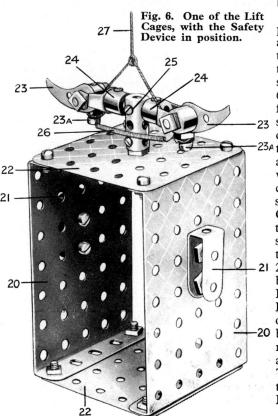

Fig. 6. One of the Lift Cages, with the Safety Device in position.

The safety devices employed in the model are of a simple yet very interesting type. They are fitted to the top of each cage and one is shown clearly in Figs. 5 and 6; it is constructed as follows. A Coupling 25 is secured to the roof of the cage by means of a ⅜″ Bolt that is locked in position by a nut 25a. In its upper transverse hole, this Coupling carries a 1½″ Rod that is secured centrally in the Coupling. The Rod carries two Fork Pieces 24 that are secured one on each side of the Coupling. Two Pawls 23 are held pivotally on bolts lock-nutted in the Fork Pieces as shown, and each Pawl has a ⅜″ Bolt 23a instead of the usual grub-screw, the bolt being held firmly by means of a nut locked against the boss of the Pawl. The Bolts 23a must not grip the pivots on which the Pawls are mounted.

A length of Meccano

Cord is attached to each of the bolts 23a and the ends of the cord are brought through the Fork Pieces behind the Pawl bosses in the manner shown in the photographs. (The two pieces of cord are later attached to the lifting cord 27). The ends of a length of Spring Cord 26 are also looped round the Bolts 23a.

When the lift cord 27 is in tension—that is, as soon as the cage is raised from the ground—the Pawls 23 are rotated slightly on their pivots and their projecting ends pulled downward clear of the lift guides. This movement bends the Spring Cord 26 so that one side of it is in tension. Now, should the cord 27 break or fail for any reason, the Pawls are no longer held down and owing to the action of the Spring Cord, which tends always to straighten out, the ends of the Pawls rise and engage with the elongated holes of the guides 7. The cage is consequently locked safely in position in the shaft, and cannot be moved until the Pawls are pulled downward and clear of the guides.

This most interesting feature of the model is closely allied in principle to the safety device usually employed on the actual lift. A demonstration of its action on the Meccano lift should enable even the most timid old lady to overcome any fears that she may entertain as to the safety of travelling in lifts!

The Operating Mechanism

The mechanism incorporated in the model for lifting and lowering the two cages is of special interest as it enables the model to be worked for an indefinite period without attention. It is entirely automatic in action, and the arrangement is such that one cage is raised while the other is being lowered.

In operation, as soon as the Electric Motor is set in motion one of the cages ascends and the other descends until both cages have reached the top or bottom positions of their respective guides, when they come to rest as though to allow for loading and unloading. Then after a short pause the upper cage descends while the lower ascends, and the process is repeated each time the limit of travel is reached.

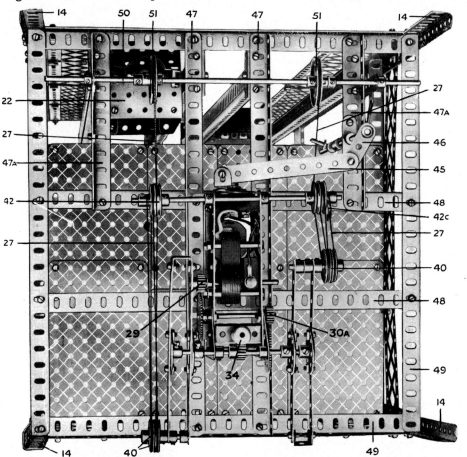

Fig. 7. **Plan view of Top Floor of Warehouse, with Roof removed to show the arrangement of the Electric Motor and the Lifting Mechanism.**

The 6-volt Meccano Motor is secured in position by bolting its flanges to the transverse Angle Girders 47 (Fig. 7). The drive is taken from the Motor armature via a $\frac{1}{2}''$ Pinion 29, the 57-teeth Gear Wheel 30, and a $\frac{1}{2}''$ Pinion 30a on the opposite end of the Rod carrying Gear 30 that meshes with another 57-teeth Gear Wheel 31 on a 2″ Rod (see also Fig. 8).

On the latter Rod is a Worm 32 meshing with a $\frac{1}{2}''$ Pinion secured to a vertical 3″ Rod 33, which is journalled in bearings consisting of a $2\frac{1}{2}''$ Strip 43 bolted across the Girders 47 beneath the Motor (Figs. 7 and 8) and a $1\frac{1}{2}'' \times \frac{1}{2}''$ Double Angle Strip 33a secured between the Motor side plates. The Rod 33 carries at its upper extremity a second Worm 34 meshing with a $\frac{1}{2}''$ Pinion on the $3\frac{1}{2}''$ Rod 35.

This Rod 35 is journalled in Corner Brackets, as shown, and carries at its ends the device whereby the automatic reversing hoist motion is obtained. It will be seen that it consists essentially of two rotating arms each of which is built up from $5\frac{1}{2}''$ Strips 31, secured rigidly to the Rod 35 by means of Bush Wheels 38, and a system of 1″ loose Pulleys 40 and 42. The Pulleys 40 are free to run on a 2″ Rod 39 journalled in each arm and the Pulleys 42 are mounted on a $4\frac{1}{2}''$ Rod attached to the Motor. A Washer is placed between the Pulleys to minimise friction and allow freedom of movement.

The spindle of the Pulleys 40 follows the circular path traced out by the end of the arm, while the spindle of the Pulleys 42 is fixed. The cord 27, which is attached to the cage, passes over the Pulleys 51 at the top of the lift shaft. It is then led under one of the 1″ loose Pulleys 42, round one of the Pulleys 40, back to the remaining Pulley 42 and thence to the second 1″ Pulley 40. After passing round the latter, it is secured to the Flat Bracket 42c.

On examining the illustration, it will be observed that the system is similar in effect to a two-sheave pulley block, in which the free end of the cord, where the power is applied, moves through four inches for every inch the load is raised. In the model, however, the load (*i.e.*, the lift cage) is attached to the cord at a point corresponding to the free end in the ordinary pulley block, and the power is applied to the movable pulley block. Consequently the reverse effect is obtained, the lift cage moving through four inches for every inch of movement of the Pulleys 40 relative to the Pulleys 42.

When the Pulleys 40 advance towards the Pulleys 42, the hoisting rope is paid out, but as the distance between the two sets of Pulleys decreases, the relative motion between them also decreases, with the result that the movement of the cage becomes gradually slower until finally, when the Pulleys 40 and 42 and the moving arm are all directly in line, all movement of the cord ceases. At this point the cage is at rest at the ground floor.

The rotating arm, continuing its motion, now commences to withdraw the Pulleys 40, with the result that the hoisting cord is hauled in and the cage begins to rise, gradually gathering speed as the increasing angle of the rotating arm increases the relative movement between the Pulleys 40 and 42.

In view of the fact that a slight movement of the rotating arm results in a greatly magnified movement of the cages, it will be apparent that the arms must rotate very slowly. This explains the use of the double worm drive from the Motor.

Owing to the considerable strains imposed upon the mechanism, the Pinion and Bush Wheels mounted on the shaft 35 should be secured very rigidly in position and, if possible, new style parts should be employed so that two set-screws can be inserted in each boss.

The extent of the travel of the cages may be varied considerably by altering the length of the rotating arms—adding to the length to increase the travel and vice versa—or by using a larger number of Pulleys. Such alteration will be necessary, for example, if it is decided to add further floors to the model, thus increasing the extent of the lift shafts.

Fig. 8. The Lifting Mechanism. This illustration shows the construction of the Rotating Arms and arrangement of the gears.

The Motor Control Gear

In the model, as in an actual lift, means are provided by which it is possible to start or stop the Motor and thus control the movement of the cages from any of the landing floors. This is accomplished by means of the control handles 10 (Fig. 1) which are secured to the Rod 9. A slight movement of any one of these handles either stops or starts the Electric Motor according to the direction in which the handle is turned. Threaded Pins 10 screwed into Collars form the handles.

The Rod 9 consists of two 11½″ and one 5½″ Rods connected together by means of Couplings. At its lower end it is journalled in a Double Arm Crank 11 (Fig. 2) that is bolted to one of the transverse Angle Girders in the base as shown. The Rod 9 extends from top to bottom of the warehouse and is connected at its upper end with the Motor switch in the following manner.

The upper end of the Rod is journalled in a 1½″ Strip bolted to the Angle Girder 47a (Fig. 7) and is held in position by means of a Collar placed on the Rod against the face of the Strip. A Crank 46, secured to the end of the Rod, is connected pivotally to one end of a 4½″ Strip 45, and the other end of this Strip is attached to an Angle Bracket that, in turn, is pivoted to the central arm of the Motor switch. It will readily be seen that movement of the control Rod is transmitted via the Crank 46 and Strip 45 to the Motor switch, with the result that the Motor can be either started, stopped or reversed as desired.

After the mechanism has been adjusted finally, the roof is placed in position and bolted to the Angle Girders 14.

The terminals of the Electric Motor should be connected to the terminals of a 6-volt accumulator or to a Transformer, whichever source is employed for the current supply.

Parts required to build the Meccano Warehouse:

38 of No.	1	4 of No.	8a	1 of No.	14	2 of No.	32	2 of No.	53a	6 of No.	103	To construct the Safety Devices the following parts are required:—	
2 "	1a	6 "	9	2 "	15a	424 "	37	28 "	59	2 "	103b		
4 "	2	4 "	9b	2 "	17	2 "	37a	1 "	62	4 "	108		
1 "	2a	4 "	9f	2 "	21	8 "	38	2 "	63	5 "	115		
9 "	6	2 "	10	8 "	22a	1 "	40	6 "	70	4 "	126	2 of No.	18a
2 "	6a	2 "	11	4 "	24	1 "	48	4 "	72	2 "	136	6″ "	58	2 of No.	140
12 "	7	1 "	12	4 "	26	8 "	52a	14 "	99	1 Electric		2 "	63	4 "	147a
26 "	8	3 "	12a	2 "	27a	4 "	53	4 "	102	Motor				4 "	147b

MECCANO SUPER MODELS

No. 13 Leaflet

No. 6 Leaflet

Our expert designers have produced for us 23 super models that reach the highest pinnacle ever attained in Meccano construction. Each model in this series is a masterpiece and there is not a boy who will not be eager to build them all.

These models are so important that we have engaged expert engineers to describe them and a special leaflet with beautiful half-tone illustrations has been written for each of them. A selection of the leaflets is illustrated on this page.

A brief description of each model in the series is given below and the number and price of the special Instruction Leaflet are indicated. Copies of the leaflets may be obtained from any Meccano dealer or direct from us, post free, at the prices stated.

No. 1a Motor Chassis. This model runs perfectly under its own power. It has Ackermann Steering, Differential, Gear-Box and Clutch, etc.

No. 2 Ship Coaler. All the movements of a real ship coaler are reproduced in this model.

No. 5 Travelling Bucket Dredger In this model trucks and wagons can run underneath the shute through which falls the material raised by the dredger buckets.

No. 6 Stiff-Leg Derrick. This model has many interesting movements, including hoisting, luffing and swivelling, which are controlled by suitable levers.

No. 7 Platform Scales. This model will weigh articles up to 4½lb. with remarkable accuracy.

No. 9 Bagatelle Table. This is an interesting model that will give hours of fun to the players.

No. 10 Log Saw. In this model the saw is driven rapidly to and fro while the work table travels beneath it.

No. 11a Single-Cylinder Horizontal Steam Engine. Fitted with balanced crankshaft, crosshead, and centrifugal governor.

No. 12 Stone Sawing Machine. The model is equipped with adjustable work table and overhead trolley with self-sustaining chain hoist.

No. 13 Meccanograph. This wonderful model will draw hundreds of beautiful designs.

No. 14a Grandfather Clock A practical example of Meccano model-building. The model keeps accurate time.

No. 18 Revolving Crane. This model is fitted with screw-operated luffing gear.

No. 19 Steam Shovel. This model embodies travelling and rotating mechanisms and jib hoisting and lowering gear.

No. 20 Mobile Crane. This model has hoisting, luffing, travelling and slewing movements. It is fitted with an automatic brake.

No. 21 Transporter Bridge. The carriage automatically travels to and fro as long as the motor is driven, pausing for a few seconds at each end of its travel.

No. 22 Traction Engine. A remarkably realistic model that will pull a boy of average weight. Fitted with two speeds.

No. 24 Travelling Gantry Crane. The movements of this model, comprise the traversing of the entire gantry, hoisting and lowering, and the traversing of the crane trolley.

No. 25 Hydraulic Crane. The hydraulic ram is represented realistically by a powerful screw mechanism.

No. 28 Pontoon Crane. The movements of this model include the operation of the three hoisting blocks, slewing of the entire crane, and luffing.

No. 29 Hammerhead Crane. This is a very realistic and powerful model, comprising traversing, hoisting and slewing motions.

No. 30 Breakdown Crane. This model is equipped with travelling, slewing, luffing, and hoisting motions, and also is fitted with laminated springs, brakes, out-riggers, etc.

No. 31 Warehouse with Elevators. The two cages are driven automatically and work alternately, pausing at top and bottom positions.

No. 35 Level-Luffing Crane. The model is provided with level-luffing gear, and an important feature is a grab that can be opened and closed automatically.

INSTRUCTION LEAFLET PRICES

Leaflets Nos. 5 6 7 9 10 11a 12 14a 18 19 20 21 22 24 25 28 29—United Kingdom 2d., Overseas 3d., Canada 5 cents

Leaflets Nos. 1a 2 13 30 31 35—United Kingdom 3d., Overseas 4d., Canada 8 cents.

No. 25 Leaflet

No. 19 Leaflet

THE "MECCANO MAGAZINE"

The "Meccano Magazine" is the Meccano boy's newspaper. It is published monthly, and each issue contains details of splendid new Meccano models and new ideas for operating Hornby model railways. Interesting model-building and other competitions are announced each month, and details of all new Meccano products appear in its pages. It is the official organ of the Meccano Guild and the Hornby Railway Company, which have thousands of boy members in all parts of the world.

The "Meccano Magazine" appeals to every boy, for it deals with Engineering in all its branches—Railways, Aviation, Ships, Motor Cars, Hydro-Electric Schemes, Bridges, Cranes, etc. Specially attractive articles are devoted to Model Railways and Model Speed Boats, and Home Experiments in Electricity and Chemistry. Other sections deal with Books of interest to boys, Stamps, New Inventions, etc.

The Magazine may be ordered from any Meccano dealer or newsagent, price 6d (Can. 10c)

MECCANO LIMITED, Binns Road, LIVERPOOL 13

Australia

Twin Cylinder Steam Engine

A Powerful Model of a
Stationary Reciprocating
Engine

Fitted with
Balanced
Crankshaft
Piston Type
Valves and
Centrifugal
Governor,
etc., etc.

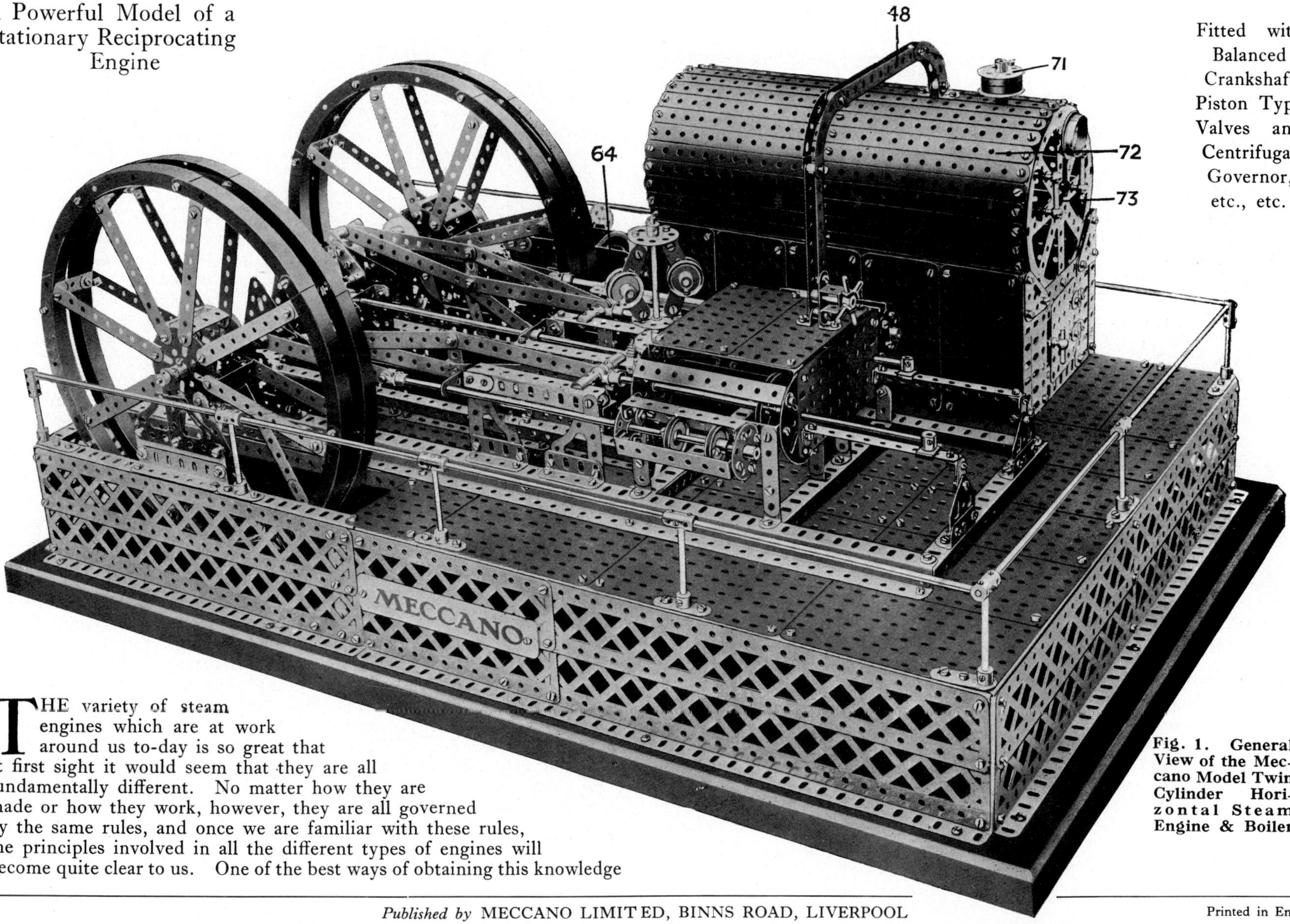

Fig. 1. General
View of the Mec-
cano Model Twin
Cylinder Hori-
zontal Steam
Engine & Boiler

THE variety of steam
engines which are at work
around us to-day is so great that
at first sight it would seem that they are all
fundamentally different. No matter how they are
made or how they work, however, they are all governed
by the same rules, and once we are familiar with these rules,
the principles involved in all the different types of engines will
become quite clear to us. One of the best ways of obtaining this knowledge

Published by MECCANO LIMITED, BINNS ROAD, LIVERPOOL

of the mechanical principles of a steam engine is to build a Meccano model such as that described in this leaflet.

The majority of steam engines are of the reciprocating type, that is, they comprise pistons which are driven to and fro by the admission of the steam into the cylinders. The to-and-fro motion of the piston rods cannot be utilised very satisfactorily, of course, until it is converted into rotary motion. This is done by means of a crank mechanism. Many Meccano boys are probably cyclists and consequently are familiar with the cranks of a cycle. Although at first glance it may appear to be a vivid stretch of the imagination, the cranks of a cycle and those in the largest marine or mill engine are similar in principle, for they both transform up and down movements into a circular one. The piston rod does not work directly on the crank, however, but is connected to it by means of a connecting rod. This consists of a massive steel bar that is mounted freely on the crank pin and on the end of the piston rod.

In the ordinary way, the crank transmits a very uneven drive, and hence a flywheel must be secured to the crankshaft. The flywheel is a wheel with a heavy rim which, when rotating, smooths out the impulses and makes the crankshaft turn at a constant speed throughout the complete revolution.

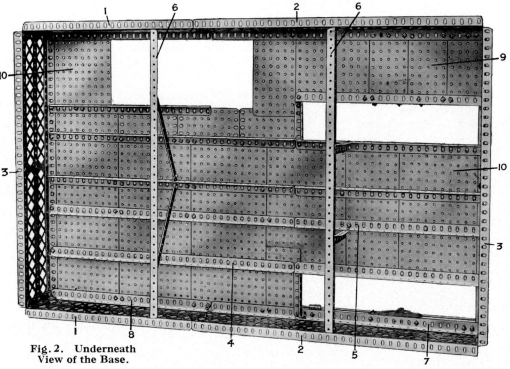

Fig. 2. Underneath View of the Base.

The energy stored in the flywheel also helps the crank over the neutral points, or "dead centres," as they are termed. The dead centres occur twice in each revolution of the crank and are formed when the piston rod, connecting rod, and crank lie in one straight line. Hence there is no turning moment applied to the crank, the tendency being for the crankpin to be sheared off.

Eccentrics are sometimes used in place of cranks to convert rotary motion into reciprocating motion. An eccentric is really a disc of metal that is mounted off its centre on a shaft. It is fitted with a metal surrounding collar that is kept well lubricated so that it can slip easily and smoothly round the periphery of the disc. This collar is attached to a rod termed the eccentric rod. When the disc is rotated the movement of the eccentric rod is exactly the same as if it were attached by a pin to the centre of the disc, or to a crank having the same throw.

An advantage of the eccentric is the fact that it can be mounted on any

ordinary shaft without dividing the latter as is necessary if a crank is used. The eccentric, however, can only be used to convert rotary motion into a to-and-fro movement, whereas the action of a crank can be reversed, that is, it can be turned by power applied to it by means of a piston and connecting rod, or it may be used like the eccentric to produce reciprocating motion. The reason for this will be clear to every boy who has handled the Meccano Eccentrics. In steam engines eccentrics are usually employed to operate the slide valves that control the admission of steam into the cylinders.

Instead of using eccentrics to operate the slide valves, an arrangement of links is sometimes used for the purpose. The principal system arranged on this method is known as Walschaerts' Valve Gear. This gear is becoming more and more popular for locomotives and it may interest the reader to know that a realistic Meccano model of it was described and illustrated in a recent issue of the "Meccano Magazine."

Nowadays there is a tendency to use steam at ever increasing pressures and this has led to the adoption of what are known as "compound" engines. This type is the result of efforts to make the fullest possible use of the expansion of the steam by taking it first to one cylinder and allowing it to expand a little and then leading it to secondary and larger cylinders to finish its expansion. The first is termed a High Pressure Cylinder and those used subsequently Low Pressure Cylinders.

If the steam is expanded in three or four stages the engine is termed a triple or quadruple expansion engine. Nowadays all reciprocating marine engines are of either the compound, triple, or quadruple expansion types. If the engine is triple expansion there will usually be three cylinders, high, intermediate, and low pressure. It does not always follow, however, that an engine having four cylinders is quadruple expansion ; it may be triple expansion with the low pressure expansion carried out in two separate cylinders. This compounding of cylinders is the only really great improvement in the design of reciprocating engines since the time of James Watt.

The Meccano Model

Coming now to the Meccano model it will be seen from Fig. 1 that it comprises two separate cylinders each of which is connected by a piston rod and connecting rod to a common crankshaft. The crankshaft carries eccentrics that are connected to and operate two separate valves of the piston type. Although this engine has two cylinders it is not "compound" as steam is separately admitted to each cylinder and does not exhaust from one to the other as would be the case in a compound engine.

The model incorporates also a centrifugal governor, the purpose of which in the actual engine is to ensure smooth running under varying boiler pressure or unequal loads. The governor consists of a pair of weights

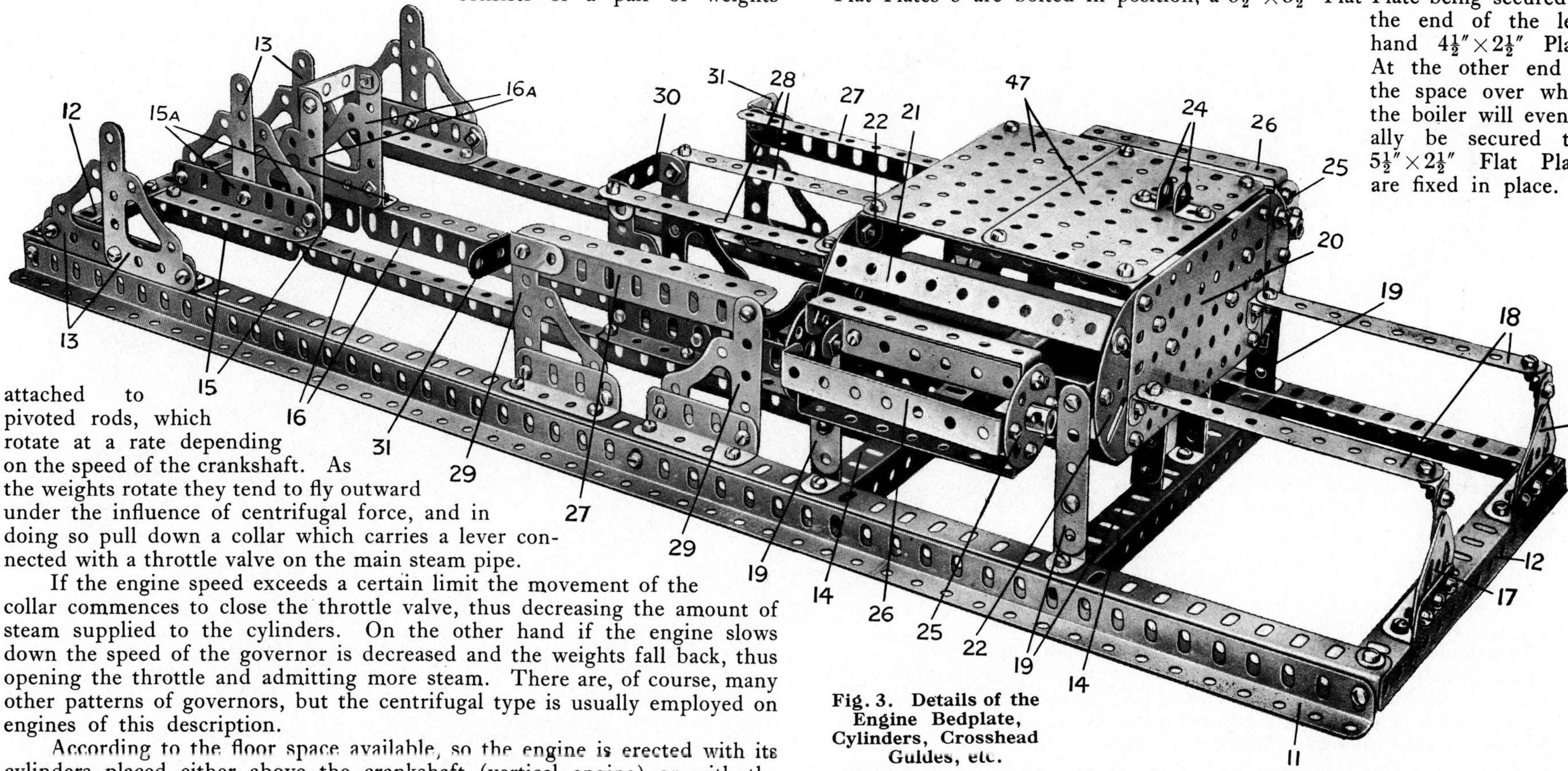

Fig. 3. Details of the Engine Bedplate, Cylinders, Crosshead Guides, etc.

attached to pivoted rods, which rotate at a rate depending on the speed of the crankshaft. As the weights rotate they tend to fly outward under the influence of centrifugal force, and in doing so pull down a collar which carries a lever connected with a throttle valve on the main steam pipe.

If the engine speed exceeds a certain limit the movement of the collar commences to close the throttle valve, thus decreasing the amount of steam supplied to the cylinders. On the other hand if the engine slows down the speed of the governor is decreased and the weights fall back, thus opening the throttle and admitting more steam. There are, of course, many other patterns of governors, but the centrifugal type is usually employed on engines of this description.

According to the floor space available, so the engine is erected with its cylinders placed either above the crankshaft (vertical engine) or with the cylinders placed on a level with it. Ships, for example, invariably have vertical engines, whilst in mills and other places, where there is usually a larger amount of floor space in comparison with a ship's engine room, the horizontal type such as the prototype of the Meccano model is preferred.

Construction of the Base

Fig. 2 shows an underneath view of the base, which, as will be seen from the illustration, is strongly constructed from Angle Girders and Plates. The bottom longitudinal Girders each consist of one $18\frac{1}{2}''$ and one $12\frac{1}{2}''$ Angle Girder 1 and 2 and the cross members are $18\frac{1}{2}''$ Girders 3. The four corners are connected together by means of $3\frac{1}{2}''$ Angle Girders, and further cross Girders 6 that are secured by $\frac{1}{2}'' \times \frac{1}{2}''$ Angle Brackets to the main longitudinal Girders 1 and 2 tend to make the structure more rigid. The Flat Plates constituting the floor of the model are attached to "joists" that consist of Angle Girders.

Commencing at the top right-hand corner, it will be seen that five $4\frac{1}{2}'' \times 2\frac{1}{2}''$ Flat Plates 9 are bolted in position, a $5\frac{1}{2}'' \times 3\frac{1}{2}''$ Flat Plate being secured to the end of the left-hand $4\frac{1}{2}'' \times 2\frac{1}{2}''$ Plate. At the other end of the space over which the boiler will eventually be secured two $5\frac{1}{2}'' \times 2\frac{1}{2}''$ Flat Plates are fixed in place. A longitudinal row of four $4\frac{1}{2}'' \times 2\frac{1}{2}''$ Flat Plates are next laid down, and then a similar row of six $5\frac{1}{2}'' \times 3\frac{1}{2}''$ Plates. It should be noted that they are all "butted" together bar one, which is overlapped four holes. A row of $5\frac{1}{2}'' \times 2\frac{1}{2}''$ Flat Plates and then a row of $5\frac{1}{2}'' \times 3\frac{1}{2}''$ are bolted down to the joists, and lastly a row of $5\frac{1}{2}'' \times 3\frac{1}{2}''$ and one $4\frac{1}{2}'' \times 2\frac{1}{2}''$ Plates are secured to the joists 4 and 8. The open spaces left at the bottom and top to accommodate the lower portions of the twin flywheels are termed the "wheel pits."

Cylinders and Steam Chests

The engine bedplate, cylinders, guides and crankshaft bearings of the engine are shown clearly in Fig. 3. It will be seen that the sides of the bedplate consist of $24\frac{1}{2}''$ Angle Girders 11 bolted in pairs back to back. The two reinforced girders thus formed are connected together by

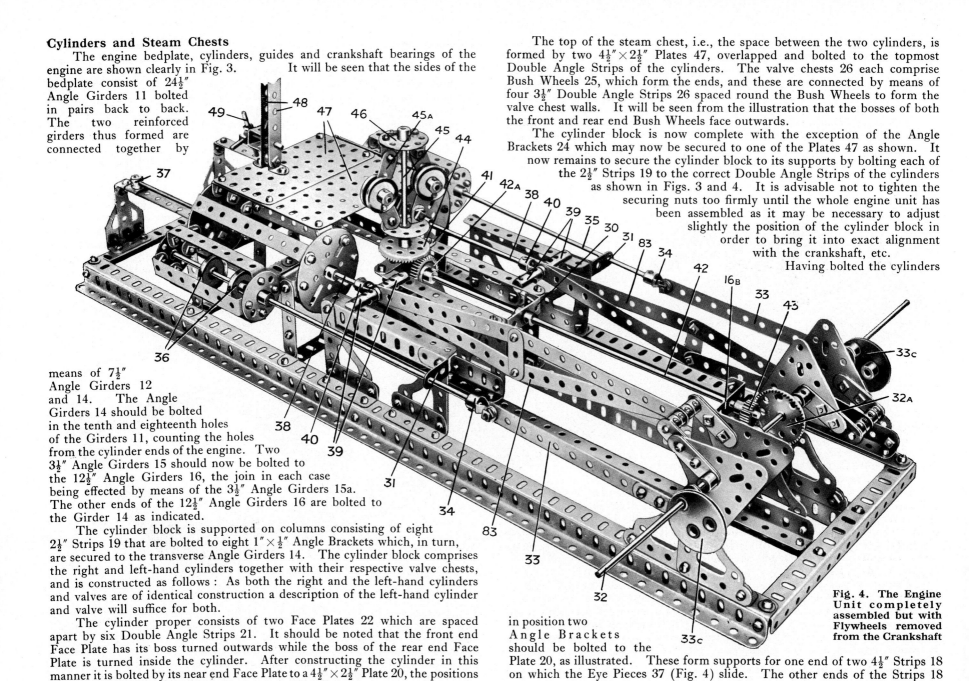

means of $7\frac{1}{2}''$ Angle Girders 12 and 14. The Angle Girders 14 should be bolted in the tenth and eighteenth holes of the Girders 11, counting the holes from the cylinder ends of the engine. Two $3\frac{1}{2}''$ Angle Girders 15 should now be bolted to the $12\frac{1}{2}''$ Angle Girders 16, the join in each case being effected by means of the $3\frac{1}{2}''$ Angle Girders 15a. The other ends of the $12\frac{1}{2}''$ Angle Girders 16 are bolted to the Girder 14 as indicated.

The cylinder block is supported on columns consisting of eight $2\frac{1}{2}''$ Strips 19 that are bolted to eight $1'' \times \frac{1}{2}''$ Angle Brackets which, in turn, are secured to the transverse Angle Girders 14. The cylinder block comprises the right and left-hand cylinders together with their respective valve chests, and is constructed as follows : As both the right and the left-hand cylinders and valves are of identical construction a description of the left-hand cylinder and valve will suffice for both.

The cylinder proper consists of two Face Plates 22 which are spaced apart by six Double Angle Strips 21. It should be noted that the front end Face Plate has its boss turned outwards while the boss of the rear end Face Plate is turned inside the cylinder. After constructing the cylinder in this manner it is bolted by its near end Face Plate to a $4\frac{1}{2}'' \times 2\frac{1}{2}''$ Plate 20, the positions of the securing bolts being clearly shown in the photograph.

The top of the steam chest, i.e., the space between the two cylinders, is formed by two $4\frac{1}{2}'' \times 2\frac{1}{2}''$ Plates 47, overlapped and bolted to the topmost Double Angle Strips of the cylinders. The valve chests 26 each comprise Bush Wheels 25, which form the ends, and these are connected by means of four $3\frac{1}{2}''$ Double Angle Strips 26 spaced round the Bush Wheels to form the valve chest walls. It will be seen from the illustration that the bosses of both the front and rear end Bush Wheels face outwards.

The cylinder block is now complete with the exception of the Angle Brackets 24 which may now be secured to one of the Plates 47 as shown. It now remains to secure the cylinder block to its supports by bolting each of the $2\frac{1}{2}''$ Strips 19 to the correct Double Angle Strips of the cylinders as shown in Figs. 3 and 4. It is advisable not to tighten the securing nuts too firmly until the whole engine unit has been assembled as it may be necessary to adjust slightly the position of the cylinder block in order to bring it into exact alignment with the crankshaft, etc.

Having bolted the cylinders in position two Angle Brackets should be bolted to the Plate 20, as illustrated. These form supports for one end of two $4\frac{1}{2}''$ Strips 18 on which the Eye Pieces 37 (Fig. 4) slide. The other ends of the Strips 18 are bolted to Angle Brackets that are secured to 2'' Strips that, in turn, are

Fig. 4. The Engine Unit completely assembled but with Flywheels removed from the Crankshaft

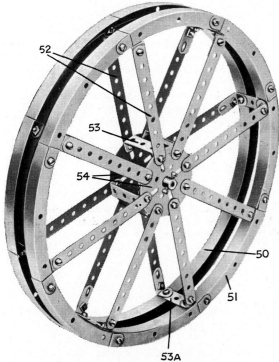

Fig. 5. One of the two Flywheels

bolted to Flat Trunnions 17. These latter are bolted to 1½″ Angle Girders secured to the Angle Girder 12 of the Base-frame.

The Crosshead Guides and Supports

Continuing the construction of the engine frame as shown in Fig. 3, proceed to build up the four crosshead guides 27 and 28. Each of the two outer guides consists of two Architraves 29 bolted to a 4½″ Angle Girder. Two 2″ Angle Girders bolted one to each Architrave provide the means whereby the whole is secured to the bed plate. To each of the outer guides 27 a 1″×1″ Angle Bracket 31 is bolted. These Brackets form supports for the valve Rods 35, as shown in Fig. 4. The two centre guides 28 are connected by a 1½″ Double Angle Strip 30. The crossheads, as will be described later, are formed by Strip Couplings 39 (Fig. 4) the slots of which slide on the flanges of the Angle Girders 27 and 4½″ Strips 28 (Fig. 3).

Before proceeding to assemble any of the mechanism it is advisable to construct the bearings for the crankshaft. These are shown at 13 in Fig. 3 and consist of Architraves bolted back to back in pairs. Each pair of Architraves is secured to the engine frame by means of 3½″ Angle Girders. The two Architraves 16a (Fig. 3) bolted to the 3½″ Angle Girders 15a are joined together at the upper ends by means of a 1½″ Double Angle Strip 16b (Fig. 4), the centre hole of which forms a journal for the Rod 42 (Fig. 4).

It is, of course, important that all bearings in this model are in perfect alignment, and this point is specially important in the case of the crankshaft bearings. Before the several pairs of Architraves are secured rigidly to the bed plate of the engine, it is advisable to pass a rod through the upper holes of all four supports, as these holes will form the crankshaft bearings proper; whilst the rod is in position it will be an easy matter to make slight adjustments in the positions of the supports in order to obtain proper alignment.

Construction of the Crankshaft

As the successful working of the model depends to a large extent on the accurate construction of the crankshaft, particular care should be paid to this important part of the engine.

Two Rods 32 (Fig. 6) each carry at their inner ends a Crank 81, to the arm of which a 1½″ Strip is bolted to add strength to the Cranks. The centre portion of the crankshaft comprises a Rod 32b on which are secured a 1½″ Contrate Wheel 32a and two Collars. The exact position of the Collars on the Rod will be arranged when the crankshaft is placed in its bearings. Each end of the Rod 32b carries a Crank 81a and these Cranks are secured to the Rod at an angle of 90 degrees to each other, as shown in the illustration. They are strengthened with 1½″ Strips in a similar manner to the Cranks 81.

The crank pin "webs", the lower portions of which form the balance weights to counter the effect of the weight of the connecting rods and crank pins, etc., are formed from four 2½″ Triangular Plates 82 bolted to the Cranks 81 and 81a. Each of the two crank pins consists of a 1½″ Rod 80a which is held securely in the bosses of two Cranks 80. The latter are strengthened by means of 1½″ Strips in the manner described above and are secured to the inside faces of the Triangular Plates 82, by the same bolts that secure the Cranks 81 and 81a. It is very important that the set-screws of all the cranks should be screwed home very tightly so as to make the crankshaft a perfectly rigid unit. To ensure reliable working a small flat should be filed on the Rod beneath each grub-screw so that the latter may obtain a better grip, and new style Cranks should be used so that two grub-screws may be inserted in each boss. Great care must be taken in filing the flats, or else the Rods will bind against the grub-screws and become very difficult to remove.

The Connecting Rods and Valve Eccentrics

Each of the two connecting rods 83 comprises four 5½″ Strips that are bolted in pairs end to end and joined together by a 1½″ Strip as shown.

Each connecting rod is connected freely to one of the crank pins 80a of the crankshaft by passing the pin through the end holes of the Strips forming the connecting rod; a Collar is placed on the pin on each side of the connecting rod for spacing purposes.

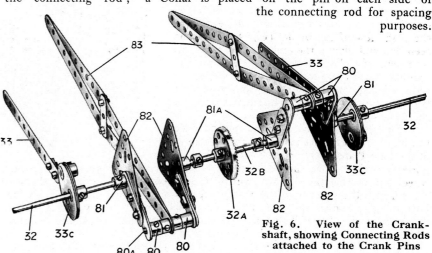

Fig. 6. View of the Crankshaft, showing Connecting Rods attached to the Crank Pins

The Eccentrics 33c control the movement of the slide valves to which they are connected as shown in the view of the completed model (Fig. 1). As the Eccentrics cannot be connected up until the model is finally assembled they may be passed over the Rods 32, the final adjustment of their position being left until all the other working parts have been secured in place.

Construction of the Flywheels

Two flywheels are required. Both are of similar construction and one of them is shown in detail in Fig. 5.

The hub of the wheel is formed by bolting two Face Plates 54 opposite to each other by means of $1\frac{1}{2}''$ Double Angle Strips 53. Each side 50 and 51 of the wheel rim comprises eight Channel Segments bolted together to form a complete circle. The two rings thus formed are then placed side by side and joined together by means of eight $1\frac{1}{2}''$ Strips 53a that are bolted on the inside of the rim.

The rim is secured to the hub by eight $4\frac{1}{2}''$ Strips 52 that are bolted at their outer ends to $1'' \times \frac{1}{2}''$ Angle Brackets secured to the $1\frac{1}{2}''$ Strips 53a. The inner ends of the Strips 52 are bolted to the Face Plates. Before finally tightening the bolts the wheel should be lined up so that it will run true on the crankshaft, and this is easily done by passing a length of Meccano Rod through the bosses of the Face Plates and adjusting the various bolts and Strips until the wheel revolves quite true on the Rod. While the wheel is still on the Rod tighten all nuts securely.

Assembly of the Engine

Commence assembly of the engine proper by placing the crankshaft together with the connecting rods in its bearings. Referring to the plan view of the model (Fig. 8) it will be seen that end play of the crankshaft is taken up by means of Collars placed on the shaft in the various positions indicated. A Collar is required also on each end of the crankshaft between the Bosses of the Eccentrics 33c and the faces of the outer Architraves 13.

The flywheels may now be passed over the ends of the crankshaft and the set-screws of the Face Plates forming their hubs tightened quite securely. Care should be taken to tighten all four set-screws in each wheel hub so that the flywheel will be firmly secured to the shaft, otherwise the wheel will move round the shaft under its own momentum—a result that is technically known as "creeping." In a real engine, "creeping" is usually due to misfitting "keys," the small pieces of metal partly sunk into the shaft which engage a slot cut in the hub of the flywheel.

The 8" piston rods 38 (Fig. 4) carry at their inner ends small Fork Pieces 40.

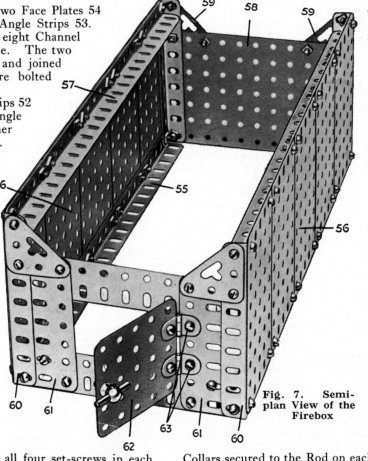

Fig. 7. Semi-plan View of the Firebox

Each of the connecting rods 83 (Fig. 6) is pivoted on a 1" Rod passed through the end holes of the rear pair of $5\frac{1}{2}''$ Strips, and held in position by securing to each of its ends a Strip Coupling 39 (Fig. 4). These Couplings form the crosshead guide shoes and as previously explained the slots of the Strip Couplings are arranged to slide on the flanges of the Angle Girders 27 and Strips 28 (Figs. 3 and 4), thus forming very effective and smooth working guides for the piston rods.

It will be noticed that each of the piston rods extends right through the cylinder and carries at its further end an Eye Piece 37 (Figs 1 and 4) which is arranged to slide freely on one of the Strips 18 (Fig. 3).

The Piston Valves

The valve gear is shown clearly in Figs. 1 and 4. The valves, which are of the piston type, each consist of two 1" fast Pulleys 36 that are secured to an $11\frac{1}{2}''$ Rod that forms the valve rod.

The valve rods pass through the bosses of the front Bush Wheels of each valve chest, through the Pulleys 36, and out through the bosses of the rear Bush Wheel 25 (see Figs. 3 and 4).

As the exact location of the Pulleys 36 on the valve rod can only be determined by experiment, that is, rotation of the crankshaft when the model is completely assembled, their set-screws should not be tightened at this stage. The valve rods pass through guides formed by the $1'' \times 1''$ Angle Brackets 31 (Fig. 4) and each Rod carries a small Fork Piece 34 to which the eccentric rods 33 are connected pivotally by a lock-nutted bolt (S.M. 263.)

The Centrifugal Governor

The $6\frac{1}{2}''$ vertical Rod 45 (Fig. 4) of the governor is journalled at its lower end in a $1\frac{1}{2}''$ Strip bolted to the inner Angle Girder 14 (Fig. 3) and a $2\frac{1}{2}''$ Strip 41 that is bolted across the ends of the Strips 28 (Fig. 3). The Rod is free to rotate in its bearings and is held loosely in position by means of Collars secured to the Rod on each side of Strip 41.

The governor weights comprise four 1" fast Pulleys that are secured on 1" Rods passed through the end holes of $1\frac{1}{2}''$ Strips 45a. The Strips 45a are attached pivotally by a bolt and two nuts to Angle Brackets that are bolted to a Bush Wheel 46 secured on the vertical Rod 45. The lower $1\frac{1}{2}''$ Strips are pivoted in a like manner to a further Bush Wheel that slides freely on the Rod 45. The latter also carries a Contrate 44 which is secured firmly in position and engages a 1″ Gear Wheel 42a that is secured on the end of a 1½″ Rod 42. This Rod 42 is journalled in the centre holes of the Double Angle Strips 30 (Fig. 3) and carries at the opposite end to the Gear 42a a ½″ Pinion 43 that is secured to the Rod in position to engage the Contrate Wheel 32a (Fig. 4) that is on the crankshaft.

As the crankshaft rotates, motion is transmitted to the vertical Rod 45, and as the speed of rotation increases, centrifugal force causes the governor weights to fly outwards, with the result that the lower Bush Wheel moves up the vertical Rod 45. In a practical engine this rising movement is made use of to shut the main steam valve or open it as the case may be, thus admitting or shutting off steam to the cylinders and so keeping the revolutions of the engine fairly constant.

Building the Boiler

Each end of the boiler is formed by a Hub Disc, to the rims of which are bolted twenty-one 12½″ Strips 72 (Fig. 1). The underneath portion of the boiler, i.e., the part that lies inside the boiler mounting, is left uncovered. The boiler fittings comprise a steam pressure gauge, a water gauge and a "dead weight" safety valve. In actual practice the water gauge consists of a length of stout glass tube mounted at each end in hollow brass sockets. The sockets are directly connected with the boiler water so that the water flows into the glass tube and takes up the same level as that of the water actually in the boiler. The gauges are, of course, fitted about 12 inches below the normal working water level. In the model the gauge consists of a 1½″ Rod (representing the glass tube), that is held in two Handrail Supports, the latter being secured to the front end plate of the boiler. The arrangement is shown clearly in Fig 1.

The pressure gauge is formed by a 1⅛″ Flanged Wheel bolted to the boiler end plate by means of a ⅜″ Bolt. The dead weight saftey valve comprises

two 1⅛″ Flanged Wheels 71 held flange to flange on a 1½″ Rod that is passed through a hole in the top Strip of the boiler, as shown, and held in position by a Collar secured to the Rod inside the boiler.

Details of Boiler Mounting, Fire Box, etc.

The boiler is mounted above the fire box as shown in Fig. 1. The fire box is illustrated in detail in Fig. 7. Each side is formed by five 4½″×2½″ Flat Plates 56 that are bolted at their ends to 12½″ Angle Girders 55 and 57. The rear end is a 5½″×3½″ Flat Plate 58 that is bolted to the Angle Girders 55 and 57 and is further secured by means of two Corner Brackets 59, which also form the saddles on which the boiler rests. At the fire door end, two 4½″ Angle Girders 60 are bolted to the Angle Girders 55 and 57, as are also two horizontal 5½″ Flat Girders. Two 3½″ Flat Girders 61 may now be secured between the latter as shown, after which two further Corner Brackets are bolted in position in a similar manner to the Corner Brackets 59 at the rear end.

The fire door is formed by a 2½″×2½″ Flat Plate that is attached by two Meccano Hinges 63 to one of the Flat Girders 61. A Handrail Support, in which is secured a 1″ Rod, serves as a handle.

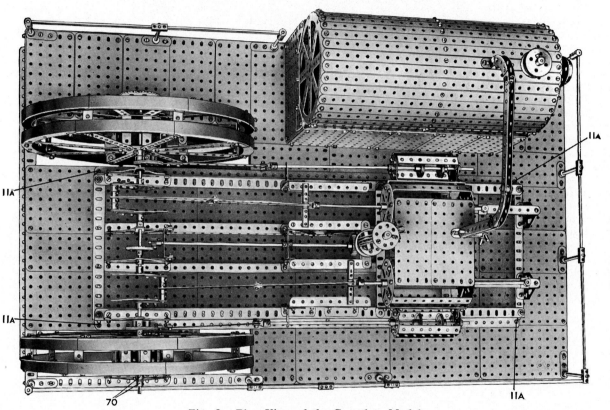

Fig. 8. Plan View of the Complete Model

The firebox unit is now complete and may be secured to the base by bolting it in the position shown in Figs. 1 and 8. The securing bolts pass through the Angle Girder 55 (Fig. 7) of the fire box and also through the Flat Plates of the base, the whole being placed so as to cover completely the space left to receive it in the base (see Fig. 2).

The boiler may next be bolted in position above the fire box. It is secured by bolting the Hub Discs to the 5½″ Flat Girder at the front end of the fire box, and to the Flat Plate 58 (Fig. 7) at the rear. One bolt in each of the above positions will be quite enough to ensure that the boiler is held firmly in position. In the prototype the steam is drawn off from the boiler via the main steam pipe 48, which is connected to the steam chest of the engine (see Fig. 4).

The pipe is made up from four 5½" Strips and four 2½" Curved Strips connected together. It is secured to the boiler by bolting the ends of the Curved Strips to two Angle Brackets that, in turn, are bolted to the boiler. At its other end it is connected to the Angle Brackets 24 (Fig. 3) bolted to the top of the steam chest.

The main steam pipe is provided with a stop-valve 49 (Fig. 4) the purpose of which is to shut off or admit steam to the engine as required. It is constructed from a 2" Rod that is journalled in a Double Bent Strip before passing through the 5½" Strips forming the steam pipe. The Rod is held in position by a Collar, secured on the Rod between the two 5½" Strips. Four Threaded Pins screwed into the spider of a Universal Coupling or Swivel Bearing secured on the 2" Rod form a very neat and realistic handwheel for operating the valve.

To complete the model and at the same time add realism to its appearance it now only remains to fix handrails round the base as shown in Fig. 1. The handrail supports are formed by eleven short Rods secured in Cranks. It will be noticed that the corner supports are secured in ordinary Cranks while the intermediate supports are held in Double Arm Cranks. Each supporting rod carries a Coupling that is secured transversely, as shown. These Couplings form sockets in which to secure the 8½" and 6½" Axle Rods comprising the handrails.

Having now assembled all the moving parts of the engine, final adjustments may be made. Each of the Eccentrics 33c are to be secured to the crankshaft at an angle of approximately 90 degrees with its respective crank pin. Careful

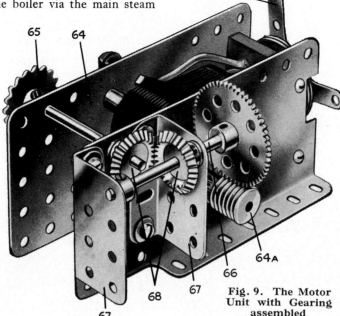

Fig. 9. The Motor Unit with Gearing assembled

attention should be paid to the alignment of the piston rods, crossheads, and crankshaft and it may be necessary to make certain minor adjustments to these parts in order to ensure that everything works quite freely. Apply a little oil to all gears, crank pins, crosshead slides, piston rods, and crankshaft bearings, etc.

It is a good plan to turn the engine by means of the Flywheel for a few revolutions, when, if it is at all hard to turn or unsteady in its movement, the trouble is generally to be found in one of the rods being out of line with its journals. Careful inspection will soon locate the fault.

Arrangement of the Driving Motor

The model is operated by a 6-volt Meccano Electric Motor. It should be bolted to the base in the position shown at 64 in Fig. 1. Fig. 9 is a detailed view of the complete Motor unit and the gears through which the drive is transmitted to the engine crankshaft.

The Motor armature spindle carries a Worm 64a engaging a 57-teeth Gear Wheel secured to the Rod 66 that is journalled in Girder Brackets 67 bolted to the side plates of the Motor. Besides the 57-teeth Gear the Rod 66 carries also a ⅞" Bevel 68 that engages a second Bevel secured on a Rod journalled in the Motor frame plates. This latter Rod carries also a 1" Sprocket Wheel 65. Both the Rod 66 and the Rod of the Sprocket 65 are held in position by Collars. Washers should be placed on the Rods behind the bosses of the Bevels 68, for spacing purposes. The drive from the Motor is conveyed by Sprocket Chain from the Sprocket 65 to a 2" Sprocket secured on the crankshaft, as shown in the plan view of the model (Fig. 8).

List of Parts Required to Build the Meccano Twin Cylinder Steam Engine

25 of No. 1	6 of No. 9a	2 of No. 14	1 of No. 27a	10 of No. 48c	4 of No. 76	4 of No. 103b	2 of No. 126a
2 ,, 1b	14 ,, 9b	2 ,, 15a	2 ,, 28	2 ,, 50a	1 ,, 81	22 ,, 108	4 ,, 130
12 ,, 2	1 ,, 9c	12 ,, 16a	2 ,, 30	17 ,, 52a	4 ,, 90a	8 ,, 109	5 ,, 133
38 ,, 2a	1 ,, 9d	1 ,, 16b	1 ,, 31	22 ,, 53a	6 ,, 94	6 ,, 111a	5 ,, 136
7 ,, 5	8 ,, 9e	5 ,, 18a	1 ,, 32	18 ,, 59	1 ,, 95a	2 ,, 111c	1 ,, 143
10 ,, 6	2 ,, 9f	5 ,, 18b	633 ,, 37	13 ,, 62	1 ,, 96	2 ,, 114	2 ,, 161
30 ,, 6a	22 ,, 12	3 ,, 20	13 ,, 37a	5 ,, 62b	8 ,, 99	4 ,, 115	1 ,, 165
4 ,, 7	2 ,, 12a	2 ,, 20a	28 ,, 38	10 ,, 63	8 ,, 99a	2 ,, 116a	2 ,, 166
15 ,, 7a	38 ,, 12b	8 ,, 22	1 ,, 45	4 ,, 63b	4 ,, 99b	2 ,, 118	1 6-volt
15 ,, 8	7 ,, 13	6 ,, 24	19 ,, 48	9 ,, 70	2 ,, 103	32 ,, 119	Electric Motor
4 ,, 8b	5 ,, 13a	1 ,, 26	8 ,, 48b	1 ,, 72			

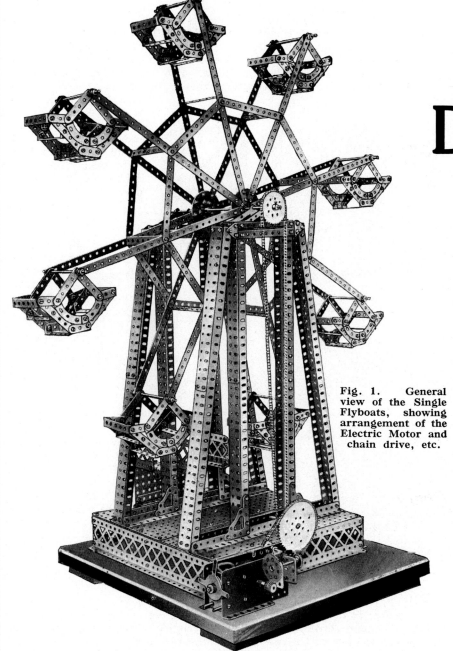

Fig. 1. General view of the Single Flyboats, showing arrangement of the Electric Motor and chain drive, etc.

Single and Double Flyboats

The two Meccano models described in this leaflet represent popular pleasure fair attractions. When set in motion by means of the Meccano Electric Motor they present a very realistic appearance, and are entirely automatic in operation.

EVERY boy will be familiar with the huge roundabouts, scenic railways and oscillating swing boats which form such prominent features at most seaside resorts and country fairs, and he will no doubt have many pleasant memories of happy hours spent riding first on one and then on another of these jolly machines. It is doubtful, however, if he will be equally familiar with the very enjoyable ride that may be had in a car of such a machine as the Revolving Flyboats, a model of which is shown on this page. This device, although not so much in evidence as various other mechanical amusements, is nevertheless a warm favourite with thousands of boys and girls in some parts of the country. It is perhaps principally on account of its necessarily huge size that it is not met with more frequently.

It is indeed an exhilarating experience to step into one of the little cars and to be carried high into the air and then as the car descends to the ground, to see the earth apparently rushing out to meet it! A typical structure of this nature stood for many years at Blackpool, in Lancashire, but unfortunately it has recently been condemned as unsafe and has had to be dismantled. It was known as the "Big Wheel" and during its long life it has been a source of pleasure to countless thousands of holiday makers. It formed a very conspicuous landmark that could be seen from many miles around.

The construction of the Blackpool Big Wheel was commenced

in February, 1896, and the following August saw the giant structure thrown open to the public. The erection was carried out by Lieutenant W. B. Bassett, R.N. and a staff of 250 men. Most of the metal used in the various ties and struts was Scotch Steel, while the spokes and driving cables were manufactured from Lancashire steel cable. From the ground to the topmost girder the height of the structure was 220 feet—the tip of the wheel being 260 feet above sea level! The total weight of the wheel with its 30 cars attached was 1,000 tons, while its superficial area for painting purposes was estimated at 2,000 square yards!

The vast size of this great wheel may perhaps be better realised when it is learned that 2½ tons of paint were necessary in order to apply two coatings to the steelwork! Each of the carriages weighed 3 tons 3 cwt., and was capable of carrying 30 passengers—giving a grand total of 900 passengers that could be carried at one time.

The rim of the wheel itself was built of steel girders bolted together and was suspended from the axle by 120 wind ties and spokes of steel cable. For rotating the wheel giant steel cables were used, the total length of which was 3,132 feet, or ¾ of a mile! The splicing on these two cables was recognised as the longest spliced joints in the world. The huge wheel was mounted on a massive steel axle, the circumference of which measured 6 feet 10 inches, the axle having a weight of 30 tons!

Although the Meccano model Flyboats differ in some

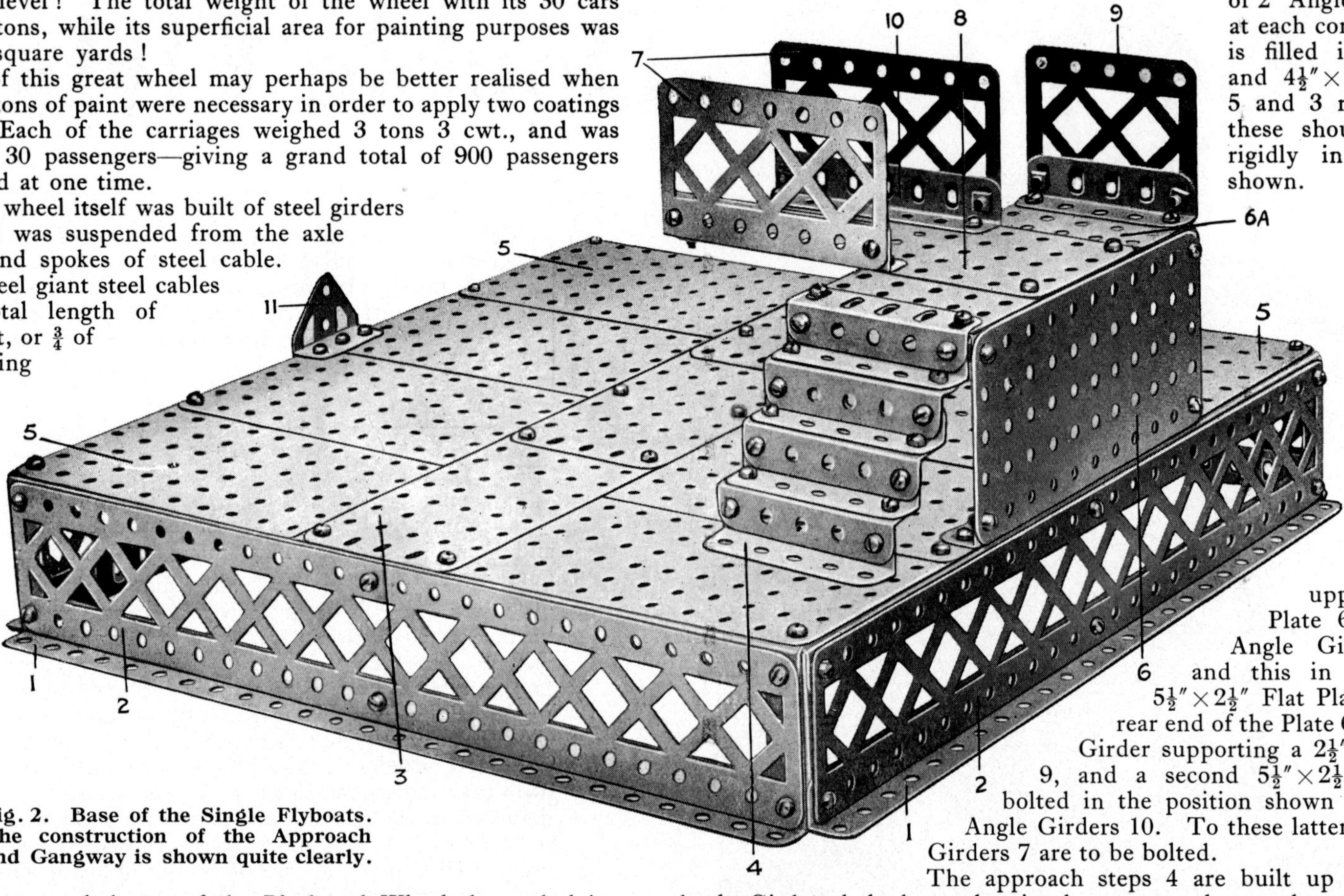

Fig. 2. Base of the Single Flyboats. The construction of the Approach and Gangway is shown quite clearly.

respects from the structural design of the Blackpool Wheel the underlying principle is the same as that on which most Big Wheels and Flyboats are designed. We would refer those boys who wish to build a more accurate model of the Blackpool Wheel to the Meccano Instructions Manual, which contains illustrations and constructional details for building a model that is fashioned to a great extent on this famous pleasure wheel (see Model No. 6.6).

Construction of the Single Flyboats

It is convenient when constructing a model of this description to commence by building up the base, which is shown in Fig. 2. It is of quite simple design and will give little trouble to the builder. The two 12½″ Angle Girders 1 are bolted to the edges of a 12½″ Braced Girder 2, care being taken to ensure that the flanges of the upper and lower Angle Girders project in opposite directions as indicated in the illustration. Four complete sides are required, and when built these may be bolted together in the form of a square, by means of 2″ Angle Girders bolted at each corner. The base is filled in by 3½″×5½″ and 4½″×2½″ Flat Plates 5 and 3 respectively and these should be secured rigidly in the positions shown.

Having completed the construction of the base, the approach and steps may receive attention as follows. A 5½″ × 3½″ Flat Plate 6 is bolted to a 5½″ Angle Girder that is in turn secured to the base. To the upper edge of the Plate 6 a second 5½″ Angle Girder is bolted and this in turn carries a 5½″×2½″ Flat Plate 6a. At the rear end of the Plate 6a is a 2½″ Angle Girder supporting a 2½″ Braced Girder 9, and a second 5½″×2½″ Flat Plate 8 bolted in the position shown carries two 3½″ Angle Girders 10. To these latter the 3½″ Braced Girders 7 are to be bolted.

The approach steps 4 are built up from eight 2½″ Angle Girders bolted together in the manner shown, the upper end Angle Girders of the stairway when complete being bolted to the Flat Plate 6a.

Details of the Main Standards

Referring to the general view (Fig. 1) of the model it will be seen that both the main vertical standards are of similar construction, so it is only necessary to describe the construction of one of them.

The standard (see Fig. 3) is built up from two 18½″ Angle Girders 13 to which are bolted two 9½" Flat Girders 14 over-lapped one hole as shown in the illustration. The four columns 13 when completed are joined together at the foot by means of two 12½" Angle Girders 12, bolted one at each side of the columns. At their upper ends the two centre columns are connected by means of Girder frames 16 and the outer "inclined" columns are secured in position by 1" Triangular Plates 17 that are bolted to the ends of the Girder Frames.

Building the Wheel and Cars

The revolving wheel that carries the eight cars is shown in Fig. 5. Each side is composed of eight arms, each of which consists of a 12½" Strip 18 that is secured by means of two Bolts to a centre Face Plate 21. 5½" Strips 20 bolted to the Strips 18 serve to hold the whole rigidly together.

After building two similar sides as described they may be joined together by means of 3½" Double Angle Strips 19, which are secured in position between each opposite pair of Strips 18. It is important that care is taken to ensure that the bosses and central bores of the two Face Plates are directly in line so that the wheel will revolve quite true about its axis when the various parts of the model are finally assembled. To correctly align the Face Plates it is advisable to place a length of Meccano Rod through their bores and then carefully re-adjust the Double Angle Strips 19 until the wheel runs free and true on the temporary axle. A little care is all that is necessary to construct a perfectly balanced wheel.

Altogether eight cars are required and each of these is constructed as follows (see Fig. 4). The lower portion is composed of 2½" × ½" Double Angle Strips 23 to the ends of which are secured 3" Strips 24 and 2" Strips 22. The backs and seats are constructed from further 2½" × ½" Double Angle Strips 23 while 2½" small radius Curved Strips 25 complete the sides of the cars.

Each car is provided with four 2½" Strips 26 that are bolted at one of their ends to the ends of the Curved Strips 25. The latter are held in the positions shown in the illustration by means of 1½" Strips that are bolted to the ends of the upper Double Angle Strips 23.

Fig. 3. One of the two Main Standards.

Assembly of the Single Flyboats

Having completed the various portions of the model it remains now to assemble them in their respective positions. The first step is to attach to the base the two vertical standards (Fig. 3) that support the wheel. As will be seen from the general view the standards are bolted one at either side of the base. The bolts securing each standard pass through the Angle Girders 12 (Fig. 3) and through the fourth and seventh holes of the Flat Plates 5, counting the holes from the sides of the base (see general view).

To ensure perfect rigidity it is advisable to further secure each standard to the base by means of bolts and nuts passed through the Girders 12 about midway along their length. Having made sure that the main standards are perfectly secure, attention may be given to the moving parts of the model.

The wheel (Fig. 5) revolves on an 11½" Rod and to place it in position between the standards, the Rod should first of all be passed through the apex holes of the Girder Frame 16 (Fig. 3) of the outer standard. The Wheel may now be placed between the standards and the 11½" Rod passed through the Face Plates 21 (Fig. 5) then through the apex holes of the Girder Frames capping the opposite standard. It is held in position by means of two Collars secured to the Rod one at each end and placed against the faces of the Girder Frames 16.

The wheel should be secured centrally on the Rod by tightening the set-screws of the Face Plates 21.

The next step is to attach the cars to the arms of the wheel. The method of doing this is illustrated in the general view (Fig. 1).

Each car is suspended pivotally on a 3½" Rod that is journalled in the end holes of the Strips 18 (Fig. 5) that form the arms of the wheel. This Rod passes through the upper end holes of the Strips 26 (Fig. 4) and is held in position in the arms of the wheel by means of two Collars. As all the cars are suspended freely on their respective pivot Rods it will be found that as the wheel is rotated the cars maintain a horizontal position.

The Chain Drive Mechanism

The mechanism for rotating the wheel is very

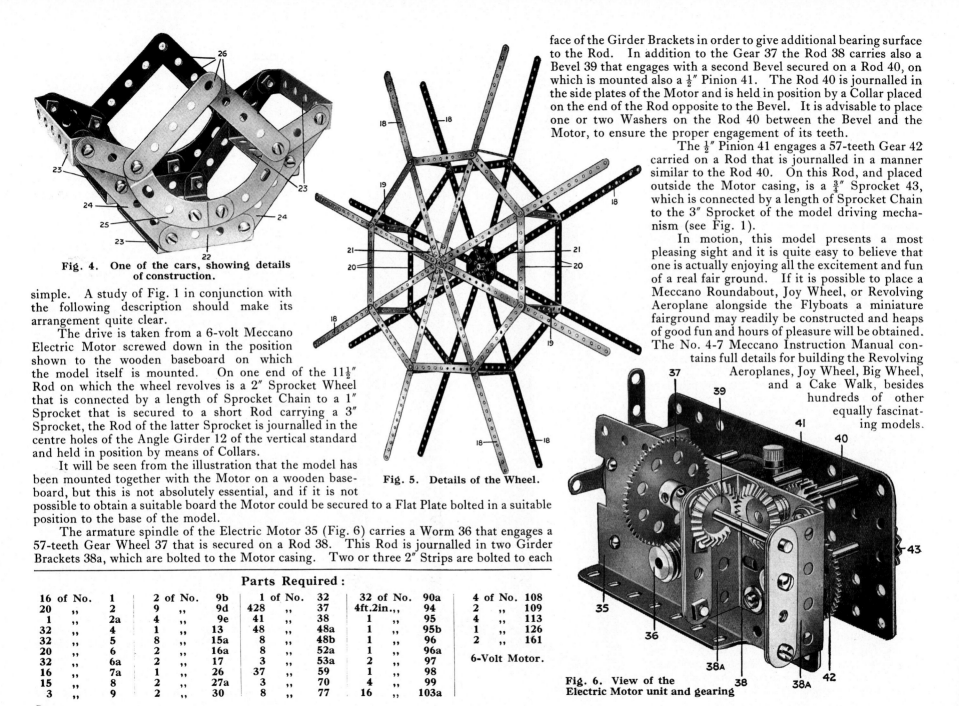

Fig. 4. One of the cars, showing details of construction.

Fig. 5. Details of the Wheel.

Fig. 6. View of the Electric Motor unit and gearing

face of the Girder Brackets in order to give additional bearing surface to the Rod. In addition to the Gear 37 the Rod 38 carries also a Bevel 39 that engages with a second Bevel secured on a Rod 40, on which is mounted also a $\frac{1}{2}$" Pinion 41. The Rod 40 is journalled in the side plates of the Motor and is held in position by a Collar placed on the end of the Rod opposite to the Bevel. It is advisable to place one or two Washers on the Rod 40 between the Bevel and the Motor, to ensure the proper engagement of its teeth.

The $\frac{1}{2}$" Pinion 41 engages a 57-teeth Gear 42 carried on a Rod that is journalled in a manner similar to the Rod 40. On this Rod, and placed outside the Motor casing, is a $\frac{3}{4}$" Sprocket 43, which is connected by a length of Sprocket Chain to the 3" Sprocket of the model driving mechanism (see Fig. 1).

In motion, this model presents a most pleasing sight and it is quite easy to believe that one is actually enjoying all the excitement and fun of a real fair ground. If it is possible to place a Meccano Roundabout, Joy Wheel, or Revolving Aeroplane alongside the Flyboats a miniature fairground may readily be constructed and heaps of good fun and hours of pleasure will be obtained. The No. 4-7 Meccano Instruction Manual contains full details for building the Revolving Aeroplanes, Joy Wheel, Big Wheel, and a Cake Walk, besides hundreds of other equally fascinating models.

simple. A study of Fig. 1 in conjunction with the following description should make its arrangement quite clear.

The drive is taken from a 6-volt Meccano Electric Motor screwed down in the position shown to the wooden baseboard on which the model itself is mounted. On one end of the $11\frac{1}{2}$" Rod on which the wheel revolves is a 2" Sprocket Wheel that is connected by a length of Sprocket Chain to a 1" Sprocket that is secured to a short Rod carrying a 3" Sprocket, the Rod of the latter Sprocket is journalled in the centre holes of the Angle Girder 12 of the vertical standard and held in position by means of Collars.

It will be seen from the illustration that the model has been mounted together with the Motor on a wooden baseboard, but this is not absolutely essential, and if it is not possible to obtain a suitable board the Motor could be secured to a Flat Plate bolted in a suitable position to the base of the model.

The armature spindle of the Electric Motor 35 (Fig. 6) carries a Worm 36 that engages a 57-teeth Gear Wheel 37 that is secured on a Rod 38. This Rod is journalled in two Girder Brackets 38a, which are bolted to the Motor casing. Two or three 2" Strips are bolted to each

Parts Required :

16	of No.	1	2 of No.	9b	1 of No.	32	32 of No.	90a	4 of No. 108
20	,,	2	9 ,,	9d	428 ,,	37	4ft.2in.,,	94	2 ,, 109
1	,,	2a	4 ,,	9e	41 ,,	38	1 ,,	95	4 ,, 113
32	,,	4	1 ,,	13	48 ,,	48a	1 ,,	95b	1 ,, 126
32	,,	5	8 ,,	15a	8 ,,	48b	1 ,,	96	2 ,, 161
20	,,	6	2 ,,	16a	8 ,,	52a	1 ,,	96a	
32	,,	6a	2 ,,	17	3 ,,	53a	2 ,,	97	6-Volt Motor.
16	,,	7a	1 ,,	26	37 ,,	59	1 ,,	98	
15	,,	8	2 ,,	27a	3 ,,	70	4 ,,	99	
3	,,	9	2 ,,	30	8 ,,	77	16 ,,	103a	

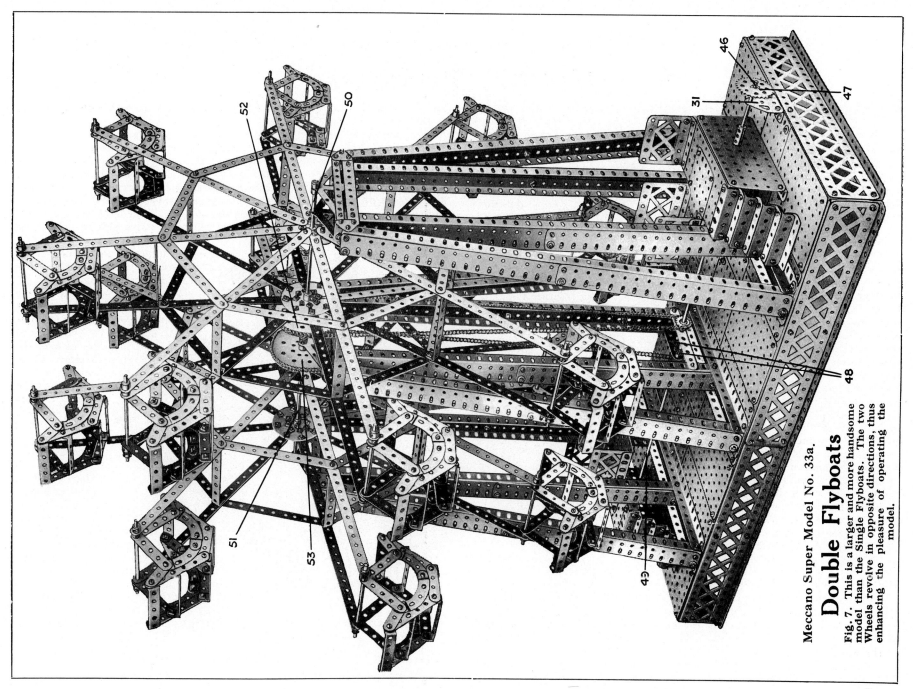

Meccano Super Model No. 33a.

Double Flyboats

Fig. 7. This is a larger and more handsome model than the Single Flyboats. The two Wheels revolve in opposite directions, thus enhancing the pleasure of operating the model.

Double Flyboats

WITH certain exceptions the constructional details of the Double Flyboats (Fig. 7) are the same as those of the Single Flyboats. Two wheels (Fig. 5) are of course required and an additional main standard (Fig. 3). The design and construction of the cars is identical with that of the smaller model, as also is the arrangement of the Electric Motor unit (Fig. 6). The base, however, is larger and the driving mechanism differs considerably from that of the Single Flyboats.

The base is constructed as follows : two 24½″ Angle Girders 27a (Fig. 8) to which are bolted two 12½″ Braced Girders 27 overlapped two holes, form each of the larger sides of the base. Each end is formed from two 12½″ Angle Girders 32a and 12½″ Braced Girders 32. The two sides and ends are connected together to form an oblong frame by means of 2″ Angle Girders used as corner pieces. The whole framework so formed may then be partially filled in with 5½″×3½″ Flat Plates 34 bolted to each side of the frame. A space down the centre remains uncovered and this is filled in with six 4½″×2½″ Flat Plates overlapped one hole at their ends and also overlapping the 5½″×3½″ Flat Plates by one hole.

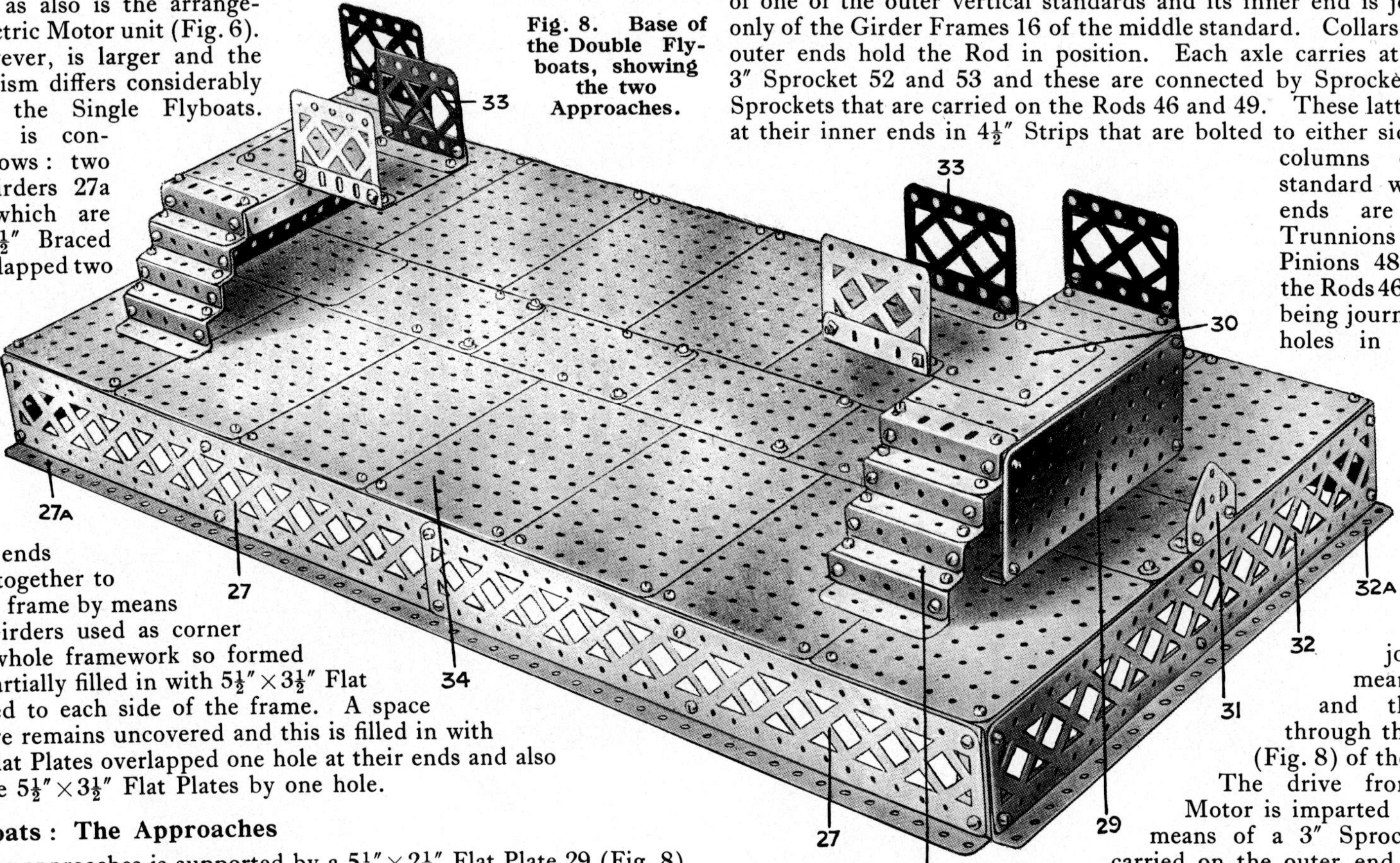

Double Flyboats : The Approaches

Each of the approaches is supported by a 5½″×2½″ Flat Plate 29 (Fig. 8) that is bolted to an Angle Girder secured to the base. A 5½″ Angle Girder supports the landing platform and the gangway 30, the Girder being bolted to the upper edge of the Flat Plate 29. Three 2½″ Braced Girders secured in the positions shown add to the appearance of the approaches.

As in the Single Flyboats the "steps" are formed from 2½″ Angle Girders 28. The two Flat Trunnions 31 are bolted to 1½″ Angle Girders that in turn

are bolted to the base, one Trunnion being secured at each end of the base in the position indicated.

In this model each of the two wheels revolves on a separate axle 50 and 51 (Fig. 7). Each of the axles is journalled in the Girder Frames 15 (Fig. 3) of one of the outer vertical standards and its inner end is journalled in one only of the Girder Frames 16 of the middle standard. Collars on the inner and outer ends hold the Rod in position. Each axle carries at its inner end a 3″ Sprocket 52 and 53 and these are connected by Sprocket Chain with 1″ Sprockets that are carried on the Rods 46 and 49. These latter are journalled at their inner ends in 4½″ Strips that are bolted to either side of the central columns of the centre standard while their outer ends are journalled in Trunnions 31. Two ½″ Pinions 48 are carried on the Rods 46 and 49, the Rods being journalled in suitable holes in the 4½″ Strips to enable the Pinions 48 to engage.

It will be observed from Fig. 7 that the Rods 46 and 49 are both composed of a long and a short Rod joined together by means of a Coupling and that they pass through the Flat Plates 29 (Fig. 8) of the approaches.

The drive from the Electric Motor is imparted to the model by means of a 3″ Sprocket 47 (Fig. 7) carried on the outer end of Rod 46, the Motor being mounted on the baseboard in a suitable position to allow the Sprocket 43 (Fig. 6) to be connected by Sprocket Chain to the Sprocket 47 (Fig. 7).

Alternative Drive Incorporating Intermittent Motion

With the aid of the ingenious yet simple mechanism shown in Fig. 9

Fig. 8. Base of the Double Flyboats, showing the two Approaches.

it is possible to make the operation of the Flyboats much more interesting and spectacular. It is a device by means of which intermittent rotary motion may be given to the Flyboat wheels, with the result that when set in motion the Wheels make one revolution or so and then come to rest for a few seconds as though to allow passengers to alight or embark. After this pause the wheels make another revolution, when the process is repeated automatically and entirely without attention. This intermittent motion gives the model a very realistic appearance and is well worth the little extra trouble required to incorporate it in the model.

The photograph shows a convenient arrangement of the gearing, although of course the layout and general assembly of the necessary apparatus may be altered as desired to suit individual requirements. The Rod 1 forms the driven shaft, which conveys intermittent motion to the model. The drive from the Motor is led to a Worm Wheel 2 that meshes with a 57-teeth Gear Wheel 3, in the face of which two Threaded Pins 4 are secured as shown. For driving the Flyboats it is advisable to use one pin only and the other shown in the photograph should be removed. In the illustration the Gear Wheel 3 is secured to a short Rod journalled in a footstep bearing consisting of a Double Bent Strip bolted to a base plate.

Either the Single or the Double Flyboats may be fitted with the device and this will entail several minor alterations in the constructional details of the driving mechanism previously described. The necessary alterations are the same for both the Single and the Double Flyboats, and are of such simple character that no difficulty should be experienced.

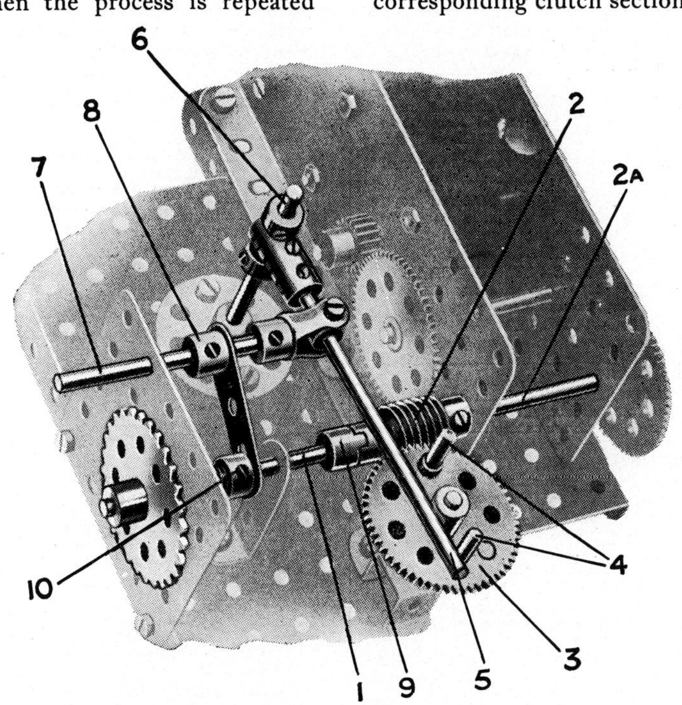

To incorporate the intermittent mechanism into the Double Flyboats it will be necessary to remove the large Sprocket 47 (Fig. 7) and to replace it with a ½″ Pinion that is driven by a Worm secured on a long Rod at right angles to Rod 46. The Rod of the Worm may be journalled in any suitable manner and must be long enough to project beyond the side of the model. This Rod carries on the opposite end to the Worm a 3″ Sprocket that is connected by a length of Meccano Sprocket Chain with the 1½″ Sprocket on the Rod 1 (Fig. 9) of the intermittent mechanism. These are the only alterations required to the standard layout of either the Single or Double Flyboats. This arrangement will result in the transferring of the Electric Motor from the position shown in Fig. 1 to the left (as seen in that view) of the base.

Automatic Operation of the Intermittent Mechanism

As the 57-teeth Gear Wheel 3 (Fig. 9) slowly rotates the Threaded Pin 4 alternately presses against the end of a 3½″ Rod 5, which is secured in a Coupling

Fig. 9. The Intermittent mechanism. One of the Pins 4 should be removed when using this mechanism in connection with the Single or Double Flyboats.

mounted on a suitable pivot 6. On this Rod 5, about ¼″ from the Coupling, is mounted the boss of a Swivel Bearing, which forms a pivotal connection between the Rod 5 and a 2½″ Rod 7. This Rod 7 carries a Crank 8, through the end hole of which is journalled the driven shaft 1. The latter slides in its bearings and carries on its inner end one section of a Dog Clutch 9, the corresponding clutch section being secured next to the Worm 2 on the driving Rod 2a. The Clutch is normally held in engagement by means of a Compression Spring mounted on the driven shaft and pressing against a Collar 10. This Spring, while retaining the Clutch in engagement, also tends to hold the lever 5 against the boss of the 57-teeth Gear Wheel 3.

When the Pin 4 strikes the lever 5, the Rod 7 is pushed back in its bearings. This movement is conveyed by means of the Crank 8 to the Rod 1, the Spring thereon is compressed and the clutch members 8 disengaged. The model is thus thrown out of gear and the Motor is free to rotate independently. It continues to do so until the movement of the Gear Wheel 3 has carried the Threaded Pin far enough to allow the Rod 5, through the action of the Spring on the Rod 1, to slip back into its normal position, when the Clutch is re-engaged. The Motor is now connected to the model and the latter is operated until the Threaded Pin again presses against the Rod 5. The cycle of operations is then repeated.

Adjusting the Frequency of Operation

The speed ratio between the Motor and the Gear Wheel carrying the Threaded Pin has a direct bearing on the rapidity with which the cycles of operations take place. An increase in the ratio will result in a corresponding increase in the time taken to complete each cycle, and vice versa. Hence, by altering the gear train attached to the Motor, it is a simple matter to vary the length of the periods during which the Model is at rest or in motion.

Parts Required :										
32	of No.	1	4	of No.	9e	72	of No.	38	2	of No.	95b
38	,,	2	1	,,	9f	96	,,	48a	1	,,	96
2	,,	2a	2	,,	13	16	,,	48b	2	,,	96a
64	,,	4	2	,,	13a	14	,,	52a	6	,,	98
64	,,	5	16	,,	15a	8	,,	53a	6	,,	99
48	,,	6	2	,,	16a	74	,,	59	24	,,	103a
64	,,	6a	2	,,	17	1	,,	63	4	,,	109
4	,,	7	3	,,	26	4	,,	70	6	,,	113
24	,,	7a	2	,,	27a	12	,,	77	1	,,	126a
16	,,	8	2	,,	30	64	,,	90a	2	,,	161
6	,,	9	1	,,	32	8ft.	,,	94	1 6-Volt Motor		
22	,,	9d	735	,,	37	1	,,	95a			

MECCANO SUPER MODELS

No. 6 Leaflet.

No. 19 Leaflet.

Our expert designers have produced for us 34 super models that reach the highest pinnacle ever attained in Meccano construction. Each model in this series is a masterpiece and there is not a boy who will not be eager to build them all.

These models are so important that we have engaged expert engineers to describe them and a special leaflet with beautiful half-tone illustrations has been written for each of them. A selection of the leaflets is illustrated on this page.

A brief description of each model in the series is given below and the number and price of the special Instruction Leaflet are indicated. Copies of the leaflets may be obtained from any Meccano dealer or direct from us, post free, at the prices shown at foot.

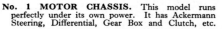

No. 1 MOTOR CHASSIS. This model runs perfectly under its own power. It has Ackermann Steering, Differential, Gear Box and Clutch, etc.

No. 2 SHIP COALER. All the movements of a real ship-coaler are reproduced in this model.

No. 3 MOTOR-CYCLE AND SIDECAR. The sidecar is of stream-line design and is mounted on springs. The motor-cycle is complete with lamps, horn, exhaust pipes, etc.

No. 4 GIANT BLOCK-SETTING CRANE. This realistic model is fitted with an accurate reproduction of Fidler's block-setting gear.

No. 5 TRAVELLING BUCKET DREDGER. In this model trucks and wagons can run underneath the chute through which falls the material raised by the dredger buckets.

No. 6 STIFF-LEG DERRICK. This model has many interesting movements, including hoisting, luffing and swivelling, which are controlled by suitable levers.

No. 7 PLATFORM SCALES. This model will weigh articles up to 4½ lbs. with remarkable accuracy.

No. 8 ROUNDABOUT. This model is most attractive when in motion. As the roundabout rotates the cars spin round and the horses rise and fall.

No. 9 BAGATELLE TABLE. This is an interesting model that will give hours of fun to the players.

No. 10 LOG SAW. In this model the saw is driven rapidly to and fro while the work table travels beneath it.

No. 11 SINGLE-CYLINDER HORIZONTAL STEAM ENGINE. Fitted with balanced crankshaft, crosshead, and centrifugal governor.

No. 12 STONE SAWING MACHINE. The model is equipped with adjustable work table and overhead trolley with self-sustaining chain hoist.

No. 13 MECCANOGRAPH. This wonderful model will draw hundreds of beautiful designs.

No. 14 GRANDFATHER CLOCK. A practical example of Meccano model-building. The model keeps accurate time.

No. 15 BALTIC TANK LOCOMOTIVE. The driving wheels are operated by an Electric Motor. An accurate reproduction of Walschaerts' Valve Gear is fitted.

No. 16 LOOM. This is perhaps the greatest Meccano success. The model weaves beautiful material.

No. 17 PLANING MACHINE. Fitted with quick-return motion.

No. 18 REVOLVING CRANE. This model is fitted with screw-operated luffing gear.

No. 19 STEAM SHOVEL. This model embodies travelling and rotating mechanisms and jib hoisting and lowering gear.

No. 21 TRANSPORTER BRIDGE. The carriage automatically travels to and fro as long as the motor is driven, pausing for a few seconds at each end of its travel.

No. 22 TRACTION ENGINE. A remarkably realistic model that will pull a boy of average weight. Fitted with two speeds.

No. 23 VERTICAL LOG SAW. While the saws are in motion, the logs are fed slowly to them.

No. 24 TRAVELLING GANTRY CRANE. The movements of this model comprise the traversing of the entire gantry, hoisting and lowering, and the traversing of the crane trolley.

No. 25 HYDRAULIC CRANE. The hydraulic ram is represented realistically by a powerful screw mechanism.

No. 26 TWIN ELLIPTIC HARMONOGRAPH. Some beautiful designs may be produced with this model.

No. 27 DRAGLINE. This imposing model of a giant excavator is fitted with travelling, luffing, slewing and dragging movements.

No. 28 PONTOON CRANE. The movements of this model include the operation of the two hoisting blocks, slewing of the entire crane, and luffing.

No. 29 HAMMERHEAD CRANE. This is a very realistic and powerful model, comprising traversing, hoisting and slewing motions.

No. 30 BREAKDOWN CRANE. This model is equipped with travelling, slewing, luffing, and hoisting motions, and also is fitted with laminated springs, brakes, out-riggers, etc.

No. 31 WAREHOUSE WITH ELEVATORS. The two cages are driven automatically and work alternately, pausing at top and bottom positions.

No. 32 TWO-CYLINDER STEAM ENGINE AND BOILER. This is a realistic working model of a complete steam plant, equipped with valve gear, governor, balanced cranks, etc.

No. 33 SINGLE AND DOUBLE FLYBOATS. These two models represent popular pleasure-fair attractions.

No. 34 THREE-ENGINE BIPLANE. This is a realistic model of an "Argosy" machine, and is fitted with ailerons, elevators and rudders.

No. 1 Leaflet.

No. 13 Leaflet.

No. 8 Leaflet.

No. 16 Leaflet.

INSTRUCTION LEAFLET PRICES.

Leaflet Nos. 3 5 6 7 8 9 10 11 12 17 18 19 21 22 23 24 25 26 28 29—United Kingdom 2d., Overseas 3d., Canada 5 cents.

Leaflet Nos. 1 2 13 14 15 16 27 30 31 32 33 34—United Kingdom 3d., Overseas 4d., Canada 8 cents.

Leaflet No. 4—United Kingdom 6d., Overseas 8d., Canada 15 cents.

MECCANO LIMITED   -   Old Swan   -   LIVERPOOL

Meccano Three-Engine Biplane

A FINE MODEL OF AN ARMSTRONG WHITWORTH "ARGOSY" THREE-ENGINE PASSENGER AIR LINER, AS BUILT FOR THE IMPERIAL AIRWAYS LONDON-PARIS SERVICE

SPECIAL FEATURES

The unit construction of the model renders wings, fuselage, tail, engines, etc., readily detachable. All controls work as on the actual machine. The three propellers are driven by a Meccano 4-volt Electric Motor mounted in the fuselage.

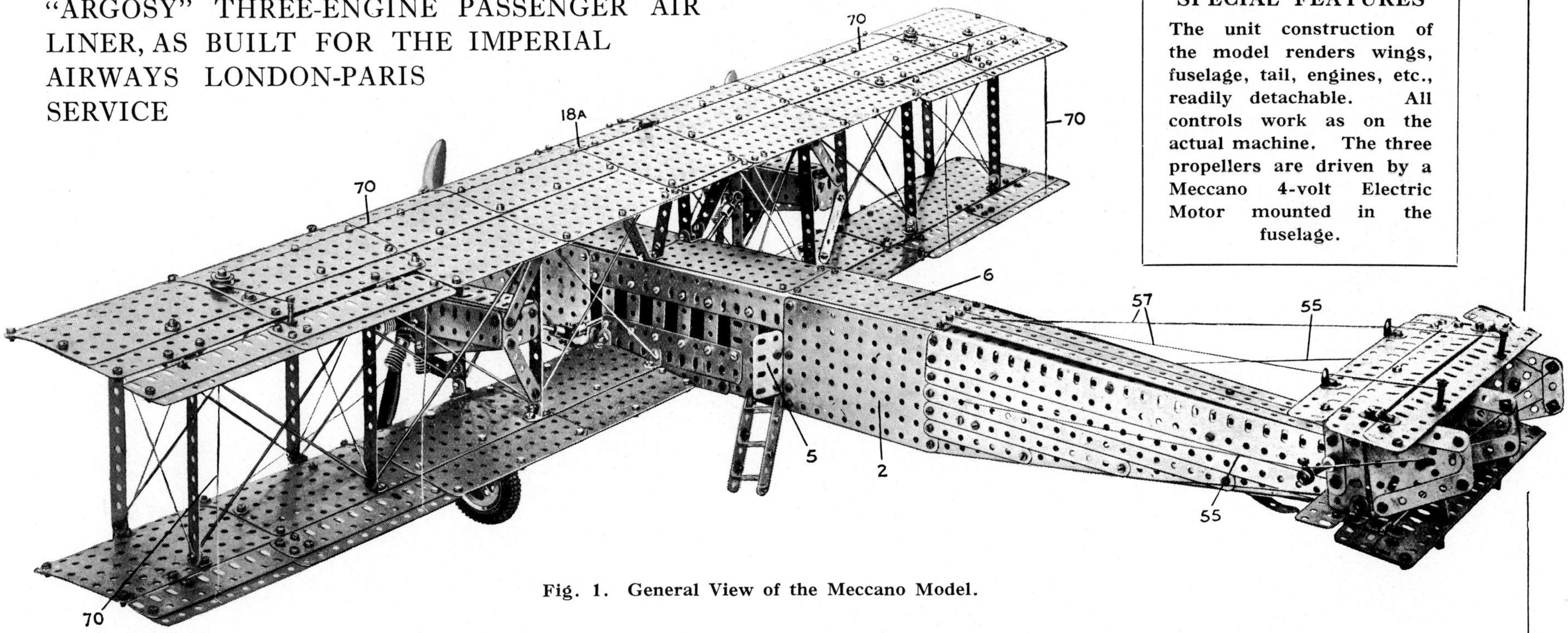

Fig. 1. General View of the Meccano Model.

THE desire to conquer the air has possessed man throughout the ages. For example, Icarus, of ancient Greek legend fame, sought to cross the Ægean Sea by fastening wings to his shoulders with wax. The sun shone so fiercely, however, that it melted the wax and Icarus forthwith did what would nowadays be described as a "nose dive," into the Ægean Sea !

Many would-be aeronauts suffered a more or less similar fate, for it was thought that successful flight could only be attained by constructing a device that imitated the actions of a bird in flight. Such machines were operated invariably by "man power," which often proved inadequate for the task and so spelt disaster !

But it was not along these lines that the conquest of the air was achieved. It was left to Lilienthal, a German who experimented with gliders, to solve successfully the problem of flight. He proved that a machine with fixed planes could be made to glide through the air. The glider was launched from a hill top or similar elevated position and flew through the air at a slight downward angle to maintain sufficient speed, making a landing some distance away. He

Published by MECCANO LTD., BINNS ROAD, LIVERPOOL

Printed in England

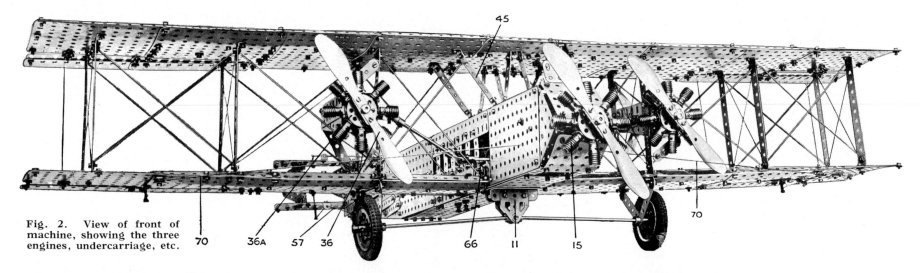

Fig. 2.   View of front of machine, showing the three engines, undercarriage, etc.

45   70   36A   57   36   66   11   15   70

made some astonishingly long flights, but eventually met with a fatal accident. Although gliders were not fitted with motors, the study of their behaviour in flight proved invaluable to the designers of the power-propelled aeroplane that was yet to come.

The rapidity with which aviation has developed, especially since the war, is one of the wonders of the twentieth century. Perhaps an idea of the tremendous strides made in aircraft design may be grasped by comparing such a machine as the Armstrong Whitworth "Argosy" type, made for Imperial Airways Limited and the prototype of the Meccano model, with say, the "Wright" aeroplane with which the first successful flight of a heavier-than-air machine was accomplished twenty-five years ago.

Features of Modern Aircraft

It has long been recognised that multi-engine aeroplanes possess a considerable advantage over the single-engine type. The former can keep on flying even if one engine stops : but the single engine machine has to come down in the event of engine failure.

The practical difficulties of employing multiple engines in aircraft are fast disappearing and it is evident that the multi-engine planes will be the aircraft of the future. The three-engine "Argosy" aeroplane, for instance, represents one of the finest examples in modern aircraft design. It is a very large machine, having a wing span of approximately 90 feet and accommodation for 20 passengers. The three Siddeley "Jaguar" engines develop 1,200 h.p., and each drives a tractor airscrew. Balanced ailerons and elevators are fitted, thereby permitting manœuvring to be carried out without undue fatigue to the pilot.

The fuselage and many other parts of the machine are of tubular steel construction. As modern research has proved conclusively, this method of construction is vastly superior to the old method of using wooden spars.

This point will be realised from the fact that a correctly shaped steel spar is nearly 25 per cent. stronger than a wooden spar weighing 20 per cent. more.

The main passenger saloon is designed on very commodious lines, being some 30 feet long and 6 feet high. Two rows of very comfortable wicker armchairs are provided, and large windows, which may be opened if desired, allow a splendid view to be obtained of the landscape when the aeroplane is in flight, besides making the saloon very light.

The total weight of each of the Argosy machines used on the "Silver Wing" service between London and Paris, is 8 tons, of which 2 tons represent paying load. A maximum speed of approximately 110 m.p.h. can be obtained, the normal cruising speed being in the neighbourhood of 95 m.p.h. This is truly a remarkable performance for so huge a machine.

The Meccano model of the "Argosy" has been designed to resemble the original as closely as possible. The ailerons, elevators and rudders are connected to their respective controls in the cockpit (in the nose of the machine) by wires, and work as in the prototype. One 4-volt Meccano Electric Motor concealed in the fuselage drives the three propellers at the armature speed of the Motor, no reduction being found necessary.

How an Aeroplane is Controlled

At this juncture it would be well to give Meccano boys a brief description of the controls of an aeroplane and the manner in which they are used.

From the bottom of the fuselage in the pilot's seat there projects a vertical bar, called the control column, or "joystick." This is pivoted about three-quarters of the way down and can be moved backward and forward and from side to side from the pivoting point. The stick controls the elevator and ailerons. The elevator is a horizontal controlling flap set parallel to the main planes at the rear of the machine and hinged so that it can be moved upward and downward. It is connected to the control column by wires so that, when the stick is pushed forward, the elevator moves downward from its hinge, thus presenting more resistance to the air when the aeroplane is in flight and sending the nose of the machine downward. When the stick is pulled back the elevator flap is raised and the nose of the machine goes up.

The control column is also connected to the aileron flaps on each of the four wings. These flaps move upward or downward according to the movements of the control column. When the stick is moved to the left, the ailerons on the right side are pulled down, setting up an additional resistance on that side and causing that wing to rise. At the same time the ailerons on the left side are slightly pulled up, assisting the downward motion of the left wing. The movement of the ailerons is slight, but sufficient to cause the machine to bank and make an effective turn.

When the lever is pushed to the right, on the other hand, the left ailerons are depressed, and those on the right slightly raised, so that the machine banks to the right.

The rudder is controlled by wires connected to the rudder bar, which is a piece of wood or metal pivoted about its centre and arranged athwartships, so that the pilot can swing it about its centre with his feet. The rudder is parallel to the fore-and-aft line of the machine when the rudder bar is square, and the machine will then fly straight, but if one side is pushed forward the rudder is swung in the same direction. For example, if the left foot is pushed forward the rudder swings to the left, more resistance to the wind being thus given on that side, so that the tail of the machine is forced to the opposite direction and the nose of the machine turns to the left. To turn the machine to any side, therefore, the foot on that side is pushed forward on the rudder bar.

In order to make a turn, however, it is not sufficient to move the rudder bar in the required direction. If the rudder only is used the machine skids, or slips outward, an effect due to the difference in speed between the inner and outer wing tips. The aeroplane must be banked so that it will not lose speed and slip outward. Thus, to make a left-hand turn the left foot is pushed forward on the rudder and at the same time the control lever is moved to the left. When the machine is to be flown level again, the control lever is pushed across again and a little past the central position, and the right foot is pressed on the rudder. The controls are then centred so that the machine flies straight and level.

These, in brief, are the actions of the controls. It would be advisable for

the reader, however, to give some consideration to the problem of what is known as the "inversion of controls."

Suppose the machine is executing a vertical turn, that is, a turn in which the aeroplane is on its side relative to the horizon. If the machine is given left rudder—which means that the left foot is pushed forward—when the aeroplane is on the turn, which we are assuming to be a left-hand one, the nose will turn toward the left wing, as it would if the machine were flying level, but, relative to the horizon, the nose will go down. If right rudder is given, the nose will go up.

Now consider the action of the elevator. If the control lever is pulled back, the nose will tend to approach the tail, as happens when the machine is flying level. But, as the machine is on its side, the action of the elevator is simply that of forcing the machine to turn, as it now occupies the position of the rudder, relative to the horizon.

Thus, on a vertical bank, the actions of the rudder and elevator are reversed—that is, the nose of the aeroplane is made to fall below or rise above the horizon by means of the rudder, and the aeroplane is made to turn by means of the elevator. In turns of 45 degrees the elevator acts, so to speak, half as rudder, and the rudder half as elevator. In steeper turns the actions of the rudder and elevator become more and more reversed.

Construction of the Fuselage

The building of the body of the model, or "fuselage," should be proceeded with first. It consists essentially of four 18½" Angle Girders 1 with four 12½"

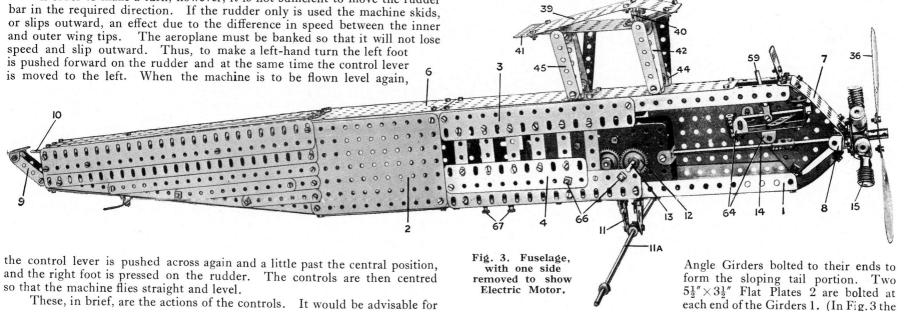

Fig. 3. Fuselage, with one side removed to show Electric Motor.

Angle Girders bolted to their ends to form the sloping tail portion. Two 5½" × 3½" Flat Plates 2 are bolted at each end of the Girders 1. (In Fig. 3 the

Plate at the front end has been removed to show the inside details of the fuselage). The saloon windows are represented by 2″ Strips bolted to a 7½″ Flat Girder 3 and also to a 5½″ Flat Girder 4, the latter being secured to another 7½″ Flat Girder that is attached to the bottom Girder 1. The construction of the windows on the opposite side of the saloon is similar to that just described, except that a door 5 (Fig. 1) consisting of a 2″ Flat Girder, is hung from the Plate 2 by means of Hinges. To accommodate the door the Flat Girders on this side are moved forward four holes and also the rearmost 2″ Strip is omitted, a 3½″ Flat Girder taking its place.

The sides of the tapering tail portion of the fuselage formed by the 12½″ Angle Girders are closed in by means of 12½″ Flat Girders and Strips, disposed as indicated in Figs. 1 and 3. The upper and lower 12½″ Angle Girders have their extreme ends held together by 1½″ Angle Girders.

The top of the fuselage is composed of 5½″ × 2½″ Flat Plates 6 bolted to the Girders 1, a space being left at the front end for the cockpit. The top of the tapering portion consists of three 12½″ Strips bolted at the rear end to a 1½″ Angle Girder that is secured across the ends of the two top 12½″ longitudinal Girders. Another 1½″ Girder is secured to the bottom pair of 12½″ Girders and two 2″ Strips 9 attached by means of Angle Brackets to this lower Angle Girder carry two Angle Brackets at the ends as shown. Two Angle Brackets 10 are secured also to the top 1½″ Angle Girder.

The bottom of the fuselage may be left open to facilitate erection, or, if preferred, it may be filled in in a similar manner to the top.

The "nose" consists of two 2½″ × 2½″ Flat Plates 7, the upper one being bolted to a 2½″ Flat Girder that is secured to the ends of the Angle Girders 1, and the other bolted directly to the end holes of the lower Angle Girders. The Plates are bent to enable their front edges to be attached by means of Flat Brackets to a 2½″ × ½″ Double Angle Strip 8. The "engine" 15, which is shown in detail in Fig. 8, is secured to the Double Angle Strip 8 by means of two ½″ Bolts passed through the holes 29a in the Bush Wheel 35. A Collar on each bolt serves to space the engine away from the Double Angle Strip.

A 2½″ × 2½″ Flat Plate on each side of the model is bolted diagonally to the end holes of the Girders 1 and to the Double Angle Strip 8 to complete

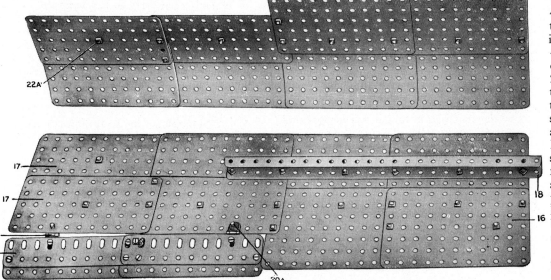

Fig. 4. Left-hand top plane "laid open" to show interior construction.

the sides of the fuselage. The controls (Fig. 6) are secured in place by means of the Angle Brackets 64 : the position in which they are bolted to the Plates 2 is shown clearly in Fig. 3.

Two Flat Trunnions 11 secured to 2½″ Angle Girders that are bolted across the bottom Girders 1 (Fig. 3) carry a Coupling, in the longitudinal bore of which two 8″ Rods 11a are secured. The Coupling is secured to the Trunnion by means of bolts that are passed through the end holes of the Trunnions and inserted in the tapped centre holes of the Coupling. A Washer is placed on the shank of each bolt between the Coupling and the Trunnion, and the bolts tightened up securely.

The centre wing section (Fig. 3) is shaped to the streamline section of the main planes and consists of two 5½″ × 3½″ Flat Plates 39, with two 2½″ Angle Girders 40 bolted between them after the manner of the Girders 18 in Fig. 4. A 3½″ Flat Girder 41 is attached to the trailing edge of these Plates. Four 2½″ Strips 42 are bolted to two Double Brackets attached to the underside of the centre section and their other ends are bolted to two pairs of Double Brackets 44 that are secured to the top of the fuselage. Four 3″ Strips 45 are bolted to the remaining portions of the Double Brackets 44. From Fig. 2 it will be seen how these Strips are arranged.

The armature spindle of the 4-volt Electric Motor carries a 1″ Gear that meshes with a second 1″ Gear 12 secured on the 4½″ Rod 13. The latter is journalled in the side plates of the Motor and projects an equal amount either side of the fuselage. The same Rod carries a 1″ Bevel meshing with a second Bevel on the Rod 14, which is journalled in a 1½″ Double Angle Strip bolted to the side plates of the Motor and connected by means of a Coupling to a 3½″ Rod journalled in the centre hole of the Bush Wheel 35 (Fig. 8) of the engine.

Construction of the Main Planes

The construction of the main planes should next be undertaken. Fig. 4 shows the construction of the top left-hand wing, Fig. 10 the complete bottom left-hand wing, whilst Fig. 5 gives the complete right-hand bottom and top wing unit, with engine, bracing wires, and interplane struts.

To describe first the construction of the portions of the dissembled top wing shown in Fig. 4. As will be seen from the illustration it is double surfaced—a feature common to all the wings—each half consisting of six $5\frac{1}{2}''$ $\times 3\frac{1}{2}''$ Flat Plates and two $5\frac{1}{2}'' \times 2\frac{1}{2}''$ Flat Plates. The Plates 16 are overlapped two holes in the direction of their length and by the same amount in regard to their width. The Plates 17, however, are overlapped one hole in length and three in width. The edges of the $3\frac{1}{2}'' \times 5\frac{1}{2}''$ Flat Plates forming the leading edges of the top and bottom halves are curved slightly, so that when they are bolted together the complete wing has a streamline section as in an actual aeroplane wing. (The profile of the centre section 39, Fig. 3, gives a good idea of the shape that the main planes, in section, should present).

The two halves of the wing may now be bolted together, $\frac{3}{8}''$ Bolts being used to draw the leading edges of the Plates together whilst ordinary bolts are used for the trailing edges of the Plates 16. The aileron 19, consisting of four $5\frac{1}{2}''$ Flat Girders, is hung from the trailing edges of the $2\frac{1}{2}'' \times 5\frac{1}{2}''$ Flat Plates 17 by means of Hinges 20. It will be found that when the two halves of the wing are fitted together there is a space between the trailing edges of the Plates 17. Therefore it is necessary to place four Washers—two on each side of the Hinge—on the $\frac{3}{8}''$ Bolt 20a (see also Fig. 4). The Hinge nearest the tip is merely bolted direct to the top of the wing surface.

It should be apparent from the various illustrations that from the end of the $12\frac{1}{2}''$ Angle Girders 18 the upper and lower wing surfaces

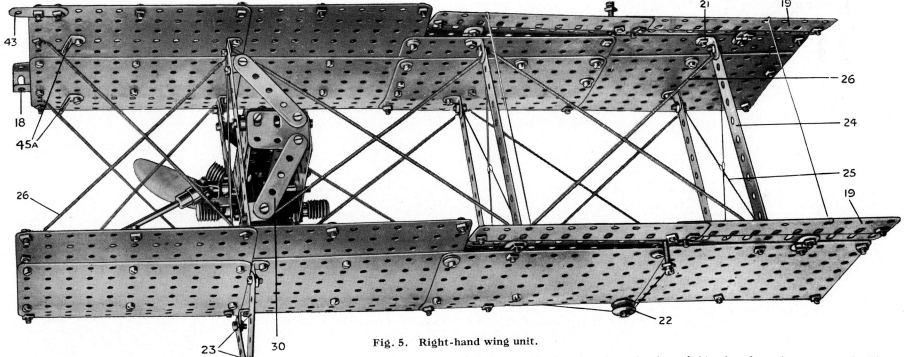

Fig. 5. Right-hand wing unit.

A channel section girder 18, composed of two $12\frac{1}{2}''$ Angle Girders, is bolted to either the top or bottom half of the wing, in the fourth row of holes from the leading edge. It will be observed that the end of the Girder projects one hole from the edges of the Plates 16. The various Angle Brackets for the attachment of the interplane struts should be bolted to the bottom half (see Figs. 1, 2 and 5 for the correct location of these Angle Brackets), and a $\frac{1}{2}''$ loose Pulley is attached to the top half by means of a $\frac{1}{2}''$ Bolt that is held in place by nuts on each side of the Plate (see Fig. 1). The Pulley is free on the bolt, of course.

taper towards the wing tips. In view of this, therefore, the curve on the Plates should gradually diminish toward the wing tips and such bolts that project inside the wings near the wing tips require their shanks to be shortened by placing Washers under their heads. The right-hand top wing is made in a precisely similar manner, of course.

As regards the construction of the lower wings the main features are the same as in the case of the top wings, but each one is only $4\frac{1}{2}''$ wide as compared with the $5\frac{1}{2}''$ of the top ones : they are also $\frac{1}{2}''$ longer. The upper and lower surface of each bottom wing consists of four $5\frac{1}{2}'' \times 3\frac{1}{2}''$ Flat Plates (Fig. 10) all overlapped one hole, thus giving the extra $\frac{1}{2}''$ in length compared with the

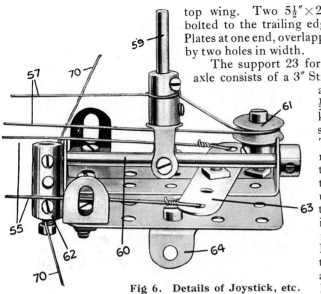

Fig 6. Details of Joystick, etc.

top wing. Two $5\frac{1}{2}'' \times 2\frac{1}{2}''$ Flat Plates are bolted to the trailing edges of the $5\frac{1}{2}'' \times 3\frac{1}{2}''$ Plates at one end, overlapping the latter Plates by two holes in width.

The support 23 for the landing wheel axle consists of a $3''$ Strip and a $2\frac{1}{2}''$ Strip, and is attached by $\frac{1}{2}'' \times \frac{1}{2}''$ Angle Brackets to the bottom surface of the wing. The Angle Brackets must be bolted to the wings before the latter are closed up, of course, a fact that should be borne in mind also with regard to the Angle Brackets to which the interplane struts are attached. The loose Pulley 22 is attached by means of a $\frac{1}{2}''$ Bolt in the front row of the holes as shown in Figs. 2, 5 and 10.

The Wing Engines

Each wing engine is housed in a nacelle or casing (Fig. 7) which is constructed as follows. The top of the nacelle consists of a $3\frac{1}{2}''$ Flat Girder 27, to the edges of which two $3\frac{1}{2}''$ Angle Girders are bolted. Each side consists of $3\frac{1}{2}''$ Flat Girders arranged in the manner shown, the bottom edges being connected together by a $1\frac{1}{2}'' \times \frac{1}{2}''$ Double Angle Strip. An Angle Bracket is secured to the centre hole of this Double Angle Strip, and two further Angle Brackets are secured to the front edges of the side Flat Girders as indicated in the figure. Three $\frac{3}{8}''$ Bolts 29 are bolted to these Angle Brackets.

The back of the nacelle is formed by a $1\frac{1}{2}''$ Flat Girder attached by Angle Brackets to the top of the nacelle (see Fig. 5). Two $2\frac{1}{2}''$ Strips 30 are attached to the $1\frac{1}{2}''$ Flat Girder, and two $2''$ Strips 32 are secured also by Angle Brackets to the front end. The nacelle is attached by the $\frac{3}{8}''$ Bolts 31 to the $5\frac{1}{2}''$ Strips 24 that form two of the interplane struts, two Washers being placed on each bolt for spacing purposes.

The $2''$ Rod 33 is journalled in the Flat Girders composing the sides of the nacelle, and carries a $\frac{7}{8}''$ Bevel 34, which is intended to mesh with a second Bevel that is secured to a $1\frac{1}{2}''$ Rod journalled in the centre hole of the Bush Wheel 35 (Fig. 8). Eight Angle Brackets are arranged round the periphery of the Bush Wheel and carry the Worms representing the cylinders, which are attached to the Angle Brackets by $\frac{3}{8}''$ Bolts. A Bush Wheel 36a (Fig. 2) is secured to the $1\frac{1}{2}''$ Rod close to the Angle Brackets and, lastly, the propeller 36, consisting of two Propeller Blades bolted to a Double-arm Crank, is secured in position on the Rod. The $\frac{3}{8}''$ Bolts 29 bolted to the Angle Brackets on the

nacelle are passed through the holes 29a in the Bush Wheel 35, nuts holding the latter in place. The left-hand wing engine nacelle is shown in Fig. 7 : the other for the right-hand wing is exactly similar.

Having made all the wings and also the two engine nacelles it remains only to assemble them into a complete unit as shown in Fig. 5. The interplane struts 24 are attached to the Angle Brackets 21 by nuts and bolts, the latter serving also to secure the various "bracing wires." The Loom Heads 25 prevent fore and aft movement of the struts, whilst the Spring Cord 26 is intended to brace the planes in a vertical direction. The complete unit should now appear as in Fig. 5.

The Controls

The controls, consisting of the rudder bar 63 and the joystick 59, are mounted together on a $2\frac{1}{2}'' \times 2\frac{1}{2}''$ Flat Plate for convenience in fixing them in the fuselage.

The joystick is a $1\frac{1}{2}''$ Rod held in the boss of a Swivel Bearing. The latter's "spider" is secured to the $3''$ Rod 60, which is journalled in a $2\frac{1}{2}'' \times \frac{1}{2}''$ Double Angle Strip bolted to the Flat Plate and carries a Coupling 62 secured to one of its ends. The $\frac{1}{2}''$ loose Pulley 61 is journalled on a $\frac{3}{4}''$ Bolt attached to the Plate by two nuts, and is retained in position on the bolt by means of a Collar. The rudder bar 63 consists of a $2\frac{1}{2}''$ Strip that is attached pivotally by means of a lock-nutted bolt (see Standard Mechanism No. 262) to the $2\frac{1}{2}'' \times 2\frac{1}{2}''$ Flat Plate. The $\frac{1}{2}'' \times \frac{1}{2}''$ Angle Brackets 64 are for the purpose of attaching the Flat Plate to the side Plates of the fuselage in the position indicated in Fig. 3.

The landing wheels each consist of two $2''$ Pulleys 65 (Fig. 9) that are held rigidly together by $\frac{1}{2}''$ Bolts and nuts, a Collar on each bolt spacing the Pulleys the required distance apart. The Wheels are shod with two $2''$ Dunlop Tyres, which are sprung in the groove formed between the two Pulleys.

The Tail Unit

As will be seen from Fig. 11, both the upper and lower elevators (fixed and moving) of the tail unit are exactly similar in construction : therefore the description of one should suffice to make the whole clear. The fixed portion of the elevator consists of a $7\frac{1}{2}''$ Flat Girder 47 and another Flat Girder 46 $8\frac{1}{2}''$ in length (obtained by bolting

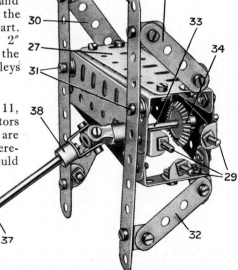

Fig. 7. Left-hand wing Engine nacelle.

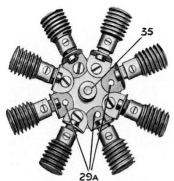

Fig. 8. One of the three Engines.

a 1½″ Flat Girder to one end of a 7½″ Girder). The two Girders are connected together at each end by means of Flat Brackets, a 1½″ Strip lending additional support in the centre. The longer Girder 46 overlaps the shorter one by one hole at each end.

The movable portion of each elevator consists of a 9½″ Flat Girder with 2″ Flat Girders bolted at right angles to its ends. It is attached to its respective fixed portion by Hinges 49. The two units—consisting of one fixed and moving plane—are spaced apart by 2½″ Flat Girders 50 attached by means of ½″ × ½″ Angle Brackets to the Flat Girders 47. Bolted to the Flat Girders 50 are Hinges to which the rudders 51 are attached. The rudders each consist of a 2½″ Triangular Plate, along the edges of which two 2½″ Strips and a 1½″ Strip are bolted.

Double-arm Cranks 53 are bolted to the two outside 2½″ Flat Girders 50, and Collars 54 are secured on the ends of 1½″ Rods held in the bosses of the Double-arm Cranks. The rudder wires 55 are to be taken round the shanks of ordinary bolts that are inserted in the set-screw holes of the Collars 54.

Two ¾″ Bolts 56 are attached to the moving portion of each elevator at the extreme trailing edge. The control wires 57 are secured to these bolts, and are led through guides 58 consisting of Angle Brackets bolted to the leading edges of the Flat Girders 46.

Erecting the Model

Having completed the various portions of the model it remains now to erect them in their respective positions. The first step is to attach the tail unit to the fuselage. It is bolted firmly to the Angle Brackets on the ends of the Strips 9 and to the Angle Brackets 10 at the end of the fuselage (Fig. 3) and should appear as in Fig. 1. Two wires 55 are now fixed to the rudder bar (one at each end), led along inside the fuselage for some distance, and then passed out through each side. They are taken round the bolts on the Collars 54 and attached to the rudders 51, the wires connecting all three together so that the movement of the rudders synchronise.

Short lengths of wire 57 are passed through the guides 58 and secured to

the ¾″ Bolts 56 on each elevator plane. The other ends of each pair of wires are connected together (see Fig. 1). Another length of wire is clamped to the joystick between the boss of the Swivel Bearing and the Collar (see Fig. 6). One end of this wire is led round the Pulley 61 (Fig. 6) and thence out through the top of the fuselage and connected to the wire yoke 57 of the upper elevator (see Fig. 1), while the other end is taken directly to the yoke of the lower elevator. If the length of the wire 57 is adjusted correctly by means of "strainers" the elevators will rise and fall in accordance with the movements of the joystick. The elevators cause the actual machine to rise or dip whilst the rudders direct its course to left or right.

Attaching the Wing Units to the Fuselage

Each bottom wing has two ½″ × ½″ Angle Brackets bolted to its upper surface at the end nearest the side of the fuselage. These Brackets are slipped on to the ⅜″ Bolts 66 bolted to the side of the fuselage (see Figs. 2 and 3). The projecting end of the Girder 18 (Fig. 5) should now be pushed into the centre section so that the Girder 18 is in line with the Girder 40 (Fig. 3), and the holes in the Girder 18 in line with those in the Plates 39 in order that a 1″ Threaded Rod 18a (Fig. 1) may be passed through the holes. The Threaded Rod is retained in place by nuts on its ends. The trailing edge of each wing is connected to the Flat Girder 41 of the centre section by the Strip 43 (Fig. 5), and the ends of the Strips 45 bolted to the Angle Brackets 45a (Figs. 2, 3 and 5).

The ends of the landing wheel axles 11a are supported in the Strips 23: the landing wheels are placed on the ends of the axles and retained in place by Collars.

Fixing the Aileron Controls

The top wing ailerons are connected together by a length of wire 70 (Fig. 1) that is attached to ¾″ Bolts secured to the trailing edges of the ailerons and passed round the ½″ Pulleys on the top surface of the wings. The length of the wire is so adjusted by means of a "strainer" that it is taut when both ailerons are perfectly level in relation to the main plane surface.

The upper ailerons are connected by short lengths of wire 70 to the lower ailerons, to transmit the motion of the former to the latter. The length

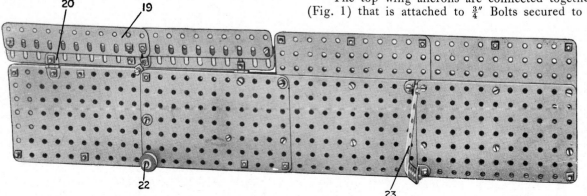

Fig. 10. Underside of left-hand bottom plane.

Fig. 9. Landing Wheel with tyre removed.

of these wires must be such that the upper and lower ailerons are parallel with one another.

A further length of wire 70 is attached to the bolt held in the end of the Coupling 62 (Fig. 6) and its ends are passed through the holes in the side Plates of the fuselage. Thence they are led round the Pulleys 22 on the bottom wing (Fig. 2) and fastened to the $\frac{3}{4}''$ Bolts that are bolted to the under surfaces of the lower ailerons. The length of the wires must be so adjusted by means of the strainers incorporated in each of them, that when the joystick is in a vertical position, the ailerons are level with the main plane surfaces.

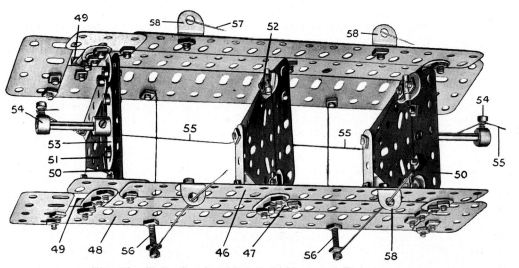

Fig. 11. Tail, showing hinged Rudders and Elevators, etc.

Therefore any side-to-side movement of the joystick should result in an up and down movement of the ailerons—those on one side of the machine moving downward whilst those on the opposite side move upward simultaneously.

The fact that one aileron is inclined downward and the other upward produces a couple that tends to roll the actual machine about its longitudinal axis. This is known as "banking," a manoeuvre that is neccessary when turning the machine in either direction. It is also necessary to operate the ailerons frequently while the machine is in flight, in order to maintain equilibrium and counteract sudden gusts of wind, etc.

Mention has been made of "strainers" incorporated in the various

control wires to adjust their length, and hence their tension, very minutely. To make a suitable strainer, the control wire requiring such an addition is cut and a loop made on each of the cut ends. A $\frac{1}{2}''$ Bolt is passed through the loops of the wire and a nut placed on the end of the bolt. By turning the bolt the nut is made to advance or recede up the shank of the bolt, so altering the tension of the control wire.

Thin wire obtained from any ironmongers or stores for an inconsiderable sum is used for all the control wires on this model. Meccano Cord is not suitable, as it stretches considerably and would prevent satisfactory working of the model.

To connect up the drive from the Electric Motor to the wing engines, the Universal Couplings 38 (Fig. 7) are secured to each end of the Rod 13 (Figs. 2, 3). All three propellers are driven at the speed of the armature of the Motor, as the ratios existing between the various gears is unity.

Two terminals 67 are provided on the bottom of the fuselage (see Fig. 3) to form a convenient means of attaching the leads from a 4-volt Meccano Accumulator. The shanks of the terminals are 6 B.A. Bolts (part No. 304) secured to and insulated from the fuselage by 6 B.A. Nuts (part No. 305) with Insulating Bushes and Washers (parts Nos. 302 and 303). The terminals are connected to those on the Motor by short lengths of wire.

Parts required to build the Three-Engine Biplane

6 of No. 1	4 of No. 9b	2 of No. 16a	489 of No. 37	5 of No. 62b	11 of No. 103d	4 of No. 140
2 ,, 1a	4 ,, 9d	1 ,, 16b	74 ,, 37a	3 ,, 63	4 ,, 103f	1 ,, 165
14 ,, 2	2 ,, 9f	2 ,, 17	2 ,, 37b	22 ,, 70	5 ,, 103g	2 ,, 302
2 ,, 3	12 ,, 10	3 ,, 18a	42 ,, 38	5 ,, 72	3 ,, 103h	2 ,, 303
6 ,, 4	6 ,, 11	4 ,, 20a	6 ,, 41	3 ,, 76	7 ,, 103k	2 ,, 304
20 ,, 5	86 ,, 12	5 ,, 23	3 ,, 48	2 ,, 82	9 ,, 111	2 ,, 305
18 ,, 6	2 ,, 13a	6 ,, 24	2 ,, 48a	12 ,, 101	3 ,, 111a	2 ,, 306
10 ,, 6a	1 ,, 14	6 ,, 30	46 ,, 52a	18 ,, 103	56 ,, 111c	8 ,, 312
4 ,, 7a	2 ,, 15a	2 ,, 31	15 ft. ,, 58	2 ,, 103a	20 ,, 114	1 Electric
12 ,, 8	3 ,, 16	24 ,, 32	8 ,, 59	4 ,, 103b	2 ,, 126a	Motor

Model No. 7.11

Level-Luffing
Automatic Grabbing Crane

Fig. 1.   The prototype of the Meccano model

SPECIAL FEATURES

Outstanding features of the crane include the Toplis level luffing gear, the crank-operated balanced jib, and the single suspension grab, which is raised, lowered, opened or closed by operating the hoisting barrel.

The four movements of hoisting, slewing, travelling and luffing are all driven at will from a 6-volt Motor through an efficient gear box. The Motor obtains its current supply from a Meccano 6-volt 20 amp. Accumulator carried in the swivelling superstructure, and its speed is regulated by means of a neat built-up 6-notch controller. A novel automatic servo brake is provided for the hoisting barrel.

IN the ordinary type of crane a considerable amount of power is necessary to raise the jib on account of its weight and the effect of the load. How the load affects the operation may be easily demonstrated by means of a Meccano crane. If the jib is luffed in and out with the hoisting barrel "braked," the load will be found to rise and fall also, so that power has to be expended in this direction as well as in lifting the dead-weight of the jib. In practice this means an increase in running costs, especially in the case of cranes engaged in the handling of ships' cargoes, etc., where it is necessary to luff the jib almost continuously.

In order to eliminate some of this waste of power, many cranes are fitted with balanced jibs and level luffing gears. The balanced jib gets over the difficulty of the dead-weight of the jib, whilst the level luffing gear counteracts the effect of the load by making the crane hook maintain always the same height from the ground whilst the jib is being luffed. Hence the luffing motor only has to overcome friction, so that the motor can be of much lower power than is necessary with the ordinary non-compensated crane. Also it will be readily appreciated that the driver can handle a load with a much clearer conception of its path when it follows a horizontal course instead of a constantly varying one.

One of the simplest and most efficient balanced-jib level luffing systems and one, therefore, that goes a large way to reducing running and maintenance costs, is the "Toplis" gear, which is the type reproduced in the Meccano model. In order to make matters quite clear to the reader we show in Fig. 9 a line drawing of the layout of the "Toplis" gear. The hoisting rope passes up from the hoist barrel to a pulley in the superstructure head B. From here it passes round one of the pulleys at the jib head A, back round the remaining pulley at B, and lastly over the second pulley at A, and so down to the load.

Now the point B is such a distance above the jib pivot that when the jib head A rises through, say, 3", the distance AB decreases by 1". Owing to the fact, however, that there are three falls of the hoisting rope passing between A and B, the shortening of the distance AB by 1" means that the end of the rope to which the hook is attached is paid out 3". Hence the load remains level throughout the entire luffing range.

Another common feature of most cranes is that the jib is luffed by a rope or ropes that are wound upon a barrel, but in the case of the

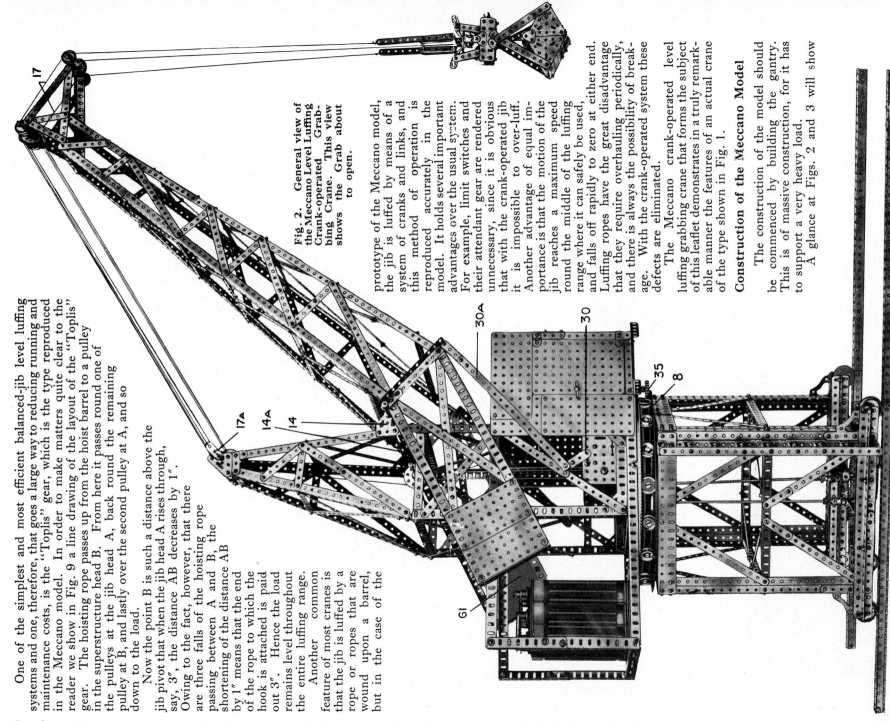

Fig. 2. General view of the Meccano Level Luffing Crank-operated Grabbing Crane. This view shows the Grab about to open.

prototype of the Meccano model, the jib is luffed by means of a system of cranks and links, and this method of operation is reproduced accurately in the model. It holds several important advantages over the usual system. For example, limit switches and their attendant gear are rendered unnecessary, since it is obvious that with the crank-operated jib it is impossible to over-luff. Another advantage of equal importance is that the motion of the jib reaches a maximum speed round the middle of the luffing range where it can safely be used, and falls off rapidly to zero at either end. Luffing ropes have the great disadvantage that they require overhauling periodically, and there is always the possibility of breakage. With the crank-operated system these defects are eliminated.

The Meccano crank-operated level luffing grabbing crane that forms the subject of this leaflet demonstrates in a truly remarkable manner the features of an actual crane of the type shown in Fig. 1.

Construction of the Meccano Model

The construction of the model should be commenced by building the gantry. This is of massive construction, for it has to support a very heavy load.

A glance at Figs. 2 and 3 will show

that the four main supporting girders 1 are each composed of a 12½″ Angle Girder and two 12½″ Strips, bolted together so as to give an "L" Section to the girder, which is one of the shapes best calculated to resist effectively the crushing or compressive stresses to which these members are subjected. The bottoms of the girders are attached near the ends of the girders 2, in which the road wheel axles are journalled. Each girder 2 consists of two 12½″ Angle Girders bolted together to resemble in section the letter "T"—a form that easily resists the stresses set up in this part of the structure. Architraves are employed to strengthen the connections between the girders 1 and 2.

It will be realised that the top cross girders or "beams," to which the lower portion of the Geared Roller Race 8 is bolted, are subjected to severe downward-acting bending stresses due to the weight of the crane proper. Consequently, each beam consists of a 9½″ Angle Girder to the downward flange of which is secured a Flat Girder of similar length. This construction, by strengthening the flanges, reduces the tendency of the lower edges of the Girders to tear asunder.

Having reached this stage of the construction, it will be found that the gantry is still far from rigid in spite of the strength of its main members. In fact, if the base be held firmly, it is possible to push the top horizontally in nearly every direction. This defect is due to a lack of strength at the corners and in order to obtain the required rigidity it is necessary to add to the structure diagonal corner "ties." The various ties in the model take the form of Strips. As in the actual crane, the forces at work are always pulling on the ends of the ties in the model, and each tie is pulling against its neighbour, or an opposing external force, so that it may be said that a continual tug-of-war is taking place, in which neither side gains the advantage, unless a bolt pulls out or a tie breaks !

Fig. 3.   View of Gantry from underneath, showing method of driving the wheels.

The idler travelling wheels are secured to Rods that are journalled in the slots of the girders 2 so that they are free to rise and fall therein, but the driving wheel axles are journalled in Strips that are bolted over the slots of the girders.   In this manner the whole weight of the model is thrown on to the driving wheels, so ensuring proper adhesion of the wheels on the rails.

The arrangement of the drive to the travelling wheels is identical on each side of the gantry, and the construction is as follows : A Rod 7 carries on its end a $\frac{7}{8}$″ Bevel, which is in mesh with a similar Gear on a 1″ Rod that is journalled in 2½″ Strips 3 and in a Coupling 5 on the Rod 7. The Coupling is, of course, quite free on the Rod, and the 2½″ Strips 3 (which are trebled for strength) are bolted across a 9½″ Flat Girder 10. The latter is attached to 4½″ Angle Girders that are secured to the top flanges of the girders 2.

The other end of the 1″ Rod is fitted with a Universal Coupling 4, and this is connected by an 8″ Rod 6 to a further Universal Coupling. The latter, in turn, is secured to a Rod that is journalled in a 2½″ × 1″ Double Angle Strip and in the Geared Roller Race and carries a ½″ Pinion. The Pinion is in constant mesh with a second Pinion 9a, which is secured to a Rod 9 (Fig. 4) that passes completely through both the upper and lower Roller Races. It will be seen that by rotating the Rod 9, the Rods 7 are both driven at the same speed via the train of three ½″ Pinions, the universally-jointed Rods 6, and the $\frac{7}{8}$″ Bevels. The drive is transmitted finally to the wheels by Sprocket Chain, which passes over $\frac{3}{4}$″ and 1″ Sprocket Wheels secured on the Rods 7 and the wheel axles. Before laying the gantry aside and continuing with the construction of the model, it is important to see that the transmission works as freely as possible. Bearings and gears should be oiled lightly, and small adjustments made if necessary with this end in view.

The Swivelling Superstructure

As will be seen from Fig. 4, the swivelling superstructure is built upon the upper portion of the slewing race 8. The two side members are 18½" Angle Girders 11 and they are joined by 9½" Angle Girders 12 at the points shown, and also at the rear by a similar Girder. The Girders 12 are secured firmly to the Race by means of 5½" Angle Girders. The vertical 12½" Girders 13 comprising side members of the tower are attached to 5½" Angle Girders on the side Girders 11 and the points of attachment are strengthened by means of Corner Brackets.

The pulleys 15 and 16 and the 1½" Strips 17a are mounted loosely on a Rod that is journalled in Corner Brackets at the top of the tower to which they are attached by 2½" Strips and Flat Brackets. The pulleys 15 are 1" fast Pulleys, which are spaced from the centre pair (1" loose Pulleys) by Collars and Washers, and guards to keep the hoisting cord in the grooves of the pulleys 16 are formed from 2½" Strips. Suitable bracing is added to the tower as indicated in the illustration.

The construction of the gear cabin should be fairly clear from the general view, with the exception of the roof, which is composed of three 5½"×2½" Flanged Plates and one 5½"×2½" Flat Plate. The rear portion of the cabin is left uncovered owing to the lack of plates in the No. 7 Outfit, but the constructor can easily obtain the necessary extra plates to fill in the whole cabin or even cardboard answers the purpose very well.

The Construction of the Jib

The main constructional features of the jib may be seen fairly clearly by a careful study of Fig. 2. The two lower longitudinal side members each consist of one 24½" and one 12½" Angle Girder overlapped eight holes, whilst each of the upper longitudinal members is composed of one 24½" and one 9½" Angle Girder overlapped 2 holes. The bottom end of the jib is extended at an angle to the main portion by 12½" Angle Girders, the ends of which are connected together by 4½"×2½" Flat Plates.

The upper extremity of the jib is extended by 7½" Angle Girders that are bolted to the end holes of the side members, and a 7½" Strip is placed over the slotted holes of each Girder in order to give a neat appearance. Bracing should now be added to the sides as shown, care being taken to ensure

Fig. 4. The Superstructure and upper Slewing Race

that the various Strips are disposed exactly as indicated in the illustration.

The completed sides may now be joined together. This is effected at the bottom end by girders, each of which is 10 inches long (one 5½" and one 7½" Angle Girder overlapped six holes) and is bolted to the top and bottom sides of the jib, 2" in front of the jib pivot pin 14a.

The extremities of the two upper longitudinal members of the jib are connected by a 3½" Angle Girder and those of the lower members are joined by a 3" Angle Girder. Having in this manner determined the taper of the jib, it is a simple matter to bolt into place intermediate cross-members of the correct length and then to add the bracing. The latter is triangulated, which makes the jib very strong, and yet permits of light construction.

The jib head has two distinct sets of pulleys. One set is at the extreme end of the jib and consists of a 1½" Pulley secured to a Rod that has a 1" fast Pulley mounted loosely on either extremity. The other set comprises three pairs of Pulleys on a common rod. The centre pair comprises two 1" loose Pulleys, on each side of which are placed Flat Trunnions to act as guards for the hoisting rope, and each of the two remaining sets consists of a 1" fast and a 1" loose Pulley. The respective groups are spaced on the Rod by Collars and Washers, and the bosses of the fast Pulleys serve to keep the Pulleys away from the supporting frame, so that all may run freely.

Construction of the Gear Box

The gear box (Fig. 5) enables the four movements of hoisting, slewing, travelling and luffing to be driven from the 6-volt Meccano Electric Motor merely by the operation of two levers. A point worthy of note is the fact that it forms a self-contained unit that is readily fitted into the model.

The 5½" Angle Girders 18, 18a, are butt-jointed together so that their vertical flanges point in opposite directions, the left-hand pair being bolted to a 5½"×2½" Flanged Plate, whilst the right-hand pair are connected together by means of a 2" Strip. The Girders 18a also are secured at right-angles to, and two holes from either end of, a 9½" Angle Girder that will eventually be secured to the ends of the Girders 11 (see Fig. 4). Cross girders, each 7½" long, are bo..ed across the Girders 18, 18a to carry the centre plate 19 and the right-hand plate of the gear box, and a 5½" Angle Girder 20. The centre plate 19 is a 5½"×2½" Flat Plate and it is secured to the cross girders by a 5½" Angle Girder.

Having now completed the constructional part of the gear box, we may turn our attention to the gearing. The mainshaft 21, which is driven by the Motor, has secured to it a 1" Gear in mesh with a similar Gear on the Motor, and also a $\frac{1}{2}''$ diameter $\frac{1}{2}''$ wide Pinion. On each side of the mainshaft are two sliding layshafts 22 and 23, each of which carries a $\frac{3}{4}''$ Pinion and a 57-teeth Gear, the latter being in constant mesh with the $\frac{1}{2}''$ wide Pinion on the mainshaft.

The layshaft 22 is moved in its bearings by the Crank 36, which is secured on an 8″ Rod that carries the lever 37. The layshaft 23 is actuated in a similar manner by the lever 39 through the medium of the Crank 38. Both Cranks carry bolts, the shanks of which locate between Collars spaced a short distance apart on the Rods.

By sliding the layshaft 23 to the right the $\frac{3}{4}''$ Pinion is brought into engagement with a 50-teeth Gear 26. This Gear is secured to a Rod carrying a $\frac{3}{4}''$ Contrate that is in mesh with a $\frac{3}{4}''$ Pinion on a Rod 41. The latter is journalled in a Flat Trunnion that is bolted to the front top edge of the gear box and also in one of the $5\frac{1}{2}'' \times 3\frac{1}{2}''$ Flat Plates forming the front of the cabin. It has secured to it a $\frac{1}{2}''$ Bevel, and this meshes with a $1\frac{1}{2}''$ Bevel on a short vertical Rod on the lower extremity of which is fixed the Pinion 35 that meshes with the teeth of the fixed slewing Race 8 (see Fig. 2). When the Pinion 35 rotates, it runs round the circumference of the Race and thus causes the model to slew.

A reinforced bearing is provided for the Rod carrying the Bevel and the Pinion 35 by bolting a $7\frac{1}{2}''$ Girder across the Girders 18a beneath the floor plates. The Rod also passes through the end hole of a Strip that is bolted to the upper member of the slewing race.

On moving the layshaft 23 to the left the $\frac{3}{4}''$ Pinion is brought into mesh with a 50-teeth Gear 27 on the hoisting barrel shaft. The hoisting barrel 31 consists of a Sleeve Piece, one end of which is passed over a $\frac{1}{2}''$ fast Pulley secured against the face of the 50-teeth Gear, and it is held firmly in place by means of a $\frac{3}{4}''$ Flanged Wheel that is pushed on to its other end.

The hoisting barrel is fitted with a novel automatic servo brake that allows the load to be hoisted with perfect freedom, but applies the brake when the barrel tends to unwind. An unequal-armed crank, composed of a 2″ Strip bolted to a Double Arm Crank, is fitted on the end of a Rod that is journalled in the gear box sideplate and in the $5\frac{1}{2}''$ Angle Girder 20. The Rod may be operated by the lever 33 that is secured to it by a Coupling ; by raising the lever the brake is released. A short length of cord is passed round the brake drum 32 and its ends tied to the shanks of bolts on the extremities of the crank. The automatic servo effect is accounted for by the fact that the points of attachment of the brake band to the crank are at different distances from the fulcrum.

A 50-teeth Gear 25 is secured to a Rod that also carries a $\frac{1}{2}''$ Pinion. The latter will mesh eventually (when the gear box is mounted in place) with a $1\frac{1}{2}''$ Contrate on the upper end of the Rod 9 (see Fig. 4). In this manner the drive will be transmitted from the gear box to the wheels.

The last movement to be considered is that of luffing the jib. The luffing cranks 30 are secured on the extremities of an $11\frac{1}{2}''$ Rod 29, which has secured to it a $\frac{3}{4}''$ Contrate that meshes with a $\frac{1}{2}''$ Pinion 28 on a short vertical Rod. The latter has a further $\frac{1}{2}''$ Pinion that meshes with a Worm on the Rod carrying the 50-teeth Gear 24. The Rod with the Pinion 28 is journalled at its bottom end in a Strip, and at its upper end in a Corner Bracket that is attached to the Flanged Plate by a $1\frac{1}{2}''$ Angle Girder. One of the bolts that serve to secure the $1\frac{1}{2}''$ Angle Girder to the Plate is also passed through a $2\frac{1}{2}''$ Angle Girder, which is bolted vertically to the Plate for strengthening purposes.

The Electrical Equipment of the Model

There are only two items that claim our attention under this heading, the Motor and its gearing, and the built-up controller, which enables six different speeds to be obtained from the Motor.

Fig. 5   Plan view of Gear Box.   Its simplicity of design is clearly apparent

The Motor is secured to the floor plates in the position indicated in Fig. 5, by nuts and bolts and by a $\frac{1}{2}'' \times \frac{1}{2}''$ Angle Bracket 40. A gear train providing a reduction ratio of 9 : 1 and consisting of two $\frac{1}{2}''$ Pinions and two 57-teeth Gears is employed to transmit the drive from the armature spindle to the Rod carrying the 1" Gear.

The controller is shown at 34 and is conveniently placed in relation to the other controls ; it is of exceptional interest as it is built up entirely from standard Meccano parts. Space precludes anything but a brief description of the device, but readers who require fuller information on the point should refer to detail No. 115 in the Standard Mechanisms Manual.

The resistance is formed from a short length of Spring Cord, drawn out so that no two adjacent turns touch, and attached to the shanks of 6 B.A. Bolts that are insulated from the Bush Wheel on which they are mounted by Insulating Bushes and Washers. A seventh insulated stud is provided ; it is not connected in any way, since it forms the "off" position of the controller. The switch arm is a Double Arm Crank, on one end of which is mounted a Spring Buffer that makes contact with the studs. The Bush Wheel is mounted on a Rod, the upper extremity of which forms a pivot for the Double Arm Crank, its lower end being secured in the boss of a Bush Wheel that is bolted to the floor.

A length of insulated wire is taken from one Motor terminal to one end of the resistance, and the other terminal of the Motor is connected to one terminal of the Accumulator. The remaining terminal of the latter is "earthed," that is, connected to the frame of the model. If coloured parts are used, it may be found necessary to remove the enamel from beneath the bolt holding the earth wire to the frame and also beneath the bolts securing the controller to the floor plates.

Final Assembly of the Model

We now come to the most interesting stage of the construction, that of fitting together the various units to form the complete model. The gear box unit should be first fixed into position on the Girders 11 and 12 and between the Girders 13. This is accomplished by arranging the holes a, b, c (Fig. 5) of the gear box to coincide with similar indexed holes on the Girders 11 and 12 (Fig. 4). Bolts should then be inserted in these holes.

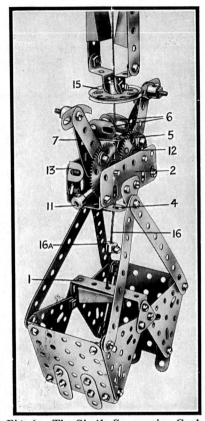

Fig. 6. The Single Suspension Grab

It will be necessary to remove the Rod 29 temporarily before sliding the gear box into place.

The superstructure is now lowered on to the $\frac{3}{4}''$ Flanged Wheels of the Ring Frame. The Rod 9 passes freely through both Races, of course, and has secured to its upper end the $1\frac{1}{2}''$ Contrate that meshes with the $\frac{1}{2}''$ Pinion on the shaft carrying the Gear 25. The upper Race should bed down quite evenly on the $\frac{3}{4}''$ Flanged Wheels and the complete superstructure should turn at a touch. The Pinion 35 must also be arranged to mesh with the teeth of the lower Race.

The jib is mounted pivotally on the front of the tower by passing the $11\frac{1}{2}''$ Rod 14a through the Flat Trunnions 14 and through the bosses of Cranks that are secured to the sides of the jib. It is now necessary to add weights at 61 in the shape of pieces of scrap lead melted into blocks of the required shape, or large quantities of Meccano parts, until the jib is accurately balanced. The connecting rods 30a may then be attached pivotally by lock-nutted bolts to the luffing cranks 30.

The hoisting cord is attached to the hoisting barrel 31, and is led over one of the pulleys 16 at the superstructure head, passing through a guide pulley on its way. The guide pulley consists of a 1" loose Pulley running between two Bush Wheels mounted on an 8" Rod that is secured by Handrail Supports to the tower. From Pulley 16, the cord passes over one of the centre pair of pulleys at the jib head, back over the remaining Pulley 16 and thence to the other centre Pulley on the jib head, after which it runs over the $1\frac{1}{2}''$ Pulley at the extremity of the jib and so down to the load hook or grab, to which it is secured.

The Single Suspension Grab

Although the model may be used as an ordinary crane by fastening a Loaded Hook to the end of the hoisting cord, its interest is vastly increased by the addition of a grab.

The grab employed on the model is known as the single suspension type, and is opened and closed merely by manipulation of the hauling rope, instead of depending for its operation, as is quite usual, upon two distinct falls of rope wound on separate barrels. An excellent example of a grab of the latter type is afforded by the Meccano High Speed Ship Coaler (see Instruction Leaflet No. 2).

Fig. 6 is a general view of the single

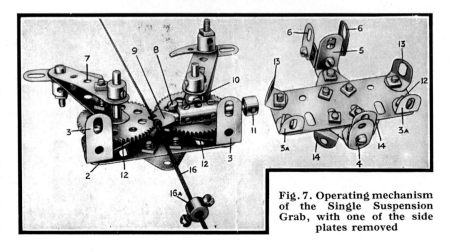

Fig. 7. Operating mechanism of the Single Suspension Grab, with one of the side plates removed

suspension grab, whilst Fig. 7 shows the grab head partly dismantled. From the latter view it will be seen that the mechanism of the grab is ingenious, yet, at the same time, remarkably simple. The construction of the jaws themselves should not present any particular difficulty since they are fairly apparent from the illustration. The apices of the Triangular Plates forming the sides of the jaws are attached pivotally by lock-nutted bolts (see Standard Mechanisms No. 263) to 1″ Triangular Plates that are bolted rigidly to each end of a 2½″ × ½″ Double Angle Strip 1, and four connecting links (4½″ Strips) are attached pivotally to the outer ends of the jaws by lock-nutted bolts. The Double Angle Strip 1 is weighted by the addition of a number of 2″ Strips or a 50-gramme weight, to make the jaws open.

The side plates 2 (Fig. 7) carrying the operating mechanism are 3″ Flat Girders, which are connected together by 1″ × ½″ and ½″ × ½″ Angle Brackets 3, 3a. On the side plate shown detached are fixed two 1″ Triangular Plates that carry 1″ × ½″ Angle Brackets 4 and 5, and to the Bracket 5 is secured a Double Bracket, with two Flat Brackets 6 bolted to it. Two Washers are placed between each Flat Bracket and the Double Bracket for spacing purposes.

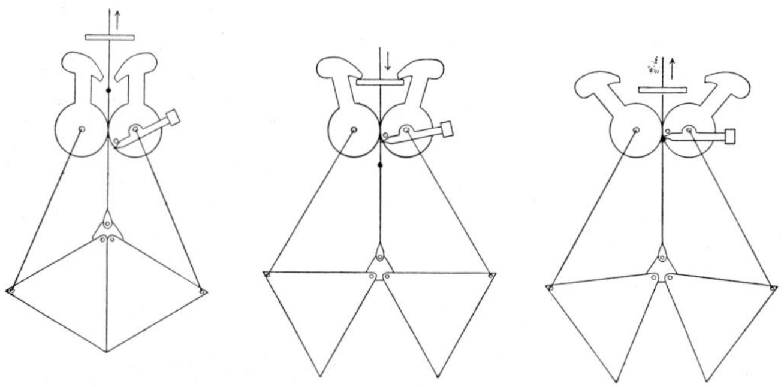

The hooks 7 are composed of 2½″ Strips bent to the shape shown in the illustrations and attached by means of ½″ Bolts to 57-teeth Gears. The ends of the Strips are each fitted with a Pawl and a Flat Bracket. The catch 9 is composed of a Centre Fork held in the end bore of a Coupling, which also carries a Handrail Support 10 and a balance weight 11 consisting of a 1″ Rod to the end of which is secured a Collar. The Gears are arranged to mesh with each other so that the Hooks 7 lie at the same angle to the perpendicular, and the Rods on which they are secured should be perfectly free to turn in the side plates 2.

The Handrail Support 10 of the catch is mounted freely on the spindle of the right-hand Gear, and a ¾″ Bolt 8 is secured by double nuts to the Gear in the third hole from that in which the 2½″ Strips are secured. Each hook is kept in the normal position by a piece of Spring Cord 12, one end of which is attached to the side plate and the other to a set-screw inserted in the boss of the 57-teeth Gear. Each piece of Spring Cord should be partially carried round the boss of the 57-teeth Gear before it is attached, so that its effort to come back to its normal state, and not its actual tension, is utilised to return the hooks. If it were used in the normal way, the tension would be too great for the purpose in view.

The connecting links between the grab proper and the grab head are attached by lock-nutted bolts to the 1″ Triangular Plates, and the hoisting cord 16 is secured to the cross member 1. The cord is then threaded through the round holes in the lower guide 4, and a large knot made in it in such a position that when the jaws are open the knot rests on top of the guide. The cord may then be passed through the upper guide 5 and through the 1½″ Pulley 15, which is termed the "suspender ring." This consists essentially of a 1½″ Pulley that is hung by two cords 17 from the jib head. These cords are each passed over the Pulleys 15 on the tower (Fig. 4) and over the outside pairs on the jib in exactly the same manner as that followed with regard to the hoisting cord, but the ends of the cords are attached to 1½″ Strips 17a at the top of the tower, and are not led down to a winch. A winch may be added if it is desired to effect discharge at different levels : otherwise it is only necessary to adjust the suspender to the most convenient height and then secure the ends of the cords to the Strips 17a. The object of the pulley system is to maintain the suspender in a horizontal position through all luffing angles in accordance with the Toplis principle.

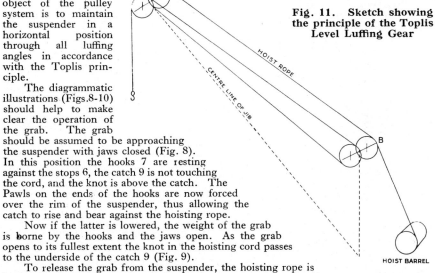

Fig. 11. Sketch showing the principle of the Toplis Level Luffing Gear

The diagrammatic illustrations (Figs. 8-10) should help to make clear the operation of the grab. The grab should be assumed to be approaching the suspender with jaws closed (Fig. 8). In this position the hooks 7 are resting against the stops 6, the catch 9 is not touching the cord, and the knot is above the catch. The Pawls on the ends of the hooks are now forced over the rim of the suspender, thus allowing the catch to rise and bear against the hoisting rope.

Now if the latter is lowered, the weight of the grab is borne by the hooks and the jaws open. As the grab opens to its fullest extent the knot in the hoisting cord passes to the underside of the catch 9 (Fig. 9).

To release the grab from the suspender, the hoisting rope is hauled in a little, thus causing the knot to bear against the underside of the catch. The latter bears, in turn, against the ⅜″ Bolt 8 and the arms of the hooks fall back on the stops 13. The grab is now freed from the suspender and it can be lowered in the open position (Fig. 10). On reaching the material to be removed, the hoisting rope is allowed to fall quite slack so as to give the weight of the Collar 16a a chance to pull the knot free from the catch, and so permit of the closing of the jaws when hoisting is commenced.

The two ½″ × ½″ Angle Brackets 14, by bearing against the connecting arms of the grab, serve to maintain the grab head in a horizontal position in relation to the jaws under all conditions of service.

We are indebted to Messrs. Stothert and Pitt, the makers of the prototype of the model, for the illustration on page 1 of this leaflet, and for valuable technical assistance in connection with the building of the model.

Fig. 8   Fig. 9   Fig. 10
Diagrams illustrating operation of Single Suspension Grab

Parts required to Build the Meccano Level Luffing Crane :

13 of No.	1	26 of No.	8	24 of No.	12	4 of No.	18b	6 of No.	27a	1 of No.	46		1 of No.	65		1 of No.	110		4 of No.	136
12	„ 1a	14	„ 8a	4	„ 12a	8	„ 20	1	„ 28	8	„ 48	7	„ 70	4	„ 111	2	„ 140
13	„ 1b	7	„ 8b	2	„ 12b	1	„ 20b	2	„ 29	1	„ 48a	2	„ 72	4	„ 111a	2	„ 147a
40	„ 2	24	„ 9	2	„ 13	3	„ 21	4	„ 30	6	„ 52	4	„ 76	4	„ 111c	1	„ 163
12	„ 2a	10	„ 9a	4	„ 13a	6	„ 22	1	„ 30a	8	„ 52a	5	„ 77	2	„ 114	2	„ 165
22	„ 3	2	„ 9b	1	„ 14	7	„ 22a	1	„ 30c	18″	„ 94	2	„ 115	1	„ 167
24	„ 4	1	„ 9c	2	„ 15a	1	„ 23a	2	„ 31	4	„ 53	4	„ 96	2	„ 116a	7	„ 302
42	„ 5	2	„ 9d	10	„ 16	4	„ 24	1	„ 32	6″	„ 53a	2	„ 96a	7	„ 120a	7	„ 303
24	„ 6	1	„ 9e	2	„ 16a	3	„ 25	594	„ 37	48	„ 59	6	„ 103	4	„ 125	7	„ 304
13	„ 6a	2	„ 9f	5	„ 16b	7	„ 26	6	„ 37a	6	„ 62	4	„ 103a	2	„ 126	13	„ 305
4	„ 7	9	„ 10	6	„ 17	1	„ 26a	130	„ 38	2	„ 62b	2	„ 103e	8	„ 126a	1	„ 306
4	„ 7a	1	„ 11	6	„ 18a	4	„ 27	3	„ 40	6	„ 63	4	„ 108	7	„ 133	1 Electric Motor

THE MECCANO SUPER MODEL LEAFLETS

The range of Meccano Super Models now embraces no less than 37 superb examples of miniature engineering construction. A special instruction leaflet has been published for each of these super models and a selection of the leaflets is illustrated on this page.

A brief description of each model in the series is given below, while the prices of the leaflets are indicated at the foot of this page. Copies of any of the leaflets may be obtained from your dealer or direct from Head Office, post free, at the prices indicated.

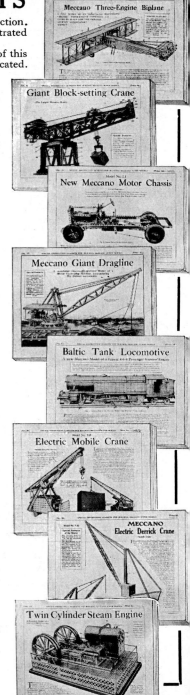

No. 1 MOTOR CHASSIS. This model runs perfectly under its own power. It has Ackermann Steering, Differential, Gear Box and Clutch, etc.

No. 2 SHIP COALER. All the movements of a real ship-coaler are reproduced in this model.

No. 3 MOTOR CYCLE AND SIDECAR. The sidecar is of streamline design and is mounted on springs. The motor-cycle is complete with lamps, horn, exhaust pipes, etc.

No. 4 GIANT BLOCK-SETTING CRANE. This realistic model is fitted with an accurate reproduction of Fidler's block-setting gear.

No. 5 TRAVELLING BUCKET DREDGER. In this model trucks and wagons can run underneath the chute through which falls the material raised by the dredger buckets.

No. 6 STIFF-LEG DERRICK. This model has many interesting movements, including hoisting, luffing and swivelling, which are controlled by suitable levers.

No. 7 PLATFORM SCALES. This model will weigh articles up to 4½ lb. with remarkable accuracy.

No. 8 ROUNDABOUT. This model is most attractive when in motion. As the roundabout rotates the cars spin round and the horses rise and fall.

No. 9 BAGATELLE TABLE. This is an interesting model that will give hours of fun to the players.

No. 10 LOG SAW. In this model the saw is driven rapidly to and fro while the work table travels beneath it.

No. 11 SINGLE-CYLINDER HORIZONTAL STEAM ENGINE. Fitted with balanced crankshaft, crosshead and centrifugal governor.

No. 12 STONE SAWING MACHINE. The model is equipped with adjustable work table and overhead trolley with self-sustaining chain hoist.

No. 13 MECCANOGRAPH. This wonderful model will draw hundreds of beautiful designs.

No. 14 GRANDFATHER CLOCK. A practical example of Meccano model-building. The model keeps accurate time.

No. 15 BALTIC TANK LOCOMOTIVE. The driving wheels are operated by an Electric Motor. An accurate reproduction of Walschaerts' Valve Gear is fitted.

No. 16 LOOM. This is perhaps the greatest Meccano success. The model weaves beautiful material.

No. 17 PLANING MACHINE. Fitted with quick-return motion.

No. 18 REVOLVING CRANE. This model is fitted with screw-operated luffing gear.

No. 19 STEAM SHOVEL. This model embodies travelling, rotating, racking and digging movements, and jib hoisting and lowering gear.

No. 19a STEAM EXCAVATOR, OR MECHANICAL DIGGER. A Meccano Steam Engine is incorporated in this model and provides the power for operating the four movements.

No. 20 MOBILE CRANE. This model has hoisting, luffing, travelling and slewing movements. It is fitted with an automatic brake on the hoisting shaft, an internal expanding brake on the front axle, and a limit switch to prevent over-winding of the jib in either direction.

No. 21 TRANSPORTER BRIDGE. The carriage automatically travels to and fro for as long as the motor is driven, pausing for a few seconds at each end of its travel.

No. 22 TRACTION ENGINE. A remarkably realistic model that will pull a boy of average weight. Fitted with two speeds.

No. 23 VERTICAL LOG SAW. While the saws are in motion, the logs are fed slowly to them.

No. 24 TRAVELLING GANTRY CRANE. The movements of this model comprise the traversing of the entire gantry, hoisting and lowering, and the traversing of the crane trolley.

No. 25 HYDRAULIC CRANE. The hydraulic ram is represented realistically by a powerful screw mechanism.

No. 26 TWIN ELLIPTIC HARMONOGRAPH. Some beautiful designs may be produced with this model.

No. 27 DRAGLINE. This imposing model of a giant excavator is fitted with travelling, luffing, slewing, and dragging movements.

No. 28 PONTOON CRANE. The movements of this model include the operation of the two hoisting blocks, slewing of the entire crane, and luffing.

No. 29 HAMMERHEAD CRANE. This is a very realistic and powerful model, comprising traversing, hoisting and slewing motions.

No. 30 BREAKDOWN CRANE. This model is equipped with travelling, slewing, luffing, and hoisting motions, and is also fitted with laminated springs, brakes, out-riggers, etc.

No. 31 WAREHOUSE WITH ELEVATORS. The two cages are driven automatically and work alternately, pausing at top and bottom positions.

No. 32 TWIN CYLINDER STEAM ENGINE AND BOILER. This is a realistic working model of a complete steam plant, equipped with valve gear, governor, balanced cranks, etc.

No. 33 SINGLE AND DOUBLE FLYBOATS. These two models represent popular pleasure-fair attractions.

No. 34 THREE-ENGINE BIPLANE. This is a realistic model of an "Argosy" machine, and is fitted with ailerons, elevators and rudders.

No. 35 LEVEL LUFFING GRABBING CRANE. A large and imposing model of novel design. The crane incorporates a level luffing gear, while the balanced jib is operated by crank action and is fitted with a "single suspension" grab.

No. 36 ELECTRIC DERRICK CRANE (Scotch Type). This imposing model is built to a scale of ¾in. to 1 ft., the jib measuring 6 ft. in length. The movements include hoisting and lowering, luffing and slewing.

No. 37 6-in. HOWITZER, LIMBER AND TRACTOR. A splendid new working model of a complete mobile artillery unit. The Tractor incorporates "caterpillars" and the Howitzer will shoot accurately.

Prices of Meccano Super Model Leaflets :—

Leaflets Nos. 3, 5, 6, 7, 8, 9, 10, 11, 12, 17, 18, 19, 20, 21, 22, 23, 24, 25, 26, 28, 29, 36—United Kingdom 2d., Australia 4d., New Zealand and South Africa 3d., Canada 5 cents.

Leaflets Nos. 1, 2, 13, 14, 15, 16, 19a, 27, 30, 31, 32, 33, 34—United Kingdom 3d., Australia 6d., New Zealand and South Africa 4d., Canada 8 cents.

Leaflet No. 4—United Kingdom 6d., Australia 1/-, New Zealand and South Africa 8d., Canada 15 cents.

MECCANO LIMITED, Old Swan, LIVERPOOL, ENGLAND

Model No. 7.32

Special Features of the Model.

This Meccano model is built to a scale of ¾in. to 1 ft., the jib measuring 6 ft. in length.

The arrangement of the mechanism closely resembles that adopted in the prototype, and the three movements of hoisting, luffing, and slewing are driven from a gear box of simple design.

The model is capable of level luffing, and a safety interlocking device controls the pawl and ratchet gear on the luffing barrel. The motive power is supplied by a 6-volt Motor, the speed of which may be varied by means of a Meccano built-up controller.

MECCANO
Australia 4.2
Electric Derrick Crane
(Scotch Type)

THE construction of this Meccano model of a Derrick Crane should be commenced by building the jib. By a careful study of the general view (Fig. 2) the main details of this portion of the model should be fairly clear. Each of the main longitudinal members of the jib consists of three 24½″ Angle Girders, bolted together and overlapped two holes. The top and bottom members of the centre portion are joined together by 2½″ Strips, whilst each end section of the jib tapers down towards its extremity. The complete sides are connected together by 2½″ Strips at points one third from either end, the bottom end tapering down to a 7½″ Flat Girder whilst the top is bridged by a 1½″ Strip. As will be seen from the illustration, the jib is very adequately braced by Strips on all four sides. The length and bracing of these Strips is the same throughout the centre section of the jib, each one consisting of two 2½″ Strips overlapped one hole. As the cross-section of the jib alters toward each end, so will the disposition of the bracing strips vary accordingly. No difficulty should be experienced, however, in putting the finishing touches to the bracing, as the general view gives a good idea of how this should be done. It should be noted that the construction of the upper tapered portion of the jib is practically identical with that of the lower, so that, bearing this fact in mind, a careful study of the latter should make the structural details of both clear to the builder.

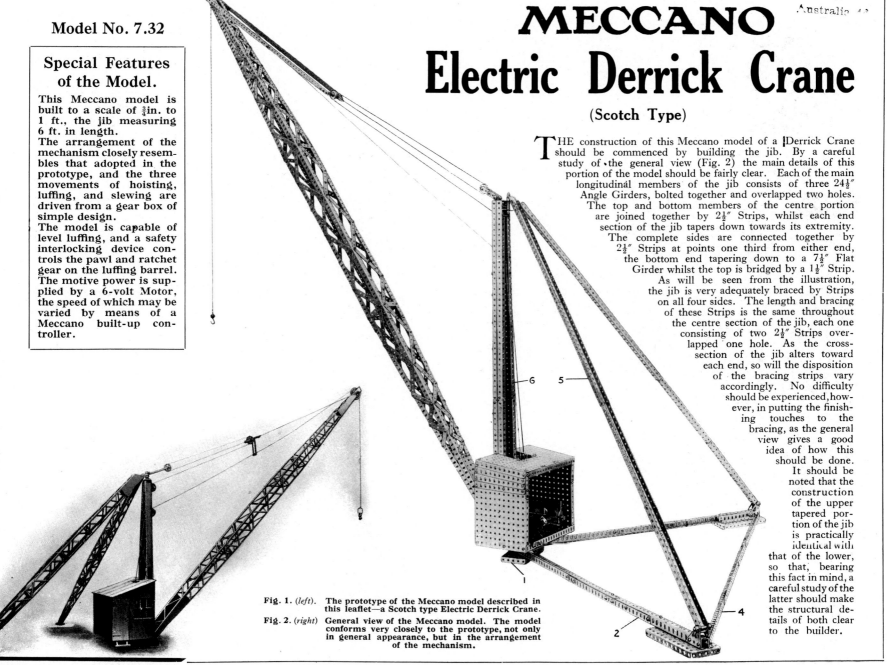

Fig. 1. (*left*). The prototype of the Meccano model described in this leaflet—a Scotch type Electric Derrick Crane.

Fig. 2. (*right*) General view of the Meccano model. The model conforms very closely to the prototype, not only in general appearance, but in the arrangement of the mechanism.

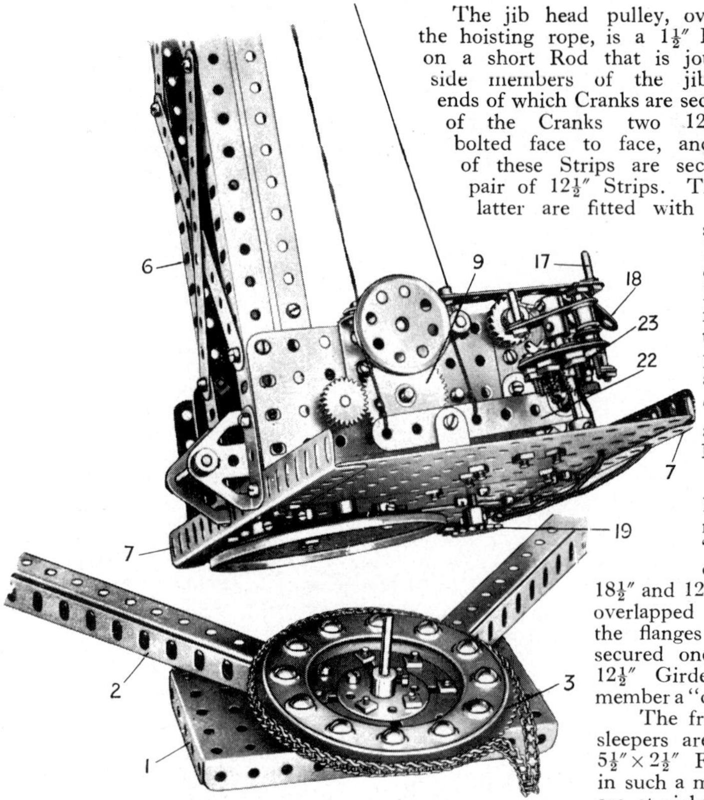

The jib head pulley, over which runs the hoisting rope, is a 1½″ Pulley mounted on a short Rod that is journalled in the side members of the jib and to the ends of which Cranks are secured. To each of the Cranks two 12½″ Strips are bolted face to face, and to the ends of these Strips are secured a further pair of 12½″ Strips. The ends of the latter are fitted with Cranks, which serve to hold a 1½″ Rod that carries a 1″ loose Pulley forming one of the luffing purchases, and also a 1½″ Strip.

The Sleepers and Slewing Race

Each of the horizontal members or "sleepers" 2 consists of an 18½″ and 12½″ Angle Girder overlapped three holes, to the flanges of which are secured one 9½″ and two 12½″ Girders, giving the member a "channel" section.

The front ends of the sleepers are attached to a 5½″ × 2½″ Flanged Plate 1 in such a manner that they are at right angles to each other. The geared portion of a Meccano Ball Bearing (part No. 168) forms one part of the slewing race, and it is secured by bolts to the top flanges of the sleepers 2, additional support being afforded by means of 1″ Screwed Rods, which pass through the Plate and race, and are secured in place by nuts. A Bush Wheel bolted to the upper side of the race carries a 2″ Rod that forms the central pivot about which the model slews.

The rear ends of the sleepers are mounted on 5½″ × 2½″ Flanged Plates, to which they are attached by means of 5½″ Angle Girders. The Flanged Plates are spaced apart by the member 4, which consists of four 12½″ Angle Girders.

Each of the rear tie members 5 is 42 inches in length and is composed of six 12½″ and two 9½″ Angle Girders. The upper extremities of both members are fitted with 3″ Strips that project three holes beyond the ends of the Girders and the ends of these Strips are bent downward slightly. The end holes will eventually be passed over a 1½″ Rod mounted on the top of the mast 6.

The Vertical Mast and Gear Box

Each side of the vertical mast 6 is composed of two 18½″ and two 12½″ Angle Girders with their flanges bolted to the edges of 12½″, 9½″, and 7½″ Flat Girders to form a channel-section girder of great strength. The top ends are bridged by means of two 1½″ Angle Girders, and a third 1½″ Angle Girder is bolted across

Fig. 3. Partial side and underneath view of Swivelling Platform and Gear Box, showing details of the Slewing Race, etc.

the rear face of the mast in the second hole from the top. This latter Girder together with the one above it, will form a bearing for the pin that serves as a means of pivotally attaching the tie members to the mast head.

The front of the mast, the lower portion of which may be seen in Fig. 3, is braced by 5½″ Strips. This view shows also how the mast is secured to the platform or swivelling base on which is built the gear box. The foot of the mast is actually attached to a 9½″ Angle Girder 7 that forms the front edge of the platform, the floor of which consists of three 5½″ × 3½″ Flat Plates. Trunnions are bolted to the foot of the mast to accommodate the jib pivot pin. The gear box sides are 4½″ × 2½″ Flat Plates, and they are attached both to the mast and to 5½″ Angle Girders that are bolted to the base, whilst to the underside of the latter is mounted the upper portion of the slewing race, which is secured in the position shown in Fig. 3 by ½″ Bolts, Collars being used for spacing purposes.

Arrangement of the Gearing

Derrick Cranes are very much alike in structural appearance, but they vary greatly in mechanical details. Some manufacturers, for example, employ a motor for each of the hoisting, luffing, and slewing movements, whereas others believe in one motor and the provision of the necessary gearing to obtain the separate motions. Each system has its advocates and they both have particular advantages which are fully appreciated by the engineer. The latter practice is, however, by far the most usual arrangement for Derrick Cranes.

The makers of the prototype of the Meccano model evidently believe in the usual practice, as a glance at Fig. 4 (which shows the gear box of the actual crane) will indicate. Two of the distinctive features of the prototype is the provision of level luffing, whereby the load maintains a constant vertical height at all luffing angles, and a patent interlocking device which precludes the possibility of the luffing barrel pawl being disengaged from its ratchet unless the luffing barrel is in gear. Both these interesting features have been reproduced in the model.

The arrangement of the gears, etc., in the model may be seen fairly clearly in Figs. 3 and 5. Fig. 5 is a semi-plan view showing the 6-volt Motor in place,

Fig. 4. An illustration of the Gears and Controls of the actual Derrick Crane

while Fig. 3 is a partial side view of the gear box unit, which is lifted to show the two portions of the slewing race, etc.

A ¾″ Pinion on the Motor armature spindle engages with a 50-teeth Gear Wheel secured on a 2½″ Rod which is journalled in the Motor side plates, and which carries at its other extremity a ½″ Pinion. The latter is in mesh with a 57-teeth Gear mounted on a Rod vertically above the first. On the same Rod is a ½″ Pinion engaging with a 57-teeth Gear on a 3″ Rod that is journalled in the gear box side plates. This Rod has, on the end seen in Fig 3, a ¾″ Pinion in constant mesh with a 50-teeth Gear 9, that is secured on what may be termed the mainshaft of the gear box.

A ¾″ Pinion 10 (Fig. 5) on the mainshaft may be engaged with either the Gear 12 on the hoisting barrel or with the Gear 13 on the slewing shaft, by sliding the mainshaft in its bearings. The sliding movement is effected by means of the lever 11, which is attached pivotally to a 2½″ Angle Girder that is bolted to the vertical girders 6 and carries a ⅜″ Bolt, the shank of which locates between two Collars that are secured on the mainshaft a short distance apart. The lever works in a quadrant composed of two 2½″ Strips that are spaced apart by Washers and secured by ½″ Bolts a short distance below a transverse 2½″ × ½″ Double Angle Strip. The latter is seen clearly in the illustration.

The slewing shaft has, in addition to the Gear Wheel 13, a Worm meshing with a Pinion 14 mounted on a short vertical Rod. The latter is journalled in a re-inforced bearing, consisting of three 1½″ Strips laid on top of each other and bolted across two parallel Z-section girders 21 ; each of these girders is composed of two 2½″ Angle Girders secured together so that their other flanges point in opposite directions. A Bush Wheel is also bolted to that portion of the Plate below the bearing so that the Rod passes through its boss. A ¾″ Sprocket Wheel 19 (Fig. 3) is secured on the lower end of the Rod.

The luffing winch barrel is a 3½″ Rod that is journalled freely in the side plates and on which is mounted in the order named, from left to right, a Ratchet Wheel, one Washer, a Collar, the 50-teeth Gear 15, a Coupling, a Collar, three Washers and a ½″ fast Pulley.

A Pawl 18 engages with the teeth of the Ratchet Wheel and so prevents the unwinding of the luffing barrel. The Pawl pivots on a ¾″ Bolt that is secured to a Corner Bracket, bolted to the end of the gear box plate.

The luffing barrel is driven from the hoisting barrel through the medium of a sliding layshaft 16, which is operated by the lever 17. The latter is attached pivotally to a 1″ × ½″ Angle Bracket on the left-hand gear box side-plate, and is

Fig. 5. Partial plan view of Gear Box, showing layout of Gears, Electric Motor, Operating Levers, Brakes, Controller, etc.

connected to the Rod that it actuates, in a similar manner to the lever 11. In its neutral position, i.e., when the layshaft Pinion is out of engagement with the Gear 12, the lever is over the top of the Pawl 18, thus preventing the latter from being raised and letting the jib fall. On the other hand, when the lever is moved over to the left to effect engagement of the layshaft pinion with the Gear 12, the Pawl is free to be lifted out of engagement with the Ratchet teeth by means of a Flat Bracket secured to its boss. This, of course, is similar to the safety interlocking device employed in the actual crane.

The hoisting barrel is fitted with an effective semi-automatic brake 22 (Fig. 3). Although this type of brake allows the load to be hoisted perfectly freely, the load cannot be lowered until the end of the brake lever is raised. It should be noted that these results can only be attained when the points of attachment of the brake cord are on opposite sides, and at different distances, from the fulcrum of the brake lever. The fulcrum is a 1″ × 1″ Angle Bracket which is bolted to the floor, and the brake lever is attached pivotally to the Bracket by a lock-nutted bolt (Standard Mechanism No. 263).

Electrical Equipment of the Model

The electrical equipment of the model is comparatively simple. The chief item, excluding the Motor, is the controller for varying the speed of the Motor. The controller is seen on the left of the gear box in Fig. 5; it is of exceptional interest for it is built up entirely from Meccano parts. The following is a brief description of the device, and readers who require further information should refer to detail No. 115 in the Standard Mechanisms Manual.

The resistance is formed by a short length of Spring Cord drawn out so that no two adjacent turns touch, and attached to the shanks of six 6 B.A. Bolts that are mounted on a Bush Wheel and insulated therefrom by means of Insulating Bushes and Washers. A seventh insulated 6 B.A. Bolt is provided. This is not connected in any way, however, for it is intended to form an "off stud."

The switch arm is a Double Arm Crank on one end of which is mounted a Spring Buffer, which makes contact with the heads of the bolts. The Bush Wheel is mounted on a Rod, the upper extremity of which serves as a pivot for the Double Arm Crank, its lower end being held in the boss of a Crank that is bolted to the platform. The sleeve portion of a Spring Buffer is secured to the Bush Wheel to form a stop for the Double Arm Crank.

A length of insulated wire is taken from one terminal of the Motor to one end of the resistance, and the other Motor terminal is connected to an insulated terminal 20.

The remaining terminal 20 is in metallic contact with the Girder on which it is mounted, and is consequently in electrical connection with the switch arm of the controller. Hence it only remains to connect the Accumulator or Transformer to the Terminals 20 by suitable lengths of flex or insulated wire.

Construction of the Cabin

The driver's cabin is illustrated upside down in Fig. 6. It will be seen that its construction is simple and no Meccano boy should find much difficulty in building this portion of the model. Each half of the front of the cabin is composed of two 5½″ × 3½″ Flat Plates over-lapped seven holes, while the roof consists of two 5½″ × 2½″ Flat Plates joined by a 2½″ × 2½″ Plate. The sides consist of 5½″ × 2½″ Flat Plates that are attached to the roof and to the platform by means of Angle Girders. Since the roof slopes down toward the rear, it is necessary to fill in the top portions of the sides with 5½″ Flat Girders so that their slotted holes may enable the necessary angles to be obtained. When the model is completed the luffing cord is passed over the ½″ loose Pulley seen mounted loosely on a Rod journalled in the roof.

Final Erection of the Model

Having completed the various units of the model it only remains to fit them together in their respective positions—a simple task, as will be seen.

The first step is to secure the cabin (Fig. 6) to the swivelling base, and then to place this portion of the model over the central pivot (see Fig. 3), care being taken to see that the Ball Casing (part No. 168c) is included in the assembly.

The tie members 5 may now be put in place, their bottom ends being attached by 2″ Rods to the rear anchorages (the Corner Brackets on the members 2) and their top ends meeting on a common pin that is journalled in the 1½″ Angle Girders at the mast head. A length of Sprocket Chain is passed round the geared periphery of the lower portion of the slewing race 3, and round the ¾″ Sprocket Wheel 19 (Fig. 3). The model should now be secured by ordinary wood screws to a suitable base, and the attachment of the jib to the model proceeded with. This is accomplished by passing a Rod completely through the Trunnions at the foot of the mast and through the end holes of the jib-foot. If the model is secured to a portable baseboard, it may be found necessary to add ballast at the rear, to prevent it over-balancing when heavy loads are lifted.

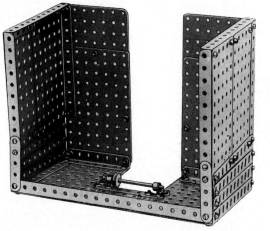

Fig. 6. Inverted view of the Driver's Cabin.

The standing end of the luffing cord is tied to the 1½″ Strip that is mounted by the side of the purchase pulley on the jib. The cord is then led over the pulley at the mast head and back round the pulley on the jib, whence it is passed over a 1½″ guide pulley that is mounted on a short Rod journalled freely in the sides of the mast, and finally secured to the luffing barrel.

The hoisting cord is attached to its barrel and led over a guide pulley on the mast to the 1½″ jib head pulley and then down to the hook. Matters must be so arranged that as the hoisting cord is wound on to the hoisting barrel, the luffing cord is simultaneously paid out or vice versa.

Owing to the fact that the luffing barrel is of a larger diameter than the hoisting barrel, and to the effect of the luffing purchase system, the load maintains a practically constant height when the jib is luffed in or out. With a non-compensated crane the load moves a considerable distance vertically, and thus power has to be developed by the motor to overcome the effect of the load as well as that of the jib. In addition, the crane driver often has difficulty in judging the exact position of the load after he has altered the angle of the jib—a matter of extreme importance in many instances.

Advantages of Crane Models

Cranes are perhaps the most popular models among the majority of Meccano boys, and it is not difficult to account for their popularity, for everyone is gripped by the fascination of handling a model that may be put through such interesting evolutions as a properly constructed crane.

The prototype of the Meccano model must be a very familiar sight to most of our readers, as its slender outline may often be observed placed on the top of some large building under construction. The appearance of the original has been well brought out in the model, as a glance at the general view and that of the prototype will show, and the weight-lifting capabilities of the Meccano model compare favourably with those of its "big brother," for it will lift 15 lbs. with the utmost ease. It should be noted that when lifting weights of this order the hoisting cord should be doubled, as a single length is very likely to break under the strain.

An interesting refinement that may easily be added to the model is a jib radius indicator. The construction of this device is fully described under detail No. 282 in the Standard Mechanisms Manual, and also in the Stiff Leg Derrick Leaflet (No. 6).

We are indebted to the Anderson-Grice Co., Ltd. (Carnoustie, Scotland), makers of the prototype, for the illustrations of the derrick crane (Fig. 1) and the gear box (Fig. 4), and also for much valuable information.

Parts Required to Build the Meccano Scotch Type Derrick Crane :—

8 of No.	1	26 of No.	8	1 of No.	12b	2 of No.	23a	4 of No.	40	1 of No.	63	2 of No.	103k	8 of No.	302
5 ,,	2	9 ,,	8a	4 ,,	16	3 ,,	24	1 ,,	48a	5 ,,	70	1 ,,	111	8 ,,	303
3 ,,	2a	12 ,,	9	3 ,,	16a	4 ,,	25	3 ,,	52	1 ,,	72	6 ,,	111a	9 ,,	304
20 ,,	3	2 ,,	9b	5 ,,	16b	3 ,,	26	8 ,,	52a	3 ,,	82	4 ,,	115	15 ,,	305
14 ,,	4	5 ,,	9d	7 ,,	17	5 ,,	27	2 ,,	53a	14″ ,,	94	3 ,,	120a	3 ,,	306
110 ,,	5	3 ,,	9f	1 ,,	18a	2 ,,	27a	1 ,,	57b	1 ,,	96a	2 ,,	126		
5 ,,	6	1 ,,	10	1 ,,	18b	1 ,,	32	3″ ,,	58	6 ,,	103	8 ,,	133	1 Electric	
11 ,,	6a	2 ,,	11	4 ,,	21	320 ,,	37	37 ,,	59	2 ,,	103a	1 ,,	147	Motor	
12 ,,	7	3 ,,	12	2 ,,	22	14 ,,	37a	5 ,,	62	2 ,,	103b	1 ,,	148		
6 ,,	7a	1 ,,	12a	1 ,,	23	48 ,,	38	1 ,,	62b	2 ,,	103d	1 ,,	168	—	

(No. 37)   SPECIAL INSTRUCTION LEAFLETS FOR BUILDING MECCANO SUPER MODELS   **Price 2d.**
(New Zealand and South Africa 3d.)
(Australia 4d.   Canada 5c.)

Model No. 6.47
6-Inch Howitzer
Equipped with
Limber and Tractor

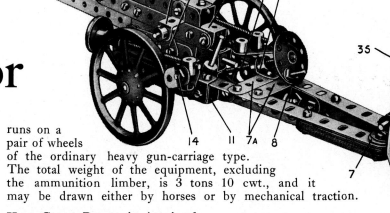

Fig. 2. The Howitzer in firing position, showing the firing lever, elevating handle, etc.

DURING the Great War howitzers were used to a very large extent in consequence of the change from open warfare, with which activities commenced, to the trench warfare that developed as the war progressed. Howitzers of 6″ and 8″ calibre are easily capable of transport on their own carriages along ordinary roads or across fairly level country. For siege operations large calibres, entailing special means of transport, are necessary.

The particular howitzer forming the prototype of the Meccano model has a calibre of six inches and is capable of firing a projectile weighing 100 lbs. Some idea of the great power of this weapon will be gained when it is learned that the projectile leaves the muzzle of the gun at a velocity of 1,250 feet per second, and when fired at an elevation of 45 degrees the range of the gun is about 10,000 yards. It is mounted on a field carriage of very massive construction, which runs on a pair of wheels of the ordinary heavy gun-carriage type. The total weight of the equipment, excluding the ammunition limber, is 3 tons 10 cwt., and it may be drawn either by horses or by mechanical traction.

How Great Range is Attained

The range of any gun depends on a number of important factors, not the least of which is the shape of the projectile and the length of the barrel.

To attain a long range it is necessary to reduce the resistance of the air to the projectile without diminishing the mass of the shot, and this result is obtained by using the well-known elongated form resembling a pointed cylinder.

Such a shot has, however, a tendency to travel sideways (this fact can be demonstrated by dropping a pointed stick from a height). By giving the projectile axial rotation before it leaves the barrel of the gun, the tendency to "tumble over" during flight may be overcome, and this is done by causing the shot or shell to fit helical grooves in the

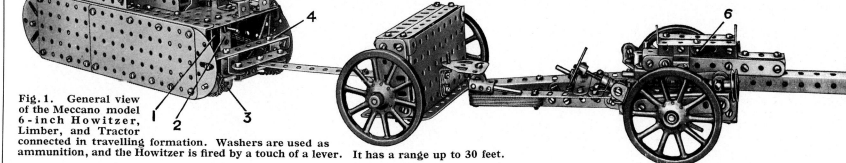

Fig. 1. General view of the Meccano model 6-inch Howitzer, Limber, and Tractor connected in travelling formation. Washers are used as ammunition, and the Howitzer is fired by a touch of a lever. It has a range up to 30 feet.

7/830/5.   *Published by* MECCANO LTD., OLD SWAN, LIVERPOOL.   *Printed in England.*

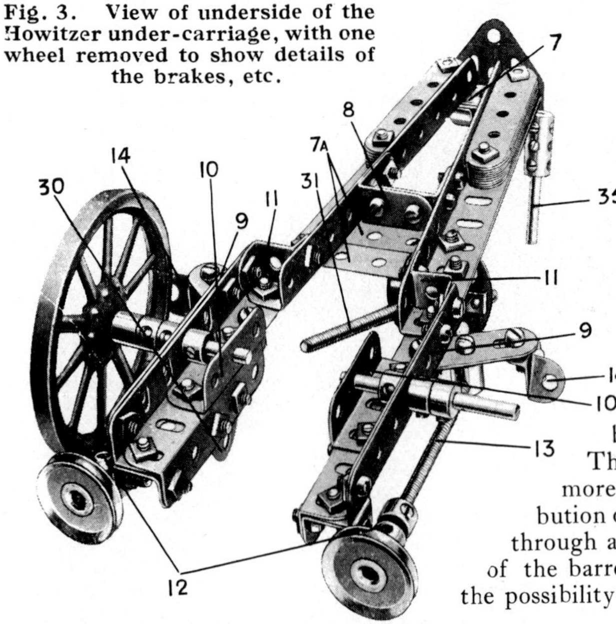

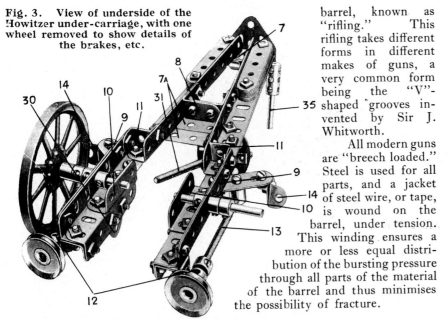

Fig. 3. View of underside of the Howitzer under-carriage, with one wheel removed to show details of the brakes, etc.

barrel, known as "rifling." This rifling takes different forms in different makes of guns, a very common form being the "V"-shaped grooves invented by Sir J. Whitworth.

All modern guns are "breech loaded." Steel is used for all parts, and a jacket of steel wire, or tape, is wound on the barrel, under tension. This winding ensures a more or less equal distribution of the bursting pressure through all parts of the material of the barrel and thus minimises the possibility of fracture.

Construction of the Model: The Howitzer

The trailing girders and gun pivot support (Fig. 3) are built up from two 5½″ Angle Girders connected by ½″ Reversed Angle Brackets 11 to two 3½″ Angle Girders. The 5½″ Girders are connected together by the Strips 7 and 7a and the 1″ × 1″ Angle Brackets 8. The 3½″ Angle Girders carry 3″ Strips 9 and 1½″ Angle Girders 10, secured in the positions indicated in the illustration, to form extended bearings for the wheel axles. The gun proper is mounted pivotally in 1″ Triangular Plates 30 that are secured to the 3½″ Angle Girders by 2½″ Angle Girders.

The brakes acting on the road wheels are built up as follows. Each brake shoe consists of two ½″ × ½″ Angle Brackets 14, which are secured to a Crank that is attached pivotally to the frame by a ⅜″ Bolt. Each brake may be applied or withdrawn from the wheel by means of a 3½″ Screwed Rod 13, which works in the transverse hole of a Threaded Boss attached pivotally to the Crank as shown, and is journalled in a Handrail Support 12 secured to the frame by a Double Bracket.

The recoil spade, consisting of a Flat Trunnion, is secured by a Collar to a 1½″ Rod. This Rod carries the handle 35 and is journalled in two ½″ × ½″ Angle Brackets bolted to the Strip 7, the securing bolts passing through the rear end of the trailing girder. To counterbalance the weight of the barrel, ten 2½″ Strips are secured by ¾″ Bolts to each limb of the trailing girder.

The gun muzzle, which together with the recoil chamber is shown sectionally in Fig. 4, is built up from two 7½″ Angle Girders 15 and 15a secured at their inner ends to a Coupling 16 by means of three set-screws and a ⅜″ Bolt 17. These set-screws and ⅜″ Bolt also retain in place inside the Coupling an 8″ Rod, which carries two Compression Springs interlocked one with the other, so as to form a short, powerful spring. The end of one of the Springs is formed into a loop which serves to secure the Spring by means of a set-screw to the Collar 18.

The firing handle 19 (a 1½″ Rod) is secured rigidly by a Coupling and ¾″ Bolt to a 2″ Strip that is attached pivotally to the Angle Bracket 20. The ¾″ Bolt slides in the elongated hole of another Angle Bracket 21, which is secured to the underside of the barrel and forms an efficient "stop" for the firing mechanism. Another Coupling, secured to the 2″ Strip by the Bolt 36, carries a ¾″ Bolt 22, the end of which engages with the Washer (representing the shot) to be fired from the gun. Hence to discharge the gun, it is only necessary to apply a very slight lifting movement to the handle 19. The shot is pushed into position by a 7½″ Strip, which, when not in use, is carried in the Double Brackets 5 (Fig. 1) on the tractor. The complete gun barrel slides between the 2½″ Angle Girder 23 and the Angle Bracket 24, each of these parts being bolted to its respective side in the recoil chamber. The latter is constructed from two 2½″ × 2½″ Flat Plates joined together at top and bottom by 2½″ Angle Girders. Two ½″ Reversed Angle Brackets 26 (Fig. 2) and two 4½″ Strips 25 (Fig. 4) are bolted to the outside of the recoil chamber, and the 1½″ Angle Girder 27 and Double Bracket 28 are secured to the Strips 25 as shown in Fig. 4 to form a cover for the recoil spring, which is secured to the ⅜″ Bolts 17 and 29.

The recoil chamber with barrel in position is pivoted to the under-carriage by passing a 2½″ Rod through the ½″ Triangular Plates 30 (Fig. 3), and through the ½″ Reversed Angle Brackets 26 (Fig. 2) and the side plates of the recoil chamber, the whole being held in place by Collars.

The elevating apparatus consists chiefly of a 3½″ Threaded Rod 31 (Fig. 2), which carries at one end a Bush Wheel and is journalled at the other end in a Threaded Boss 32 (Fig. 4) that is attached pivotally to the lower corner of the recoil chamber. The Threaded Rod is prevented from moving laterally by two Collars clamped to the Rod, one on each side of an Angle Bracket 33 that is secured in the position indicated.

An efficient sighting apparatus is attached

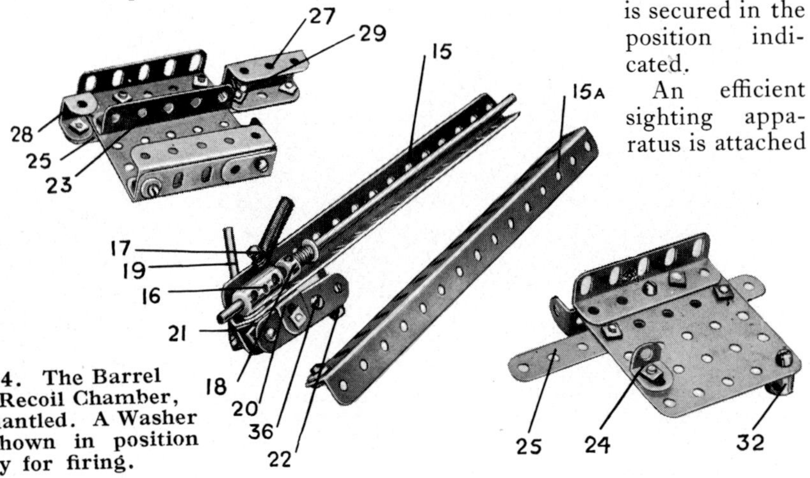

Fig. 4. The Barrel and Recoil Chamber, dismantled. A Washer is shown in position ready for firing.

to the gun. The $2\frac{1}{2}'' \times \frac{1}{2}''$ Double Angle Strip 34 (Fig. 2) is bolted to an Angle Bracket 6 (Fig. 1), and the latter is attached by lock-nuts (see Standard Mechanism No. 262) to the recoil chamber, so as to allow a fairly stiff swivelling movement. A very fine wire, about 36 S.W.G. is secured perpendicularly across the hole A and a piece of paper over the hole B, the paper having a pin hole punched in its centre. In view of the fact that the centre line of the sighting arm is to one side of the centre line of the barrel, it is necessary to move the arm inward or outward when altering the range. At extreme range, which is approximately thirty feet, the sighting arm should point inward at an angle of half a degree to its own centre line. For every decrease of 6 ft. in the range the arm should be moved inward half a degree, so that at 6 ft. range it will be at an angle of $2\frac{1}{2}$ degrees. In addition to this movement, the sights may be raised or lowered for the convenience of the operator without interfering with the laying of the gun. Small protractors, marked so that at different angles the range will be indicated, may be fitted to the sights and elevating movements. Such details will facilitate the working of the gun.

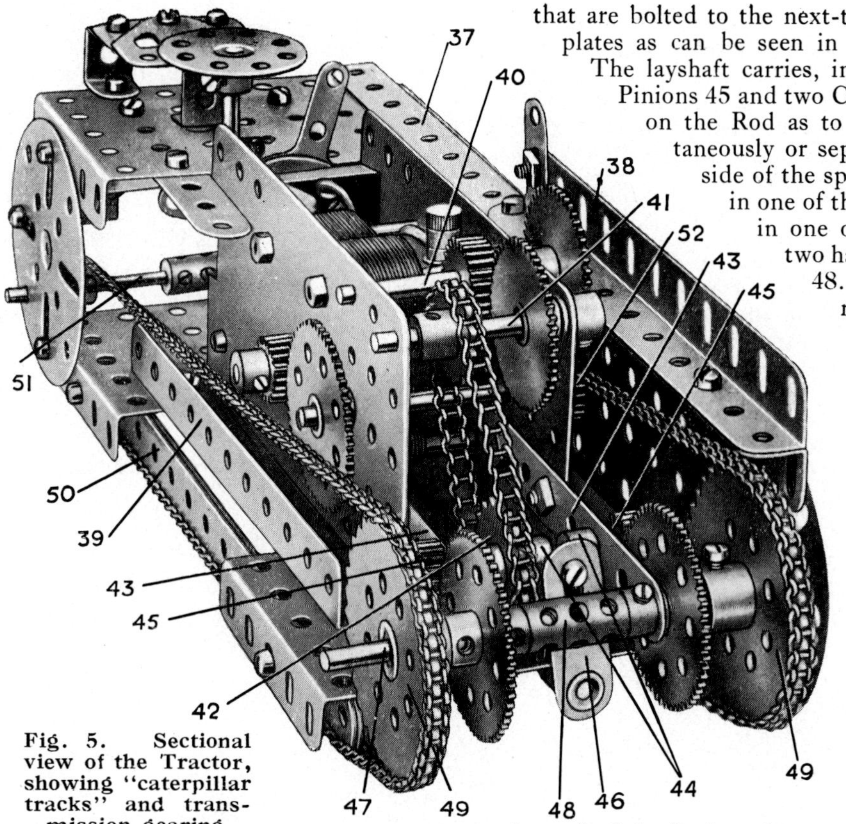

Building the Tractor

Each side of the tractor consists of two $5\frac{1}{2}'' \times 2\frac{1}{2}''$ Flat Plates over-lapped five holes, and two Face Plates, bolted one at each end. Four $3\frac{1}{2}'' \times 2\frac{1}{2}''$ Flanged Plates and one $3\frac{1}{2}'' \times \frac{1}{2}''$ Double Angle Strip 4 (Fig. 1) are used to connect the two sides together, two of the Plates being used for the top and two for the bottom. The $3\frac{1}{2}'' \times \frac{1}{2}''$ Double Angle Strip 4 is secured between the rear pair of Face Plates and carries two $\frac{1}{2}''$ Reversed Angle Brackets. These are for use when coupling the gun limber to the tractor. The upper edge of each side carries a $9\frac{1}{2}''$ Angle Girder 37 (Fig. 5) to which is bolted a $5\frac{1}{2}''$ Angle Girder 38. Two further $5\frac{1}{2}''$ Angle Girders 39 are bolted across the two lower $3\frac{1}{2}'' \times 2\frac{1}{2}''$ Flanged Plates and form a bed for the Electric Motor as shown.

The next stage is the assembling of the mechanism, which is carried out as follows. A $\frac{1}{2}''$ Pinion on the Motor armature shaft engages with a 57-teeth Gear that is secured to a $2\frac{1}{2}''$ Rod carrying a $\frac{3}{4}''$ Pinion 52. This Pinion meshes with a 50-teeth Gear on the Rod 40, and this Rod carries also a $\frac{3}{4}''$ Sprocket Wheel that is connected by Sprocket Chain to a $1''$ Sprocket Wheel 42 on a slidable lay-shaft. The latter is journalled in two $3\frac{1}{2}''$ Strips 43

Fig. 5. Sectional view of the Tractor, showing "caterpillar tracks" and transmission gearing.

that are bolted to the next-to-bottom row of holes in the Motor side plates as can be seen in Fig. 5.

The layshaft carries, in addition to the $1''$ Sprocket 42, two $\frac{1}{2}''$ Pinions 45 and two Collars 44. The Pinions must be so spaced on the Rod as to engage the 57-teeth Gears either simultaneously or separately. The Gears are secured on each side of the split rod 47, each half of which is journalled in one of the Face Plates on the side of the model and in one of the Strips 43. The inner ends of the two halves of the rod 47 are carried in a Coupling 48. Each carries also a $2''$ Sprocket Wheel, round which is passed a length of Sprocket Chain to form the "caterpillar" track. Each of the two chains passes round a $\frac{3}{4}''$ Sprocket Wheel that is loose on the Rod 51, and also along the lower edges of two $7\frac{1}{2}''$ Strips 50 that are bolted face to face. The Strips 50 hold the tracks in contact with the ground. They are secured to the sides of the model by means of $\frac{3}{4}''$ Bolts, and are spaced from the sides by Collars.

The two Collars 44 on the lay-shaft are spaced apart so as to allow a set-screw, carried in the elongated hole of the Crank 46, to move easily in the intervening space. The Crank 46 is nipped on an $8''$ Rod that is journalled in Angle Brackets bolted to the under-side of the $3\frac{1}{2}'' \times 2\frac{1}{2}''$ Flanged Plates joining the sides of the tractor, and the opposite end of the Rod carries a second Crank 3 (Fig. 1) to which is secured a $2''$ Strip 2 carrying a Threaded Pin in its upper end hole. The portion of the shank of the Threaded Pin that protrudes beyond the securing nut may be engaged, when desired, with the hole in a $\frac{1}{2}'' \times \frac{1}{2}''$ Angle Bracket 1, which is secured to the top casing of the tractor by a bolt through its elongated hole. When the Threaded Pin rests in the hole of the Angle Bracket both 57-teeth Gears are in engagement with the Pinions 45 (Fig. 5) but on moving the lever to the right the right-hand Pinion is thrown out of mesh while the left hand Pinion remains in mesh, thus causing the tractor to make a right-hand turn. A left-hand turn is carried out by moving the lever 2 over to the left, thus disengaging the left-hand Pinion and bringing the right-hand Pinion into mesh with its appropriate 57-teeth Gear.

The engine cover consists chiefly of two $3\frac{1}{2}'' \times 2\frac{1}{2}''$ Flanged Plates connected together along their edges by means of $5\frac{1}{2}''$ Strips and across the top by a $5\frac{1}{2}'' \times 3\frac{1}{2}''$ Flat Plate. The ends of the cover are fitted with $3\frac{1}{2}'' \times \frac{1}{2}''$ Double Angle Strips; the front Double Angle Strip carries also a $3\frac{1}{2}''$ Flat Girder. Two Double Brackets 5 (Fig. 1) are bolted to the $5\frac{1}{2}'' \times 3\frac{1}{2}''$ Flat Plate and the complete engine housing is secured, by means of four Flat Brackets, to the Angle Girders 38 (Fig. 5).

The tractor is completed by the addition of a dummy steering wheel and driver's seat. The steering wheel consists of a Bush Wheel secured to a $5\frac{1}{2}''$ Rod that is journalled in the rear end pair of $3\frac{1}{2}'' \times 2\frac{1}{2}''$ Flanged Plates (Fig. 5). The driver's seat comprises two Flat Trunnions bolted together to form a square, and secured to the rear of the tractor by means of three Double Brackets, the positions of which are shown clearly in Fig. 5.

The Gun Limber

The bottom of the Limber (Fig. 6) consists of a $4\frac{1}{2}'' \times 2\frac{1}{2}''$ Flat Plate, to which is bolted, by means of a $4\frac{1}{2}''$ Angle Girder, a second similar Plate to form the back. A second $4\frac{1}{2}''$ Angle Girder 53, bolted to the top edge of the latter plate, is connected by two Flat Brackets to a $4\frac{1}{2}''$ Strip that, in turn, is secured to two $2\frac{1}{2}'' \times \frac{1}{2}''$ Double Angle Strips 54, the other ends of which are secured to the bottom of the limber. Each side is enclosed by a $2\frac{1}{2}''$ Flat Girder, which is secured by means of four $\frac{1}{2}'' \times \frac{1}{2}''$ Angle Brackets to the top and bottom of the limber.

The Flat Girders carry also four $\frac{1}{2}'' \times \frac{1}{2}''$ Angle Brackets 55, these being spaced from the Double Angle Strips 54 by Washers so as to allow a $4\frac{1}{2}'' \times 2\frac{1}{2}''$ Flat Plate 56 (shown separately) to slide in the intervening space. A $1'' \times \frac{1}{2}''$ Angle Bracket, carrying a $\frac{3}{8}''$ Bolt 57 is bolted by set-screws spaced by Washers to this sliding plate, and will be used later for connecting the gun to the limber.

The road wheels are free to turn on an $8''$ Rod 58 that is journalled in the $2\frac{1}{2}''$ Flat Girders forming the sides of the limber. The wheels are held in place on the Rod by Collars.

The Washers which represent the shot to be used in the gun are carried on $\frac{3}{4}''$ Bolts secured inside the limber, and are prevented from falling off the

bolts by means of Spring Clips. Three of the $\frac{3}{4}''$ Bolts are secured to the bottom of the model and two are secured to $1'' \times 1''$ Angle Brackets that are bolted to the back Plate of the limber.

The draw-bar, by means of which the gun limber is attached to the tractor, is shown in detail in Fig 6. A $5\frac{1}{2}''$ Strip is attached by means of a Flat Trunnion at one of its ends to two $1\frac{1}{2}'' \times \frac{1}{2}''$ Double Angle Strips 59, one of which is secured to the base of the gun limber by the Bolts shown in position in Fig. 6. A $2\frac{1}{2}''$ Strip is attached pivotally to the other end of the draw-bar and carries a $\frac{3}{8}''$ Bolt in each end hole.

Operating the Model

When the gun, limber and tractor have been completed they may be assembled into travelling formation as shown in Fig. 1. The gun is coupled to the limber by raising the recoil spade 35 (Fig. 3) until it is in a horizontal position and passing the end hole of the Flat Trunnion over the Bolt 57 on the limber (see Fig. 1). The tractor is coupled to the limber by passing the two $\frac{3}{8}''$ Bolts in the pivoted Strip of the drawbar, through the end holes of the $\frac{1}{2}''$ Reversed Angle Brackets bolted to the $3\frac{1}{2}'' \times \frac{1}{2}''$ Double Angle Strip 4 of the tractor (Fig. 1). The model is now a self-contained unit capable of moving with wonderful mobility.

When the desired firing position is reached the limber and tractor are uncoupled from the gun, the shells exposed by raising the sliding door in the limber, and firing proceeded with as described earlier in the leaflet. It may be found that the sights will need a little adjustment, but after careful attention to this point objects up to thirty feet range may be hit with precision. A little lubricating oil should be applied to the guide rod in the howitzer muzzle so as to reduce the friction between it and the "shells."

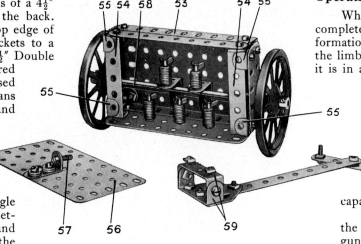

Fig. 6. The Limber, with "shells" in position. The cover-plate and drawbar are shown detached.

Parts required to build the Meccano 6-inch Howitzer, Limber, and Tractor :

HOWITZER								LIMBER				TRACTOR					
2 of No.	2a	3 of No.	11	62 of No.	37	2 of No.	77	1 of No.	2	34 of No.	37	5 of No.	1b	2 of No.	16a	4 of No.	48b	3 of No.	96a
2 ,,	4	15 ,,	12	1 ,,	37a	2 ,,	80a	1 ,,	2a	9 ,,	37a	2 ,,	2	6 ,,	17	1 ,,	52a	4 ,,	109
21 ,,	5	2 ,,	12a	8 ,,	38	1 ,,	80b	1 ,,	5	4 ,,	38	4 ,,	3	1 ,,	24	5 ,,	53	4 ,,	111a
2 ,,	6	1 ,,	13a	1 ,,	43	4 ,,	111	2 ,,	9a	2 ,,	48	2 ,,	25	12 ,,	59	1 ,,	111c
1 ,,	6a	1 ,,	16a	1 ,,	48a	2 ,,	111a	2 ,,	10	2 ,,	48a	2 ,,	8a	2 ,,	26	2 ,,	62	1 ,,	115
2 ,,	8b	2 ,,	17	15 ,,	59	4 ,,	111c	10 ,,	12	3 ,,	53a	2 ,,	9	2 ,,	27	2 ,,	63	2 ,,	125
2 ,,	9	3 ,,	18a	2 ,,	62	1 ,,	115	1 ,,	12a	2 ,,	59	4 ,,	10	3 ,,	27a	4 ,,	70	2 ,,	126a
2 ,,	9b	2 ,,	19a	4 ,,	63	2 ,,	125	1 ,,	12b	2 ,,	103f	5 ,,	11	2 ,,	35	50" ,,	94	1 Electric
6 ,,	9d	2 ,,	22	3 ,,	64	1 ,,	126a	1 ,,	14	5 ,,	111	1 ,,	13a	69 ,,	37	2 ,,	95	Motor
4 ,,	9f	1 ,,	24	2 ,,	72	2 ,,	136	2 ,,	19a	1 ,,	111a	1 ,,	16	8 ,,	38	1 ,,	96	
								5 ,,	35	1 ,,	126a						

Complete Publication Data

MANUAL MODELS PUBLISHED WITHOUT INSTRUCTIONS; REFERENCE TO EARLY LEAFLET INSTEAD.

Date of publication of manual.

	1916	1921	1925	1926 & 7	Late 1927
Motor Chassis	320	429	701	701	701
High-Speed Ship-Coaler			734	729	728
Loom		446	725	725	724
Grandfather Clock					720

In addition, the Meccanograph model in the 1919 manual (Model 315) and the 1926 manual (Model 318), though providing reasonable instructions, recommended the purchase of the Meccanograph Manual for fuller details.

SPECIFIC LEAFLETS CONTAINED IN STANDARD OUTFITS

Early Series; in Numbered Outfits

In 1925, the 6a & 7 outfits contained both Chassis and Loom leaflets.
In 1926, the High-Speed Ship Coaler leaflet was also included.
In late 1927, a Grandfather Clock leaflet was added.

Main Series; in Numbered Outfits

In 1928, the 5a & 6 outfits included Leaflets 7, 9, 10, 11, & 12. The 6a outfit had in addition Leaflets 1, 2, 3, 5, 6, 13, 14, 16, 17, 18, 19, 20 (listed as 'Aeroscope'), 21, 22 (listed as 'Tractor'), 23, 24, 25, & 26. All the above leaflets were of course included in the 7 outfit.
In 1929, Leaflet 22 was omitted, but Leaflet 31 was added to the 6a & 7 outfits. Leaflet 20 was by now listed as 'Electric Mobile Crane'.
In 1930, Leaflets 14 & 16 were replaced by revised Leaflets 14a & 16a. Leaflet 22 was reinstated, but now entitled 'Traction Engine'. Leaflets 28, 29, 30, 35, & 36 were added to the 6a & 7 outfits. Leaflet 31 was temporarily omitted from the contents list, though still retained in the main body of the manual.
In 1931 & 1932 Leaflet 31 was reinstated to the 6a & 7 outfits, and Leaflet 37 was added to the 5a, 6, & 7 outfits.
In 1935, Leaflet 1 was replaced by revised Leaflet 1a.

Main Series; in Lettered Outfits

In 1934, outfits Ha & K contained Leaflets 7, 9, 10, 11, 12, & 37.
Outfit Ka contained Leaflets 1a, 2, 5, 6, 13, 14a, 16a, 17, 18, 19, 20, 21, 22, 23, 24, 25, 26, 28, 29, 30, 31, 35, 36.
Outfit L of course contained all the above Leaflets.
In 1935 Leaflet 11 was replaced by revised Leaflet 11a.
By 1937, Leaflets 16a, 17, 23, 26, 36, & 37 were omitted, and there seems some doubt as to whether Leaflets 7, 9, 10, & 12 in addition were any longer included.
It is perhaps relevant to mention here that a free 'sample' Leaflet from the main series was given away with the issue of 'Meccano Magazine' for December 1934.

MANUAL MODELS PUBLISHED WITHOUT INSTRUCTIONS; REFERENCE TO LEAFLET INSTEAD.

Date of publication of manual.

Leaflet Number	1928	1929	1930	1931 & 2	1934 & 5	1936	1937
1	7.1	7.1	7.1	7.21			
1a				***	L23	L34	L35
2	7.28	7.30	7.28	7.45	L31	L22	L22
3	7.31	7.33	7.33	7.43			
5	7.2	7.35	7.39	7.31	L33	L33	L34
6	7.9	7.10	7.31	7.41	L38	L25	L25
7	6.21	6.20	6.9	6.41	K42	K41	
9	6.16	6.15	6.46	6.45	K45	K42	
10	6.22	6.21	6.45	6.44	K44	K40	
11	6.29	6.28	6.43	6.42	K43**		
11a					K43	K39	
12	6.43	6.42	6.44	6.43	K40	K43	
13	7.8	7.9	7.26	7.26	L42	L19	L33
14	7.19	7.21					
14a			7.32	7.33	L26	L32	L32
16	8.21	7.23					
16a			7.24	7.39 & 37+	L29 & 34+		
17	7.5	7.5	7.23	7.35	L25		
18	7.6	7.7	7.21	7.27	L21	L31	L31
19	7.7	7.8	7.40	7.44	L36	L36	L23
20*	7.11*	7.15	7.35	7.30	L35	L28	L28
21	7.12	7.14	7.36	7.34	L30	L21	L21
22	7.13		7.38	7.25	L32	L23	
23	7.14	7.6	7.27	7.38	L41		
24	7.23	7.25	7.34	7.29	L27	L30	L30
25	7.24	7.4	7.22	7.23	L24	L20	L20
26	7.29	7.31	7.37	7.40	L40		
28			7.42	7.42	L22	L35	L19
29			7.44	7.22	L37	L24	L24
30			7.43	7.32	L28	L29	L29
31		7.12	7.29	7.24	L20	L27	L27
35		7.11	7.36		L39	L26	L26
36***				7.41	7.28	L43	
37			6.47	6.46	K41		

These were the only Leaflet Models which could be made from the contents of Standard Outfits. Many manual models were 'shuffled around' from year to year, which resulted in the many number changes which will be observed in the above list.

* In 1928, Model 7.11 was the Aeroscope; from 1929 onwards the correct 'Electric Mobile Crane' was shown for the manual model numbers which related to Leaflet 20.

** The only difference as far as the Leaflet models were concerned, between the 1934 and 1935 Manuals, was that model K34 changed from Leaflet 11 to Leaflet 11a.

*** There were 1935 editions of the Numbered Outfit Manuals; the only difference as far as the Leaflet Models were concerned, between these and the 1931 and 1932 editions, was that Model 7.21 was changed from Leaflet 1 to Leaflet 1a.

**** Leaflet 36 bears a reference '7.32' but no manual has been found listing the model under this number.

+ The Loom and Beaming Frame were listed as separate models in the manuals. Instructions were usually given for the Beaming Frame, but from 1931 to 1935 there was a reference instead to Leaflet 16a, which of course included both models.

EARLY SPECIAL MODEL LEAFLETS WITH SUPPLEMENTARY PUBLISHING DATA

	Number of pages	English Language.
Motor Chassis	1	(NR; original article dated 7/7/1915) 621/5 1124/1 326/1
Loom	2	1121/2 1124/1 326/1
High-Speed Ship-Coaler	2	125/1 427/1
Clock	2	124/1

'SPECIAL INSTRUCTION LEAFLETS FOR BUILDING MECCANO SUPER MODELS' WITH SUPPLEMENTARY PUBLISHING DATA.

Leaflet Number		Number of pages	English Language U.K.	U.S.A.	French Language	German Language	Spanish Language
1	(With accumulator)	8	328/5		328/2.5		
1	(Amended – no accumulator)	8	2/430/5 1/432/2.5	0-1228/5	9/1230/2	629/2.5	2/530/5
1a		8	21/1134/5		135/2/A 4760		
2		8	428/5 1228/5 1/636/.5		628/4		
3		4	328/5 628/5	0-028/2	428/5		
4		12	628/5		728/4		
5		4	528/5 828/5 1/736/.5	0-0828/1	828		
6		4	628/5 828/5 6/432/1 1/836/.5	0-0928/1	129/4		
7		4	(NR) 1/132/1 (1R) 21/934/4.5	0-0728/2	928/4		
8		4	(NR) 528/5 528/10		528/10 828/		
9		4	528/10 21/934/4.5	0-0728/2	728/4		
10		4	528/5 1228/5 21/934/4.5	0-0728/1	1028/4		
11		4	528/10 7/1130/1 7/931/1 6/432/1.5 21/934/4	0-0728/1	1128/4		
11a		4	(NR) 1/836/.5				
12		4	528/5 1028/5 7/1130/1 6/432/1.5 21/934/4	0-0728/1	828/4		
13		8	628/10 1/636/.5	0-0928/2	828/4		
14		8	428/5. 729/1	0-0928/2	429/4	7/729/2.5 929/2.5	
14a		4	1/331/3		6/1231/4		
15		8	1128/5		429/4		
16		8	628/5 928/5	0-0928/1	928/4		
16a		8	(NR)		1/132/1.5		
17		4	928/5		129/4		
18		4	1028/5 1/736/.5		129/4		
19		4	828/5 21/934/4		229/4 1/935/.5		
19a		8	7/1229/5		7/930/4		
20		4	7/1229/5 1/836/.5		7/730/4		
21		4	1128/5 1/836/.5		228/4		
22		4	1128/5 231/7/1.5 21/934/4.5		229/4		
23		4	1028/5		192/4		
24		4	828/ 828/33 21/1034/7.5 1/736/.5		3/829/4		
25		4	828/5 1/736/.5		129/4		
26		4	1228/5		1228/5 429/4		
27		8	1228/5		7/929/4		
28	(Bearing built with Part 119)	4	1128/5		3/829£6		
28	(Revised with Part 167)	4	1/936/.5				
29	(Bearing built with Part 119)	4	1228/5		429/4		
29	(Revised with Part 167)	4	1/1136/.5				
30		8	7/929/5 1/736/.5		7/1030/4		
31		8	3/729/5 1/836/.5		7/1230/2		
32		8	729/5				
33	(Includes 33a)	8	429/5		7/330/4		
34		8	028/5		629/4		
35		8	7/730/5 1/836/.5		6/132/4		
36		4	3/130/5		7/531/4		
37		4	7/830/5.		1/132/1.5		

'NR' indicates the existence of a Leaflet with no printing reference.

Index

Illustrations and Source Material

Index

BE = 'The Meccano Book of Engineering' Page Number.